C000180475

OBSERVERS AND NAVIGATORS

and other non-pilot aircrew in the RFC, RNAS and RAF

OBSERVERS AND NAVIGATORS

and other non-pilot aircrew in the RFC, RNAS and RAF

Wing Commander
C.G. Jefford MBE, BA, RAF Retd.

THIS BOOK WAS
SLIGHTLY DAMAGED IN
TRANSIT AND IS NOW
BEING SOLD AT A
SPECIAL BARGAIN PRICE

Airlife
England

Copyright © 2001 C.G. Jefford

First published in the UK in 2001
by Airlife Publishing Ltd

British Library Cataloguing-in-Publication Data
A catalogue record for this book is available from the British Library

ISBN 1 84037 275 3

The information in this book is true and complete to the best of our knowledge. All recommendations are made without any guarantee on the part of the Publisher, who also disclaims any liability incurred in connection with the use of this data or specific details.

All rights reserved. No part of this book may be reproduced or transmitted in any form or by any means, electronic or mechanical including photocopying, recording or by any information storage and retrieval system, without permission from the Publisher in writing.

Typeset by Gray Publishing, Tunbridge Wells, Kent
Printed in England by Butler & Tanner Ltd., London and Frome

Airlife Publishing Ltd
101 Longden Road, Shrewsbury, SY3 9EB, England
E-mail: airlife@airlifebooks.com
Website: www.airlifebooks.com

Foreword

This book is a most welcome addition to the bibliography of military aviation and is long overdue. *Observers and Navigators* at long last pays tribute to the thousands of non-pilot aircrew, the often unsung heroes of two World Wars and the years between and since. It is a remarkable and impressive story and one that will, without doubt, both enlighten and surprise readers from outside and inside the Service.

It is quite clear from the evidence within these pages that both the Royal Flying Corps and the Royal Air Force have good reason to be ashamed of their treatment of their non-pilot crew. 'It's a pilots air force' has been the mantra of the back-seater for many years and, although an 'equal careers' policy for pilots and navigators was introduced in 1948, pilots have always been more equal than others. In the context of equality, it is, of course, not without significance, that the RFC and RAF have always insisted that their non-pilot aircrew should wear the strange 'half wing', unlike the more enlightened RNAS and USAF, which never adopted it, and the RCAF and RAAF, both of which inherited the design but subsequently abandoned it.

But in real terms, apart from the relatively limited world of single-seat fighters, it never has been a pilot-only air force. Had it not been for its very large numbers of observers, navigators, wireless operators, air bombers, flight engineers and air gunners the Royal Air Force would have played a very limited role indeed in the world of air power.

From the earliest days of the First World War, observers were playing a vital role in the bloody battles on the Western Front. Readers will be astonished to discover that more than 10 000 men flew as non-pilots during that war and that 25% of all commissioned aircrew were wearing the observers badge at the time of the Armistice.

As the size, complexity and range of aircraft grew so did the roles that they were capable of carrying out, but this potential could be realised only by a substantial increase in the numbers and specialisation of non-pilot aircrew.

With the introduction during the Second World War of heavy, four-engined aircraft into Bomber, Coastal and later Transport Commands, the requirement for rear crew was considerably increased. The standard bomber crew at that time consisted of two air gunners, a flight engineer, a wireless operator, an air bomber and a navigator; six crewmen to one pilot. Of the 55 500 aircrew that were killed during the bomber offensive fewer than 10 000 will have been pilots.

In addition to braving all the risks associated with flying, whether in peace or in war, 'other' aircrew must place their lives unreservedly in the hands of the pilot and in a full career they will fly with a great variety of different pilots of varying level of skills. As Capt J.M. Steel, the Commandant of the large RNAS training establishment at Eastchurch, wrote to the Admiralty's Director of Air Services in 1917, being non-pilot aircrew 'requires a standard of courage which the majority do not possess.'

The requirement for large numbers of 'other' aircrew continued well into the post-war years with the V-bombers, Shackletons, Hercules, VC10s, Nimrods and Tornados. In this era air electronics officers and air electronics operators were introduced into the V-bomber and maritime patrol fleets. But with the introduction of increasingly sophisticated electronic devices and a reduction in the numbers of aircraft in service the requirement for 'other' aircrew began to decline during the 1990s,

Now, the Air Force Board in its 'wisdom' has decided to abolish the historic, prestigious and highly valued title of navigator and replace it with the totally inept 'Weapons Systems Operator'. This was a decision that could only have been reached by a Board composed entirely of pilots. It is significant that, in the entire history of the Royal Air Force, no navigator was ever appointed to serve on the Air Council, and only one to the Air Force Board. Indeed, despite their oft proclaimed 'equality', only three navigators have ever been promoted to air marshal. In terms of prestige, influence and recognition it really has always been a 'pilots air force'.

Thanks to this book, however, some degree of recognition has finally been given to all the very many 'other' aircrew who gave invaluable service, and often their lives, to their country, the Royal Flying Corps, the Royal Naval Air Service and the Royal Air Force.

Air Marshal Sir John Curtiss
KCB KBE FRAeS FRGS

Preface

Compared to the millions of words which have been written by and about the British pilots who fought in the First World War, very little space has been devoted to the men who flew with them – men who shared in (at least) equal measure the risks involved in air combat – the observers. The most likely reason for this will be the public's fascination with the exploits of a handful of outstandingly successful pilots, practically all of whom flew single-seat fighters. The achievements of these 'aces' were so spectacular that they reflected a measure of glory on all pilots, even those who flew the relatively pedestrian two-seaters. Unfortunately, they also cast a shadow which completely obscured the considerable contribution to success that was being made by the even less glamorous occupants of rear cockpits. Another possible explanation for the activities of non-pilot aircrew having been overlooked could lie in an impression that there were relatively few of them. If so, this was based on a misunderstanding. At least 10 000 such men flew on operations between 1914 and 1918.

In view of the fact that so many men actually flew as backseaters it is rather surprising that so few of them subsequently saw fit to record their experiences. There are a handful of first-hand accounts written by observers, of course, but nothing like the number penned by pilots. Since the early observers declined to sing their own praises, and since no one else has ever bothered to do so, they have faded into relative obscurity to become little more than a footnote to the history of the Great War. In writing this book my original aim was to sharpen the focus on these sadly overlooked aviators, thus disposing of some long-standing myths (without, I hope, creating any new ones).

It is conventional to regard the observer of WW I as the forerunner of the navigator of WW II and after. In practice, however, until quite late on, very few first-generation observers had much to do with navigation. Nevertheless, because responsibility for it was eventually vested in the second generation of observers, some space has been devoted to the evolution of the art of air navigation. In fact, since they were not navigating, most of what the observers of 1914–18 actually did had far more in common with specialisations which would come to be recognised as quite separate trades during the 1939–45 War. To reflect this, some consideration has been given to the development of the other categories of early non-pilot aircrew, the aerial gunner/gunlayer and the kite balloon observer. Since it was fundamental to the provision of non-pilot aircrew, the narrative also includes frequent references to the evolution of the associated training organisation. In order to maintain some sort of perspective, despite the disproportionate amount of publicity which they have already been afforded, some reference to pilots proved to be unavoidable.

Having painted what I believe to be a reasonable likeness of the non-pilot aircrew of WW I, it was almost inevitable that I would be seduced into considering how rapidly that picture faded after the war and the steps which had to be taken to restore it in later years. These developments are covered in rather less detail, in the second and third sections of the book which continues the story to the turn of the century.

I should perhaps add that I embarked on this project with a reasonably open mind – I really did. As a latter-day backseater myself, however, I was so surprised to discover the extent of the RFC's institutionalised lack of regard for its observers (an attitude which was so wholeheartedly endorsed by the RAF in its formative years that its ramifications can still be detected today) that this book may occasionally read as something of a polemic. If it does, so be it.

I hereby offer my thanks to the many colleagues within the mafia of aviation historians who assisted me in this project but I must make specific mention of Graham Day, of the Air Historical Branch, and of Mike O'Connor, who pointed me at a number of particularly useful files at the Public Record Office. It is also appropriate to acknowledge the contribution made by the staff of the PRO itself, since it would be impossible to write a book of this nature without the access to essential documents and data which only they can provide.

One last thought. It is a moot point whether or not the word 'observers' should have an apostrophe when used, for instance, to identify an emblem (as in 'an observers badge') or an item of equipment (as in 'observers cockpit') or within the title of a unit (as in Observers School) and, if so, whether it should go before or after the 's'. From an examination of contemporary documents relating to such matters during WW I, it is quite plain that those who drafted them were undecided, as examples of all the options can be found. Throughout this book, where appropriate, the word 'observers' (and 'pilots', 'navigators', etc) has been used in its adjectival sense as a plural attributive noun, i.e. *sans* apostrophe.

C.G. Jefford
Postcombe
November 2000

Contents

Part I – The Rise of the Observer 1914–18

Part II – Fall and Rise Again 1919–42

Part III – The Post-Observer Era 1942–2000

Epilogue

Annexes

Part I

The Rise of the Observer 1914–18

Chapter 1

Genesis

In the beginning there were pilots – only pilots. In the beginning, that is, of the British Army's involvement with powered flight. In point of fact, officially sponsored experiments with balloons having begun as early as 1878, there had been aviators of a sort in the British Army long before the advent of the aeroplane. Military balloonists of the Royal Engineers had seen active service during the Boer War and in the Sudan, while others had been deployed as far afield as India and China. The use of aerostats had provided commanders with their first opportunities to see what was happening 'on the other side of the hill' but the arrival of the aeroplane was to revolutionise every aspect of the conduct of war. While it was axiomatic that the first soldiers to fly in powered aircraft would be pilots, they did not bring about the eventual revolution unaided and once the fighting started, indeed even before that, they would be assisted at practically every turn by others, the observers and gunners, whose part in the development of early military aviation has for too long been overlooked.

Doubtless there are several candidates for the title of being the 'first British air observer' but a reasonable claimant must be a far-sighted junior staff officer serving in India, Capt W.S. Brancker. He managed to engineer events so that on 15 January 1911 he was able to fly in a privately-owned Bristol Boxkite during manoeuvres held in the Deccan. Piloted by H.M. Jullerot[1] and operating under the direct orders of Sir Douglas Haig, Brancker took off to search for an 'enemy' column. He found it in the vicinity of Jalna, some thirty miles away. Less than 1½ hours after briefing, the General was handed a full report identifying all the units involved. An attempt to repeat this exercise the following day ended in a crash shortly after take-off.

While this obscure exploit in far-off India had been instigated largely by the personal enthusiasm of one man, the potential of air reconnaissance had not been lost on the small band of professional aviators of the Air Battalion at home. Here the question was being actively discussed during 1911, the focus of attention at that time being the possibilities represented by the airship *Beta*. Flying hours were a precious commodity at that stage, however, and those that were available had to be husbanded for pilot training. Nevertheless, if little effort could be devoted to live practice, the theoretical possibilities continued to be examined. Thus the first Military Aviation Course, which ran at Farnborough between April and August 1912 (i.e. as the Royal Flying Corps was actually being formed), included reconnaissance and aerial photography among the topics being studied, albeit still primarily in the context of lighter-than-air craft.

[1]A Frenchman, Henri Marie Jullerot was employed by the Bristol and Colonial Aeroplane Company as a test and demonstration pilot and flying instructor. As supervisor of the Bristol flying schools at Larkhill and Brooklands for four years, Jullerot was probably responsible for the training of more pre-war RFC pilots than any other individual. Returning to France to enlist on the outbreak of war, he was back in England by May 1915 when he was commissioned into the RNVR. Rather surprisingly, in view of his considerable flying experience, he was initially employed as an observer, first appearing as such in the RNAS Disposition List for October 1915. On 4 August 1916 he was graded as a pilot and transferred to the RNAS, spending most of the remainder of the war at Dover and Greenwich on (mostly ground) instructional duties.

Sefton Brancker (on the left) may well have been the 'first British air observer'. He is seen here, as a major, talking to Lt-Col Frederick Sykes at the RFC 'Concentration Camp' in June 1914. These two officers were to be very influential in the development of early British aviation; within four years both of them would be major-generals. (J.M. Bruce/G.S. Leslie collection)

The increased autonomy conferred by the creation of the RFC stimulated its members to find ways of persuading a sceptical General Staff to accept the military worth of aeroplanes. The first significant opportunity to do this was provided by the annual Army Manoeuvres held in the summer of 1912 when, among others, Majs Trenchard, Brooke-Popham and Sykes, Capt Webb-Bowen and Lt C.J. L'Estrange Malone RN could all be found occupying the second seats of aeroplanes from time to time, all of these men later becoming influential figures in British military aviation. Once play had begun, Lt-Gen Sir James Grierson, commanding the 'Blue' defenders, was more successful than his opponent in exploiting his air assets, leading directly to the early defeat of Lt-Gen Haig's 'Red' offensive.

The manoeuvres had clearly demonstrated that, weather and daylight permitting, reconnaissance could be successfully conducted from the air. It had been convincingly shown that it was possible not only to detect troop movements but to establish much additional associated intelligence, such as the numbers involved and the rate and direction of advance. This information was of little value, however, if it could not be placed in the hands of the field commander while it was still current. Thus, the need for reliable and much faster communications links was demonstrated with equal clarity, the successful exploitation of the wireless equipment carried by the 'Blue' airship *Gamma* having contributed significantly to Grierson's 'victory'. Many other lessons were learned, notably about the logistic problems involved in operating aeroplanes on a relatively large scale in what was still very much a horse-drawn era – it was probably still easier to find fodder than petrol in the rural England of 1912.[2]

1913. Early indications of a possible need for professional observers

As its first birthday approached, and with the previous year's manoeuvres having provided a sound basis of practical field experience, Lt-Col F.H. Sykes, the commander of the RFC's Military Wing, decided that it was time to arrange its affairs on a more formal basis. On 5 February 1913 he proposed the publication of four key documents: Standing Orders for the Military Wing and the Central Flying School, a Training Manual and a War Manual. By April the first draft of the latter had been circulated, the following (slightly edited) extract being of particular significance:

> 'In order that good results may be obtained from aerial reconnaissance, it is essential that the same pilot and observer should always work together as far as possible, at all events in the case of aeroplanes (*i.e. as distinct from airships – CGJ*). Mutual confidence is of the utmost importance.
>
> It is inadvisable to lay down hard and fast rules as to the respective duties of pilots and observers, as it must depend largely upon the personality of the individuals. As soon as the orders have been received, the pilot and observer should consult together with the aid of a map, as to the best manner of carrying out their task, and the route to be followed.
>
> Compass bearings, distances and times must be worked out, and, if necessary, tabulated and fixed to the machine, so as to be clearly visible during flight. As regards the former, allowance must be made for the probable drift due to the wind at the height the aeroplane will fly.
>
> (*The pilot*) will mark the route on his map and place it in readiness. The observer will also mark his map, and in certain cases, such as where a detailed reconnaissance is required, will make an enlargement of it and duplicate it with the aid of carbon paper. He will collect and get ready all his apparatus, notebook or writing block, pencils, sharpened at both ends, weighted message bags, watch, field glasses and in some cases a camera.
>
> Finally both pilot and observer will commit their orders to memory and then burn them. On return from the reconnaissance, the observer is responsible for seeing that the information gained is transmitted to its destination by the most expeditious means.'

All of this represented sound practical guidance for observers (and pilots) and it is interesting to see that the crucial importance of flight planning had already been clearly identified. What the draft signally failed to provide, however, was any indication of who 'the observer' was to be. Would he continue to be a second pilot, as in the 1912 manoeuvres, or was it the intention to employ specialists in the future? The first paragraph rather suggests the latter but, as yet, no arrangements had been made to recruit such men.

By June the 'War Manual' had been extensively revised and renamed the RFC Training Manual, Pt II (Military Wing). On 3 September proof copies of this document were issued to at least forty-eight of the officers participating in the 1913 manoeuvres. The guidance on techniques was practically unchanged from the original draft but the following additional paragraph had been included:[3]

> 'Pilots will always be provided from the personnel of the Royal Flying Corps; officers for duty as observers will be provided by the Royal Flying Corps or, temporarily, from the General Staff and other units, as occasion demands.'

It would seem from this proposal (the document had not yet been formally approved for publication) that the RFC acknowledged that it might need to 'borrow' outsiders from time to time but that it intended to provide its own observers whenever possible. Since the RFC had no professional observers, however, this implied that it was content to misemploy its pilots.

This concept was put to the test during the 1913 war games, this time between 'White' and 'Brown' forces. Most of the officers who flew as observers were relatively inexperienced pilots drawn from recent intakes; they included Capts B.R.W. Beor and W. Picton-Warlow, and Lts R.O. Abercromby, J.E.G. Burroughs, R.G.D. Small, F.G. Small, R.P. Mills, P.H.L. Playfair, M.W. Noel and E.R.L. Corballis, and 2/Lts G.F. Pretyman, C.W. Wilson and W.C.K. Birch. Significantly, however, three students from the current Staff College course also participated. They were Capts E.W. Furse, L.P. Evans and H.C. Jackson, who thus became the first non-pilots to fly quasi-operationally with the RFC. This was only a temporary arrangement, however, and once the manoeuvres had ended these three men resumed their studies.

Following the manoeuvres, HQ Military Wing received a number of constructive criticisms and comments on the Flying Training Manual, Pt II. Despite their 'amateur' status, incidentally, the three part-time aviators from Camberley had been among those issued with a proof copy. In the main the observations offered were confined to minor amplifications and changes in emphasis. Since there was little disagreement with the bulk of its content, on 19 May 1914 the document was published, without amendment, as the 'provisional' manual.

[2]While its participation in the 1912 manoeuvres represented the RFC's first substantial involvement in a formal exercise, it had not been the Army's first experience of working with aeroplanes in the field. Apart from the exploits of Jullerot and Brancker in 1911, a privately owned Farman and a pair of Bristol Boxkites loaned by the manufacturers had taken part in Army manoeuvres held as early as September 1910. A particularly significant event on that occasion being Mr Robert Loraine's demonstration of air-to-ground communication by W/T, using a transmitter devised by Mr R. Thorne-Baker. The range achieved at the time was a mere quarter of a mile, although that would be quadrupled in early post-exercise experiments. The potential demonstrated by aeroplanes in 1910, amplified by the possibilities represented by the use of radio, were probably instrumental in hastening the early elevation of British military aviation from battalion to corps status.

Building on the experience gained in 1910, it was intended to use Army-owned aeroplanes during the annual manoeuvres planned for the following year. In the event, in view of the international tensions which had been aroused by the Agadir Crisis, it was considered inadvisable to mount any significant display of military force and the 1911 manoeuvres were cancelled.

[3]AIR1/785/204/558 contains draft copies of the War Manual and of the original version of the Training Manual, Pt II.

This Breguet G3, 211, of No 4 Sqn participated in the 1913 Army manoeuvres during which it crashed on 25 September. Note that, in common with most aeroplanes of this era, when an observer was carried he would have occupied the front seat. (J.M. Bruce/G.S. Leslie collection)

1913–14. The need for professional observers is recognised

Capt G.S. Shephard, another future general, had flown both as pilot and as observer during the 1913 manoeuvres and he subsequently committed his thoughts to paper. In his view, which was probably shared by many of his colleagues, pilots, particularly experienced ones, made poor observers because they disliked flying as passengers and tended to become preoccupied with monitoring the efforts of the man driving the aeroplane. Shephard suggested that the ideal observer would be an experienced ground-based officer, preferably one possessing some technical skill which might be of value in the event of mechanical failure, who had previously flown several times with the same pilot or group of pilots. He also urged that the observer's station should be provided with a compass 'as the observer is ultimately held responsible for finding the way.'[4]

Shephard had, in effect, set out the case for the creation of a cadre of professional observers who would be at home in the air and who knew what they were about. It is not known how much direct influence his paper had, but shortly afterwards an infantry officer was attached to the RFC to be trained as just such an observer. He was Capt H.H. Shott DSO of the Royal Berkshire Regiment, who appears to have been the first non-pilot officer to be specifically trained for observation duties from aeroplanes. He reported to HQ Military Wing on 6 November 1913 but, because of a shortage of machines at South Farnborough, Lt-Col Sykes redirected him to Montrose to be looked after by No 2 Sqn; Shott rejoined his battalion on 17 December.[5]

So far as this writer has been able to ascertain Shott's was an isolated case and the RFC does not appear to have run another lengthy one-man course. On the other hand, provision was made for individuals to be taken up for a flight as part of the RFC's continuing effort to 'sell' the advantages of aerial observation. Officers who showed an interest, typically engineers, artillerymen and those concerned with intelligence, could apply for a flight 'through channels' and several are known to have been taken up from Farnborough over the next few months.[6]

With tensions rising in Europe the War Office finally decided to take positive steps to ensure that a group of trained observers would be available in the event of war. On 13 July 1914 the ten officers listed at Fig. 1 reported to Netheravon for a month's course of instruction.[7] They were to draw an additional three shillings per day while under training and, assuming that they passed the course, they would subsequently be entitled to draw flying pay at a rate of five shillings *per diem* throughout any period during which they were seconded to the RFC for observation duties.

A second course was scheduled to commence on 12 August but this one was to be overtaken by events.[8] Meanwhile, on 27 July the first course had moved to South Farnborough where it was attached to No 6 Sqn. Four days later the War Office suspended observer training and directed that all ten of the officers concerned were to return to their units. On 4 August Great Britain declared war on Germany and the following day the second observers course was cancelled before it had even begun.

Name	**Regiment**
Maj C.A.L. Yate	2nd Yorks Light Infantry
Capt A.F. Attwood	4th Royal Fusiliers
Capt N.P. Clarke	2nd Royal Dublin Fusiliers
Capt D.W. Powell	3rd Northants Regt
Capt H.S. Walker	3rd Cheshire Regt
Capt C.P. Heywood	3rd Coldstream Guards
Capt E. Hewlett	1st Devonshire Regt
Capt H.F.S. Amery	1st Royal Highlanders
Capt H.H. Hughes-Hallett	3rd North Staffs Regt
Lt C.G. Forsyth	2nd Yorkshire Regt

Fig. 1. *The ten members of the first formal observers course to be run by the RFC.*

[4]*Memoirs of Gordon Shephard*, edited by Shane Leslie and published privately in 1924. Key extracts, including Shephard's thoughts on the provision of air observers, were reproduced in an article by Marvin L. Skelton in *The Cross & Cockade Journal*, Vol 8, No 1 (1977).

[5]AIR1/771/204/4/280. War Office letter 43/Flying School/92(MA1), dated 4 November, directed that Capt Shott should report to Farnborough two days later. In an undated HQ Military Wing memo, RFC HR 4859, Lt-Col Sykes notified the War Office that Shott had returned to his unit on 17 December.

[6]*Ibid*. Officers who are known to have been flown from Farnborough under these terms included:

Name	**Corps/Regt**	**Date**
Lt W.G. Welch	RFA	28/11/13
Capt E. Hope Carson	(Rhodesian)	5/12/13
Lt J.A.C. Pennycuick	RE	?/2/14
Lt C.W.M. Firth	1st Sigs Coy RE	9/3/14
Capt H.G. Gandy	RE	?/4/14
Lt S. StQ. Fullbrook-Leggatt	1st Royal Berks	?/5/14
Lt G. Cheetham	11th Fd Coy RE	?/5/14

[7]AIR1/683/21/13/2234. The ten officers listed at Fig. 1 were nominated for the course by War Office letter 43/Flying School/119(MA1) dated 6 July 1914.

[8]AIR1/365/15/231/5. The officers nominated for the second observers course, which was to take place at South Farnborough, were identified in War Office letter 43/Flying School/123(MA1) dated 24 July 1914. They were:

Rank/Name	**Corps/Regt**
Capt F.G. Spring	Lincolnshire Regt
Capt H.E. Trevor	Northamptonshire Regt
Capt E.T. Welchman DSO	West Yorks Regt
Capt Hon. C.M. Hore-Ruthven DSO	Royal Highlanders
Capt R.J. Kentish	6th London Infantry Bde
Capt D. le G. Pitcher	39th Central India Horse

They were to draw the same rates of pay as the students on the first course, apart from Pitcher who, being a qualified pilot, was already permanently in receipt of full flying pay.

Chapter 2

1914. The RFC goes to war

Although the RFC had clearly accepted that it was going to need dedicated airborne observers, by the time that it began to cross the Channel in the second week of August 1914 it still had no designated aircrew other than its pilots. Concerned to fill this gap, the War Office exercised its option on the three Staff College students who had flown as observers during the 1913 manoeuvres. Because they were still at Camberley, these officers were not carried on the immediate fighting strengths of their own regiments, making them readily available for employment elsewhere. Capitalising on its investment, the RFC had already earmarked these men for flying duties in the event of general mobilisation.

As early as 5 August Capts Evans and Furse had been directed to report to Nos 3 and 5 Sqns respectively but this order was rescinded on the 7th. Three days later they were summoned to Farnborough again, this time accompanied by Capt Jackson. Henry Jackson was sent to France on 19 August, thus gaining the distinction of becoming the first designated observer to be attached to the RFC on active service overseas. He was assigned to No 3 Sqn on the 21st, on which date Edmund Furse sailed to be allocated to No 5 Sqn on the 22nd. For a month, Lewis Evans was obliged to exercise his newly acquired skills as a staff officer at the Department of Military Aeronautics (DMA) in London before following his colleagues across the Channel on 20 September. He was to spend three month with No 3 Sqn before rejoining his regiment, the Black Watch.

With the obvious exception of the RFC's pilots, the only other officers with any experience of aerial reconnaissance work were the members of the observers course which had been interrupted by the declaration of war. An effort was made to recall these officers but this met with only limited success, as most of them were serving with their own units. The first to be released was Capt Hughes-Hallett, who was despatched to join the BEF on 1 September, being assigned to work with No 4 Sqn from the 8th. Capts Walker and Powell left England two days after Hughes-Hallett, both of them being allocated to No 3 Sqn on the 9th. The fourth and last member of the one and only pre-war observers course to return to the fold was Capt Hewlett. He had the distinction of being the first observer to go to France as part of a constituted unit, No 6 Sqn, which left South Farnborough in three daily waves beginning on 6 October. Hewlett was part of the first element and he was formally taken on strength by the RFC in the field ten days later.

As yet there were no laid-down rules as to what constituted a 'qualified' observer. It was simply left to the common sense and subjective judgement of those supervising operations in France to decide when a man was competent. Since all the officers named above had had a modicum of previous experience, all seven were considered to be fully qualified more or less as soon as they arrived. In this respect they were to be (almost) unique. It would be the late summer of 1918 before the RFC/RAF was prepared to accept that an observer could be fully qualified as soon as he arrived in France.[1]

The first 'unqualified' observer to be attached to the RFC was Capt Theodore Crean (Northamptonshire Regt) who sailed for France on 4 September. Having been seconded to the Sierra Leone Battalion of the West African Frontier Force since February 1913, he had arrived back in England within days of the outbreak of war. There had clearly been no opportunity for him to have received any training and, like many of those who were to follow him, he was effectively thrown in at the deep end after joining No 4 Sqn on 9 September. He had still to be certified as fully qualified when he became the first observer to be killed in action with the RFC. He was shot down in a BE2 on 26 October.[2]

Late 1914. The characteristics of aerial warfare begin to crystallise

The first two months of the war were characterised by hectic movement and intense activity. Despite the exploratory work which had been done before the war, it was inevitable that, with no previous operational experience on which to build, there was little method to the earliest sorties flown by the RFC in France. This is not to say that these missions were ineffective. Indeed, timely response to aerial reconnaissance reports led to the British Army being ordered to withdraw from its line on the Condé-Mons Canal, preventing its envelopment by a German pincer movement. British aerial reconnaissance was equally important in the context of the Battle of the Marne when the RFC's contribution was publicly acknowledged by the French. Furthermore, several important operational 'firsts' were achieved during the Battle of the Aisne in September – the first use of aerial photography; the first attempt to direct gunfire by using pyrotechnics; the first use of wireless telegraphy (W/T) to report enemy troop movements; and the first use of W/T to control artillery – all of which were to figure large among the activities which would routinely fall to observers in the future.

[1]There were a few, a very few, exceptions to this rule. The earliest example appears to have been 2/Lt J.O. Andrews who spent some time at Netheravon with No 1 Sqn before being despatched to France to join No 5 Sqn on 15 January 1915, his 'Qualified in England' annotation being immediately endorsed by HQ RFC. It happened again when No 7 Sqn moved to France, its five observers (Capt W. O'Gowan, Lts W.E.G. Murray and G.D. Hill, and 2/Lts F.H. Hyland and R.H. Peck) all being recognised as being fully qualified with effect from 8 April 1915, the day *before* they joined the BEF. There were other anomalies too, such as Lt J.A. Johnstone, who was killed in action on 20 March 1915, still notionally uncertified. The following day his qualification was announced, backdated to 17 December 1914 which must have reflected experience gained at home as Johnstone was not attached to the BEF until 13 March.

[2]This BE2 (612) was not the first aeroplane to be lost by the RFC in France, nor was Crean the first 'observer' to fail to return from an operational sortie. Crean's unique distinction was that he was the first British non-pilot aviator to be lost in action, his predecessors having been qualified pilots flying in the second seat.

The experience acquired during the 'Retreat from Mons' and the subsequent 'Race to the Sea' had clearly demonstrated the potential of the aeroplane. It had also revealed the inadequacy of the available role equipment, such as it was, and the need for operating procedures (particularly those involving co-operation between aeroplanes and artillery) to be more clearly defined and mutually agreed. Many other lessons had been learned, the most important being that there could no longer be any doubt about the value of aeroplanes for reconnaissance. It was equally plain, however, that identifying a target by using terms such as 'one hundred yards south of the second 'e' in Zillebeke' was hardly a satisfactory means of relaying vital intelligence. What was required was a simple, uniform and unambiguous means of defining a geographical location which could be used by both aviators and ground troops. This need was satisfied by a grid system, devised by the Experimental Wireless Unit and adopted in October 1914.[3]

Thereafter, with the Front stabilised and the opposing armies becoming increasingly entrenched, the previously mobile campaign rapidly stagnated into a form of mutual siege warfare in which the RFC/RAF was to play a key role for the next four years, finding targets for the British guns and reporting the fall of shot. The latter required something more precise than the grid system and in January 1915 an adaptation of the existing artillery 'Clock Code' was introduced. In brief, range was indicated by reference to a series of imaginary concentric circles centred on the target, while bearings were reported relative to a clock face with its 12 o'clock aligned with True North (whereas the original 'gunners' 12 o'clock had been based on a line drawn from the battery through the target).

Since air-to-ground communications facilities were very limited, e.g. message bags, Aldis lamps and coloured flares or smoke, it was possible to send only relatively crude messages in the early days, although even these had the potential to enhance the effectiveness of artillery fire to a significant degree. With the increasing availability of wireless during 1915, however, it became possible both to extend the selection of pre-(Morse)-coded signals and to refine their content, permitting aircrews to exercise increasingly precise control over the activities of the gunners. The standardised grid and the Artillery Code were to become the basic stock-in-trade of the many aviators who flew in direct support of the army for the remainder of the war.

While these and other procedural refinements were being hammered out, other work was in hand with a view to redressing the RFC's initial shortcomings. During the winter of 1914–15 its responsiveness and flexibility were improved, by decentralising its organisation, while significant technical advances were being made in the fields of aerial photography and wireless telegraphy, and in the design of bomb sights and gun mountings. There were practical limits to what could be achieved, given the limited capabilities of the available aeroplanes, but substantial progress had been made by the time that the 1915 campaigning season opened in March with the Battle of Neuve Chapelle. Shortly afterwards another task was allocated to the RFC, that of 'contact patrols' – keeping track of the precise location of the leading troops during an offensive. This was first tried, with mixed results, at Aubers Ridge in May 1915. From the lessons learned, the techniques were refined and contact patrol work was conducted much more successfully the following year during the Battle of the Somme and after.

Late 1914. The shortage of professional observers obliges the RFC to use pilots to fill the gap

As previously noted, the RFC had been only partially successful in obtaining the services of those officers who had been given an insight into the techniques of aerial reconnaissance before the war and the seven men who did eventually return to the fold were not nearly enough. For several months, therefore, when it was necessary to carry a 'passenger' in an aeroplane he often had to be another pilot. As a result, the first 'observer' to be killed in action, Lt C.G.G. Bayly, was actually a pilot who was flying a reconnaissance sortie in the second seat of one of No 5 Sqn's Avros when it was shot down on 22 August.

Other pre-war pilots who flew as observers on occasion included Maj L.B. Boyd Moss, Capts G.I. Carmichael and L.E.O. Charlton, Lts R.O. Abercromby, K.P. Atkinson, I.M. Bonham Carter, D.S.K. Crosbie, W.R. Freeman, H.D. Harvey Kelly, T.L.S. Holbrow, L. da C. Penn-Gaskell, F.G. Small, R.G.D. Small and R.M. Vaughan and 2/Lts C.E.C. Rabagliati, L.A. Strange, A.A.B. Thompson and C.W. Wilson (this list being far from comprehensive). Some pilots were specifically identified as being intended to serve as observers, a document dated 28 September, for instance, noting Capts R.A. Boger and H.L. Reilly as being in this category. Boger was another pilot who was to become an early casualty while flying as an observer, being taken prisoner on 5 October.

When additional pilots began to be sent out to France, some of these were also earmarked as observers. The first such pilot to arrive was 2/Lt R. Loraine who, as a member of the RFC Special Reserve, was called to the colours and commissioned as a probationary 2nd lieutenant with effect from 15 August. Despite his being a qualified pilot, when Robert Loraine was initially sent overseas on 1 September it was as an observer.[4] This situation was very short-lived, however, as his commission and his status as a pilot had both been confirmed by the time that he was assigned to No 3 Sqn on the 6th.

Over the next few months the strength of the four squadrons which were on active service was maintained, even increased, by a steady flow of reinforcements, some of the pilots involved evidently being either of indifferent quality or only part-trained. In late September, for instance, a batch

[3]The RFC's limited pre-war expertise in the use of airborne wireless equipment had been concentrated within its Headquarters Unit. On mobilisation the most experienced W/T personnel were formed into a flight which was attached to No 4 Sqn and flew to France with its new parent on 13 August. On 27 September the autonomy of this flight was restored by redesignating it as the Experimental Wireless Unit and making it directly subordinate to HQ RFC. Having grown substantially in the meantime, on 8 December 1914 the unit became No 9 Sqn which was commanded by Maj H. Musgrave. The officers who constituted the original staff of the Experimental Unit were Lts D.S. Lewis, B.T. James and S.C.W. Smith and 2/Lt O.G. Lywood, James generally being given the credit for having developed the grid system.

[4]AIR1/823/204/5/48. War Office letter 79/4878(MA1) dated 17 September identified all officers who had been ordered to join the Military Wing (in any capacity) since the beginning of the war. Annex C listed the eight men who had been sent to the Expeditionary Force as observers, including 2/Lt R. Loraine, the only pilot among them. This was a little surprising as Robert Loraine had qualified for (French) Aviator's Certificate No 126 as early as 21 July 1910. He had been a particularly prominent pre-war aviator, making the first crossing of the Irish Sea (although he had had to swim the last twenty yards or so) and handling the first significant W/T transmissions made from an aeroplane in the UK (see Chapter 1, Note 2). In view of his substantial experience as a pilot, it is assumed that Loraine's initial assignment as an observer will have been some sort of temporary bureaucratic device or, then again, it might simply have been a clerical error.

of five new pilots was despatched from Southampton of whom two, Capts H.T. Lumsden and J.R.C. Heathcote, were annotated as being 'fair pilots who will probably be useful as observers.' Similarly, the despatch note accompanying Capt H. Wyllie, who left for France a month later, noted that he had flown the Longhorn but clearly stated that he was being sent to France 'as an observer.'[5]

Another slightly unusual case was represented by a small group of colonial officers who had been seconded to the RFC before the war to learn to fly. Four of them, two from the Indian Army (Capt D. le G. Pitcher and Lt H.L. Reilly) and two from the South African Defence Force (Lt K.R. Van der Spuy and 2/Lt C.F. Creed), were attached to Nos 2, 4 and 5 Sqns in August 1914 and accompanied them when they first crossed the Channel. In October the War Office required that one of these men, Capt Pitcher, be sent back to England. Although Pitcher was a qualified pilot, in his response Brig-Gen Henderson (Commanding the RFC in the field) stated that he had actually been 'employed exclusively on observation duties.' The General went on to agree to release him, but only after a replacement observer had been received. London repeated its request, stating that Capt Wyllie, who had just arrived in France, was to be regarded as the necessary replacement.[6]

Name	Date Attached	Initial Unit	Date Qualified
Capt H.C. Jackson	21/8/14	No 3 Sqn	21/8/14
Maj E.W. Furse	22/8/14	No 5 Sqn	22/8/14
Capt H.H. Hughes-Hallett	8/9/14	No 4 Sqn	8/9/14
Capt D.W. Powell	9/9/14	No 3 Sqn	9/9/14
Capt H.S. Walker	9/9/14	No 3 Sqn	9/9/14
Capt L.P. Evans	20/9/14	No 3 Sqn	20/9/14
Capt E. Hewlett	16/10/14	No 6 Sqn	16/10/14
2/Lt C. Cooper	25/9/14	No 2 Sqn	28/10/14
2/Lt E.W. Powell	15/11/14	No 3 Sqn	24/11/14
Capt C.S.A. Akerman	2/11/14	No 3 Sqn	28/11/14
2/Lt A.J. Capel	14/11/14	No 4 Sqn	30/11/14
Capt P.R.C. Groves	25/11/14	No 4 Sqn	30/11/14
Lt A.E.G. MacCallum	5/11/14	No 2 Sqn	3/12/14
2/Lt A. Lees	14/11/14	No 2 Sqn	5/12/14
2/Lt R. Pierson	14/11/14	No 6 Sqn	5/12/14
2/Lt I.T. Lloyd	14/11/14	No 2 Sqn	10/12/14
Maj F.W. Ramsay	11/12/14	No 4 Sqn	21/12/14
2/Lt M.H. Monckton	25/11/14	No 3 Sqn	24/12/14
Lt K.H. Harbord	6/12/14	?	28/12/14

***Fig. 2.** Officers known to have flown as qualified observers with the RFC in the field during 1914.*

Late 1914. Early efforts to provide additional observers from home

Although the RFC had been prepared to use pilots as observers when it had to, this had always been a matter of necessity rather than choice. In December 1914 Lt-Col H. M. Trenchard commented adversely on this unsatisfactory practice when he wrote:[7]

> '... in my opinion it is absolutely unnecessary for the squadrons out here to have more pilots. 15 pilots per squadron is ample and we should get 9 observers who are not pilots to go with them, as it is manifestly a waste of time to train a man as a pilot and then when he comes out here not to allow him to fly a machine, and only use him as an observer...'

Apart from anything else, it was clearly uneconomic to risk losing two pilots when only one was necessary to fly the aeroplane. Already well aware of this, the War Office had been doing its best to find additional officers to fly with the RFC. This early recruiting campaign included the experiment of selecting a batch of Gentleman Cadets from the Royal Military College at Sandhurst and sending them straight to France as observers. The first six (I.T. Lloyd, A. Lees, J.C.W.A. Pinney, A.J. Capel, A.C. Wilson and R. Pierson) arrived at GHQ on 14 November. They were all gazetted as subalterns a few days later, their back-dated seniority anticipating their attachment to the RFC by three days.

Including all of those named above (but excluding the misemployed pilots), by 11 December a total of twenty-three officers had been sent to France as observers and a few more would arrive before the end of the year. To these should be added 2/Lts E.W. Powell and C.A. Gladstone who had originally been sent abroad to serve the RFC in their professional capacity as Intelligence Officers. Sailing for France as early as 17 August, they had been attached to the staff of HQ RFC but on 15 and 21 November, respectively, they had been reassigned to fly as observers with Nos 3 and 5 Sqns.

It should be appreciated that the men being sent to France to serve as observers would have had very little, if any, previous experience of aviation. Some of them may have been given a few days of indoctrination training at South Farnborough (although this has not been confirmed) but, in essence, they were expected to learn the tricks of the trade as best they could in the course of flying operational sorties. Once they were considered to have made the grade, this process taking anything from a week to a month, this was certified by an announcement in HQ RFC's Routine Orders.[8] Those officers who flew as fully qualified observers during 1914 are listed at Fig. 2. It should be stressed that Fig. 2 does not reflect the whole picture, as it was quite normal for observers to fly on operations before they had completed their certification; there were, for instance, a further eighteen officers in this category entitled to draw flying pay during December.[9]

[5]AIR1/814/204/4/1257. Officers proceeding to France at this time carried a note from Military Wing Headquarters at South Farnborough. It was to be handed to Brig-Gen Henderson (or his representative) when the bearer arrived at HQ RFC. Most of these missives simply stated that the bearer was at the General's disposal but some contained a brief amplifying observation, occasionally accompanied by a copy of a CFS Report. The two notes specifically referred to in the narrative were unreferenced memoranda of this nature dated 29 September and 26 October 1914.

[6]AIR1/864/204/5/506. This correspondence was terminated by War Office letter 100/Flying Corps/28(MA1) dated 29 October 1914, repeating London's request that Pitcher be sent back to England. Capt Pitcher returned to the UK shortly afterwards. By the following March he was a lieutenant-colonel and Deputy Commandant of the Central Flying School.

[7]AIR1/1283/204/11/13. The quotation is taken from an apparently private, and therefore unreferenced, letter dated 4 December 1914 from Lt-Col Trenchard to his successor at South Farnborough, Lt-Col E.B. Ashmore, who now commanded the recently established Administrative Wing.

[8]AIR1/827/204/5/188. Although the information had been available previously elsewhere, e.g. in a memorandum despatched to the War Office by Maj-Gen Henderson on 8 January 1915, a consolidated list of the twenty-one observers who had qualified to date was published, along with their effective dates of qualification, in HQ RFC's Routine Orders for 12 January 1915 (AIR1/829/204/5/219). Thereafter, until mid-1916, the certification of each individual observer was usually announced in Routine Orders more or less as it occurred.

[9]AIR1/1057/204/5/1555. These figures, and the data at Fig. 2, have been extracted from monthly nominal rolls identifying all commissioned observers available for operations in France, including those who were not yet fully qualified. These lists were maintained by HQ RFC from December 1914 until at least the following August.

Typical of the relatively primitive aeroplanes available for operations in the spring of 1915 was this BE2a, 206, which was allotted to No 6 Sqn at Bailleul in December 1914. (J.M. Bruce/G.S. Leslie collection)

In the meantime a training scheme, of sorts, had been introduced at home. Before the end of 1914 a number of junior officers had been attached to the rump of the RFC, which had been left behind in England, with a view to their becoming observers. The first to arrive at Netheravon was 2/Lt J. Robertson (RFA) who reported to No 1 Sqn on 28 November; he was followed the next day by 2/Lts F.H. Jenkins (RFC Special Reserve) and W.E.B. Wright (KOYLI) and they were joined on 1 December by Lt E.M.I. Buxton (Royal Fusiliers) and 2/Lt H.F.T. Blowey (RFA). There is some evidence to suggest that others went to No 7 Sqn, although, if they did, this writer has failed to establish their identities. Early in December another four were sent to Chelmsford to join an RFC flight which had recently been established there. They were Lt W. Milne (Loyal North Lancs), 2/Lt H.W. Medlicott (Rifle Bde), 2/Lt W.P. Knowles (Manchester Regt) and 2/Lt W.E. Gardner (DLI).[10] Of these nine men only Blowey, Medlicott and Milne appear to have seen active service as observers in France, all three crossing the Channel during January 1915.

There were no courses as such at Netheravon (or at Chelmsford), not even a formal syllabus. These proto-observers were simply expected to develop their map-reading skills and to become familiar with the practice of troop reconnaissance conducted from the air by exercising with soldiers training on Salisbury Plain or elsewhere. Fortnightly reports as to each student's progress and efficiency were called for, which suggests that their stay was expected to be of several weeks' duration. Few other specific references to this early phase of observer training appear to have survived but it is evident that one lesson was learned very quickly. The following instruction appears among No 1 Sqn's Routine Orders for 8 December 1914 – 'Officers and NCOs acting as observers will invariably have their maps tied to them if they are not attached to the aeroplane.' Thereby, no doubt, hung a tale, but while one of these early trainees may well have been the first observer to lose his maps in the slipstream he was certainly not the last.

It is interesting to note that this anecdote clearly indicates that some NCOs were already being trained for observation duties. It was generally assumed, however, that the levels of intelligence and education required to perform satisfactorily in the air were more likely to be exhibited by officers. While there was never any prohibition on non-commissioned personnel flying as observers (or as pilots), the RFC/RAF always preferred its aircrew to be officers, NCOs tending to be used only when this was necessary to balance the supply and demand equation. Nevertheless, it should be noted that two of the first three wartime casualties to be sustained by the RFC were non-commissioned personnel. 2/AM H.E. Parfitt was killed, along with his pilot, when their BE8 crashed on a non-operational sortie on 16 August 1914 and Sgt-Maj D.S. Jillings was wounded by rifle fire six days later.

[10]AIR1/823/204/5/48. These four officers were directed to report to Chelmsford by War Office letter 121/1181(MA1) dated 3 December 1914.

1914–15. Intimations of the need to grant observers a degree of formal recognition

As soon as it began to become apparent that the war was unlikely to be 'over by Christmas' after all, some consideration began to be given to the long-term implications of attaching officers to the RFC as observers. As early as 17 November it was pointed out that six of the observers currently flying with the RFC were Staff College graduates but that, apart from their rank, their standing was no greater than that of the half-dozen Gentleman Cadets who had reported to GHQ three days before. Soldiers are very fond of hierarchies and the RFC had signally failed to create one for its handful of observers. To redress this situation to some degree, it was suggested that provision should be made for the more senior officers to be employed on specialist liaison duties at corps or division level and that this service should be regarded as being at a Staff Officer grade.

This proposal appears to have been acted upon as soon as it was received, as Maj Furse and Capts Hughes-Hallett and Hewlett were all graded as staff officers (GSO3) with effect from 18 November. They were assigned, respectively, to HQ RFC, and to Headquarters 1st and 2nd Wgs with effect from 16 December.[11] The real significance of this event was not appreciated at the time but, in effect, it had served notice that something would eventually have to be done about recognising the status of observers – all of them.

[11]AIR1/829/204/5/219. The RFC's squadrons had been grouped into wings with effect from 29 November 1914, these arrangements being publicised by Army Order 62 of 16 January 1915.

Although the assignment of observers to staff appointments never became a common practice, this is not to say that the first few made no worthwhile contribution. The topic on which they concentrated at first was the ability of aviators to direct artillery fire effectively, a fact that was far from being universally recognised at the turn of 1914–15. Writing to Lt-Col Ashmore in December 1914, Trenchard described the situation as follows (the passage is quoted *verbatim*).[12]

> 'The co-operation with artillery is fairly good and will undoubtedly get rapidly better as soon as the gunners realise that our observers in the air are to be trusted in marking shots, but at present there is a certain amount of distrust placed in the observer who signals short, and the battery only creeps up to the target instead of making a bold increase in range. Also it very often happens that a battery is ordered to fire at a certain target and when the observer is in the air finds that the target does not exist or has been moved, and he finds the enemies battery five or six hundred yards away. The battery really comes under the control of the observer and can be put on to the new target with the greatest of ease, if batteries will tumble to it. Some of the Division Generals and Battery Commanders are good in letting the observer do this; others say, "Oh the observer does not know what he is doing," and refuses to alter range or line, and it is a waste of valuable time and machines if batteries do not trust the observer.
>
> Whenever I send up a senior gunner as observer batteries trust him more, but the gunner observer will tell you that it is just as easy for the infantry Officer to observe for artillery fire as it is for him, and in this I agree.'

It is evident from the gist of this piece of tortured (pre-Maurice Baring) Trenchardian prose that the first three observers-cum-staff officers would have plenty to do over the next few months, selling the concept of air observation to often very sceptical field gunners. Furse, whose credibility would have been considerably enhanced by the fact that he was a professional gunner himself, is reported to have been particularly effective in preaching the RFC's gospel.[13]

In the event, the need to provide suitable ground appointments for senior observers turned out to be a transient requirement because the supply of such officers soon began to dry up. In mid-December 1914 50% of all observers attached to the RFC had been majors or captains. By the following August there were no majors and the proportion of captains had declined to a mere 10% of the total. Why? Because by that time any officer wise enough to consider the practical implications of RFC policy had concluded that volunteering to fly as an observer was not a sound career move. (The basis of this conclusion is examined in more detail below.) It was fortunate for the RFC that such long-term considerations failed to deter ample numbers of energetic, but trench-bound, youngsters from seeking a more satisfying and dynamic (and comfortable?) occupation. For the time-being, therefore, an adequate supply of volunteers continued to come forward, but by 1915 being an observer was already perceived to be a job for subalterns and lieutenants.

[12]AIR1/1283/204/11/13. The passage quoted is taken from a letter dated 4 December 1914, written just four hours after that at Note 7.

[13]For reference to Maj Furse's efforts, see, for instance, Maurice Baring's *Flying Corps Headquarters 1914–1918*, (1920). While at the Front co-ordinating ground signals for contact patrols being flown by No 3 Sqn during the Battle of Loos, Furse sustained very serious head injuries on 30 September 1915.

Early 1915. The RFC begins to recruit and train observers in the field

By the end of 1914 it was clear that the trickle of observers being sent out from England would be insufficient to meet the requirements of the operational squadrons. Furthermore, the demand for additional pilots, both to permit the formation of new squadrons and to replace casualties, had begun to exceed the capacity of the training system. In January 1915 the War Office acknowledged that the Central Flying School (CFS) could no longer cope with the task alone and it was decided that home-based Service Squadrons working up to operational status would also have to function as advanced flying training schools. To satisfy the urgent need for additional pilots it was also directed that 'training with artillery, and other similar duties, *and the training of observers* will be cut down to the lowest minimum possible' (author's italics).[14]

This major change in training policy will not have been introduced on a whim and it is almost certain that HQ RFC would have been at least aware of, if not actively consulted in, the War Office's deliberations. Anticipating that the flow of additional observers was likely to dwindle, HQ RFC was obliged to take matters into its own hands by launching what amounted to a local recruiting campaign. Late in December authority was granted for Wing Commanders to arrange for two artillery officers to be attached to each of their squadrons for periods of up to twenty-one days.[15] The aims of this initiative were ostensibly to promote an appreciation of the advantages of aerial observation and to foster a mutual understanding of the operational limitations imposed by the contemporary state of the arts of aviation and field gunnery, but it was clearly hoped that some of the participants might also be enticed into volunteering to fly on a permanent basis. Attached officers were entitled to an additional three shillings per day (the instructional rate of flying pay) while they were with the RFC and any who showed an interest in becoming full time observers were invited to apply through their COs once they had returned to their units.[16]

While the opportunity to spend three weeks among aviators served to attract a number of gunner officers, the upper echelons of the artillery community regarded the RFC's scheme with some misgiving. Suspecting that the RFC was plotting to 'poach' some of its men, HQ Second Army wrote to GHQ seeking clarification as to the long term implications of such attachments. The letter was passed to Col Sykes (by now Chief of Staff and deputy to Maj-Gen Sir David Henderson) who explained that the RFC considered that there were two classes of observer; those who were fully trained and who were 'attached permanently' to the RFC, and those

[14]AIR1/1288/204/11/53. The revised arrangements for flying training, including the reduction of effort to be devoted to role training and the instruction of observers, were announced by War Office letter 87/4469(MA1) dated 9 January 1915.

[15]AIR1/829/204/5/219. The opportunity for artillery officers to be attached to fly with the RFC was announced in HQ RFC's Routine Orders for 27 December 1914, further amplification being provided on 5 and 6 January 1915.

[16]*Ibid.* It is interesting to observe that, in the interests of its recruiting drive, the RFC had gained permission to offer a financial inducement before it had even been granted authority to pay the men it was already employing. Although rates of flying pay for observers had been established before the war it took several months for the War Office to authorise issues to be made. The procedure to be followed was eventually promulgated in HQ RFC's Routine Orders for 5 January 1915.

who, trained or otherwise, were only temporarily attached.[17] The officers currently being 'borrowed' from the artillery were regarded as being in the second category but Sykes admitted that, once trained, he would be glad to offer them employment within the first group. If this offer were to be accepted, however, it would have to be on a permanent basis; the RFC could not afford to commit itself to observers who might subsequently be withdrawn.

With hindsight it can be seen that Sykes' real problem was that (barring one or two who were Special Reservists) the RFC was actually in the rather vulnerable position of not having *any* observers that it could really call its own and it was therefore having to beg, borrow or steal them from other arms of the Service. From HQ RFC's immediate perspective, however, the only problems were quantity and quality and, so long as volunteers were forthcoming, it was content. No one could see that it was of any consequence which cap badge an observer wore, but time would eventually show that it really did matter.

So far as quantity was concerned there appears to have been little difficulty in obtaining volunteers. Taking advantage of the relatively subdued level of operational activity imposed by the winter of 1914–15, the RFC decided to replace its relatively low-key individual attachments with a concentrated formal training programme. To meet this requirement, three-week courses were organised by 1st and 2nd Wgs during February, all the students being drawn from the Royal Artillery.

Quality, however, turned out to be a rather different matter. In March the wings reported that, of the two dozen or so men they had recently trained, only ten were considered to be suitable candidates for permanent employment as observers. In the event only four of these officers, 2/Lts W.S. Douglas, G.S.M. Ashby, R. Balcombe-Brown and C.H. Awcock, actually exercised this option and two of them (Douglas and Ashby) had already committed themselves well in advance of their courses, having been attached to the RFC at their own request from 26 December and 7 January, respectively. It was a disappointingly small return for what had turned out to be a major diversion of effort and no further large-scale courses were laid on.

In the light of this experience, Col Sykes reflected further and in April he recommended to GHQ that there should be three recognised categories of observer.[18]

a. A highly trained group of eight men per squadron attached permanently to the RFC.
b. Two further men per squadron, undergoing training and forming a first reserve.
c. A group who, although fully trained, would return to their parent units whence they could be attached to the RFC for specific tasks as required by their own commanders while also representing a second tier of reserves.

In effect, the existing arrangements already included the first and second groups (although there were only seven, rather than eight, men in the first) and Sykes was granted authority to create the third.[19] This was done by HQ RFC's running a course for sixteen officers, again all artillerymen, between 16 and 25 April. Once this course had graduated the immediate needs of the RFC in France had been virtually satisfied, although, in the event, only three of the officers who had attended HQ RFC's course were subsequently to fly as observers.[20]

Sykes had one more card up his sleeve, however – the cadets who had been sent out from Sandhurst in November (see page 8). Stating that 'the experiment has so far proved distinctly successful', he wrote to the War Office requesting that another six be sent out in May, noting that they 'should not be heavier than ten stone, seven pounds.'[21] These men were equally successful and the RFC would soon begin trawling for much larger numbers of graduating cadets, although most of these would be required as pilots rather than as observers.

Since there were deemed to be adequate numbers of trained observers available by the spring of 1915 and a system was in place to provide replacements, there could no longer be any justification for misemploying pilots. Instructions were therefore issued to the effect that 'two qualified pilots are not to ascend in the same aeroplane, except by special permission of a Wing Commander.'[22]

The manning situation was further improved by the availability of limited numbers of non-commissioned personnel. Although the RFC instinctively preferred to use officers for flying duties, it had not ruled out the use of soldiers. Some of these men were volunteers from the trenches but most tended to be the more capable of the RFC's own NCOs and air mechanics. While it may have been tentative at first, in view of the aptitude and enthusiasm shown by these men, this practice became quite widespread. Many of these men would eventually be formally recognised as qualified observers and, following a successful period of active service, it was not uncommon for them to be sent home to be commissioned and trained as pilots.

[17]AIR1/2148/209/3/199. HQ RFC letter G/155/1 dated 4 January 1915. Col Frederick Sykes had originally gone to France as deputy to Brig-Gen Henderson. In November 1914 Henderson was promoted to major-general and posted to command 1st Division, leaving Sykes in charge of the RFC. This situation was to be short-lived, as Henderson resumed his original post on 20 December. He fell ill shortly afterwards, however, and, although he did not actually relinquish his appointment, Sykes continued to function as the *de facto* GOC until May 1915, signing much of his correspondence (including this particular letter) as 'Colonel, Commanding the RFC in the Field.'

[18]*Ibid.* HQ RFC letter CRFC 1578(A) dated 15 April 1915.

[19]AIR1/366/15/231/6. The official establishment (i.e. the officially approved manpower allocation) of a standard RFC Service Squadron, had been published by the War Office as 87/4040(MA1), dated 8 December 1914. It provided for seven permanently attached observers per unit.

[20]AIR1/831/204/5/225. The sixteen officers who attended the course run by HQ RFC are listed below. The three who subsequently served as observers were Kennedy, Ryan and Prickett who flew with Nos 4, 6 and 1 Sqns respectively.

Name	Unit
Capt E.H. Marshall	19th Bty RFA, 2nd London Div
Capt G.P.R. McMahon	3rd Siege Bty RFA, 3rd Div
Capt R. Archer Houblon	32nd Bty RFA, 8th Div
Capt G. Weldon	43rd Bty RFA, 6th Div
Capt M. Farrant	22nd Bty RFA, 23rd Div
Capt J.C. Dixey	3rd Worcester Bty RFA, S Midland Div
Capt V.A.H. Taylor	105th Bty RFA, 7th Div
Capt G.G. Walkden	4th Howitzer Bde, N Midland Div
Capt K.E. Kennedy	10th Bty RFA, 1st Canadian Div
Lt D.A. Buchan	2nd Bty RFA, Meerut Div
Lt H.S. Ellis	126th Bty RFA, 4th Div
Lt C.E. Ryan	67th Bty RFA, 27th Div
Lt G. Burrard	64th Bty RFA, Lahore Div
Lt A.G. Parsons	51st Bty RFA, 1st Div
Lt L. Prickett	71st Heavy Bty RGA, 5th Div
Lt J.R. Cleland	48th Bty RFA, 2nd Div

[21]AIR1/122/15/40/116. CRFC 934/3(A) dated 23 April 1915. The six men sent in response to this request left for France on 18 May. They were 2/Lts J. Parker, M.W. Greenhow, G.C. Levick, E.W. Leggatt, J.E. Evans and C.S. Whitworth.

[22]AIR1/831/204/5/225. HQ RFC's Routine Orders for 10 May 1915. This order actually represented a reminder, suggesting that there may have been some reluctance to comply with an earlier edict.

1915. The nature of observer training in the field

While Sykes' endeavours had ensured that each squadron would continue to be furnished with an adequate supply of officer observers, his reference to some of them being 'highly trained' smacked of wishful thinking. In fact, with no further courses being organised, there was no formal training system whatsoever to prepare later arrivals for their duties and new observers were more or less obliged to fend for themselves. An impression of what this meant in practice can be gained from the experience of 2/Lt C.F.A. Portal (RE) who had been in France since the beginning of the war as a Motor Cyclist Officer attached to the Signals Company serving HQ I Corps.[23]

When he reported to No 3 Sqn on 5 July 1915 Portal already knew the Morse code and considered that he could read a map – on the ground. He had never seen a Lewis gun, however, nor had he ever been up in an aeroplane, and he had 'only the vaguest idea' of what his new employers might require him to do. He joined A Flight, which was commanded by another relative newcomer, Capt T. O'B Hubbard,[24] who instructed him to familiarise himself with the Lewis gun, as they would be flying together in two days' time. Doing as he was bid, Portal devoted the next several hours to studying the machine-gun. Wiser counsels soon prevailed, one of the older hands pointing out 'that the Morane could not carry it and me' and recommending the more practical alternative of a stripped 0.303 rifle.[25]

The next day Portal was briefed on the Artillery Code by another observer and on the third morning the crew flew their first mission, a reconnaissance which took them as far east as Lille. Portal found his first exposure to anti-aircraft fire somewhat disturbing and the engine's tendency to cut out intermittently was sufficiently alarming to frustrate some of his attempts to count rolling stock. Despite getting lost twice, they eventually returned safely to Lozinghem. As Portal later recalled:

> 'At the time, it did not appear strange that a reconnaissance should be performed by a pilot who had only once before flown the type of aeroplane used (and wrecked it) and had never been over the objective or any other part of the enemy's lines, accompanied by an observer who had never been in the air at all.'

After a few more reconnaissance sorties, Hubbard and Portal progressed to gunnery control. The squadron's reigning artillery co-operation expert gave them a thirty-minute briefing on what was involved, the theory subsequently being backed up by two demonstration shoots. That was it. The crew was now considered to be fully trained. Charles Portal was officially accredited as a qualified observer with effect from 4 August. His experience had been typical. A new observer was simply thrown in at the deep end. Whether he succeeded in learning to swim in his strange new environment, and how strongly, depended almost entirely upon his enthusiasm, aptitude and resourcefulness, reinforced by any advice that might be offered by sympathetic colleagues. By mid-1915 there were certainly some relatively *experienced* observers in France but Sykes' 'highly trained' was a misnomer.

When 2/Lt 'Peter' Portal joined No 3 Sqn in 1915 it was flying Morane Ls but shortly after he had qualified as an observer it re-equipped with Morane LAs like this one. (J.M. Bruce/G.S. Leslie collection)

The nacelle of a wrecked Vickers FB5 used by No 5 Sqn at Abeele during 1915 to familiarise new observers with the rudimentary appointments of their battle station.

Another first-hand account of squadron-based training in 1915, albeit rather later in the year, has been left us by E.M. Roberts.[26] An American, and a volunteer from the trenches, Cpl Roberts, like Portal, also learned his trade with No 3 Sqn. He found that he had to work 'fourteen hours each day' in order to absorb all that he was required to learn about gunnery direction, aerial gunnery and W/T work. He was also obliged to spend several days with an artillery battery, although he records that 'nobody had explained to me so far why I had been attached to the battery and nobody ever did, but I surmised that they wanted me to get up some acquaintance with artillery practice.'

Attaching observers to artillery batteries was to become quite a common procedure, both for trainees learning the ropes and, later on, in the interests of maintaining a close working relationship between each squadron and the batteries which it served. It was typical of the RFC's makeshift approach to training in 1915, however, that no one seemed to have bothered to provide Cpl Roberts with any specific guidance.

Before leaving the RFC's early in-house training system, one more anecdote is offered to show just how inept it could

[23]AIR1/2386/228/11/1. Taken from an account of his previous Service experience, written by Sqn Ldr C.F.A. Portal when a student on No 1 Course at the RAF Staff College in 1922.

[24]Hubbard was no novice, as he had qualified for Royal Aero Club Certificate No 222 as early as 4 June 1912. He had spent much of the next three years instructing at the Central Flying School but, having only recently taken up his appointment as a Flight Commander with No 3 Sqn, he had little experience of flying in France.

[25]AIR1/829/204/5/219. HQ RFC's Routine Orders for 6 January 1915 had specified the officially approved armament for aeroplanes at this stage of the war. Pilots were supposed to carry a standard Service revolver or a Webley Scott automatic pistol, as and when the latter became available. When a machine-gun was fitted, observers were supposed to carry the same sidearm as pilots but, if a Lewis gun were unavailable or impractical, the recommended weapon was a French carbine.

[26]E.M. Roberts, *A Flying Fighter* (1918).

sometimes be. On 3 January 1916, Lt the Hon E.F.P. Lubbock, then an observer with No 5 Sqn, noted in his diary that:[27]

> 'We had a lecture today on "Co-operation between aeroplanes and artillery". The man got up and opened his lecture by saying "I don't know much about artillery and I have never been in an aeroplane, nor have I ever seen an aeroplane working with the artillery, but I have been ordered to lecture to you." After that we had to listen for half an hour to his lecture on work which we had all been doing for months!'

1915. The beginnings of an observer training system at home

Despite its obvious limitations, in the absence of any better solution, an essentially pragmatic approach to the provision of air observers for the squadrons already in France was sustained, substantially unchanged, until early 1917. New squadrons arriving from home brought their own observers with them but, as yet, there were still no dedicated training facilities in the UK. The most common practice was for prospective home-grown observers to be initially attached either to a Reserve Aeroplane Squadron or to a Service Squadron acting as a training unit prior to its mobilisation. On completion of their 'courses' they were posted to a unit which was preparing to deploy.

Some idea of the scope of the basic training being provided at home in the summer of 1915 is conveyed by the recollections of (then 2/Lt) R.R. Money. An impatient infantry subaltern, Money had applied to serve in the RFC as a means of getting into action. He was accepted as an observer, a significant factor being his light weight.

The limited power of the aero-engines of the day placed very real constraints on the weight-lifting capabilities of early aeroplanes and contemporary observers were expected to weigh no more than eleven stone. This point was laboured by an amply upholstered Lt-Col J.F.A. Higgins (then commanding 3rd Wg) at an RFC conference held in August.[28] Maj-Gen Henderson acknowledged that the weight of an observer was important but considered that 'we ought not to reject first class officers merely because they happen to weigh over 11 stone,' pointing out, a trifle tartly, that he needed 'to keep the supply of future Wing Commanders in view.'

Money was posted to Fort Grange in June 1915 where his instruction was supervised by Capt H. Wyllie of No 17 Sqn. There were ...[29]

> '... about eight of us on the course, and for the next fortnight we practised signalling, attended lectures and went up on practice reconnaissances on which we had to write reports. We also practised artillery observation, both from the air and in a hangar where a model village and trench system had been built, enabling the would-be observer, mounted in the roof, to spot and locate the flashes of tiny bulbs concealed variously over the ground. Locations and corrections were signalled down by buzzer.'

By late 1916 the sort of training aid described by Money was available at most home-based units involved in the training of observers. Known as Artillery Targets their design varied in detail, as they were locally produced, but a typical target was described as being made 'of wood, about 10 feet square, with scenery painted on it. Small holes are pierced in the wood and the electric bulbs placed under to represent the shot exploding. This target should be raised a few feet off the ground to allow for repairs, etc.'[30] Some units made their targets even more sophisticated, using the light bulbs to represent enemy gunfire and adding a means of producing puffs of smoke to simulate the impact of outbound shells. To supplement this piece of hardware it was also necessary to produce a gridded map, representing the area of simulated terrain. Trainees were required to report the location of targets using the grid system and to estimate aiming corrections, converting these into Clock Code. Messages were transmitted to the 'battery' using a silent Morse key – silent to simulate the conditions in a noisy, open cockpit where the operator would be unable to hear his own transmissions.

The facilities available elsewhere in 1915 were not always as sophisticated as those at Gosport but, wherever they were sent, all observers were supposed to be taught something about the arts of aerial reconnaissance, photography and artillery direction, to practise Morse, to be introduced to the Lewis gun and to acquire some familiarity with the airborne environment. Unfortunately, very few flying hours could be dedicated to the training of observers, as it was even more important that their equally green pilot colleagues should accumulate as much airborne time as they could before they were committed to action. While some will have managed to squeeze in a few trips, many observers found out much of what they knew about the business of flying through a process of osmosis rather than through actually getting airborne.

While the unstructured, makeshift training methods being applied, both at home and in the field, inevitably produced varied results, they sufficed to build up numbers. By 31 August 1915 there were 113 officers serving as observers in France. Of these, forty-six were recognised as being fully qualified.[31] It is interesting to note that by this time the previously overwhelming predominance of artillerymen had largely disappeared and only 20% of the observers flying on operations were 'gunners'. While it is highly unlikely that any fault will have been found with their knowledge of gunnery, the group of men trained locally (and hastily) early in 1915 may have turned out to have been rather too specialised, and thus less flexible, compared to those drawn from the infantry and elsewhere – or perhaps it was simply that the RA preferred to keep its officers on the ground.

[27]In the course of preparing a brief biography of Eric Lubbock, his family kindly granted this writer access to his papers, including the journal from which the quotation is taken.

[28]AIR1/920/204/5/884. Minutes of a Wing Commanders Conference chaired by Sir David Henderson. The document is undated but, since the implications of the recently introduced observers badge was the main topic under discussion, the meeting will probably have been held during the last week of August 1915.

[29]The extract is taken from the first of a series of articles entitled *With the Royal Flying Corps* which appeared in five successive editions of *The Royal Air Force Quarterly* from October 1930 onwards. The by-line is a cryptic 'GOM' but the text is strewn with clues as to who the author really was. He states, for instance, that he was one of the original seven observers who crossed over to France with No 12 Sqn in September 1915 and, since he names the other six, it is quite clear who the writer must have been. Money subsequently revealed his identity himself when these articles became the basis of the first half of his book, *Flying and Soldiering* (1936). 'GOM', incidentally, was a reference to his post-war service at Leuchars where he was known as the Grand Old Man of C (Reconnaissance) Training Flight, a unit with which he flew, and which he intermittently commanded, in the mid-1920s.

[30]AIR1/1266/204/9/61. This description was circulated to all units controlled by Headquarters Northern Group by the officer responsible for W/T training in his NG/100 dated 17 December 1916.

[31]These figures have been drawn from a late edition of the nominal rolls referred to at Note 9.

Unit	Qualification State				Total
	A	B	C	D	
Squadrons in France					
No 1 Sqn	9	2	–	–	11
No 2 Sqn	10	2	–	–	12
No 3 Sqn	9	2	–	–	11
No 4 Sqn	8	3	–	–	11
No 5 Sqn	4	6	–	–	10
No 6 Sqn	8	3	–	–	11
No 7 Sqn	7	2	–	–	9
No 8 Sqn	2	7	–	–	9
No 10 Sqn	7	6	–	–	13
No 11 Sqn	5	4	–	–	9
No 12 Sqn	2	10	–	–	12
No 16 Sqn	5	6	–	–	11
Squadrons in the UK					
No 9 Sqn	–	–	–	4	4
No 13 Sqn	–	–	15	–	15
No 14 Sqn	–	–	6	–	6
No 15 Sqn	–	–	–	3	3
No 17 Sqn	–	–	1	–	1
No 18 Sqn	–	–	–	2	2
No 21 Sqn	–	–	4	–	4
No 22 Sqn	–	–	–	8	8
No 23 Sqn	–	–	–	7	7
Totals	76	53	26	24	179

Fig. 3. *Distribution of commissioned observers serving with RFC Service Squadrons on 15 October 1915. Nos 19, 20, 24, 25, 26, 30 and 31 Sqns also existed, their status varying from embryo to fully operational, but none of these had any observers on strength on this specific date.*

A – *Fully qualified and on active service.*

B – *On active service but still on probation.*

C – *Training complete, awaiting mobilisation.*

D – *Under training.*

Apart from those who were being killed or injured in combat and in flying accidents, there was further considerable wastage among observers due to many of the more experienced men returning home to become pilots. Nevertheless, the numbers of commissioned observers available continued to increase as the RFC expanded and by the middle of October the grand total had risen to 179; the distribution of these officers is shown at Fig. 3.[32] Note that by this time the average strength of the operational squadrons was approaching eleven observers per unit, somewhat higher than the authorised nine (seven qualified plus two under training). The effective figure was actually closer to sixteen as there were now substantial numbers of non-commissioned personnel serving as gunners or as *de facto* observers, a survey establishing that there were forty-nine flying operationally during October.[33]

Since this BE2a (336) served with the Wireless Flight and Nos 2, 4, 8 and 9 Sqns between August 1914 and October 1915, it is likely that a good many of the RFC's earliest observers will have flown in it. (J.M. Bruce/G.S. Leslie collection)

1915. Men only

While nothing ever came of it, it should be recorded that at least one woman volunteered to fly as an observer, a Miss E.M. Pearson (of Old House, Southam) offering her services to the War Office in August 1915. It is possible that she had been inspired by the Marchioness of Londonderry who had recently suggested that a Women's Legion should be formed to relieve soldiers of some of their more mundane domestic chores – cooking and cleaning, for instance. Shortly afterwards women did begin to work for the military, and in increasingly technical trades, but they were not formally enlisted until 1917 when they began to be employed, initially as drivers, by the RFC and the ASC.[34]

Needless to say, the War Office declined Miss Pearson's offer, Lt-Col E. Turner's polite but firm letter of rejection stating that it was 'quite impossible to consider (her) application as an observer in the Royal Flying Corps, as only officers are employed in that capacity.'[35] While this rationale may not have been scrupulously accurate, after all there were non-commissioned personnel flying as observers, it neatly avoided having to invoke the sensitive issue of gender. It should be remembered that in 1915 women had yet to be enfranchised. While the suffragettes were being relatively docile during the war years in the national interest, this represented only a truce, not a capitulation.

[32]AIR1/377/15/231/18. The data used at Fig. 3 is taken from a nominal roll of all officers serving with the RFC as at 15 October 1915, covered by War Office letter 114/Returns/1869(MA1) dated six days later.
[33]AIR1/1169/204/5/2591. The number of NCOs has been extracted from returns submitted by 1st, 2nd and 3rd Wgs in response to HQ RFC letter CRFC 934/19(A) dated 30 October 1915.
[34]AIR1/2433/305/33/1. Air Organisation (AO) Memorandum 338 dated 15 February 1917 granted immediate authority for the RFC to begin enlisting women for employment as cooks, waitresses, clerks and drivers.
[35]AIR1/373/15/231/14. War Office letter 87/670(MA1) dated 9 August 1915.

Chapter 3

Summer 1915. The RFC's provisional 'War Manual' is revised and republished

When the RFC had gone to war it had been operating to procedures which had been devised in 1913 and published in the provisional edition of the Flying Training Manual, Pt II of May 1914 (see page 4). In the meantime a number of pamphlets had been introduced to cover new techniques and procedures, notably artillery co-operation and contact patrols. Although the nature of aerial warfare was constantly changing, in 1915 an attempt was made to update the Manual to reflect the latest state of play. On 11 June proof copies of an extensively revised edition were circulated for comment. Chapter III began as follows:[1]

> 'Observation from aeroplanes can be carried out by the pilot single-handed, but as undivided attention is necessary for observing, it is usually advantageous to carry a passenger who is free to devote his whole attention to this task.
>
> The observer requires air experience and special training. He should have good eyesight, and possess sufficient military knowledge to enable him to recognise units of all arms in their various formations, and to be able to discern the most probable places in which to search for them.
>
> He should be able to read the Morse code.'

Although it was expressed in remarkably moderate terms,[1A] this passage reflected the fact that the RFC had completely abandoned its pre-war concept of using spare pilots and/or part-timers. There was no longer any question that observers needed to be professional *and* trained.

The new edition continued to stress many of the principles that had featured in the original draft of 1913. The importance of mutual confidence, for instance, and the consequent need for crews to fly together regularly, but in many respects it appears that the RFC still considered it 'inadvisable to lay down any definite rules as to their respective duties.' The draft stated, for instance, that 'the responsibility of finding the way must be shared by the pilot and observer.'

While the updated manual declined to allocate responsibility for navigation, it did provide positive guidance in another increasingly significant field of activity. It directed that 'as the attention of the observer is necessarily absorbed by his work in watching the ground, it is the special duty of the pilot to keep a lookout in the air for hostile aircraft.' This statement reflected the fact that sightings of enemy aircraft were becoming increasingly common and that these often resulted in aerial engagements, although most tended to be inconclusive as a result of the limited combat potential of the machines being flown by both sides. This situation was not to last for long, however. Experience, and the availability of more capable aeroplanes, would soon show that what had seemed sensible in June 1915 would turn out to be quite the opposite of what was required. No one could forecast this development at the time, of course, but within a year it would be increasingly the observer who spent his time scanning the skies while the pilot concentrated on events on the ground.

A major problem with the Flying Training Manual, Pt II was that it was virtually impossible to keep current. Air warfare was changing so rapidly that each edition was bound to be out of date almost as soon as it was published. Nevertheless, having attracted few adverse comments, the revised edition of June 1915 was eventually published on 15 November. It is perhaps worth pointing out, however, that this document had long ceased to be the 'War Manual' that Sykes had envisaged early in 1913. As its title indicates, it was now intended primarily for use within the training system at home, providing a framework of basic concepts and techniques with which to indoctrinate the next generation of aviators. As such it served its purpose well enough, but there was much still to be learned by these young men when they reached France.

Summer 1915. The skills required by an observer are identified

By mid-1915 the accumulated experience of air operations over France had made it possible to identify with some confidence the core skills that an observer needed to possess. At the end of July Lt-Col H.M.R. Brooke-Popham (Sykes' successor as GSO1 at HQ RFC) wrote to OCs 1st, 2nd and 3rd Wgs to ensure that all concerned were fully aware of what was required.[2] While it apparently failed to grasp the nettle very firmly (see Note 1A), this document represented the RFC's first attempt at defining a uniform training standard. It read:

> 'Although it is undesirable to lay down hard and fast rules as regards the qualifications of observers, it is considered that the same general standard of proficiency should be maintained throughout the RFC. Normally an officer should not be recommended for grading as a qualified observer unless:
>
> a. He knows the Lewis Gun thoroughly.
>
> b. Can use the RFC camera successfully.

[1]AIR1/785/204/558. This file contains a copy of the revised, June 1915, edition of the Flying Training Manual, Pt II.

[1A]It is noticeable that edicts handed down by the RFC's senior officers (and probably those of the other arms too) tended to use language which seems surprisingly moderate today. It was presumably taken for granted that any Public School-educated Edwardian gentlemen would automatically conform to the wishes of another who was acknowledged to be in a position of authority within the hierarchy. It would, therefore, have seemed boorish, unnatural and quite unnecessary to use vulgar imperatives like 'must' when an advisory 'should' was quite sufficient to secure compliance. After 1915 the proportion of officers who had attended Public Schools declined rapidly and the harsh realities and increasing complexity of warfare meant that it became inadvisable to rely on gentlemanly understandings. As a result, later regulations tend to be expressed with far greater precision and the use of executive language becomes increasingly common.

[2]AIR1/997/204/5/1241. HQ RFC letter CRFC 1938, dated 29 July 1915. Prior to this the definition of training standards had been left to the discretion of individual Wing Commanders. In 2nd Wg, for instance, Lt-Col C.J. Burke had published appropriate guidance to OCs Nos 1, 5 and 6 Sqns in his SW 252 of 19 April 1915 (AIR1/920/204/5/884).

While pilots tended to handle photography in tractor aeroplanes, observers were always obliged to do it in pusher types because of their layout. This FE2b, 4903 of No 18 Sqn, has a C Type camera mounted alongside the 'pulpit'. The gun, a stripped Mk I Lewis with a 47-round magazine, is carried on a No 2 mounting. (via Barry Gray)

c. Can send and receive by wireless at the rate of 6 words a minute with 98% accuracy.[3]
d. Knows the method of co-operation between aeroplanes and artillery thoroughly.
e. Has carried out two reconnaissances or has ranged batteries successfully on two occasions.'

The need for observers to be familiar with cameras would appear to have been axiomatic but aerial photography was far from being their exclusive preserve. Practical cameras had first begun to appear in substantial numbers in the spring of 1915, the Type A being a robust, if cumbersome, hand-held device which the observer had to lean out of his cockpit to use. This was more easily said than done, as it proved to be quite difficult to manipulate the camera's complex controls (each exposure required ten actions) in the often freezing slipstream while simultaneously having to support its weight, which was about 10 lb. The issue was further complicated by the fact that the observer occupied the front cockpit of most early aeroplanes, notably that of the ubiquitous BE2-series. This meant that his downward view was obscured by the lower wing which restricted him to taking oblique photographs, rather than the vertical shots which the map-makers would have preferred. To overcome these problems, the camera began to be carried on a fixed, external, vertical rack positioned well aft of the wings. This placed it alongside the rear cockpit where it was accessible only to the pilot who was therefore obliged to assume responsibility for its operation.

The introduction of the Type C camera in mid-1915 meant that pilots subsequently became permanently involved in photography. The Type C was much easier to operate but it was also too big and heavy (26 lb) to be used very effectively in the hand-held mode and it was almost always carried on a fixed external rack. Thereafter pilots continued to handle the majority of vertical photographic tasks, even in later types of aircraft in which the seating arrangements had been reversed. On the RE8, for instance, the camera mounting frame was generally fitted on the starboard side, alongside the front (pilots) cockpit, the fabric being removed from a section of the lower wing surface to provide an unrestricted field of view downwards. With the introduction of remote-controlled, semi-automatic cameras in 1917, however, it became possible to mount them internally within the rear fuselage (which may account for the fact that, while the RE8's external camera rack is often discernible in photographs, very few of them show a camera actually mounted on it). These later models could be operated by either crew member, but it remained the usual practice for the pilot to do it, sighting directly 'over the side' or, when available, via a Negative Lens Bomb Sight installed in the cockpit floor.

Although pilots may actually have taken the majority of wartime reconnaissance photographs, observers were always directly involved in this activity. They had, for instance, sole responsibility for the cameras carried internally in BE2s and 1½ Strutters which had been locally modified for long-range reconnaissance work, and for those which were occasionally mounted externally on the rear fuselage decking for oblique shots, as, for example, on some Nieuport 20s. Furthermore, it was invariably the observer who operated fixed cameras mounted alongside the 'pulpits' of pusher types engaged on photographic tasks and they also looked after later models of hand-held cameras – notably the purpose-built P14s and P18s. Even the introduction of internally-mounted, remotely-operated cameras did not cut them out of the loop entirely. These devices were totally inaccessible to the pilot of an RE8 or FK8 and, even if he actually took all the pictures, it was the back-seater who was responsible for changing the plate

[3]For test purposes a word was defined as having five characters.

A Type 52 wireless, the 'Sterling set', installed in the rear cockpit of a DH 9. Note the aerial wound on a drum with the business end disappearing through a fairlead on the floor.

magazines, for making any adjustments and for clearing jams. When Bristol Fighters were tasked with photographic work, the internally mounted camera tended to be operated exclusively by the observer. (For a summary of the evolution of British aerial cameras during WW I, see Annex A.)

Another noteworthy item featured in Brooke-Popham's list was the requirement for an observer to be able to use wireless equipment. This reflected the fact that by mid-1915, pyrotechnics, the Aldis lamp and the Klaxon horn had been largely superseded by radio for air-to-ground communication. The use of W/T had therefore become a key feature of the work of crews co-operating with the guns. Two points should made regarding the RFC's application of this relatively new technology. First, the most widely used equipment, the Sterling set,[4] provided only transmission facilities. A complementary system of signals was therefore necessary to permit ground-to-air communication. Many methods were employed, including heliographs, signal flares, Aldis lamps, Panneau shutters and strips of white cloth laid out on the ground in pre-arranged patterns (Popham panels). Secondly, although all observers were originally trained to use W/T, radio was never their exclusive preserve. Many pilots preferred to handle the 'buzzer' themselves and this became an increasingly common practice from the autumn of 1916 onwards. Since observers were becoming progressively less involved in using wireless equipment, from late 1917 onwards comprehensive instruction in W/T techniques was confined to observers earmarked for specific roles – of which more anon. (For a summary of later developments in British wireless technology during WW I, see Annex B.)

Before leaving the list of essential skills published in July 1915 it should be noted that the last item turned out, perhaps quite unintentionally, to have major long-term implications in terms of employment policy. The list's final provision had established the principle that an observer should not 'normally' be regarded as being qualified until he had flown in action. Before very long, however, the 'normally' had been forgotten and this principle had become an unconditional prerequisite. The problem was not that this regulation existed, but that it was applied selectively. It was not unreasonable for the RFC to require its observers to demonstrate their competence in action before they were regarded as being fully qualified, but it *was* unreasonable that newly trained pilots, some of them barely capable of flying their aeroplanes, were not required to clear the same hurdle. As will become apparent, this discriminatory approach was to cause problems in the future.

1915. Early attitudes towards observers

The RFC's attempt to impose some sort of standardisation on the training of its observers in mid-1915 implicitly acknowledged that these men had a vital role to play if a crew was to be fully effective and that they were certainly not mere passengers. While this was clearly the view of the responsible staffs, there is some anecdotal evidence to suggest that it was not held universally. The following passage probably overstates the case, but it was written by one who was there at the time and it conveys a clear impression that a different attitude prevailed at the working level, in some quarters at least. As Robert Money wrote in 1930 (see Chapter 2, Note 29):

> 'Observers were of no account in those days (*i.e. the summer of 1915*). This was not the official view, of course – merely the much more important social one. Observers were ballast, useless heavy impedimenta, ullage, who must be sat upon and squashed and made to feel their inferiority. As practically every observer looked with longing to the day when he would himself be a pilot, this attitude seemed quite natural to him.'

In view of the relatively primitive, underpowered and virtually unarmed aeroplanes which were available at the time, it is hardly surprising that some of the more aggressive and/or less perceptive pilots may well have had real reservations about the value of carrying the 'dead weight' of an observer. On the other hand, it is likely that many more expressed similar views out of a sense of playful 'pilot solidarity' and in a spirit of youthful banter, rather than from any deep-seated conviction – after all, until quite recently a significant proportion of them had been observers themselves. The facts were that in 1915 the RFC's primary functions were reconnaissance and artillery co-operation and there could be no real doubt that these roles could be fulfilled far more effectively by two men than by one.

Nevertheless, there was clearly perceived to be something 'second class' about being an observer, this perception being reinforced (as will become clear later) by the very real constraints which were imposed on his advancement by the RFC's administration. As a result, as Money makes plain, practically all observers aspired to become pilots, leading many to regard

[4]More formally designated as the Type 52, the Sterling set was a simple, robust spark transmitter. Devised by Lt B. Binyon RN at Eastchurch in October 1914, it had been adopted by the RFC as the standard equipment for artillery co-operation work by mid-1915 and it remained in large-scale use until the end of the war. Its name derived from the fact that the initial production contract went to the Sterling Telephone Company.

The evolution of the observers badge. On the left, the design as originally proposed by Maj-Gen Sir David Henderson in his letter of 15 June 1915 to GHQ BEF. At some stage an unknown hand has indicated that some of the lower feathers should be trimmed off. In the centre, the more muscular version covered by Field Marshal Sir John French's letter of 26 June to the War Office. On the right, the design as finally approved by Col Brancker on 23 July. Messrs Hobson & Co were subsequently paid seven shillings and sixpence to manufacture examples to what became the 'sealed pattern'. The prototypes were offered as (diagonally) six-inch and four-inch options; the smaller version being selected for production. The badge was formally introduced on 23 August 1915. As in WW II, although there was an officially registered pattern, individual haberdashers were not averse to running off their own interpretations and there were a number of subtle variations on the theme (see page 51).

their first flying tour as a means to an end and no more than an interim stage in achieving their ultimate ambition.

Much of this was probably inevitable at the time but the temporary nature of an observer's employment had a very unfortunate consequence. It delayed the early development of a sound basis of professionalism among non-pilot aircrew. The need for competent and skilled observers became increasingly apparent as the air war grew in complexity and intensity but the RFC never did see fit to acknowledge them properly. It was not until after the formation of the RAF in 1918 that the status of the observer's trade was to be afforded an appropriate degree of recognition. Even then it was granted only grudgingly, largely as a concession to the ex-RNAS faction, and it turned out to be more apparent than real.

1915. The RFC introduces a distinguishing badge for observers

Regardless of the disdain with which some junior pilots may have regarded their lesser brethren, observers were an increasingly prominent fact of life by mid-1915. They were still a rather ill-defined group, however, and it was time to do something about tidying them up. Maj-Gen Henderson brought this problem to the attention of GHQ in June when he suggested that observers should wear an appropriate badge. His letter included a sketch of a possible lop-sided, single-winged design, very like that which was eventually approved.[4A] The CinC concurred and wrote to the War Office as follows:[4B]

> '... some confusion is caused by the variety of uniforms and badges worn by officers of the different regiments who are now attached to the Royal Flying Corps for observation duties, and it is desirable to adopt a distinguishing mark for the qualified observer.'

He enclosed a new sketch, of a rather muscular unipinioned 'O' which could, he suggested, be 'worn in the same way as the existing pilot's badge'. If Field Marshal Sir John French wanted his observers to have a badge, no one at the War Office was disposed to argue and, after a little tinkering, the final version was approved by Col Brancker on 23 July.[4C]

[4A]AIR2/15/55/RFC/16. Letter CRFC 1701(A) dated 15 June 1915 from Maj-Gen Henderson to the Adjutant General at GHQ BEF.
[4B]*Ibid.* Letter Q/3276 dated 26 June 1915 from Field Marshal French to the War Office.
[4C]*Ibid.* Although the badge that was eventually introduced was embroidered in white on a black ground, it is interesting to observe that this file contains two examples of early prototypes which are embroidered in beige on khaki.

An initial order was placed for 100 to cover the immediate notional requirement which was for eighty-four – twelve squadrons each having up to seven observers. The badge was formally introduced in August 1915.[5] Its design, which, promptly attracted the *soubriqet* of 'the flying arsehole', was at first considered by some to add insult to injury. Money (probably overstating the case again) thought it 'bad enough to be an observer at all, without having to carry the badge of infamy.'

Nothing overt ever seems to have been said but the not-so-subtle implication of a *single*-winged badge was plain enough. An observer was simply not considered to be a fully-fledged aviator. He would become one only when he qualified as a pilot, which most were expected to do, at which point he would be given the 'other half' of his badge. Nevertheless, while the introduction of a badge had certainly represented a step in the right direction, it had been a relatively small one. If the standing of observers was really going to be raised it would be necessary for them to be accepted as full members of the RFC. For the time being, however, this privilege was still withheld.

By this time Sgt Maj F.C.V. Laws, who had been flying, both at home and overseas, since 1912, had already logged nearly 300 hours in aeroplanes, mostly on photographic work, not to mention his extensive experience in balloons and airships. Since he was almost certainly the most experienced non-pilot aviator in the RFC, on 22 September he submitted a formal request 'through channels' that he be permitted to wear an observers badge.[6] This raised the question of whether or not to recognise the efforts of other non-commissioned personnel being employed on flying duties and this was duly

[5]Army Order 327 of 23 August 1915, promulgated just two and half years after the introduction of the pilots flying badge (by Army Order 40 of 1 February 1913), authorised the wearing of a single-winged 'O' by officers qualified as observers. Interestingly, in the article referred to in Chapter 2, Note 29, Money claims that he and 2/Lt J. McArthur were the very first observers to be authorised to wear the flying 'O'. If so, this distinction was to be short-lived, as they were posted to Netheravon within a matter of days where their new CO, No 12 Sqn's Maj C.L.N. Newall, required them to remove their badges, as neither officer had yet flown in action and thus could not be recognised as being fully qualified in accordance with the requirements published on 29 July (see page 15).
[6]As explained in the Preface, within this book apostrophes will not be associated with the words 'observers', 'pilots', 'navigators', etc. when they are used as plural attributive nouns.

sanctioned in October.[7] Laws himself was specifically authorised to wear an observers badge on the 17th.[8]

This was not quite the end of the matter, however. Only three days later HQ RFC sought guidance as to whether *all* personnel engaged on airborne photographic work were entitled to wear an observers badge, on the grounds that they were just as much at risk as any other aviators. It was evidently decided that Sgt Maj Laws' case had been exceptional and that it did not represent a precedent. The DMA ruled that the only personnel entitled to wear observers badges were those who were considered to be fully qualified and who were regularly employed on 'artillery work, reconnaissance (or) machine gunnery.'[9] It was argued that any of these men ought to be perfectly capable of operating a camera and that it was therefore both unnecessary and inappropriate for unqualified personnel to fly operationally.

Having formally acknowledged the fact that the RFC was employing non-commissioned personnel other than pilots on flying duties, the War Office decided that they ought to receive an appropriate allowance. Flying pay for NCO observers and those drawn from the ranks was introduced at the beginning of 1916, the rates being a shilling per day while under instruction and two shillings once qualified. To begin with, the allowance was paid on a strictly *per diem* basis, i.e. only for those days on which the recipient actually flew.[10] In December this proviso was removed and NCOs and other ranks who were 'specially selected for continuous employment on observation duties' became eligible to draw flying pay permanently while so engaged.[11]

1915–16. The RFC joins the side-show campaigns

Thus far we have considered only those observers who flew in France. In fact they were to fly in every theatre in which the RFC was engaged, including Egypt, Palestine, Mesopotamia, Salonika, East Africa and Italy. Although the nature of warfare, both on the ground and in the air, was rather different in these 'side-show' campaigns, most airborne practices and procedures were similar to those employed on the Western Front. The major differences in the style of operations stemmed from the much smaller numbers involved and the fact that mobility was not totally denied to the ground forces involved. Thus, for instance, while artillery co-operation did take place, barrages were on nothing like the same scale or frequency as in Picardy or Flanders. While the fighting may have been less focused, however, it covered much larger areas and reconnaissance was at least as important as it was in France. Other very significant factors were the climate and the terrain. Ranging from jungle, through desert, to the mountains of the Balkans and the Trentino, operating conditions were generally more extreme and more hostile than those to which British aviators were accustomed and they brought their own associated hazards.

The first British military air presence in Egypt was established as early as November 1914 when a small detachment arrived from England. Although it brought no observers with it, the 'Air Unit, Egypt' soon acquired the services of a number of personnel formerly serving with the Anglo-Egyptian Government, including, for instance, Lt H.G. Hillas who had been with the Ministry of Finance, Lt D.R. Tweedie of the Coast Guard and 2/Lt Sir J. Paul of the Irrigation Dept. Like their contemporaries in France, they were totally untrained as aviators, but they did know the country. At least a dozen observers had been recruited by mid-January but by the end of that month eight of them had, in effect, been seconded to the RNAS as they had been assigned to Port Said to fly with the French Seaplane Flight based on the SS *Aenne Rickmers.*[12]

A second flight was set up in Mesopotamia during April 1915 but, while this and the flight in Egypt both saw some action, the RFC did not become deeply involved in the more remote theatres until the autumn, by which time the two original units had been reorganised and merged to become No 30 Sqn.[13] In November 5th Wg's Headquarters arrived in Egypt accompanied by two fully equipped units, Nos 14 and 17 Sqns. Both of these squadrons were more or less manned to establishment, their combined strength including twenty-one observers. At much the same time No 26 Sqn had sailed from England bound for Mombassa, while No 31 Sqn began to move to India, one flight at a time. It was July 1916 before No 31 Sqn's third flight reached its destination and in that month No 17 Sqn moved to Macedonia, so that the RFC now had a presence in most of the theatres in which British forces were currently engaged. The only significant exception had been the Dardanelles, the Aegean being an RNAS preserve.

Neither of the two units which had been most recently posted abroad had brought any observers with them but a head count in August 1916 revealed that, apart from those in France, sixty-five officers were serving with overseas RFC units as nominal observers, twenty-one of them being rated as fully qualified. The distribution was as follows: No 14 Sqn had twenty-eight (fifteen qualified); No 17 Sqn had fifteen (three qualified); No 1 Sqn AFC (later No 67 Sqn RFC) had fourteen (three qualified); No 26 had eight, all unqualified, while Nos 30 and 31 Sqns had none. The next influx of trained men did not arrive from England until October 1916 when

[7]Army Order 404, published on 11 October 1915, authorised the wearing of the observers badge by suitably qualified 'Warrant Officers, Non-Commissioned Officers and Other Ranks'.

[8]Laws, who was commissioned in November 1915, just a month after he had acquired his flying 'O', subsequently became one of the RAF's experts in photography. He eventually retired in 1946 as a group captain but, as his rank implies, he had by that time long since traded in his 'O' for a pilots badge.

[9]AIR1/997/204/5/1241. War Office letter 87/6370(MA1) dated 27 October 1915.

[10]AIR1/874/204/5/557. The introduction of daily flying pay for non-commissioned observers was announced by War Office letter 20/RFC/97(MA1) dated 10 January 1916, although implementation had to await the publication of a Royal Warrant and it was two months before the procedure for claiming was announced in HQ RFC Routine Orders for 14 March.

[11]AIR1/983/204/5/1167. Non-commissioned aircrew became eligible to draw flying pay on a permanent basis on the authority of a Royal Warrant which was reproduced in HQ RFC's Routine Orders for 22 December 1916.

[12]The *Aenne Rickmers* was a 4000 ton German steamer which had been seized by the British on the outbreak of war. Pressed into service as a seaplane carrier, her initial equipment was a pair of Nieuport IVs of *l'Aviation Maritime Française*. In August 1915 the ship was commissioned into the Royal Navy as HMS *Anne* for service with the East Indies and Egypt Seaplane Squadron.

[13]For much of 1915 the RFC's organisation in the Middle East was rather vaguely defined. The original flight in Egypt had been designated as No 30 Sqn with effect from 24 March, although no one seems to have bothered to notify the CO of this fact until as late as 31 July [War Office letter 87/4469(MA1)]. The other independent flight, which was operating in Mesopotamia, was sponsored by the Government of India. Following negotiations between London and Delhi, 'air unit personnel' in Mesopotamia were gazetted to the RFC on 5 August. Eventually, on 7 November, the unit in Mesopotamia was reorganised and redesignated to become the Headquarters plus A and B Flights of No 30 Sqn. Having been relieved by the arrival of No 14 Sqn at about the same time, No 30 Sqn's Egypt echelon moved to Basra to become C Flight.

No 47 Sqn was sent out to Salonika. Thereafter, few (if any) reinforcements or replacements were sent out and, as in France, most additional observers were obtained from local volunteers and trained in-house under squadron arrangements. A formal flying training organisation began to take shape in Egypt during 1916 but, as described later, it would be some time before this turned its attention to the provision of observers.

Meanwhile, a new observer in the Middle East had to cope as best he could. His situation would have been much the same as that encountered by 2/Lt Portal in France in 1915 (see page 12), although, if anything, the facilities were even less sophisticated. Flt Lt R.M.C. Macfarlan recalled his initiation into the mysteries of aviation with No 30 Sqn as follows:[14]

> 'In contrast to the training observers were given at home (*sic*) we were what might be called "self-taught". No instruction was given in Lewis gun or aerial firing and the procedure for Artillery Co-operation we had to pick up for ourselves, assisted by any other observer who was willing to spare the time. After five days with the squadron I was detailed to carry out a shoot without ever having been taken up for air experience, however, on explaining the situation, I was given a short flight and then sent up.'

Typical armament of an FE2d, a pair of Lewis Mk IIs. The front gun, which lacks an ammunition drum, is carried on a simple pillar mounting, possibly a No 4 Mk III. The other weapon, which has a 97-round magazine, is carried on a swan-necked telescopic No 10 mounting, the Anderson arch, which supported this, being hidden beneath the cockpit coaming. The rear gun could be handled by either crew member but it was of most use when wielded by the observer/gunner for rear defence. In order to fire backwards over the upper wing the gunner had to stand up, leaving him totally exposed above the knees, his only security being his grip on the gun plus whatever purchase he could gain from bracing his legs against the aircraft's structure. (J.M. Bruce/G.S. Leslie collection)

1915–16. The introduction of the two-seat fighter

Meanwhile, while the RFC had been establishing itself further afield, air operations in France were becoming increasingly sophisticated. During 1915 the RFC introduced several more warlike two-seaters, first the Vickers FB5, followed by a few of Farnborough's FE2as and, before the end of the year, the first of the far more numerous FE2bs. Although their primary functions were still reconnaissance and photography, these aeroplanes had been designed as gun-carriers so that they could also be used to engage the enemy in the air. Their arrival in France raised the profile of the observer significantly, as it was he who generally wielded the armament in these pusher types.[15]

The pusher concept was an exercise in lateral thinking which, by outflanking it, effectively solved the problem of providing a forward-firing gun in the absence of a satisfactory means of avoiding damage to the propeller of a tractor design. This layout afforded the occupant of the front cockpit, the observer, a virtually unrestricted field of fire to both sides and ahead of the aircraft and, by firing backwards over the upper mainplane (of an FE2), it was also possible for him to provide some sort of defence of the rear sector. Since the latter required him to stand up in a violently manoeuvring aeroplane while attempting to bring his gun to bear in an icy 70 mph slipstream, however, this can scarcely have been very effective.

Even so, if the crews of these pusher aeroplanes remained vulnerable to attacks from the rear, they were still much better off than those of most contemporary tractor types (like RE7s and BE2s) who were hard-pressed to draw a bead in *any* direction. The oblique angles at which fixed guns had to be installed (to avoid hitting the propeller) made 'aiming off' extremely difficult for the pilot and the need to allow additionally for deflection rendered the chances of his actually hitting the target very small indeed. Flexibly mounted guns were not the answer either, as it was almost impossible for the pilot to manipulate and fire these effectively as well as fly the aeroplane.

Nor was providing the observer with a flexibly mounted gun a satisfactory solution. Occupying the front cockpit, he was closer to, and therefore even more hampered by, the propeller than the pilot, and further boxed-in by the wings and a cat's cradle of struts and bracing wires. This resulted in a hopelessly restricted field of fire in most directions, although, by shooting over or past the pilot's head, he could provide some sort of rearward defence. Ingenious attempts to provide these early observation types with a means of defending themselves continued but, while they may have served to boost morale, none of them really overcame the fundamental limitation inherent in the unsatisfactory seating arrangements for the crew.[16] (Some additional notes on the evolution of aircraft gun armament are at Annex C.)

The enemy's early, unarmed, B-Type two-seaters had suffered from exactly the same drawbacks as the RFC's BEs, but the *pfennig* dropped much more quickly on their side of the lines. The Germans soon abandoned pre-war orthodoxy

[14]AIR1/2388/228/11/88. Taken from an account of his previous Service experience, written by Flt Lt R.M.C. Macfarlan at the RAF Staff College in 1926. Macfarlan flew as an observer with No 30 Sqn from September 1916 to March 1917 before returning to the UK to train as a pilot.

[15]Provision was sometimes made for the pilot of a Vickers FB5 or an FE2 to have access to a gun but this option was not often exercised.

[16]The practice of putting the 'passenger' in the front seat originated with early aircraft designers who sought to locate the disposable load more or less at the centre of gravity, so that it would make no difference to an aeroplane's balance whether or not the seat was occupied. Putting the pilot in the front cockpit meant that ballast often had to be carried in the back seat if the aeroplane were flown solo, hence the prominent warning notices which were frequently to be seen stencilled beneath the sills of the observers cockpits of, for instance, RE8s and Bristol Fighters.

These photographs convey some impression of the practical problems involved in mounting a machine-gun effectively in the front (observers) cockpit of a BE2. The left picture shows a Lewis Mk II on a No 1 Mk II swivel mount; there would have been a similar facility on the opposing (port) front strut. The right picture shows the same gun mounted on a telescopic Strange mounting; the gun could be swivelled through 180°, permitting the pilot in the rear cockpit to fire forwards and upwards. One should not, however, underestimate the difficulty involved in dismounting, transferring and remounting the gun, while dressed in bulky leather clothing at sub-zero temperatures in a 70 mph slipstream. (J.M. Bruce/G.S. Leslie collection)

and the observer in their more powerful, armed, C-Types, which began to appear in the spring of 1915, occupied the rear cockpit, permitting him to use his gun to considerable effect. It was to be another two years before the RFC followed suit, large numbers of late-model BE2s soldiering on well into 1917 before they were finally replaced by RE8s, DH4s and Armstrong Whitworth FK8s in which the allocation of cockpits was reversed.

Because of the lack of recognition which their efforts have generally received, the point needs to be made that, although pilots have tended to be given (or to have claimed?) most of the credit for the victories scored by the RFC's first generation of (pusher) two-seat fighters, practically all of them were actually shot down as a result of the marksmanship of observers. Furthermore, the introduction of the tractor-powered Sopwith 1½ Strutter from mid-1916 made very little difference to this pattern.

With a forward-firing Vickers gun, synchronised to fire through the propeller's arc, and with the observer's Lewis transferred to the rear cockpit, the layout of the Sopwith had established the classic two-seat fighter format. Unfortunately the 1½ Strutter had neither the power nor the manoeuvrability to cope with the Halberstadt and Albatros scouts by which it was opposed. By early 1917, although the Sopwith squadrons continued, like the rest of the RFC, to pursue a doggedly offensive strategy, they were being increasingly obliged to employ defensive tactics. As Sholto Douglas, OC No 43 Sqn at the time, later wrote, '... we found that it was necessary ... to lure him into attacking us; and then we would trust to the good shooting of our observers to pick off the Huns ... .'[17]

Thus, despite the availability of a more efficient fighting aeroplane, it had been introduced into service too late. For long-range reconnaissance work, the Sopwith's primary task, it became essential to fly in formation (usually five to seven aeroplanes, ideally with airborne reserves). While the defensive cross-fire which this provided increased the chances of survival, in terms of tactics it was very restrictive and presented the pilot with few firing opportunities. Thus it was

Lt P.E. Foot of No 15 Sqn demonstrating a Lewis Mk II, fitted with a Norman vane sight and a 97-round magazine, mounted on a No 3 Mk II barbette. More commonly known as the Scarff ring, this arrangement became the standard means of mounting defensive armament from 1917 until the mid-1930s. (J.M. Bruce/G.S. Leslie collection)

[17]Sholto Douglas, *Years of Combat* (1963).

still the observer who was actually inflicting most of the damage on the enemy in aerial combat.[18] The performance of the Sopwith's replacement, the remarkable Bristol Fighter, was such that it could hold its own in combat, even against single-seaters. Once its capabilities had been fully recognised, its crews were freed from the constraints imposed by the need to maintain formation and the Bristol's manoeuvrability did permit its pilots to bring the front gun to bear on occasion but, even then, the contribution made by back-seaters continued to be very substantial.

1916. The emergence of role specialisation

Some of the skills which had been identified in the summer of 1915 (see pages 15–16) were obviously essential for any observer operating over France but role specialisation had already begun to emerge. Despite the constraints imposed by the relatively limited capabilities of the available aeroplanes, two distinct styles of RFC activity had evolved. These could be broadly characterised as short- and long-range work, i.e. that which took place in close proximity to the trenches and that which penetrated some distance into enemy airspace. Depending upon their assignments, therefore, the duties of individual observers had begun to differ significantly.

Reflecting this development, and to improve the control and administration of the growing number of squadrons deployed (sixteen by the end of 1915), the RFC in France was reorganised in January 1916.[19] A brigade structure was introduced with one brigade being assigned to each of the armies in the field, of which there were four by April. Each brigade controlled two wings of aeroplanes. One, designated as an (Army) Wing, was concerned with relatively long-range work (reconnaissance in depth, bombing and air fighting). The other undertook shorter-range tasks (contact patrols, artillery co-operation and trench photography) and was designated a (Corps) Wing. Each wing had three or four squadrons.[20]

In this context it would be as well to give some scale to the rather imprecise terms 'long' and 'short'. With the armies deadlocked and dug in, it became possible to assign, more or less permanently, clearly defined areas of tactical control to each military formation. When the system was fully developed a typical corps had responsibility for a sector with a front of about 5000 yards while an army might control four such

An early Sopwith 1½ Strutter, 7777, with a Nieuport mounting for the rear gun. The Sopwith established the classic two-seat fighter configuration, the pilot (now in the front cockpit) having a fixed forward-firing Vickers gun and the observer a flexibly mounted Lewis. It only remained to move the cockpits closer together (as in the Bristol Fighter) to permit the crew to communicate more easily and thus co-operate more closely. (J.M. Bruce/G.S. Leslie collection)

sectors. In general the RFC's aerodromes were located within thirty miles of the lines (often much closer), and offensive operations penetrated a similar distance into enemy airspace. The activities of the majority of military aviators took place, therefore, within an airspace box roughly fifty miles long by twenty miles wide. Once the significant local landmarks had become familiar, navigation within this fairly confined area presented little problem – so long as the crew could see the ground. This meant that, for all practical purposes, flying was confined to the hours of daylight and could be severely curtailed by adverse weather.

While the reorganisation of early 1916 had served to define more precisely the role of each squadron, change did not end there. Over the next twelve months the accumulation of experience and developments in the nature of air warfare also began to raise questions over the specific functions of the individual members within a crew. Ever since mid-1915, when radio equipment had become generally available, it had been conventional for the observer to conduct an artillery shoot, since he usually handled 'the buzzer'. This had never been a rigidly enforced doctrine, however, and by late 1916 it was becoming increasingly common for pilots to carry out this task, leaving their observers to scan the skies for enemy fighters.

This trend was most marked within the corps squadrons assigned to IV Bde, those which had born the brunt of the fighting over the battlefields of the Somme, where they had suffered badly at the hands of an enemy whose more numerous and more potent single-seaters had begun to hunt in packs (*Jagdstaffeln*). While its hopelessly inefficient seating arrangements meant that the docile BE2 was incapable of putting up much of a fight, its crew's chances of survival were marginally improved if they could at least see the enemy coming – hence the emphasis being placed on maintaining a good look out. For the future, the early prospect of more effectively armed RE8s made it even more likely that the role of the observer would become one of using his own gun, rather than of directing the fire of those on the ground.

[18]The author's *The Flying Camels* (1995) contains a summary of all combat reports submitted by No 45 Sqn, these providing ample evidence to support the contention that observers inflicted far more damage on the enemy than pilots. It is a matter of record that between June and August 1917 (the squadron's last three months flying, by then seriously outclassed, 1½ Strutters) a total of fifty victories was claimed, fourteen of these being recognised as confirmed 'kills'. An analysis of the reports indicates that of the overall claim of fifty, thirty-three were probably attributable to the guns of observers and fifteen to those of pilots. The surviving documents do not permit an attribution to be made in the remaining two instances but it is quite clear that the ratio of claims was about 2 : 1 in favour of back-seaters. If the assessment is confined to the fourteen confirmed victories the contrast is even more marked. Twelve of these aircraft were destroyed by observers, only two by pilots. The ratio of two out of fifteen possible claims by pilots, versus twelve out of thirty-three by observers, further suggests that pilots may have been more prone to making optimistic claims (see also page 74).

[19]The decision to reorganise the RFC on a brigade basis was announced by Army Order 385 of 1 October 1915. Home-based units had been marshalled into II (soon to be renumbered as VI) and V Bdes before the end of the year but the RFC in the field did not adopt a brigade structure until the following January.

[20]The strength of a wing was not fixed and it could be adjusted as necessary to meet tactical needs. Wings also tended to become larger as the war progressed and by November 1918 some were controlling as many as eight squadrons.

Chapter 4

1914–15. Slow progress in the RNAS

Before the war the Naval Wing of the RFC had been as keen to demonstrate its potential to the Admiralty, as the Military Wing had been to sell itself to the War Office. Having previously experimented with launching aeroplanes from ships, the use of airborne W/T and bomb dropping, the flying sailors' first opportunity to make a practical contribution was presented by the Naval Manoeuvres of 1913. Although the impact of the aeroplane on the conduct of this exercise was not as marked as it had been in the Army's War Games of the previous year, valuable lessons were certainly learned. The need for more robust machines was underlined, as was the tactical value of wireless and, most significantly, it had been shown that aeroplanes might well be able to detect submarines. In marked contrast to the Army, however, the RN did not conclude that a need for specialist observers had been demonstrated.

Thus, while the RFC had taken steps shortly before the war to prepare a handful of officers to act as airborne observers, the RNAS had not. The navy began its war unconvinced that it was necessary to have people dedicated to being observers at all and, even if it was, it was certainly not persuaded that they needed to be officers. To begin with, therefore, the RNAS was content to use another pilot or a ground tradesman to fill up its two-seaters. Eventually, however, the navy did begin to address the question of observers when it approached the Royal Marine Artillery in January 1915, seeking volunteers for flying duties in France.

Five men came forward of whom four (2/Lts L. Innes-Baillie, R.F. Ogston, A.R. Collon and J.H. D'Albiac) were selected. They reported to OC No 1 (Naval) Sqn, Wg Cdr A.M. Longmore, at Dover on 3 February. There was evidently some uncertainty as to how best to use these men and D'Albiac later recalled that they spent their time boning up on Morse and semaphore while gaining some airborne experience in the available Avros, 'Bloaters' and Vickers fighters before moving to St Pol on 27 February.[1] These four men were included in a nominal roll of all officers serving with the RNAS as at 15 March. Clearly identified as observers, they were the first to be formally acknowledged as such by that Service.

Early productive employment was found in spotting for the guns of HMS *Revenge* and HMS *Bustard*, using the RFC's Clock Code and communicating initially by Aldis lamp, pending the acquisition of W/T equipment. In the early days the RNAS's first four observer officers encountered similar credibility problems to those which their RFC counterparts had experienced with the field artillery. The results spoke for themselves, however, and the navy's Gunnery Officers did eventually learn to trust the instructions that were being passed by their airborne colleagues. By June there were still only four commissioned observers flying with the RNAS, still all with No 1 (Naval) Sqn, although by this time the first naval officers had appeared, Ogston and Collon having been replaced by Sub-Lts F.D. Casey and H.W. Furnival, both of the RNR.

In the meantime, like the RFC, the RNAS was finding that role specialisation was beginning to emerge. In the navy's case the contrast between different styles of operation could be quite marked and significant differences in emphasis would gradually become apparent between the functions of crews flying shore-based airships and seaplanes, those flying ship-based floatplanes and those operating landplanes over the Belgian coast and elsewhere. For the first year of the war, however, the naval approach to the training of aircrew other than pilots was even more haphazard than that of the army, and its manning situation was considerably worse.

In the autumn of 1915 Capt O. Schwann brought this matter to the attention of his immediate superior, VAdm Sir George Warrender (commander of the Second Battle Squadron). His specific complaint was that, while commanding the seaplane carrier HMS *Campania*, in the absence of any appropriately trained personnel, he had been obliged to employ totally inexperienced RNR midshipmen as air observers. Before they could be sent aloft it had been necessary to provide these young men with some inkling of what was required of them, which included teaching them such basic skills as signalling.[2]

It seems clear that prior to 1916 most admirals of the old school were prepared to tolerate professional pilots and even to accept that for the odd RN officer to spend a few years associating with aeroplanes was a relatively harmless diversion from his proper employment, that is to say serving on the bridge of one of HM warships.[3] On the other hand, it is also evident that the admirals had little appreciation of what observers were supposed to do and sitting in the 'other' seat of an aeroplane was not perceived to be a suitable pastime for a 'proper' naval officer.

The prevalent view in the upper reaches of the naval hierarchy seems to have been that flying was simply an *avant garde* form of seamanship. The captain of an aeroplane was expected, therefore, much like the captain of a ship, to be in possession of a kind of Watchkeeping Certificate which endowed him with the ability to undertake all airborne activities. The reality, of course, was that a pilot, even one who had once been a sailor, could not actually *do* everything himself and he obviously needed to be accompanied by an assistant. Prior to the formation of the RAF, however, most naval flyers other than pilots were petty officers or ratings, many of whom had received little, if any, specialist training in aviation, especially in the early days.

[1]AIR1/2390/228/11/128. Taken from an account of his previous Service experience, written by Sqn Ldr J.H. D'Albiac at the RAF Staff College in 1929.

[2]AIR1/636/17/122/132. Letter 31/E/15 dated 8 October 1915. Schwann's letter worked its way rapidly up the chain of command and four days later it was on its way to the Admiralty under cover of a note from Admiral Jellicoe.

[3]The notional length of a period of secondment to the RNAS was four years or the duration of the war, whichever was longer.

Late 1915. The beginnings of a training system for naval observers

Throughout 1915 the RNAS continued to supplement its small group of commissioned observers by employing RNVR officers, ideally those already possessing what were thought to be appropriate qualifications and/or experience. There were, however, no dedicated instructional facilities for them until October when a unit was set up to co-ordinate the training of selected officers. Housed in the requisitioned Clement Talbot Works near Wormwood Scrubs,[4] the school was established as an element of the RNAS Central Depot at White City. In addition to carrying out a range of logistic functions, including the direct support of the RNAS Armoured Motor Car Section, the White City Depot also accommodated an Armament Training Establishment and provided facilities for training RNAS W/T operators.

With an experienced pre-war pilot in charge, Flt Cdr E.T. Newton-Clare, the first six students were in residence at the Talbot factory by the end of October. They were: Lt R.G. St John and Sub-Lts H.A. Furniss, E.B.C. Betts, R.M. Inge, C.J.A. Mullens and J.A. MacNab, all of them being members of the RNVR.

Details of this early phase of naval observer training are obscure but it seems likely that the establishment at White City would have been more concerned with providing an introduction to Service procedures and the responsibilities of being an officer than with professional instruction. What is known is that, having spent a few weeks at the Clement Talbot Works, students were detached to a variety of RN schools, mostly in and around Portsmouth, and it was here that they were introduced to the arts of naval gunnery, signalling, navigation, Fleet tactics, ship recognition and the like.

In the meantime an attempt was being made to respond to Capt Schwann's earlier complaint. While HMS *Campania* was being refitted in late 1915 her next class of midshipmen had been sent to Dunkirk to gain some initial flying experience, their practical instruction in signals and other applied skills subsequently being carried out, still under local arrangements, after they had rejoined their ship. About half of this group turned out to be satisfactory. They were eventually supplemented by a handful of RNVR officers who had spent a short time at the RNAS Gunnery School at Eastchurch. Since they had never been to sea, however, Schwann regarded most of these men as being somewhat ill-prepared for life afloat.

Since neither the home-grown midshipmen nor the RNVR officers had been entirely successful, it was decided to try internal recruiting among experienced W/T operators. The Admiralty called for volunteers and received 120 responses against its requirement for twenty. Those who were selected (four Signals Boatswains, one Chief Yeoman and fifteen Yeomen of Signals) began training on board *Campania* on 25 January 1916. The course ended in May, by which time five of its members had fallen by the wayside. Of those who were successful, eight were allocated to *Campania* and the seaplane station at Scapa Flow (Houton Bay), four went to *Engadine* and three to *Manxman*. To make up the shortfall another five signallers began training in July but *Campania* was called away in August and their course had to be completed ashore at East Fortune. All of the second batch were successful and the twenty men trained in 1916 were to constitute the core of the Grand Fleet's team of seagoing 'W/T Operator Observers' until 1918.

Early 1916. The shortage of naval observers persists and pressure increases for their status to be recognised

Similar problems over the availability of trained naval observers had occurred in the Mediterranean theatre where the East Indies and Egypt Seaplane Squadron had been obliged to employ attached army officers (see page 19), this arrangement persisting for much of the remainder of the war. Attention was drawn to this generally unsatisfactory situation in Sqn Cdr C.J. L'Estrange Malone's report on operations conducted by the seaplane carrier *Ben-my-Chree* during March/April 1916. Noting that most of the navy's handful of observers were a rather motley collection of failed pilots, RNVR recruits and RNAS petty officers, he advised that their trade needed to be provided with a much firmer foundation.

Ideally, Malone thought that all observers should undergo a familiarisation course as pilots, although he accepted that this refinement could be deferred until after the war, except, taking a leaf from the RFC's book, (see Chapter 5) for those who were selected to fill executive appointments. Much more significantly, he also recommended that the professional training of observers should be substantially improved and that they should be recognised as fully accredited members of the RNAS, rather than being treated as mere RNVR appendages. In other words, that, like pilots, observers should be 'graded'.[5]

Like the War Office, the Admiralty had appreciated from the outset that if it was going to be in the flying business at all it would need full-time professional pilots and the grading system had been introduced to reflect their individual levels of seniority and skill. With little experience to go on, however, neither wing of the pre-war RFC had foreseen that there would also be a permanent need for *professional* observers so no proper provision had been made for them. Since they were not graded, naval observers, in common with their army colleagues, had no status and no career structure. As a result, as the RFC was also beginning to discover, (see Chapter 5), it was difficult to attract and retain high quality personnel for employment in an occupation which offered virtually no opportunities for advancement.

Concern over the unsatisfactory position regarding naval observers was also being expressed in other quarters. In January 1916 the Admiralty's Civil Secretariat (as distinct from its uniformed Naval Staff) had pointed out that, unless

[4]At the time Wormwood Scrubs still boasted a double 'b', i.e. Scrubbs, but the more familiar modern rendering will be used here. The actual address of the Clement Talbot Works, previously a motor car factory, was Barlby Road, Ladbroke Grove, North Kensington.

[5]The grading scheme for officer pilots, which was applicable to both the Military and the Naval Wings of the RFC, had been introduced before the war. Although the army and navy went their separate ways in 1914, both retained the grading system virtually unchanged. Within the RFC (and later the RAF) a qualified pilot was graded as a Flying Officer, officers of this grade being ranked as subalterns and lieutenants. The same term was originally used in the RNAS but with the passage of time Flight Officer became increasingly common. Higher grades, those of Flight, Squadron and Wing Commander, were associated with the ranks of captain, major and lieutenant-colonel (or their naval equivalents). In most cases, wartime promotions to fill higher grade appointments were made on a temporary basis.

It should be appreciated that because an officer was graded as, for instance, a Squadron Commander this did not necessarily mean that he would be in command of a squadron. Technically, it indicated only that he was considered to be capable of exercising command at that level, although in nearly every case, he would actually have done so at some stage.

the situation were redressed, once the war ended all RNVR personnel would be demobilised, leaving the RNAS very short of expertise and with at least one of the seats in many of its aeroplanes empty.[6]

Observations such as these, raised by experienced commanders at sea and informed civil servants alike, were symptomatic of the fact that the Admiralty was still reluctant to recognise the need for dedicated observers. Under the circumstances it is hardly surprising that no distinguishing badge had been authorised for them, making it, perhaps, equally surprising that from April 1916 observers were authorised to wear the RNAS eagle.[7] The tide was turning, however, and the pleas of L'Estrange Malone, Schwann and others for more and better observers were beginning to induce a slow change in the Admiralty's conservatism.

[6]AIR1/668/17/122/773. This argument was put forward in a minute (CW36998 dated 6 January 1916) raised by Mr W.A. Medrow.

[7]The first regulations governing the wearing of naval 'wings', i.e. a gilt eagle, were contained within Admiralty Weekly Order 55 of 26 June 1914. It was to be worn on the left sleeve, above the rank distinction lace, by naval officers and on the left cuff by Royal Marine officers. At this stage the eagle signified not so much that the wearer was an active pilot but that he was a member of the Military (i.e. the Executive) Branch of the RNAS – although this usually amounted to the same thing. Nevertheless, it appears that it may well have been the original intention to confine the wearing of the eagle to pilots but that the regulations had been expressed with insufficient precision. In any event, by late 1915 eagles were commonly being sported by non-graded officers and, presumably in imitation of the RFC, the badge also began to be worn on the left breast. This, and another malpractice concerning the improper use of RNAS rank titles, drew an adverse comment from the Director of the Air Service, RAdm C.L. Vaughan-Lee, in February 1916. The regulations were suitably revised and republished in Weekly Order 756 of 21 April.

The new rules were quite specific. RN officers graded as Flying Officers, i.e. pilots, were to wear the eagle on the left sleeve, above the rank lace, as before (and, when appropriate, on the left epaulette), but graded RM officers were now to wear it on the left breast. Observers were not addressed as such but were covered by a provision which stated that other naval officers 'under a continuous liability to make ascents in aircraft' were also entitled to wear the eagle on the left sleeve and left shoulder; RM and attached Army officers who fell into the same category were to wear the badge on the left breast. The Order went on specifically to direct that all other non-graded officers serving with the RNAS were not to wear the eagle. Weekly Order 1865 of 11 August 1916 subsequently authorised RNVR officers who were not graded within the RNAS but who held pilots certificates as Acceptance Officers (non-operational pilots employed since February 1916 to test new and repaired aircraft) to wear the eagle. This Order specifically stressed once again the exclusive link between the eagle and flying personnel.

It is of interest to note that the 'continuous liability' provision also covered aircrew who were as yet unqualified so that naval pilots and observers were entitled to wear the eagle while they were still under training. Thus, whatever its original significance may have been, by early 1916 the RNAS eagle indicated only that its wearer was a flyer. It was impossible to tell by inspection whether he was a pilot or an observer or even whether he was qualified. This represented a marked contrast to RFC practice where the wearing of 'wings' was a jealously protected privilege and a sometimes contentious issue. (For reference to the introduction of the naval observers badge, see Chapter 11, Note 3).

The situation was complicated further by the publication of Weekly Order 2842 of 11 November 1916 which authorised naval officers serving ashore overseas to wear an army-style khaki uniform. Provision was made for the normally gilt naval buttons and cap badge to be in bronze. The RNAS eagle is not specifically mentioned but, since the precedent had been established, it would seem possible that some of these may also have been produced in bronze. The November Order specifically directed that on khaki jackets distinction marks relating to Branch were to be worn 'as on blue uniform.' This clause would have embraced the RNAS eagle which should, therefore, have been worn on the left sleeve. Nevertheless, from the evidence of contemporary photographs, it is quite clear that, on khaki, the eagle was commonly worn on the left breast *à la* RFC. While this practice appears to have been improper, it was clearly condoned and may have been justified by stretching the conditions governing the wearing of eagles by RM and Army officers to cover the case of sailors dressed as soldiers.

Name	First Assignment
Sub-Lt E.B.C. Betts	No 3 Sqn, Dunkirk
Sub-Lt N.W. Frames	No 8 Sqn, A Gp, Dover
Sub-Lt H.A. Furniss	Dover Seaplane Station
Sub-Lt R.W. Gow	No 3 Sqn, Dunkirk
Sub-Lt C.L. Hains	No 3 Sqn, Dunkirk
Lt R.G. St John	No 1 Sqn, A Gp, Dover
Sub-Lt R.M. Inge	Dover Seaplane Station
Sub-Lt J.A. MacNab	No 7 Sqn, A Gp, Dover
Sub-Lt C.J.A. Mullens	No 7 Sqn, A Gp, Dover
Sub-Lt G.H. Nelson	No 3 Sqn, Dunkirk
Sub-Lt J.T. Sims	No 3 Sqn, Dunkirk
Sub-Lt L.H. Slatter	Dunkirk Seaplane Station
Sub-Lt E.M. Wright	No 8 Sqn, A Gp, Dover

Fig. 4. *The initial assignments of the first thirteen RNVR officers to graduate from the RNAS training system; all were in post by 3 March 1916.*

Nevertheless, despite their poor prospects, the number of commissioned observers serving with (as distinct from being members of) the RNAS was steadily increasing. At the end of December 1915 there were fifty-seven of them, of whom twenty-four were actually available for duty, the other thirty-three still being on the books of the training school at the Clement Talbot Works.[8]

By mid-March 1916 the total of observers available to the RNAS had crept up to seventy-eight. They were distributed as follows.[9]

a. Nine were at Dover, seven with Nos 2, 7 and 8 Sqns of A Gp and two at the Seaplane Station.
b. One was at the Central Flying School.
c. One was with No 2 Wg in the Aegean.
d. Twelve were in France, eleven with No 1 Wg and one at the RNAS Headquarters at Dunkirk.
e. Two were with Force D in Mesopotamia.
f. Five were assigned to seaplane carriers, three to *Ark Royal*, one to *Campania* and one to *Engadine*.
g. Forty-eight were under training. Thirteen were at the White City Depot; twenty-four were attending courses at RN establishments and eleven were at Eastchurch.

In arriving at this disposition it is informative to consider what had become of the thirty-three RNVR officers who, as noted above, had been under training at the end of 1915. Having been attached to the RNAS on a variety of dates between October and December, they had been organised into two batches. Running about one month apart, each batch did an initial stint at the Talbot factory, followed by a month or more attached to RN establishments. The subsequent progress of each group followed different patterns with individuals sometimes breaking away to pursue separate courses. By late-January 1916 the leading group was at Dover but a few weeks later, still under training, several of them moved to Dunkirk. By the end of February they were all deemed to be qualified. The initial assignments of the first thirteen observers to be formally trained by the RNAS are listed at Fig. 4.

Following their initial training at the White City Depot and elsewhere, half of the second, and rather larger, group went to Eastchurch at the end of February. At the beginning of April they moved to Roehampton where they were joined by the

[8]AIR1/2108/207/49 series. RNAS Disposition Lists, which permit the movements of all officers serving with the RNAS to be reconstructed, were published at relatively frequent, if irregular, intervals from April 1914 onwards.

[9]*Ibid.*

One of the first batch of observers to be formally trained for service with the RNAS, Sub-Lt R.W. Gow RNVR, photographed at Dunkirk alongside a Nieuport 10. (J.M. Bruce/G.S. Leslie collection)

rest of the course a week later. Most of this group graduated from Roehampton at the end of the month. Three joined the recently reformed No 3 Wg at Detling, two were assigned to HMS *Campania* and one to *Ark Royal*; one was sent out to Egypt; two were retained at Roehampton until early June before joining HMS *Empress*, the remainder being distributed between Dover, Westgate, Yarmouth, Manston, Felixstowe and the Isle of Grain.

It is interesting to note that by May 1917, only fourteen of these thirty-three men were still serving as observers. Of the rest: three appear to have left the Service altogether; one (no longer annotated as an observer) was on the staff of the RN Air Department in London; three had been killed in action and one was a prisoner of war. The other eleven had all become pilots; two were already operational, the remaining nine still being at various stages of training.

1916–17. The RNAS revises its observer training sequence and sets up dedicated schools at Eastchurch

If the granting of formal authorisation for observers to wear the RNAS eagle in April 1916 had been a sign that the Admiralty was becoming increasingly aware of them, the introduction of revised rates of pay only a month later was another.[10] The chief innovation in the latter case was that the new pay scales belatedly recognised the contribution that had been made by the previously overlooked midshipmen who had been ordered into the air by Capt Schwann and others. There was a curious anomaly in the new rules, in that officers and midshipmen who were deemed to be fully trained observers drew five shillings per day continuously while being employed as such (as in the RFC), whereas warrant officers and petty officers drew three shillings and two shillings respectively but only on those days on which they actually flew, unless they happened to be in 'an area of operations', effectively, at sea or overseas.

Nevertheless, it was clear that the navy was finally beginning to come to terms with the idea of observers – and other non-pilot aircrew. Despite these positive developments, however, the naval aircrew problem was actually getting worse, because, in contrast to the RFC, the RNAS was beginning to operate relatively large aircraft. These flying boats, airships and, later on, heavy bombers, required crews of three, four or even more men. The RNAS was a much smaller-scale operation than the RFC, of course, but in relative terms naval pilots tended to need much larger numbers of competent airborne assistants – wireless operators, gunlayers[11] and engineers, as well as observers – than their opposite numbers in the Army.

Along with acceptance of the need for more crewmen came an appreciation that their training needed to be improved and a more seamanlike approach was adopted with the opening of a dedicated Gunnery School at Eastchurch under the overall command of Wg Cdr J.L. Forbes. The first CO, Sqn Cdr A.C. Barnby (another pre-war pilot), arrived in April 1916 and the school officially opened for business on 31 May.[12] Although most new naval observers passed through the Gunnery School between June and December, this still did not involve very large numbers. This was of little consequence, however, as the school had not been set up solely for their benefit, the bulk of its throughput actually consisting of pilots and non-commissioned crewmen.

Since the Gunnery School was now able to provide a focal point for the training of all naval back-seaters, it was decided to dispense with the establishment at White City.

[10]Regular and casual rates of flying pay for 'officers and men who do not belong' to the RNAS but who were obliged to go aloft as observers in naval aircraft had originally been authorised on 26 June 1914 by Admiralty Weekly Order 55. The revised rates were published by Admiralty Weekly Order 894 of 12 May 1916. The latter amplified and extended the pre-existing regulations and, in the case of the previously omitted midshipmen, provided for flying pay to be backdated to as early as 1 April 1915, where applicable.

[11]Although the RNAS had been employing *de facto* non-commissioned gunners ever since the beginning of the war, as with its observers, the Admiralty had been slow to acknowledge them. A specific date for the introduction of the rate of aerial gunlayer has not been established but it was probably in 1916, as an appropriate badge was authorised for them late in that year; see Admiralty Monthly Order 3319 of 1 December. The badge consisted of a single gun with a star above; it was to be worn on each collar by chief petty officers and on the right sleeve by all other ranks.

[12]Prior to this there had been a less formally organised Gunnery School at Eastchurch. This had been operating there since October 1915, apparently in association with a collocated element of No 4(N) Sqn commanded by Sqn Cdr A. Ogilvie (although, because the RNAS tended to apply designations in such a hapahazard manner, it is possible that Ogilvie's unit *may* actually have been a part of No 4 Wg). Whatever it was called, it was this unit which had looked after the group of trainee observers who had been at Eastchurch in February–March 1916 before moving on to Roehampton. By the time that the next batch of observers began to arrive at Eastchurch in late May/early June, some of them from the Clement Talbot Works and some from Roehampton, the new Gunnery School was being set up under Sqn Cdr Barnby.

At the beginning of June the students in residence at Wormwood Scrubs were transferred to Eastchurch and the Clement Talbot Works closed down shortly afterwards.[13]

For the remainder of 1916 the training of naval observers embraced a series of courses which appear to have been attended on a somewhat selective (or random?) basis, few students completing the whole sequence. A substantial proportion of naval observers continued to be obtained by the appointment of suitably qualified officers from other Branches and by reselecting pilots who had been unsuccessful in flying training. Direct recruiting was taking place, however, and most of the RNVR officers involved began their careers at the RNAS Depot at Crystal Palace which had been commissioned in May 1916. Mostly concerned with the initial training of prospective pilots, the number of directly-recruited observers needing to attend this 'Disciplinary Course' was relatively small, the monthly intake rarely exceeding half-a-dozen.

With or without having spent some time at Crystal Palace, the specialist training of observers involved attendance at some or all of the following.

a. The RN Gunnery School at Whale Island.
b. The RN Navigation School in Portsmouth.
c. The RN Signals School in Portsmouth.
d. The RNAS Kite Balloon Depot at Roehampton.[14]
e. The RNAS Gunnery School at Eastchurch.

Two points are worth making. First, although most of these courses appear to have been about four weeks in duration, the time that individuals spent at each location varied considerably. Secondly, while observers could spend as long as eight months under training, they acquired very few flying hours. Only Eastchurch offered practical training facilities and even here the amount of flying provided was minimal in 1916.

While the RN would doubtless have done its best to adapt the content of its courses to meet the peculiar needs of its aviators, the use of traditional schools, more accustomed to dealing with seafarers, was clearly a second-best solution. What the RNAS really needed was a school of its own, one which could provide instruction tailored to fit the specific requirements of its back-seaters. This approach was finally adopted in December 1916 when Flt Cdr K.S. Savory was posted to Eastchurch to set up an Observers School. Savory was a pilot, the senior qualified specialist on his staff being Lt Cdr F.H. Swann who was to become CO himself a year later.[15]

When Savory's unit began training in January 1917 the RNAS already had more than one hundred observers on its books. Almost half of these were ineffective, however, as they were attending a variety of courses: ten were at Roehampton; eleven were in Portsmouth; seventeen were with the Observers School at Eastchurch where there were a further eleven, still annotated as observers, who were actually being retrained as pilots.

By this time much more attention was beginning to be paid to air navigation techniques and a course of six week's duration was set up at Cranwell early in 1917 to train specialist instructors who were then posted to the various flying schools to pass on the good word. While this refinement was aimed primarily at pilots, the Observers School at Eastchurch was to have been included in the programme. Once the new specialists were in post it was intended to withdraw the two air instructors on the staff of the RN Navigation School at Portsmouth, although, as it happened, they had already become redundant by that time (see page 67).

Some idea of the complex and disjointed nature of naval observer training in 1916–17 can be gained by considering the progress of a typical individual. Sub-Lt Gordon Keigthley's career as an aviator began at the RNAS Depot on 9 July 1916. From Crystal Palace he went to Portsmouth for two specialist courses. The first of these started on 13 August and dealt with signals procedures. It was followed immediately by the second, which was concerned with navigation and started on 8 September. From Portsmouth Keigthley moved to Roehampton on 28 October and from there to the RNAS Gunnery School on 19 November. During his time at Eastchurch, probably in January, he will have been transferred to the books of the newly established Observers School. He finally graduated on 17 March 1917, more than eight months after entering training. His initial posting was to HMS *Empress,* then assigned to the East Indies and Egypt Seaplane Squadron based on Port Said. Keigthley never reached his ship, however, as he was killed in action flying in a Farman of No 2 Wg on 20 May.[16]

Despite the establishment of a dedicated school and a gradual increase in numbers, progress was still painfully slow. Furthermore, it was not until as late as the spring of 1917 that the RN felt able to take the long overdue step of formally recognising its air observers as *graded* aircrew. Thus, despite the demands of the future having been recognised in some circles, whenever a second man flew in an RNAS aeroplane during the first three years of the war he was far more likely to be another pilot, a bewildered midshipman, a seaman rating, a misemployed ground tradesman or a seconded army officer than a properly trained, commissioned naval observer.

Later developments in the provision and employment of naval observers are discussed in Chapter 11.

[13]At much the same time as the student observers were being moved to Eastchurch, i.e. late May, Admiralty Monthly Order 411 of 1 June 1916 announced that the Armament Training Establishment and the W/T Operators being trained within the White City complex had been moved to the new RNAS Depot at Crystal Palace and the recently opened RNAS Central Training Establishment at Cranwell, respectively. Now redundant, closure of the Clement Talbot Works was announced (in arrears) by Admiralty Weekly Order 2022 of 25 August 1916.

[14]The facilities at Roehampton were exploited to provide practical instruction in map-reading from free balloons and in ship recognition and gunnery control from tethered balloons, the latter involving model ships floating on a lake and simulated procedures in much the same way as the RFC employed its Artillery Targets.

[15]Despite its specialist role, and the availability of an appropriately qualified senior officer, the Observers School at Eastchurch had to be commanded by a pilot (as had the earlier one at the Talbot Works) because the Admiralty did not recognise observers as being members of the Executive Branch of the RNAS until 1917, and until they were so recognised they could not exercise command of a unit.

[16]The sortie in which Keigthley was engaged when he was shot down involved spotting for the guns of HMS *Raglan*, bombarding the town of Kavalla on the coast of Macedonia. It is quite possible that Keigthley may have been formally reassigned to No 2 Wg at some stage, but evidence for this appears to be lacking and it is just as likely that he had simply been temporarily pressed into service locally to meet an urgent operational requirement while passing through the Aegean on his way to Egypt.

Chapter 5

Late 1915. The observer is granted a degree of formal status within the RFC

In the meantime, while the navy was still dragging its feet, the level of formal recognition granted to observers flying with the army had been significantly increased. This change had been introduced in an effort to redress an unfortunate consequence of the way in which military personnel were managed. In short, internally-recruited observers were 'attached' to the RFC, unlike the majority of pilots who were 'transferred' to it. This apparently obscure distinction had significant implications in terms of career management because officers *attached* to the RFC were effectively *transferred* to the General List. This meant that they no longer figured in the promotion lists which were periodically raised by their original regiment or corps. Their attached status meant that they did not figure in the RFC's calculations either so that, in practical terms, no one had any direct responsibility for fostering their further advancement.

This problem was actually even more complicated. The majority of wartime officers held temporary commissions in the 'New Armies'. Since they were serving only 'for the duration', relatively few of these men would have expected to gain significant advancement in any case but, even as 'amateurs', they could reasonably have expected to attain the rank of lieutenant. Even this modest ambition would be unrealised, however, unless someone was told to look after their interests. Suitable arrangements had been made for the RFC's 'own' junior officers, those serving on the Special Reserve, in August 1915 but it was not until December that commanders were formally required to consider recommending subalterns of the General List for promotion to lieutenant.[1]

In real terms the problem of promotion, or the lack of it, was far more acute for professional officers of the Regular Army who were serving as observers, all of whom would have had reasonable expectations of fairly rapid advancement in time of war. To avoid being overtaken in the promotion stakes by their less enterprising colleagues, an increasing number of older, more senior, observers had begun to request that they be permitted to return to their original units. The loss of these capable, ambitious and experienced men caused considerable concern but nothing could be done to alleviate the situation within the existing regulations, as RFC policy dictated that promotion leading to executive appointments was restricted to Flying Officers, that is to say, to pilots.

The obvious solution was to arrange for observers to be *transferred* to the RFC so that they too could be graded. From November 1915, therefore, it was ruled that all seven fully accredited observers held against the establishment of each squadron could be formally gazetted to the RFC.[2] Two conditions applied. First, all observers graded as Flying Officers were to undertake to be retrained as pilots at 'the earliest opportunity.' Secondly, any observer selected for Flight Commander grade (which implied an automatic captaincy) would be obliged to retrain as a pilot *before* he could fill such an appointment.

The imposition of these constraints is very revealing of the RFC's ambivalent attitude towards its observers. While it had quite clearly accepted that it needed them for the efficient and economic operation of its two-seaters, it is equally plain that the concessions it had granted were calculated to be the bare minimum necessary to ensure that an adequate flow of volunteers was maintained. It can also be seen that the RFC still did not regard its observers as professional aviators in their own right; much of their value was seen to be in their potential as additional pilots. That the RFC had little real regard for its observers is heavily underscored by the second condition it had imposed which ensured that for all practical purposes the rank ceiling for an observer was fixed at lieutenant.[3]

Since they plainly had very little respect for back-seaters, it is perhaps unsurprising that the War Office's mandarins appear to have been quite unconcerned at the likely effect that all of this negativity might be having on their morale. Perhaps they thought that no one would notice that observers were being short-changed. If so, they were mistaken, as Sqn Ldr J.O. Andrews recalled some ten years later:[4]

> '... the observer began to find that the interest of his work and the pleasant relations in a squadron did not counterbalance the unhappy feeling that, in the eyes of the superior RFC Authority, he was a very inferior person. His prospects of promotion were negligible, his pay less than that of the most recently

[1]AIR1/404/15/231/45. The earliest (pre-war) reservists, having been called up and commissioned as 2nd lieutenants in August 1914, were becoming eligible for consideration for promotion a year later. War Office letter 100/RFC/46(MA1) dated 9 August 1915 therefore requested recommendations to be made regarding the promotion to lieutenant of subalterns of the RFC (Special Reserve). Letter 100/RFC/103(MA1) of 1 December extended this provision to cover officers of the New Armies holding temporary commissions on the General List who happened to be serving with the RFC.

[2]*Ibid*. Authority for observers to be graded was contained within War Office letter 100/FC/95(MA1) dated 13 November 1915, although the regulation was made effective retrospectively from 21 October.

It should be appreciated that, despite their having been gazetted as Flying Officers, observers (and pilots) who were transferred to the RFC, i.e. those who had not been directly recruited as aviators, retained some tribal loyalty to their parent regiment or corps. This was reciprocated and, despite their names being included in the RFC section of the Army List, they continued to appear under their original units as well. It was well into 1917 before 'straight through' RFC flyers began to outnumber the transferees.

[3]Some of the observers (and pilots) who transferred to the RFC from other organisations were already captains, or even majors, as a result of their previous service. This did not 'count' in aviation circles, however, since a captaincy in the RFC was specifically associated with the employment grade of Flight Commander. Thus, although a few observers (and some relatively inexperienced pilots) certainly wore the rank insignia of captains or majors, this was an anomaly, carrying with it no privileges beyond those conferred by normal military protocol. Similar provisions applied within the RNAS.

[4]AIR1/2388/228/11/91. Taken from an account of his previous Service experience, written by Sqn Ldr J.O. Andrews at the RAF Staff College in 1926. Andrews had spent nine months flying as an observer with No 5 Sqn before training as a pilot at the end of 1915.

joined pilot, very rarely was he awarded any mention or decoration. The consequence was that an observer, as soon as he became valuable, either learned to fly or returned to his regiment.'

A closer examination of the new rules makes it plain that Andrews' complaints about inferior status and rates of pay were fully justified. For instance, while it had been conceded that *some* observers would be gazetted the conditions were not to be the same as those which applied to pilots, *all* of whom automatically became Flying Officers as soon as they qualified for their 'wings'. Until his training was complete, whether it had begun at home or on active service in the field, an observer was merely 'on probation' and receiving flying pay at the reduced (instructional) rate of three shillings per day. He had still to win his spurs in action before, on his CO's recommendation, he could finally be awarded his flying 'O' and be accredited as a Qualified Observer,[5] at which point his flying pay was increased to the full daily rate of five shillings. 'Full' for observers that is; pilots were paid eight shillings.

Even this did not automatically make an observer an acknowledged member of the RFC. Gazetting as a Flying Officer required his CO's further recommendation, following the appearance of a vacancy in the seven-man establishment of his unit – and until he was gazetted an observer was still serving on attachment and thus still forfeiting seniority.

Furthermore, it seems that the full implications of the increased degree of recognition which had been accorded to observers may not have been appreciated in some circles. Observers were no longer ephemeral beings who existed only while they were serving on the strength of a squadron in France. Like a pilot, an observer was now a permanent fixture and he had to be recognised as such wherever he happened to be serving. To clarify the situation, OC Administrative Wing was obliged to point out to Accounting Officers at all home-based units that 'observers who have qualified as such overseas, and who are employed on observation duties in England are entitled to receive Flying Pay at five shillings *per diem* for each day of ascent.'[6]

Accounting Officers were not the only people who were having trouble adjusting to the new policy and it was to be January 1916 before the War Office's bureaucrats began to include observers in the RFC section of the Army List. That month's edition featured fifty-one Flying Officers annotated with an '(O)' in front of their names; three of them had their seniority dated with effect from 11 November 1915, the remainder from the 22nd. A month later the total had risen to eighty-nine but thereafter the system of recording was changed. It had evidently been decided that a degree of segregation was called for and observers began to be listed separately under the heading of Flying Officer (Observer).[7]

The March 1916 List notes only nine names in the new category, the remainder, still with their (O) prefixes, still being embedded among the pilots. The conversion process took some three months but by June all graded observers had been weeded out and listed separately. In the meantime some detailed amendments had been incorporated and twenty-three Flying Officer (Observers), the total having risen to 220 by then, had had their seniority backdated to the earliest possible date of 21 October 1915 (see Note 2).

Thereafter the number of observers required grew at an accelerating rate to keep pace with the formation of new squadrons and to meet an increased unit establishment which was raised from seven to twelve per squadron in mid-1916.[8] This development was particularly significant as it meant that, apart from the demands of new squadrons working up in the UK, all of those already in France would each immediately be entitled to five additional men.

Increasing an establishment could be achieved at the stroke of a pen, of course, but the manpower resources required to match the revised scale were not immediately available. It would take several months to find and train all the additional men who were now required and before this exercise had been completed the goalposts would have been moved again. Until mid-1916 the majority of aircrew being accepted directly into the RFC had been regarded as prospective pilots, relatively few being taken on as observers. The suddenly increased demand for them (the additional requirement was initially put at one hundred[9]) now justified a significant proportion of the intake being earmarked for observer duties on entry. Another innovation was that some of these directly recruited observers were expected to undergo an initial ground-based aviation course at Reading or Oxford alongside, but separate from, officers destined for pilot training.[10]

1916. The Bailhache Report

In mid-1916 the RFC was placed under close scrutiny in response to a degree of public disquiet. This had been stirred up by a group of activists with Mr Noel Pemberton-Billing MP acting as their chief spokesman. As a result, a Committee on the Administration and Command of the RFC was appointed, under the chairmanship of Mr Justice Bailhache, to investigate a variety of specific allegations. Taking evidence from May 1916, the Committee's final report was dated

[5]The term 'Qualified Observer' had been in widespread use as a convenient, self-explanatory and universally understood label since the autumn of 1914, but it had never acquired the same official standing as the equivalent 'Flying Officer'. From November 1915, however, it had a precisely defined meaning and became an officially endorsed interim employment grade – a half-way house between being a probationary (albeit operational) trainee and a fully accredited member of the RFC.

[6]AIR1/1305/204/11/184. Headquarters Administrative Wing Routine Orders for 18 March 1916.

[7]When it had first been announced that a proportion of RFC observers were to be graded (see Note 2) the letter of authority had stated that they were simply to become Flying Officers. It would appear, however, that the term 'Flying Officer (Observer)' must have been formally sanctioned at some time in early 1916. Although this writer has failed to discover a specific reference to fix the date of its introduction, its appearance in the Army List and in official correspondence from March onwards suggests that the new title was probably coined in February.

[8]AIR1/1291/204/11/83. A draft establishment for an enlarged, eighteen-aircraft squadron was forwarded to Maj-Gen Trenchard by the DMA on 31 March 1916. The final version was published under cover of War Office letter 87/6023(AO1) dated 1 June 1916. Among other changes, this raised the number of fully qualified observers from seven to twelve per unit and introduced the post of a Recording Officer to assist with routine administration at squadron level.

[9]AIR1/404/15/231/45. The requirement for one hundred observers, *some* of whom were to go to Reading (see Note 23), was notified to OC Administrative Wing at Farnborough by War Office letter 87/7632(MA1) dated 1 April 1916. In acknowledging this directive, Lt-Col H.C.T. Dowding indicated that he considered that it would be more appropriate for observers to attend the new school at Oxford, rather than that at Reading (see Note 10), but in the event both were used.

[10]Commanded by Capt A.E.G. MacCallum, the RFC Officers Training School, the first unit to provide an introductory aviation course (for pilots) had opened at Reading on 20 December 1915. It was restyled the RFC School of Instruction in February 1916 and a second was opened at Oxford under Maj C. Saunders on 3 April. Shortly afterwards they were given individual designations as Nos 1 and 2 SofIs, respectively.

17 November; it was published a month later.[11] In essence, while noting that some honest mistakes had been made, particularly in the early days, the Committee dismissed the charges and upheld the reputations of both the Corps and its commanders. This is not to say that the RFC had no shortcomings, however, and among its many observations the Committee had a number of interesting things to say about observers.

a. Having first pointed out that the observers employed by the RFC in the early days had been almost totally lacking in training and experience, the Committee's report went on to accept that, under the circumstances, this had been almost inevitable. It was noted that steps had been taken to remedy this situation and the Committee considered the current training system to be 'fairly satisfactory, except in regard to the use of the machine-gun and fighting in the air.'
b. The report stated, quite unequivocally, that 'the importance of the observer cannot be overestimated' and that the Committee had been given to understand 'on unimpeachable authority' that, because he needed to be skilled in interpreting the military significance of what he saw on the ground, as well as being an expert in the direction of artillery fire, his work was actually 'more difficult....than that of the pilot.'
c. The Committee had also concluded that, since he was not in control of his own destiny, it was far more 'trying to the nerves' to fly as an observer than as a pilot.
d. The Committee considered that, in view of his importance, it was 'strange that no encouragement by way of promotion' was offered to an observer, unless he became a qualified pilot. As a result, it was observed that many of them gave up their duties to enter flying training, thus depriving the RFC in the Field of their invaluable experience.
e. Following on from the previous comment, the Committee suggested that 'after the war, the ideal to be aimed at is that pilots and observers should be interchangeable. Meanwhile we think more encouragement should be given to observers to remain observers.'

From these very penetrating observations it is evident that, lacking any preconceived ideas about airmen and their activities, Bailhache's unbiased investigators had been able to see them in perspective. His Committee had concluded that, while pilots and observers had very different responsibilities, they were essentially two of a kind. Since the activities of pilots and observers were mutually complementary, and each was dependent upon the other, it followed that they were of equal importance. The Committee considered, therefore, that the RFC had been somewhat short-sighted in allowing itself to evolve into an exclusively pilot-dominated organisation. While this had probably limited the RFC's vision and distorted its perception, the Committee was in no doubt that undervaluing its observers had resulted in their being both underprivileged and inadequately represented.

To put all of these matters right it would be necessary only to acknowledge the considerable contribution that observers were capable of, indeed were, making. If this were done the Service would benefit from having a more balanced personnel structure while simultaneously permitting individual observers to realise their full potential. It was this finding that inspired the Committee's only specific recommendation regarding observers, '...that observers should receive promotion without having to become pilots and that a corps of observers be formed with a regular establishment graded for promotion among themselves.'

Had this far-sighted recommendation been implemented promptly it would have neutralised the impact of the prejudice inherent in the existing system. It would also have provided the incentive that was essential to foster the creation of a professional class of permanent specialist back-seaters. Although Bailhache did not actually say so, it followed that his recommendation would, by permitting observers to attain ranks at which their voices could be heard, have ensured that some of them would surely have become members of the 'air establishment'. Had this happened, the long-term implications for the RAF in the inter-war period could have been both positive and far-reaching. Sadly, it was not to be.

In the meantime, since the RFC's senior management had been deeply involved in the Bailhache Committee's investigations from the outset, it was well aware of the weaknesses that were being revealed in 1916. As a result, a number of remedial measures had already been implemented by the time that the final report appeared. So far as observers were concerned, for instance, steps had been taken to improve machine-gun training. Unfortunately, it would take another eighteen months for the idea of recognising the vital role of observers, and of raising their status to acknowledge this, to gain official endorsement. By then it was already too late; attitudes had become far too deeply entrenched and some very senior officers were quite unable to accept that an observer could ever really be anything other than an assistant to his pilot. The post-war mould had already been made; it would take another war to break it.

1916. The RFC introduces formal training courses for its observers at Reading, Oxford, Brooklands and Hythe

It will be recalled that in January 1915 it had been deemed necessary to reduce the amount of time and effort devoted to the training of observers to the 'minimum possible' (see page 10). A year later, although military aviation had become a much more complicated business, this edict was still in force. The January 1915 policy, never really a practical proposition, could no longer be sustained. By the spring of 1916 there was a growing realisation that something would have to be done about the content of observer training, and soon, but an even more urgent requirement was an increase in output. This was the case in the air arms of both Services but the need for additional numbers was particularly acute in the RFC where, apart from meeting the demands of expansion, it was also necessary to replace substantial losses, many of the latter being caused by inadequately trained pilots.[12] At one point Sir David Henderson neatly summed up the paradox inherent in this situation when he said, 'The loss rate is high because training is short, but training is short because the loss rate is high.' Although he had actually been talking about

[11] AIR1/2405/303/4/5 contains a copy of the Committee's Final Report, one of at least three preserved at the PRO; AIR2/9/87/7661 contains a copy of the final draft, which included several unpublished Annexes. The report's recommendations and final remarks were reproduced in *Flight* for 21 December 1916. The section of the body of the report dealing specifically with observers was reproduced in the issue of 4 January 1917.

[12] If Trenchard's dictum of 'a full breakfast table, with no empty chairs' was to be complied with to the letter – see p. 190 of Andrew Boyle's *Trenchard, Man of Vision* (1962) – all casualties had to be replaced as soon as they occurred. The GOC believed that the arrival of new faces served to divert the attention of the survivors and thus prevented excessive brooding over fallen comrades. He was probably right but, while his policy may have had a positive effect on morale, it also increased the pressure on the training machine and was one of the reasons why it often became necessary to send pilots to France before they had been adequately trained.

pilots, much the same was true of observers. But, even the most capable of observers obliged to fly with an incompetent pilot was bound to share the latter's almost inevitable fate – hence Bailhache's comment on the stress of flying as an observer.

First-hand testimony as to the plight of the observer can be found in the autobiography of one who flew with No 3 Sqn as an NCO. Recalling a flight made in January 1916, he wrote:

> '... one morning I went up with a certain pilot in a forty mile an hour wind, and as soon as we were off the ground he turned and flew down wind about ten feet high, past trees, ditches and houses, made one circuit and landed again. I don't know what he did it for, but I do know that I was absolutely terrified, for by now I had done a lot of passenger flying, and I knew whether a machine was being properly flown or not, and this was certainly not.'

This pilot, whom the author forbore to identify, was plainly dangerous but the observer's existence could be made almost as uncomfortable by those who were simply thoughtless. As an example, the same writer has this to say about a flight he had made with Lt C.A. Ridley in September 1915, '... to tell the truth, I did not enjoy it much, for the pilot was one of the most dashing and enterprising kind. Such flying is all very fine for the pilot, but not always for the passenger.' The observer who was having his nerves tested so thoroughly was James McCudden.[13] If a man of his calibre could be frightened flying as an observer, what of lesser mortals?

Leaving aside the question of the competence of pilots, some attempt began to be made to improve the training being offered to observers by exploiting the facilities of two RFC training units which had been set up towards the end of 1915, the Machine-Gun School at Dover (later Hythe)[14] and the Wireless School at Brooklands.[15] The primary tasks of these schools were to produce, respectively, armourers, and wireless operators and technicians (of all ranks), plus specialist technical instructors. Virtually from the outset, however, Hythe had also provided some academic and practical instruction in aerial gunnery, but only for pilots and for only very small numbers of those.

With a view to improving the training of observers, it was decided to send a small batch to Brooklands on a trial basis in March 1916. They were 2/Lts T.S. Pearson, C.E. Barrington, C.B. Pratt, E.J.H. Douch and H.W. Girdlestone.[16] The results of this experiment were so promising that the War Office immediately extended an invitation for prospective observers volunteering in France to attend the Brooklands course. HQ RFC declined this offer on a number of grounds.[17] For instance, Trenchard (it was said) suspected that officers sent home for two or three weeks would treat the interlude as quasi-leave and not 'do any work at all'.

This somewhat uncharitable opinion reflected a certain lack of confidence in the volunteers themselves and a lingering suspicion among those in France that people 'back home' could not always be trusted to do the right thing. It is difficult to substantiate these misgivings but there can be no doubt that they existed. In August 1915, for example, Lt-Col Higgins had complained that the best observers being trained at home were often retained there, rather than being sent out to France. He further alleged that many of them subsequently became pilots without ever having seen active service, thus depriving the squadrons in the field of their expertise.[18]

A more soundly based objection was that HQ RFC did not wish to be excluded from the quality control process. Lt-Col J.M. Salmond had been recalled from France in February to take charge of home-based training, assuming command (as a brigadier) of VI Bde on 9 March. With the very capable Jack Salmond in charge, early improvements were anticipated but VI Bde had yet to establish its credibility and it remained something of an unknown quantity. For the time being, therefore, HQ RFC preferred to make its own assessment as to whether a trainee observer had, or had not, made the grade. There were certainly grounds for doubting the effectiveness of the training being provided at home. In May, for instance, Trenchard wrote to the War Office to complain about the inadequacy of all aspects of W/T training, noting in particular that large numbers of aerials were being lost through newly arrived aviators forgetting to wind them in before landing.[19]

This widespread malpractice was another consequence of the War Office's policy decision of January 1915 which, apart from minimising the effort devoted to observers, had also directed that the instruction of pilots should concentrate on pure flying at the expense of all aspects of tactical training. Since then, gunnery, bombing, photography and the use of W/T had all become routine operational activities, but they were still receiving scant attention at home. Salmond would address these shortcomings in due course (as described in Chapter 7) but it could not be done instantly and it would be mid-1917 before the squadrons in France would be able to detect much improvement in the abilities of replacement pilots.

In the meantime, since HQ RFC had little regard for the capabilities of the home-based training machine, it was hardly surprising that it saw little point in sending probationary observers back to England. Furthermore, as a result of a directive issued by General Haig shortly after he had assumed command of the BEF at the end of 1915, the RFC was confident that it had an ample waiting list of high quality volunteers from which to select replacement observers and the Headquarters was therefore content to continue to conduct its own training.[20]

[13]James McCudden, *Five Years in the RFC* (1918 – later republished under the title *Flying Fury*). McCudden had been with No 3 Sqn as a mechanic since before the war. As a corporal he began flying as a gunner on an occasional basis from early 1915. While still primarily a fitter, he flew with increasing frequency and, by then a sergeant, his formal qualification as an observer was eventually promulgated in HQ RFC's Routine Orders, the effective date being 1 January 1916. Before the end of the month he had been posted home to retrain as a pilot. Commissioned at the beginning of 1917 he was eventually killed in a flying accident in July of the following year. By that time he was a major with fifty-seven victories to his credit and had been awarded the VC, DSO and Bar, MC and Bar, MM and Croix de Guerre.

[14]The RFC Machine-Gun School was set up at Broadlees, Dover under 2/Lt H.E. Chaney on 27 September 1915, starting its first course on 3 October. Its initially limited flying requirements were met by units of VI Bde but shortly after the school had moved to Hythe on 27 November it was established to operate its own aeroplanes, the initial entitlement comprising three BE2cs and a trio of Vickers fighters.

[15]The nucleus of the Wireless School, which was formally established under Maj R. Orme on 20 November 1915, had been provided by a group of specialist W/T technicians left behind at Brooklands when No 9 Sqn had moved to Dover in the previous July.

[16]AIR1/1288/204/11/48. These names appear in a nominal roll of officers on the strength of the Wireless School as at 22 March 1916. All were annotated as 'observers under instruction'.

[17]AIR1/502/16/3/4. Unreferenced letter, dated 6 April 1916, from Lt-Col F. Festing (AA&QMG at HQ RFC) to Capt B.C. Fellows at the War Office.

[18]From the minutes of the Wing Commanders Conference referred to at Chapter 2, Note 28.

[19]AIR1/1266/204/9/61. HQ RFC letter CRFC 2047G dated 15 May 1916. The GOC actually identified newly trained pilots as the culprits but the blame was obviously shared in (at least) equal measure by observers.

[20]AIR1/522/16/12/8. Shortly after taking up his appointment as CinC, Gen Haig directed that the COs of all BEF units were, 'without fail', to forward the application of any volunteer who wished to fly as an observer, GHQ reserving to itself the sole right to decide whether or not he could be released.

The War Office had a very different perception of the current and future manning situation and it would soon become clear that HQ RFC had been overoptimistic. This was probably a result of differing perspectives. HQ RFC was concerned only with its short-term need to find the relatively small numbers of observers needed to replace losses on the twenty-three squadrons which constituted its Order of Battle at that time. London saw the problem rather differently, as its task was to provide the considerable numbers of people needed to build completely new units. Despite the bland assurances coming from St André-aux-Bois, the War Office knew that the long-term outlook was far from satisfactory. In fact, the manning situation was so bleak that it was about to resort to using non-commissioned personnel as back-seaters in order to make up the numbers required (see Chapter 6). Nevertheless, since HQ RFC was content to solve its own problems, and was confident that it could do so, London chose not to make an issue of its decision.

Even though HQ RFC had elected not to participate in the new scheme, observers being trained at home began to attend the Brooklands course in substantial numbers from the spring of 1916 and Hythe was soon co-opted into the programme as well. Considerable thought was now being devoted to devising the best means of training observers, and not only in the corridors of power. In April, for instance, 2/Lt C. Court Treatt (then Assistant Adjutant with No 1 Reserve Squadron at Farnborough) submitted a comprehensive proposal for a dedicated scheme.[21] An accredited observer himself, and well aware of the inadequacies of the existing instructional facilities, both at home and in the field, Court Treatt had strong views. Arguing from the premise that a poorly trained observer was virtually useless, his proposals emphasised the following key points:

a. It was impractical to train pilots and observers within the same unit.
b. An observer training school needed to be adjacent to a large training centre for troops of all arms, to facilitate the co-ordination of realistic co-operation exercises.
c. It was essential that observers be provided with a substantial amount of practical flying experience.
d. There was a need for a special school, similar to those at Reading and Oxford, to provide an introductory aviation course designed to meet the specific requirements of observers.

Court Treatt's paper was returned to him with due acknowledgement but it was deemed 'not practicable to put it into force at present.'[22] Nevertheless, in August it was decided to send all prospective observers being recruited at home to either Reading or Oxford, which was at least a step in the right direction.[23]

At this stage the three-week academic syllabus at both of these schools was as shown at Fig. 5. This curriculum had been designed for pilots, of course, and it was intended to adjust the balance of its content to suit the particular needs of observers as quickly as possible. The ideal answer, as 2/Lt Court Treatt had proposed, would have been to set up a dedicated preparatory school for back-seaters. This approach would eventually be adopted, but not until January 1918.

By July 1916 a discernible pattern had emerged for many of the observers being trained at home. After passing through

Theory of flight	3 hrs
Aero-engines (seven types)	43 hrs
Rigging	9 hrs
Sailmaking and splicing	3 hrs
Instruments	3 hrs
Artillery observation	9 hrs
Troop formations	3 hrs
Map-reading and reconnaissance	3 hrs
The Lewis gun	6 hrs
Bombs and bombing	4 hrs
Photography	3 hrs
Wireless	3 hrs
Signalling (mostly Morse practice)	15 hrs
Meteorology and astronomy	2 hrs
Military law	3 hrs
Miscellaneous topics	10 hrs
Total	122 hrs

Fig. 5. *Syllabus of RFC Schools of Instruction in the summer of 1916.*

Reading or Oxford, they were posted to a quasi-operational squadron which was approaching the end of its period of service as an advanced flying training school. From there they would be detached to Brooklands and/or Hythe to attend courses of about three week's duration. Once this sequence had been completed a few were posted to France to take the place of the fallen but the majority returned to their parent squadrons, remaining with them while they mobilised and accompanying them across the Channel as part of their initial operational establishment.

Late 1916. HQ RFC begins to accept the limitations of its field training system

While the training sequence which was now operating at home represented a considerable improvement over that which had been available previously, the various specialist courses were still not considered to be capable of teaching an observer all that he needed to know, leaving much still to be learned when he reached France. Nevertheless, the observers being trained in England in the latter half of 1916 were now far better prepared than their contemporaries in France who were still being trained in-house under relatively *ad hoc* arrangements which had changed little since 1914.

Although HQ RFC was reluctant to accept the assistance of VI Bde to help with its instructional commitment, at unit level the field training system had long been seen as an increasingly irksome imposition.[24] Indeed, the additional burden which it placed on the squadrons sometimes inhibited

If he could, his name would be passed to HQ RFC who would interview likely candidates and place the names of those selected on a waiting list.

[21]AIR1/404/15/231/45. Farnborough letter 7329 dated 3 April 1916.

[22]*Ibid.* War Office letter 87/7632(MA1) dated 24 April 1916.

[23]AIR1/405/15/231/46. The decision to send *all* direct entrant observers to Reading or Oxford, rather than just some (see Note 9), was notified by AO 138 dated 25 July 1916.

[24]It may be helpful to summarise the evolution of the RFC's home-based training system. Salmond's original formation, HQ VI Bde, was redesignated HQ Training Brigade on 20 July 1916. To cope with its subsequent expansion, a degree of devolution became necessary and on 1 January 1917 the Brigade was subdivided into Northern, Southern and Eastern Training Groups. Having continued to grow, on 5 August 1917 the three regional Groups were redesignated as Brigades, their controlling formation becoming HQ Training Division. Salmond remained in overall command until October 1917 when he succeeded Sir David Henderson as Director General of Military Aeronautics (DGMA) at the War Office, his place at HQ Training Division being taken by Maj-Gen C.A.H. Longcroft. With the creation of the RAF the training structure was reorganised again. The newly created post of Director of Training, the first incumbent being Brig-Gen J.G. Hearson, assumed overall responsibility for training policy, implementation being devolved to numbered Training Groups via the various Headquarters of the five geographical Areas into which the metropolitan RAF had been divided. Now redundant, HQ Training Division was disbanded on 20 May 1918.

Name	Squadron
Lt K.B. Brigham	No 2 Sqn
Lt H.J. Duncan	No 5 Sqn
Lt W.R. Haggas	No 12 Sqn
Lt A.H. Stradling	No 11 Sqn
2/Lt D. Clarke	No 7 Sqn
2/Lt G. Diamond	No 16 Sqn
2/Lt F.A.A. Hewson	No 18 Sqn
2/Lt C.E. Pither	No 23 Sqn
2/Lt C.G. Riley	No 22 Sqn
2/Lt B.K.D. Robertson	No 9 Sqn

Fig. 6. *The first batch of observers to be sent back from France to attend a course at the Machine-Gun School, 12–29 June 1916.*

their ability to carry out their operational tasks. As early as August 1915 Lt-Col Higgins had written to HQ RFC, requesting that those prospective observers who were being recruited locally be given two or three days of preparatory instruction on the Lewis gun before they were posted to a squadron. He had received a rather curt reply to the effect that there were no facilities to run such a course at St Omer and that the GOC was of the opinion that the squadrons had 'ample time' to cope with this task.[25]

Despite this dismissive response, by the following summer the staffs were beginning to accept that something did need to be done to alleviate the situation. So, when the War Office extended an invitation for observers being trained in France to attend the Hythe course, HQ RFC accepted on a trial basis. The first batch of ten (see Fig. 6) reported to the Machine-Gun School on 20 June 1916 to join thirty-nine other students on No 20 Course. Eight more observers from France attended No 21 Course the following month.

Partly to improve the training of those observers who were obliged to remain in France and to enhance the skills of newly qualified pilots, and partly to gain some feedback on current combat tactics from the operational squadrons, it was also decided to set up an Aerial Musketry Range at Camiers, near Etaples. For air-to-air work there were to be towed banners and fixed targets suspended from kites and/or a balloon, these facilities being complemented by air-to-ground ranges and fixed targets to be fired at from a mock-up cockpit mounted on a rail car travelling on a closed circuit track. The scheme included a small aerodrome at Cormont to support the operation of banner-towing RE7s and to provide a base for visiting units, it being anticipated that operational squadrons would use the ranges by detaching a flight at a time. Cormont also had butts for testing and harmonising guns and a miniature firing range on which aircrew could indulge in target practice and clay pigeon shooting.

This project, which had been conceived as early as August 1916, took some time to bring to fruition. Nevertheless, with Capt A. Higson-Smith in command, supported by an Assistant Equipment Officer,[26] Lt H.J.C. Smith, and a detachment of twenty air mechanics to serve as a labour party, the range finally opened in November.[27] The first live firing trials were conducted on the 13th and 14th. Thereafter, weather permitting, the ranges were in regular use until the following March when they were closed down, most of the manpower being withdrawn during April, although the facilities were retained on a care and maintenance basis.[28] In the meantime they had permitted many of the observers being recruited from the trenches to be provided with a week's gunnery course locally before they were faced with the prospect of having to fly on operations.

Several gunnery practice facilities were established behind the British lines in Artois and Picardy. These provided continuation training for newly arrived aircrew awaiting assignment to operational units and refresher and/or remedial instruction for those already in action. This synthetic training device, a rail mounted 'cockpit' which could provide back-seaters with a fairly demanding exercise without the complications, risks and expense of flying, was at Rang-du-Fliers, near Berck-sur-Mer. (Chaz Bowyer)

[25]AIR1/1169/204/5/2591 contains copies of Lt-Col Higgins' letter of 18 August and of HQ RFC's blunt response of the following day.

[26]AIR1/405/15/231/46. The RFC term Equipment Officer (EO) is sometimes misunderstood; it was an employment grade, not a job description. Although originally introduced in January 1915 to 'mind the Quartermaster's Stores' the responsibilities of EOs soon grew to embrace all aspects of engineering, maintenance, transport and logistics. As the system evolved, courses were introduced which permitted EOs (some of whom were grounded aircrew) to gain specialist qualifications enabling them to fill appointments as Wireless, Armament, Photographic and, later on, Compass and Air Navigation Officers. A Royal Warrant of 26 March 1915 announced rates of pay for both EOs and Assistant Equipment Officers (AEOs) who were to serve at wing and squadron level respectively. War Office letter 11/FC/208(AO2) of 13 September 1916 introduced a third grade and revised the nomenclature to EO1s, EO2s and EO3s, the latter serving at squadron level. When the RAF came into being its EOs were redesignated as Technical Officers.

[27]AIR1/867/204/5/522. Range Orders for Camiers were published under cover of HQ RFC letter CRFC 2047/2G dated 8 November 1916.

[28]AIR1/398/15/231/39. It had always been envisaged that the ranges at Camiers would be a temporary affair, the aim presumably having been to provide a continuation training facility during the quieter months of the winter of 1916–17. Their availability had evidently been appreciated, however, as the ranges were reactivated in the winter of 1917–18, but this time on a permanent basis. On 15 January 1918 an establishment was issued which provided for Camiers to be commanded by an Equipment Officer (EO3), with additional responsibility for the administration of the detachment at Cormont. The resident flying staff was to comprise a Flight Commander, four Flying Officers and six NCO observers.

A similar unit was also set up to the south of Etaples. Specific details are lacking but this facility is known to have been functioning by November 1917 and it was still there in February 1919. The aerodrome and air firing ranges were at Berck-sur-Mer and there were supporting ground training facilities at Rang-du-Fliers.

Chapter 6

Late 1916. The RFC introduces non-commissioned aerial gunners

When appropriate, the RFC had been employing its mechanics as *de facto* observers/gunners since pre-war days but, despite authority having been granted for them to wear a flying 'O' in 1915, relatively few of these men had actually been awarded this distinction. Some idea of the numbers involved can be gained from HQ RFC's Routine Orders for January and February 1916. During those two months the names of nine NCOs and other ranks were promulgated as having qualified as observers. By comparison, during the same period the qualifications of more than fifty officers were recognised and at least eight more were shot down while still on probation. These figures show that, while the RFC was still content to use non-commissioned aircrew, a ratio of about 6 : 1 in favour of officers makes it quite clear where its preference lay.

By April 1916, however, despite HQ RFC's confident assurance that it had ample numbers of potential officer observers on its waiting list (see page 31), demand was actually beginning to outstrip supply. In that same month, therefore, having reconsidered its manning policy, the War Office instructed HQ VI Bde to begin making arrangements to train sufficient NCOs and men as gunners to fill 'up to 50% of the establishment' of two-seat fighter squadrons.[1] This amounted to six per squadron, since the establishment of observers was about to be raised from seven to twelve per unit (see Chapter 5, Note 8). In May it was agreed that before going to Hythe to learn about gunnery these men, all of whom were expected to be found among the soldiers serving with the Expeditionary Force, ought to pass through the ground school at Reading alongside officers undergoing their initial aviation training. It is not known how many soldiers were lucky enough to enjoy the luxury of a prolonged detachment to the UK but it is doubtful whether many (any?) did.

During the summer of 1916 two policy decisions were to aggravate the already serious shortage of manpower, making it increasingly necessary to substitute non-commissioned personnel for officers. In June General Haig requested that the number of squadrons serving with the BEF be virtually doubled to fifty-six. This expansion was approved and three months later the establishment of qualified observers/gunners was raised to eighteen per unit with the proviso that 'not more than twelve will be officers, the remainder to be Serjeants.'[2]

The numbers volunteering from the ranks of the BEF had been nothing like enough to keep pace with this sort of demand and in October the War Office decided to start selecting its own gunners from the pool of soldiers being recruited directly into the RFC at home. This time the requirement was expressed as 'six gunner observers' per squadron, all of whom were to be formally trained at Hythe. Furthermore, it was now being envisaged that gunners might fly with squadrons of all types, not just those operating in the fighter role as had originally been intended. It is perhaps worth pointing out that, despite the label that was sometimes rather carelessly applied to these prospective non-commissioned aircrew to begin with, they were not actually intended to be regarded as 'observers' and they were not fully trained as such.

Training of RFC men at home eventually began at the end of 1916, the first course, whose members are listed at Fig. 7, graduating from Hythe on 22 December on which date they were transferred to the Recruits Depot at Farnborough for onward posting. The increased training commitment which this had imposed upon Hythe meant that a corresponding reduction had to be made elsewhere. The School of Aerial Gunnery[3] therefore became a dedicated aircrew training establishment, ceasing to train tradesmen as of 1 January 1917 on which date the RFC School of Armourers was set up at Farnborough. Thenceforth all armourers were to be trained at Farnborough, those selected as prospective gunners then being detached to Hythe for an appropriate course.

The restructuring of the armament trade had evidently created some confusion and the War Office clarified the situation by circulating a summary of the new arrangements in February. This document outlined the responsibilities of

Name	Ser No
A/Cpl D.C. Green	49139
1/AM W. Bond	19789
2/AM H.W. Tilley	45441
2/AM S. Brett	46685
2/AM T.H. Lea	49338
2/AM W.J. Batten	46731
2/AM V.N. Barrie	40213
2/AM H.G. Bassenger	23052
2/AM R.H. Jones	44854
2/AM J.T. Mackie	23050
2/AM H. McMillan	P/7394
2/AM R. Griffiths	39001

Fig. 7. *The first group of RFC gunners to be formally trained; they graduated from Hythe on 22 December 1916.*

[1]AIR1/1169/204/5/1291. War Office letter FS/444(MA1) dated 26 April 1916.
[2]AIR1/405/15/231/46. Approval for an increase in the overall establishment of observers from twelve to eighteen per squadron was notified by War Office letter 87/RFC/37(AO1a) dated 8 September 1916.

[3]To reflect its increasing involvement with aircrew training, the Machine-Gun School at Hythe had been upgraded in status and restyled the School of Aerial Gunnery on 13 September 1916, Lt-Col L.A. Strange being appointed as its first Commandant. Although its role did not change substantially after it had become an exclusively aircrew training facility in January 1917, it was to be redesignated twice more before the Armistice (see Chapter 12, Note 3). Later COs were, from 6 February 1917, Lt-Col H.E. Chaney, and Lt-Col G.R. Moser from 1 August 1917 until 9 March 1918, by which time Hythe had ceased to be the sole gunnery training centre and had become just one of a growing number of tactical training schools.

the various grades of armourer and stated how many of each were to serve with each type of squadron, and in what ranks.[4] Since gunner observers were included in this digest, it would seem that they were initially regarded as armourers who flew, rather than as aviators who operated a gun. This perception was to change over the next few months, however, and these men would eventually come to be regarded as professional aircrew, the first indication of this shift in emphasis coming before the end of February when the term 'gunner observer' was superseded by that of 'aerial gunner'.[5]

1917. Squadron-trained non-commissioned gunners

Although the RFC had begun to recruit and train its own gunners at home by the beginning of 1917, Hythe had the capacity to handle only ten-man courses to begin with and this was hardly enough to meet the demand. Inevitably, therefore, it proved necessary to sustain the practice of on-the-job training for those men who were still being recruited in France. For the remainder of the year, therefore, two-seater squadrons, particularly those assigned to the (Army) Wings, continued to misemploy some of their own mechanics and to receive a trickle of bombardiers, fusiliers, riflemen, drivers, sappers and so on whom they were supposed to turn into airmen as best they could, using their own resources.

These locally-recruited men did not fall into quite the same category as the professional gunners graduating from Hythe, but they were expected to do the same job. Since quality control was a local problem, it fell to HQ RFC to lay down a qualification standard for its squadron-trained gunners.[6] They were to complete one month's probationary service during which they were required to pass a series of tests which were to be administered (nominally) at brigade level. The tests examined both technical knowledge and practical skill, requiring, for instance: a grasp of the general principles of sighting theory; considerable familiarity with the Lewis gun (including the ability to clear stoppages and to change certain components within set time limits); satisfactory camera-gun work; and assessed live firing exercises, both on the range and air-to-ground. On clearing these hurdles, squadron-trained gunners were certified as being competent and authorised to wear an observers badge.

Rather surprisingly, no formal requirement was laid down as to how much time a gunner needed to spend in the air before being awarded his flying 'O'. In practice, however, it seems that fifty hours was commonly regarded as the minimum. This figure certainly crops up repeatedly in the memoirs of Arch Whitehouse. Whitehouse was a soldier, an American, with some previous knowledge of machine-guns, who transferred to the RFC and was immediately posted to No 22 Sqn as a prospective gunner. Some extracts from one of his books, in which he describes the training he received, provide an interesting comment on the way in which the formally promulgated procedures were actually implemented.[7]

> 'We learned that we were supposed to take certain lectures in our spare time, and we were given more instruction in the Vickers gun as well as in the air-type Lewis. At times we were shown the various aerial cameras and how to use them. Map-reading and some primary instruction in Morse code were also given, but since we were not equipped to carry out artillery shoots, any form of telegraphy was wasted on us… Then there was some vague programme of camera-guns and bombs… above all we were first-class machine-gunners. We were blindfolded and placed behind Lewis guns and timed to see how fast we could take them apart and assemble them again. Blindfolded we fingered different types of ammunition until we could tell without looking at the base markings whether we were handling ordinary, tracer or armour-piercing rounds… All these periods of instruction were used to grade us. After the tests the results were considered, and when we had put in our fifty hours over the line we could claim our observer's wing.'

Considering that few of the men transferring to the RFC from elsewhere had received any previous instruction of any relevance, the training standard being demanded of them was very high. Furthermore, becoming an aviator could involve a considerable degree of 'culture shock', the sudden contrast between being stationary *in* a trench and travelling at high speed several thousand feet *above* one proving to be an

Designed by Maj D. Geddes, the Hythe camera gun took a photograph instead of firing a bullet. This is an early version; in its fully developed form, the Mk III of 1917, the camera was built into the 'gun barrel'. (J.M. Bruce/G.S. Leslie collection)

[4]AIR1/1266/204/9/64. The revised arrangements for personnel employed as armourers were contained in AO 323 dated 1 February 1917. While this document had been intended to clarify the situation, in one respect it may actually have added to the confusion. As a result of its having been carelessly expressed, the section dealing with assignments had allocated six gunner observer sergeants to all squadrons, specifically including those flying single-seaters. Fortunately, this error was not reflected in subsequent formal amendments to unit establishments.

[5]AIR1/997/204/5/1241. The term 'aerial gunner' was introduced to identify the professional non-commissioned machine-gunners serving on two-seater squadrons by AO 336 dated 13 February 1917.

[6]AIR1/1135/204/5/2224. The qualification standards to be achieved by locally-trained gunners were notified to all five Brigade Headquarters by Brig-Gen P.W. Game in HQ RFC letter 2047G dated 16 March 1917.

[7]Arch Whitehouse, *The Fledgling* (1965).

overwhelmingly disorientating experience for some. Under the circumstances, it was hardly surprising that a significant proportion of locally-trained soldier-gunners failed to make the grade. It was only to be expected that, being familiar with aeroplanes, air mechanics would be much more successful in adapting to the airborne environment and this proved to be the case. In May 1917, for instance, although only 60% of the gunners on strength were RFC men, they represented a disproportionate 89% of those who were qualified.[8]

Despite these problems, the numbers involved grew steadily. At the end of March 1917 there were thirty-nine qualified gunners serving with the squadrons in France alongside another seventy-one who were still on probation.[9] By the end of August the total had risen to 202, 105 of them being fully qualified.[10]

One other point should perhaps be made. As noted above, the letter of 8 September 1916, which had announced the establishment of six gunners per squadron, had specifically stated that they were to be sergeants (see Note 2). This had been an error, however, necessitating the immediate despatch of a second letter stating that 'although approval is given for these additional Observers to hold the rank of Serjeant, it does not of necessity follow that they should be of that rank.'[11] Nevertheless, when referring to these men generically, there was a tendency to use the term 'NCO gunner', creating the impression that many of them wore three stripes. In fact, only a handful of gunners were senior NCOs, the vast majority of them flying as humble privates; of the 202 non-commissioned gunners serving in France at the end of August 1917, for instance, fewer than a dozen were sergeants.[12] This situation did not change until 1918 when, the gunner's trade was absorbed by that of the non-commissioned observer, all of whom automatically became sergeants on qualification (see page 76).

1917. Social problems arising from the introduction of aerial gunners and crews of mixed-status

Apart from the difficulty of finding enough of them, there was another problem associated with the introduction of non-commissioned gunners which should not be overlooked. The comparatively relaxed atmosphere which prevailed within the RFC, along with the considerable erosion of social distinctions brought about by the shared experience of war, had been insufficient to overcome entirely the ingrained class consciousness of the era. As a result, some of the more Edwardian- (even Victorian-) minded among the officers found it difficult to accept the presence of NCOs, let alone private soldiers, on anything like equal terms. Nevertheless, operating as it did at the leading edge of contemporary technology, the RFC was as liberal as any branch of the Services in recognising and exploiting potential, as was clearly demonstrated by the long-established practice of squadrons encouraging their groundcrew to fly. For a pilot, however, there was a world of difference between flying with a familiar and respected mechanic of proven ability and entrusting his life to a total stranger whose level of proficiency had been certified by some remote higher authority whose own competence was sometimes regarded as being questionable. Some idea of the perceived limitations of gunners can be gleaned from the recollections of Flt Lt M. Moore, writing of his experiences with No 45 Sqn.[13]

> 'Officer observers were very scarce (*in early 1917*) and increasing use was made of air gunners. Though some of these were very efficient they were unable to "mother" fresh pilots in their work as could the experienced observer, and consequently they were at a disadvantage in a fight. The use of these inexperienced personnel cost us dearly and heavy losses were not without effect on the morale of newcomers. Short of curtailing operations, however, it is difficult to see how it could have been avoided.'

Moore was certainly not alone in expressing reservations about the value of the new breed of aviator. Seventy years after reporting to No 100 Sqn as an observer in mid-1917, (then Lt) J.A. Stedman was to recall his Flight Commander's initial briefing.[14] Capt H.D. Harman's inspiring message reportedly ran along the lines of, 'We've got some Aerial Gunners here and they're no bloody good – might as well carry a couple of sandbags as ballast, now you my lad have got to earn your keep.'

There were three factors which made it almost inevitable that gunners would be held in relatively low esteem – at least to begin with. First, they were an innovation and, as such, regarded with suspicion by the more conservative members of the community. Secondly, their training was restricted in scope, compared to that of a fully qualified observer and, finally, the deference which a non-commissioned gunner was obliged to show an officer pilot could make it difficult to work in close harmony, which was essential if a crew, especially a fighter crew, was to be successful.

The back-seater (of, in this case, a DH 4) often had to stand up in order to bring his gun to bear. Lacking a safety harness, he was clearly at risk of being thrown out of the aircraft by a violent or unexpected manoeuvre. It was very difficult to communicate in a combat situation, so a great deal depended upon the level of trust and understanding which existed between the members of a crew. It was very difficult to establish the necessary degree of mutual confidence if they lived on different sides of a rigid social divide. (Sqn Ldr H. Cockerall via W.H. Wiggins)

[8]AIR1/1297/204/11/140. Nominal role of officers and non-commissioned aircrew serving with the RFC overseas, dated June 1917.
[9]AIR1/1297/204/5/139. Nominal roles of officers and non-commissioned aircrew serving with the RFC overseas, dated January–April 1917.
[10]AIR1/1301/204/11/158. Nominal role of officers and non-commissioned aircrew serving with the RFC overseas, dated August 1917.
[11]AIR1/1291/204/11/83. War Office letter 87/RFC/37(AO1a) dated 8 September 1916.
[12]AIR1/1301/204/11/158. Nominal role of officers and non-commissioned aircrew serving with the RFC overseas, dated August 1917.

[13]This extract is taken from the first edition of *The Hawk*, published in 1928.
[14]As told to Trevor Foreman and reported in an article describing Stedman's wartime experiences published in 1989 in *The Cross and Cockade Journal*, Vol 20, No 2.

There is some evidence to suggest that this lack of regard was reciprocated. If the testimony of Arch Whitehouse is to be accepted, it would appear that some officer observers were not above putting pressure on gunners to take their place on patrols. Furthermore, there was a perception among non-commissioned gunners that officers had an easy ride, as most of them were shipped home to become pilots after accumulating relatively few flying hours, whereas gunners had to resign themselves to flying 'for as long as we last.'[15] It is doubtful whether the first of these practices was very widespread but, although some gunners were commissioned and/or became pilots, there is some truth in the second allegation.

To minimise the social problems, gunners were often paired with NCO pilots but the extent to which this could be achieved was very limited. Operational sergeant pilots were a comparative rarity in the RFC, whereas non-commissioned gunners became quite numerous and there was no alternative but for the surplus to fly with officers. There was a lot more to being a crew than simply flying and fighting together, however; ideally, its members also played together, lived together, often sharing a hut or tent, and they ate and drank in the same mess. Almost every aspect of their lives was conducted in close proximity and on quite intimate terms, all of which contributed to a successful partnership in the air.

To put some of this into the words of one who was actually there, consider the writings of Lt Walter Noble, who flew with No 20 Sqn in 1918:[16]

> 'Nothing is worse for an Observer's nerves than to fly with a varied assortment of Pilots – good, bad and indifferent. Co-operation between the occupants of a fighting-plane is essential, if their names are not to adorn the list of Missing.' and '... every useful Observer paired off with a pilot with whom he would invariably fly. Not only that, but in many cases they would become like David and Jonathan, inseparable during the intervals of flying. Thus they got to know one another intimately, and as a result became very dependable and useful.'

Noble was referring to all-officer crews, of course, but there were, perforce, many crews of mixed status. Since officers and NCOs had separate messes and private soldiers were quartered elsewhere, it was virtually impossible for a mixed crew to share their off-duty hours. As a result, they cannot have experienced the essential intimacy which Noble describes and the consequent lack of mutual understanding must inevitably have degraded their effectiveness in combat. This problem will have been compounded in units where non-commissioned personnel were not even permanently assigned to a particular pilot, their names merely appearing on a roster when they were required for flying.

Even if they had wanted to, it would have been quite impractical, for instance, for a sergeant (let alone a private) to try to introduce an officer into his own social group on informal terms or *vice versa*. Apart from embarrassing his colleagues, such behaviour would have flown in the face of normal Service protocol to such an extent that any CO would have felt obliged to curtail it on the grounds that it was prejudicial to discipline and good conduct.

The inevitable sense of separateness did little to foster a close working relationship, as later described by No 6 Sqn's Sgt G. Eddington:[17]

> 'I knew what time I was going up but I didn't even know what job I was on until the observer came out – always an officer in my case. I said, "Good morning, Sir" and we got on with our job. When we came down he got out and went to make his report. He did all the reporting – what he'd found, what he'd seen, what he'd photographed. I went to the sergeants mess and I had no further contact.'

Eddington was a pilot, but the air of detachment and lack of involvement that he recalled would have been much the same for a gunner. Unfortunately, the sense of alienation could extend beyond the working environment as, in contrast to the officers mess, where most of the members were aircrew, the sergeants mess and the billets of other ranks were inhabited largely by technical and administrative personnel. Where only a handful of aviators was involved, the scarcity of colleagues with similar interests and with whom to share mutual experiences could heighten the feeling of isolation.

The authorities were certainly aware of this problem but it was symptomatic of the general antipathy towards back-seaters that their plight failed to provoke any positive action. It was not until the last few months of the war that any serious consideration was given to the provision of messes exclusively for the use of NCO aircrew, and only then because (as discussed later) it was anticipated that there would be a substantial influx of sergeant *pilots*. Where NCO observers were present, they too were entitled to use these facilities, but no instructions were ever issued to provide messes for back-seaters alone. In the event, few of these dedicated messes were ever established. Most non-commissioned aircrew were obliged to use the mess appropriate to their rank and when they represented only a small proportion of its membership it could be a very lonely existence. George Eddington again:

> 'I couldn't make friends. I had nothing in common – I didn't have access to the officers mess; I didn't know what they thought. In the sergeants mess they were all fitters and riggers – I wasn't in their world any more than they were in mine.'

None of these difficulties should be overstated – but neither should they be ignored. While the officer/NCO/other ranks relationship could be awkward, this did not have to be the case if the situation was handled with a little tact and understanding. Mixed status crews were certainly not universally regarded as being a problem; if they had been the system would simply have become unworkable. Most of the problems eased with the passage of time. Growing numbers made the gunners seem progressively less strange, the newcomers gradually merging into the background to become a familiar and unremarkable feature of the system. Furthermore, the quality of gunnery training improved significantly during 1917, making it quite clear that marksmanship had nothing whatever to do with rank.

Even the differences which were rooted in class prejudice eased as the war dragged on. Having virtually exhausted the nation's supply of Public School boys, it became increasingly necessary to recruit officers from much lower layers of the social strata and to commission large numbers of men from the ranks, both trends further serving to dilute the old distinctions.

[15] Arch Whitehouse, *op. cit.*
[16] W. Noble. *With a Bristol Fighter Squadron* (1920).
[17] Eddington's personal recollections are in the Sound Archives of the Imperial War Museum. The extracts reproduced here are taken from passages reproduced in Nigel Steel's and Peter Hart's *Tumult in the Clouds* (1997).

Chapter 7

1914–17. Pilot training in the RFC

It will have become clear from much of the foregoing that, from being virtually non-existent in 1914, over the next two years the training of observers had progressed to being something less than adequate, substantial improvements not being introduced until the middle of 1916. Understandably, far more effort had been expended on the instruction of pilots, but even so their training had been of indifferent quality, and there had never been enough of it. As a result, while a new pilot arriving in France had always been more competent than a new observer, his capabilities were still very limited. So far as the practicalities of acquiring vital operational expertise were concerned, therefore, a pilot joined the very steep operational learning curve only slightly above his companion. The training of pilots is arguably beyond the scope of this book but the fact that no observer ever went flying without one is considered to justify a digression to examine how the 'other' member of a two-seater crew learned his trade.

While some pre-war military (and naval) pilots had learned to fly with the CFS at Upavon, most had gained their initial experience at a civilian school at their own expense. Having obtained their Royal Aero Club (RAeC) Certificates, they were then able to recover their investment, up to a maximum of £75 (equivalent to about £4375 at the end of the 1990s[1]), from public funds.[2] These 'private' pilots subsequently went either to the CFS, to undergo a more advanced formal flying course, or joined one of the handful of pre-war squadrons to consolidate their skills.

General mobilisation immediately created a demand for additional pilots and it was quite clear that the existing system would be unable to cope. To provide extra training capacity, on 17 August the War Office took over the civilian aerodrome and facilities at Brooklands for *ab initio* instruction and set up a similar military school at Netheravon shortly afterwards, several pilots being recalled from France in September to serve as instructors. These units were later given military designations as Reserve Aeroplane Squadrons (RAS).[3] The RNAS did much the same, creating the foundations of its wartime pilot training system by co-opting the civilian schools at Eastbourne and Hendon to support the relatively long-established naval presence at Eastchurch.

Despite the subsequent growth of the military flying training organisation, the RFC (and the RNAS, and later the RAF) continued to make use of civilian schools to provide elementary instruction until 1918. Examples of such enterprises included the Hall, the Ruffy-Baumann, the Grahame-White and the Beatty schools at Hendon, the London and Provincial School at Stag Lane and the Northern Aircraft Company at Lake Windermere. The precise arrangements varied. Some of these concerns worked under direct contract to the War Office or Admiralty, while in other cases students continued to pay their own tuition fees.[4] Another early adjunct to the scheme was HQ RFC's School of Instruction at le Crotoy which operated throughout much of 1915. This unit provided remedial training for pilots who were considered to need it and permitted many observers to be given an initial insight into the art of flying before being sent home to be retrained as pilots.

Although Brooklands' remit was soon extended to permit it to train to 'wings' standard the training machine was still incapable of meeting the RFC's numerical requirement. In January 1915, therefore, the system was reorganised and expanded with a view to increasing its output.[5] No 3 RAS moved from Brooklands to Shoreham, another pre-war aerodrome (operated by the Pashley Flying School) which had been among the civilian facilities taken over in the previous August, and land was acquired elsewhere for further new units. The RASs were all intended to function as elementary flying schools. In addition to practical flying training to (at least) RAeC Certificate standard, they were also to provide all the associated theoretical and technical ground instruction. The significance of the certificate, incidentally,

[1]This comparison in prices, and others which appear elsewhere in this book, have been derived from the Office of National Statistics' Long Term Retail Price Index (RPI). The edition used by this writer, which covers the period 1850–1999, assumed the RPI to have been 100 in January 1974. The base date is of little significance, however; another tabulation based on January 1956 gives very similar results.

[2]AIR1/806/204/4/1189. It is interesting to note that in the early days of the war the Treasury was predictably tight-fisted about using public money to underwrite a private (and possibly even frivolous) activity. Although pilots enlisted in the RFC for a nominal four years, it was far from certain in 1914 that the war was going to last that long. War Office letter 100/FC/30(MA1) of 10 September 1914 announced, therefore, that any wartime pilot who failed to complete his four-year engagement would be liable for the refund of the full £75 cost of his licence and that he would also have to pay back his uniform allowance at the rate of £10 for each year of the four which was not served. This information was promulgated in HQ Administrative Wing's Routine Orders on 12 October 1914. It is assumed that, once the war had become a permanent fixture, these regulations will have been relaxed.

[3]The schools at Brooklands and Netheravon complemented the Reserve Aeroplane Squadron which had been set up at South Farnborough during August. In November the original unit was given a numerical designation as No 1 RAS, those at Netheravon and Brooklands becoming Nos 2 and 3 respectively. On 13 January 1916, by which time there were eighteen of them, the RASs were redesignated as Reserve Squadrons. Neither title described the function of these units very precisely, however, and on 31 May 1917 they were given the more appropriate designation of Training Squadrons. There were more than sixty of them in the UK by then, with others in Canada and Egypt.

[4]For the first two years of the war there was an anomaly in the regulations under which serving personnel were able to reclaim their tuition fees in that they applied only to those seeking a transfer to the RFC (Military Wing). While similar arrangements had certainly existed for those wishing to fly with the pre-war RFC (Naval Wing) and the early RNAS, these would appear subsequently to have lapsed. Parity was restored on 7 November 1916 when the *London Gazette* published an Order in Council authorising the refund of fees up to £75 to any officers and warrant officers possessing RAeC Certificates who wished to transfer to the RNAS. See also page 976 of *Flight* for 9 November and Admiralty Weekly Order 3136 of the 24th.

[5]AIR1/1288/204/11/53. The new scheme was described in some detail in War Office letter 87/4469 (MA1) dated 9 January 1915.

reflected the fact that the Royal Aero Club was the only body empowered to license a British pilot, military as well as civilian.[6]

Having completed his elementary course at an RAS a student proceeded either to the CFS or, and this was a major innovation, to one of the Service Squadrons working up to operational readiness (in January 1915 these were Nos 1, 7 and 8 Sqns). There they were expected to spend up to two months flying, ideally, one type of aircraft, rather than gaining experience on a variety of different aeroplanes which had been the favoured practice in the past. By this means the number of pilots on the strength of a Service Squadron acting as an advanced flying school increased progressively until it was some 50% above establishment. At this point the surplus was detached to form the nucleus of a completely new unit, leaving its parent squadron free to proceed overseas. The cycle then repeated itself.[7]

The major weakness in this system was its use, really its misuse, of Service Squadrons. The DMA was aware of the limitations which this might impose but considered that these would have to be accepted. The main drawback, and one which had certainly been foreseen, was that imposing a major flying training commitment on units which were supposed to be preparing for active service might well overload them. Nevertheless, while these squadrons were still supposed to practise operational techniques, it was ruled that, where conflict arose, priority was to be given to pilot training. As a result of this policy, and as we have already seen, tactical role training, and the instruction of observers, were to become increasingly secondary considerations.

In essence, the training philosophy adopted by the RFC in January 1915 represented an attempt to get a quart out of a proverbial pint pot and it inevitably resulted in a short measure. While this approach did serve to sustain the flow of new pilots, it became increasingly difficult to maintain a satisfactory balance between quantity and quality. The problem grew worse as the war progressed because the introduction of increasingly sophisticated aeroplanes, equipment and techniques meant that the amount that a new pilot needed to assimilate grew inexorably.

Furthermore, while some of those who had to teach this steadily expanding syllabus were relatively experienced pilots, few of them could be regarded as skilled instructors. As Maj R. Smith-Barry put it, the flying instructors of 1916 were those pilots who 'were resting, those who were preparing to go overseas and those who had shown themselves to be useless for anything else. The first two classes had other interests paramount; the third had no interests at all.'[8] In fact, the sole qualification required of an instructor was that he had to be a licensed pilot and, on an advanced training squadron, it was not at all unusual for a pilot to be teaching his juniors to fly the day after he had himself qualified for his 'wings'.[9] The inevitable result was that the competence of most newly graduated pilots failed to meet the standards which were (should have been) required. This is not to say that the RFC had no capable pilots. It had, but they were either naturally gifted or lucky enough to have survived unscathed for long enough to have acquired a worthwhile amount of experience.

By early 1916 the War Office was receiving 'serious complaints' from Maj-Gen Trenchard 'concerning the insufficient training of some of the replacement pilots sent out as reinforcements.' By this time two major initiatives (references to both of which have already been made) had already been taken with the aim of raising training standards. First, RFC Schools of Instruction had been established at Reading and Oxford and from early 1916 these began to make a significant contribution by providing a comprehensive ground-based foundation course in aviation theory and technology. Secondly, Brig-Gen Salmond had been given overall responsibility for the conduct of training and his influence soon began to make itself felt. One of the earliest indications of more positive control being exercised was a clear restatement of what was required to qualify as a pilot. From March a pilot had to have:

a. flown solo for a minimum of fifteen hours;
b. flown a service (as distinct from a training) aeroplane 'satisfactorily';
c. made a cross-country flight of at least sixty miles, making two landings (at RFC supervised aerodromes) en route;
d. climbed to 6000 feet and remained there for at least fifteen minutes before descending to land, with his engine switched off, touching down within a circle of 50 yards diameter; and
e. landed twice in the dark with the assistance of flares, although this requirement could be waived if delays would have been incurred by waiting for suitable conditions.

[6]Since it was the only responsible aeronautical organisation in the country at the time, the RAeC had assumed (with the approval of the Government) responsibility for licensing all pilots in the United Kingdom with effect from 1 March 1910. To obtain his 'ticket' a pilot had to complete, to the satisfaction of an official observer appointed by the Club, three separate flights around a five-kilometre closed circuit course. Each flight had to terminate with the engine being switched off at or before touch-down which was to be within 150 metres of a point previously nominated by the candidate.

These requirements were later amended to reflect the increasing capabilities of aeroplanes. From February 1911, a pilot had to make only two five-kilometre flights but they were now to be flown around two posts located not more than 500 metres apart, with the direction of flight being reversed at each turn so that the course became a series of five 'figures of eight'. A third sortie was still required, the object of this one being to attain an altitude of at least fifty metres. All three landings were to be made engine-off within fifty metres of the position nominated by the candidate. The rules were amended again in January 1914, the altitude test being raised to 100 metres and on this sortie the engine was to be switched off at height, the entire descent, approach and spot landing being carried out dead-stick.

At both military and civilian schools, given favourable weather and an appropriate degree of urgency, it was quite feasible for an *ab initio* student to obtain his ticket within a week.

[7]This practice was to be sustained for the next two years, some quite complex genealogies being established. No 8 Sqn, for instance, begat No 13 Sqn, which spawned No 22 Sqn, which provided the nucleus for No 45 Sqn, which passed on its genes to No 64 Sqn – by which time it was August 1916. A similar system was used in 1917 except that the parent unit was more likely to be a Training than a Service Squadron.

[8]This description is taken from a document, advocating an entirely new approach to flying training, written by Smith-Barry in November 1916. In John W.R. Taylor's *CFS, Birthplace of Air Power* (1958) the author quotes this document, which he describes as a letter to an unidentified correspondent in the UK, in full. In his biography of the writer of this document, *Pioneer Pilot, The Great Smith-Barry* (1976), F.D. Tredrey refers to it as 'a paper' which found its way to Trenchard who, having made appropriate arrangements in advance with Jack Salmond, had Smith-Barry posted home to take command of No 1 Reserve Squadron at Gosport where he was to put his theory into practice on a trial basis. It would be interesting to know who it was that Smith-Barry actually approached and what degree of informality was involved, but this author has failed to unearth a copy of Smith-Barry's original correspondence.

[9]In his autobiography, *Recollections of an Airman* (1933), Louis Strange notes that, while commanding No 23 Sqn in late 1915, 'I put four of my best pupils on to instructing as soon as they were competent.' This practice was widespread, another example being provided by No 45 Sqn in the summer of 1916 where Lt L.W. McArthur, Lt E.F.P. Lubbock and 2/Lt B.P.G. Beanlands were all retained to fly as instructors after having gained their 'wings' with the unit.

With hindsight it is plain that this remarkably short list defined no more than a minimum standard. It should be appreciated, however, that at the time it was considered to represent a '*raising* of the standard of the graduation test' (author's italics).[10]

In order to keep the units conducting, what was known as, training in Higher Aviation fully manned, student pilots were, if necessary, to be withdrawn from the elementary flying schools before they had even qualified for their RAeC Certificates, although these were still supposed to be obtained before final graduation. Clearly, quantity was still taking priority over quality, this being heavily underlined by the fact that the graduation standard still omitted any reference to tactical or operational skills. No mention was made, for instance, of combat manoeuvring, indeed of manoeuvring of *any* kind. Similarly, formation flying, cloud flying and practical experience of bombing, gunnery, photography and W/T work were all considered to be non-essential. Admittedly, pilots were encouraged to indulge in such activities if time permitted but, unfortunately, it seldom did. In short, if the trainee pilot of early 1916 could get an aeroplane off the ground, keep it in the air and then land again, with or without power, he was considered to be ready for active service.

At much the same time as the graduation standard was being 'raised', three qualification certificates were introduced, these being additional to the RAeC Certificate. These were:

Certificate A. A written examination on the theory of flight, RFC organisation, artillery co-operation procedures, etc. The papers were set by Commandant CFS, the exams being held under local arrangements at the Headquarters of each Training Wing every Tuesday.

Certificate B. Tests of practical skills, involving aero-engines, rigging, Morse, machine-guns and the like, held at the CFS on Tuesdays and at Reading and Oxford on Saturdays.

Certificate C. Flying tests, conducted in accordance with instructions issued locally by Wing Commanders. In effect Certificate C simply involved progressive completion of the exercises which had been laid down in March (see above).

Certificates A and B had to be gained in that order but the flying test could be completed at any time. Once he had obtained all three certificates a student was awarded his Graduation Certificate of the RFC by the CFS. The War Office was notified that he had qualified and shortly afterwards the new pilot would be gazetted as a Flying Officer. Once he had been gazetted (and not before) he was entitled to wear a flying badge.[11]

By the summer of 1916 the majority of trainee pilots were passing through Reading or Oxford and the certification system was changed to reflect this. In June Certificates A and B were combined into a single Certificate A which had to be obtained before commencing flying training.[12] The original procedure had to be sustained for several months, running in parallel with the new scheme, for the benefit of students who had begun their training under the old arrangements, i.e. those who had not had the opportunity to spend a period at one of the Schools of Instruction.

Cadets learning how an aeroplane was put together in the airframe shop of No 2 School of Military Aeronautics at Oxford, this picture dates from 1918 but facilities like these had first become available at the end of 1915. The aeroplane in the centre of the room is a Camel with an engineless DH 4(?) beyond it. In the right foreground is the tail of an Avro 504 and at the far end of the room, a Dolphin, a fully rigged BE2c and the stripped fuselage of another. (Chaz Bowyer)

While the RAeC 'ticket' had been worthwhile when it had first been introduced in 1910, subsequent advances in flying techniques had made it increasingly irrelevant and it now represented only the first hurdle in the training sequence, and a very low one at that. In fact it was actually becoming counterproductive, because it required about three-quarters of an hour to complete the test and all other flying was usually suspended while one was being flown. To cut down on what HQ II Bde described as a 'lamentable waste of time', in October 1915 OC 5th Wg, Lt-Col W.G.H. Salmond, had suggested that, while retaining the requirement to fly the course twice, the five figures-of-eight might be reduced to just two.[13] When it was put to them, the RAeC Committee promptly acceded to this request.[14]

This had been the thin end of a wedge, however, and, since the RFC had long been adjudicating the tests on its behalf, the RAeC (still the sole official licensing authority) was on the point of relinquishing its jurisdiction over military pilots in any case. Recognising that the Graduation Certificate of the RFC required a far higher standard of competence than its own, the RAeC agreed to issue its 'ticket' to a pilot who could produce evidence to show that he had been certified by the military.

By the summer of 1916 more than 3000 RAeC Certificates had been issued but it was becoming increasingly common for pilots to neglect to inform the Club authorities that they

[10]AIR1/387/15/231/28. The list of requirements (and the associated quotations) are taken from War Office letter 87/7094(MA1) dated 23 March 1916.

[11]AIR1/1273/204/9/148. Although it was frequently stressed in the orders routinely published by training units that the wearing of 'wings' was conditional upon being gazetted, e.g. 5th Wg's Orders No 245 of 18 October 1915, it appears to have been a common practice for pilots to sew on their badges as soon as they knew that they had qualified, hence the need for repetition. This illicit practice will no doubt have been encouraged by the fact that, in order to give them some credibility, newly qualified pilots who were selected to act as instructors were granted local dispensations to wear their 'wings'. Lt E.F.P. Lubbock, for instance was authorised to wear his badge on 6 June 1916, although his formal appointment as a Flying Officer did not appear in the *London Gazette* until 12 July (albeit with an effective date of 22 May).

[12]AIR1/405/15/231/46. War Office letter 43/FS/417(AO1a) of 22 June 1916 announced the introduction of the new Certificate A which covered all basic theoretical and practical work.

[13]AIR1/138/15/40/283. In an unreferenced letter dated 30 October 1915, HQ II Bde requested that the War Office seek a reduction in the content of the RAeC test.

[14]*Ibid.* In a letter of 1 December 1915, the RAeC Committee agreed that the distance to be flown on each test, previously 5 km, could be reduced to 2 km.

had graduated, often because they were packed off to France as replacements before they had had time to attend to this chore. Since they lacked their RAeC 'ticket', these pilots were technically unlicensed. It was recognised, however, that by this time the RAeC was merely 'rubber-stamping' the CFS Certificate and that this procedure had become redundant. All pilots who had qualified up to and including August were, therefore, automatically and retrospectively granted their RAeC Certificates (although not all of them were claimed). For pilots who qualified thereafter, the CFS documentation alone was deemed to be sufficient proof of their competence to fly military aeroplanes.[15]

The measures which had been introduced thus far were all worthwhile, since they had served to put pilot training on a more formal basis and to streamline the associated administrative procedures. They had not addressed the fundamental problem, however. The training system was still failing to keep pace with the demands of front-line service, indeed the gap was becoming progressively wider. Much more needed to be done and these requirements can be summarised as follows:

a. Training needed to be broadened to embrace operational activities in addition to pure flying.
b. Training needed to be adapted to reflect the increasingly specialised nature of aerial warfare.
c. Pilots had to be given much more time in the air.
d. Pilots needed to taught how to be the complete master of their machines, rather than merely having some measure of influence over them. This demanded a more scientific and professional approach to training, including the provision of properly qualified flying instructors.
e. An all-through system of dedicated flying training schools was required, permitting Service Squadrons to be divorced from the system.

The first steps towards realising these aims were taken with the introduction of a substantially expanded syllabus in December 1916.[16] Prior to this, as described below, more attention had already, if belatedly, begun to be paid to operational techniques and procedures. The new syllabus, as well as revising the content of the practical flying tests, now laid down the level of expertise that pupils had to be able to demonstrate in the fields of bombing, photography, signals and so on. It also raised the minimum number of solo hours needed to qualify for a flying badge to twenty, with the addition of further solo time 'on type' for pilots destined to fly certain nominated aeroplanes.[17]

For the first few months following the introduction of the new syllabus the necessary facilities were not universally available and this and other circumstances dictated that many short cuts had to be taken. The most serious deficiency was in flying hours and as late as June 1917, in order to make good the heavy losses sustained by the RFC during the previous April, replacement pilots were still being sent to France with less than thirty hours' flying time; that is *total* flying time, let alone solo hours.

1918. Pilot training in the RAF

Despite the early setback caused by the aftermath of 'Bloody April', the quality of flying training continued to improve thereafter. Suffice to say that, largely due to the positive influence of Maj Smith-Barry (see Chapter 12), all the outstanding points listed above had been addressed by mid-1918 and, as a result, the capabilities of newly-qualified pilots had been completely transformed. Before leaving this topic, however, it might be as well to provide a brief summary of the three-phase training sequence that had been adopted by the RAF and which remained in force for the rest of the war. The details and timing varied according to role but the procedure was broadly as outlined below.

a. Basic training, which was undertaken as a flight cadet[18] at a Training Depot Station (see page 71), involved at least 25 hours of airborne time on Avro 504s accumulated over a period of about three months. On successful completion of this phase, during which a student drew the four shillings per day instructional rate of pay, he was graduated 'A'.
b. The second phase, which occupied up to two months, was conducted at the same unit with the student retaining his original status. On completion of the course he should have accumulated a further 35 hours in the air of which at least five would have been flown on a 'service' type. Apart from pure flying instruction, he would have passed practical tests in cross-country, formation and cloud flying, the conduct of reconnaissance and air-to-ground firing. On successful completion a student was graduated 'B' and gazetted as a 2nd lieutenant in the Flying Branch, although he still drew the instructional rate of flying pay.
c. The third phase was conducted at a school specialising in providing instruction appropriate to a particular operational role, i.e. single-seat fighter and fighter-reconnaissance, day and night bomber, army co-operation or maritime. Content and duration differed but on completion a student graduated 'C' whereupon he was entitled to put up his 'wings' and draw flying pay at the full rate of eight shillings per day.

In all, when the preliminary ground-based courses are added, by 1918 it was taking about eleven months for a pilot to progress from enlistment to gaining his 'wings'. At that stage he should have logged at least 70 hours and often substantially more.[19]

[15]While the War Office and Admiralty were recognised as being competent to license their own pilots from August 1916 onwards, this did not preclude a military flyer obtaining an RAeC Certificate on his own initiative. For the payment of a nominal sum, a military certificate was still negotiable and by 11 November 1918 the Royal Aero Club had approved a total of 6308 aviator's 'tickets' in addition to having issued certificates to 206 aeronauts (balloonists) and thirty-nine airship pilots. Some of the recipients will have been civilians but the majority were (or became) military personnel.

[16]AIR1/676/21/13/1773. War Office letter 87/7094(AO1a) of 15 December 1916 redefined the practical flying tests to be passed by student pilots while Training Brigade letter TB/861 of 30 November had laid down the tests to be passed in a variety of operational techniques.

[17]*Ibid*. Before being sent overseas, pilots flying BE12s, DH 2s and FE8s were required to have logged at least twenty-five hours solo of which not less than five were to have been on type. For Sopwith, SE5 and Morane pilots the corresponding figures were twenty-eight and eight.

[18]AIR1/398/15/231/39. Until the end of 1917 the Army commissioned its directly recruited officers on graduation from a Cadet Wing, so that they underwent their flying training as subalterns. This was at variance with later naval practice, since RNAS trainees were not formally commissioned until they were professionally qualified (see Chapter 11, Note 5). The RFC eventually adopted a similar approach, War Office letter 87/RFC/1049(F6) of 2 January 1918 announcing that the Air Council had decided that all prospective RFC officers would in future undergo all their basic training as Flight Cadets, although, through some bureaucratic oversight prospective *ab initio* Kite Balloon Officers continued to be trained as subalterns until late May when they too were subjected to the flight cadet regime.

The RFC cadet system was subsequently carried over into the RAF, at some notional disadvantage to ex-naval Probationary Observer/Flight Officers, since they lost their previous ability to acquire antedates of seniority in recognition of high standards being achieved during training, the RFC/RAF scheme having no provision for this refinement, see AMWO 251 of 15 May 1918.

[19]AIR10/64. This information has been condensed from Field Service Publication (FS) 39, *Training Courses in the RAF for Commissioned and Non-commissioned Personnel, showing Status and Pay*, which was published in October 1918. See also Chapter 14, Note 15.

While it was obviously of considerable concern to any observer that his colleague should be able to fly their aeroplane well, it is considered that the foregoing provides sufficient background on the way in which pilots gained their basic flying skills during WW I. On the other hand, because it had a direct impact on the division of responsibility within a crew, it is worth examining the way in which pilots acquired increasing expertise in the handling of radio and in the conduct of aerial gunnery, both of which had originally been regarded as being the province of the observer.

1916–18. Wireless training for pilots

While most of the observers being trained at home were being provided with a reasonable grounding in operational skills by the summer of 1916, pilots did not begin to attend dedicated courses, such as those being run at Brooklands and Hythe, until the following year. Nevertheless, they too were expected to be able to cope with wireless and to handle a machine-gun.

For pilots trained prior to mid-1916 their instruction in W/T procedures had been a pretty haphazard affair. The syllabus (such as it was) was poorly defined and the amount of time devoted to the subject was largely dependent upon the enthusiasm of the individual instructors, Squadron and Wing Commanders involved. Having done their operational flying in 1915, before W/T had become firmly established as a basic tool of the aviator's trade, however, many of these officers would have had little personal experience of using wireless and some would still not yet have recognised its importance. It will be appreciated, therefore, that the instruction being provided could be variable in both quality and quantity.

The lack of familiarity with wireless displayed by new pilots had been causing concern at HQ RFC and the reform of the W/T content of the syllabus was high on Salmond's list of priorities. In May 1916 a formal system was introduced.[20] Units tasked with training in Higher Aviation (by now selected Reserve Squadrons as well as Service Squadrons awaiting mobilisation) were to be provided with sufficient resources to permit each of them to have two aircraft fitted with transmitters. Each squadron was also to have a ground receiver station which was to be manned by three wireless operators. In addition, each Training Wing was established to have a dedicated AEO to co-ordinate wireless activities at squadron level. To supervise them, there was to be an EO at a scale of one per three wings and, in overall charge, there was to be an Inspecting Officer at HQ Training Brigade.

The specific skills which a pilot needed to acquire were much the same as those being taught to observers. He had to learn Morse and the Artillery Code and demonstrate his ability to transmit using a silenced key. In the air he had to become accustomed to letting out and reeling in an aerial and practise making live transmissions simulating artillery co-operation messages. This basic syllabus was progressively expanded and within a few months it included the ability to read ground signals and practical work with 'Artillery Targets', similar to those being used to instruct observers in the techniques of ranging and spotting. As previously noted, from the autumn of 1916 onwards it was becoming increasingly common for pilots to assume responsibility for operational W/T work. While it was not the only reason (see, for instance, page 52), there can be little doubt that the much improved wireless training that pilots were now receiving served to encourage this trend.

Until mid-1916 the key functions of military aviation had been reconnaissance and artillery co-operation and all pilots had undergone the same sequence of training. By that time, however, the influence of role specialisation was becoming increasingly apparent, bringing with it an appreciation that what was an essential skill for one pilot was largely superfluous to another. Early in 1917, therefore, the wireless training sequence was revised and a phased system was introduced.[21]

Since all pilots needed to have some facility with W/T, Morse training (at six words per minute) was introduced at the elementary stage and each of the Reserve Squadrons concerned was required to have ten aircraft equipped with winches and aerials so that all pilots would become familiar with the chore of having to wind out an aerial on every sortie. More importantly, they would also have drilled into them the importance of having to reel it in again! This approach, supplemented by appropriate lectures and building on the foundations laid at Oxford/Reading, served to provide all pilots with a reasonable grasp of wireless techniques. The amount of W/T training provided at the advanced stage was now varied, however, depending upon the next unit to which a student was posted.

The main users of wireless continued to be the corps reconnaissance squadrons and several advanced training units were now required to concentrate on producing pilots for this particular role. They flew Avros and a selection of 'service' types, typically BE2s and Nieuport two-seaters until these could be replaced by RE8s and FK8s as they became available. Half of the Avros and all the quasi-operational machines were scaled to be fitted with transmitters for practical airborne exercises. At these units Morse (at eight words per minute), Panneau signalling, Artillery Target work and the like continued to be a central feature of the curriculum.

As the system evolved, other squadrons began to specialise in producing pilots for single- and two-seat fighters, and for day and night bombers. At these units the amount of practical W/T training was adjusted to reflect the extent to which students would actually use radio once they had joined an operational squadron, although consolidation training in reading Morse continued to be a universal requirement.

1916–18. Gunnery training for pilots

Until the spring of 1916 gunnery training for pilots had been at much the same low level of intensity as wireless work. The provision of ground-based instruction on the Lewis gun as part of the Reading/Oxford syllabus was considered to represent sufficient improvement, as, in practice, it was usually the observer who actually handled these weapons in action. The introduction of synchronising gears during the summer meant that this approach was no longer adequate. As well as continuing to need some familiarity with the Lewis gun, a pilot now had to be able to deal with the Vickers. Furthermore, he also had to be introduced to the concept of aiming his whole aeroplane at the target.

While a few more pilots began to pass through Hythe during the early summer, these courses continued to be largely the preserve of observers and specialist ground

[20]AIR1/1266/204/9/61. HQ VI Bde letter 6BP/356 dated 26 May 1916 detailed the measures to be implemented to improve wireless training facilities.

[21]*Ibid.* Training Brigade letter TB/837, dated 29 January 1917, provided details of the extended W/T training system for pilots which was to be implemented with effect from 1 February.

tradesmen. In August it was decided that Hythe should also assume formal responsibility for the gunnery training of pilots, although the actual instruction was to be conducted remotely.[22] Each advanced training squadron was to be provided with an NCO instructor and each wing was to have a similarly qualified, Hythe-trained, pilot to act as the Wing Gunnery Officer. These officers were responsible to the Wing Commander for the effectiveness of the gunnery training being carried out at all squadrons within his organisation. They were, however, only assigned to wings on attachment; technically they remained on the strength of the School of Aerial Gunnery, which meant that they also reported to the Commandant at Hythe. In addition there was to be an Inspecting Officer at HQ Training Brigade to oversee all gunnery training activities.

These arrangements were not entirely satisfactory, as the (often very junior) Wing Gunnery Officers were in the uncomfortable position of having to serve two masters. Furthermore, because the School of Aerial Gunnery reported directly to the DMA, rather than to the Training Brigade, the Inspecting Officer lacked the authority to direct Hythe's activities.

So far as facilities were concerned, increased attention began to be paid to improving marksmanship. Each advanced training squadron was now required to maintain a .22 firing range and small numbers of Hythe gun-cameras began to be issued as they became available. Lectures were introduced to cover sighting theory, deflection shooting and the like and there was practical instruction on the mechanics of both Lewis and Vickers guns and on the gearing which permitted the latter to fire through the disc swept by the propeller. The new system began to establish itself during the autumn of 1916 but it still did not fully satisfy the requirement.

The chain of command problem was eventually solved on 18 December when Hythe was subordinated to the Training Brigade, the latter thereafter assuming responsibility for all aspects of training in aerial gunnery. This enabled Salmond to implement a progressive system similar to that already being applied to W/T training. A phased syllabus was devised which introduced gunnery theory and practical work on machine-guns as early as the Cadet Wing stage (see Chapter 8, Note 27). This foundation was subsequently reinforced at the Schools of Instruction and built on during elementary flying training. Clay pigeon shooting and machine-gun practice on ground ranges were added at the advanced stage, further tuition being provided by employing pilots with recent combat experience as visiting lecturers and to provide demonstration flights.

All of this represented a considerable improvement but the system still failed to provide student pilots with first-hand experience of live air-to-air gunnery or of simulated air combat. It was envisaged that this sort of practical training would eventually take place at Loch Doon where a new School of Aerial Gunnery was being built with extensive and sophisticated training facilities, both live and synthetic, for both ground and air firing. Unfortunately, this project proved to have been ill-conceived and it did not run smoothly.[23]

Since Loch Doon failed to open for business in January 1917, as planned, No 2 (Auxiliary) School of Aerial Gunnery [(Aux)SAG] was set up at Turnberry to provide pilots with some practical experience.[24] It took some time to decide on the format of the exercises to be flown at Turnberry but a formal syllabus had been agreed by the late spring of 1917. While this had solved the gunnery problem, there was still a requirement for tactical flying practice. This need was not really satisfied until the autumn when Nos 1 and 2 Schools of Aerial Fighting were opened at Ayr and Driffield, respectively.

Meanwhile, to satisfy the ever-increasing demand for dedicated gunnery training, two more interim units had been set up, No 3 (Aux)SAG at New Romney to deal with back-seaters and No 4 (Aux)SAG at Marske for pilots. With the collapse of the Loch Doon programme these 'auxiliary' schools became permanent fixtures and their designations were changed to reflect their independent status. Nos 1 and 3 (Aux)SAGs merged to become No 1 (Observers) School of Aerial Gunnery in March 1918 and in May the resources of Nos 2 and 4 (Aux)SAGs were pooled with those of Nos 1 and 2 Schools of Aerial Fighting to form Nos 1, 2 and 3 Schools of Aerial Fighting and Gunnery.[25] Thankfully, these rather cumbersome titles were short-lived and before the end of the month they had been redesignated as Nos 1, 2 and 3 Fighting Schools.

By mid-1918 the relatively sophisticated training system no longer had to get by with second-hand obsolete aeroplanes.This state-of-the-art Bristol Fighter, A7195, belonged to No 1 Fighting School, a unit which ran courses for observers as well as pilots. (J.M. Bruce/G.S. Leslie collection)

[22]*Ibid.* War Office letter 87/Schools/28(AO1a) dated 26 August 1916 provided details of the system being introduced to improve the gunnery training of pilots.

[23]The Loch Doon scheme had been approved in August 1916, civil engineering work commencing the following month. It had originally been anticipated that the new School of Aerial Gunnery would open for business early in 1917 and Hythe's Lt-Col L.A. Strange was appointed to command on 12 January. Since it was a peat bog, the chosen site was fundamentally unsuitable. Despite the efforts of Messrs McAlpines, who employed a labour force of 3000 men and laid 56 miles of field drains, the airfield was never a practical proposition. Strange had little option but to start training at a temporary alternative location at Turnberry. With little of substance having been achieved at Loch Doon, Strange moved on to the CFS in April, leaving his successor, Lt-Col E.B. Gordon, to supervise building work and capital expenditure, both of which continued remorselessly. By late 1917 No 6 School of Military Aeronautics was slated to move to Loch Doon but whether this was as a part of the original grandiose scheme, or merely a late attempt to find some practical use for the barracks which had been built, is uncertain. In any event the move was cancelled on 11 January 1918 and all further civil engineering work on the site had ceased before the end of that month.

AIR6/16 contains a lengthy report (from which much of the above has been condensed) by Lt-Col Gordon detailing the inadequacies of the Loch Doon site which, apart from anything else, suffered from a particularly poor weather factor. The budget originally authorised for the project in August 1916 had been £150 000. The actual expenditure appears never to have been clearly established but it was probably at least £550 000 (roughly £16 M in 1999 money) and it has been suggested that it might have been as much as £3 M.

[24]'Auxiliary', that is, to the non-effective establishment at Loch Doon. At the same time, January 1917, and for the same reason, the original school at Hythe became No 1 (Aux)SAG, now exclusively dedicated to the training of back-seaters.

[25]No 1 SofAF&G operated from both Ayr and Turnberry; No 2 was at Marske and No 3 at Driffield.

Chapter 8

1916. The RFC's observer training system begins to mature

Reverting to the theme of observer training, activities at the Wireless School were being increasingly influenced by Brig-Gen Salmond and his staff and direct command of the unit was eventually transferred to Headquarters Training Brigade with effect from 1 September 1916. By this time the throughput at Brooklands was running at about twenty observers per month and to reflect the increasing importance of the aviation syllabus the unit was renamed the Wireless and Observers School on 24 October.[1]

The observers course had been extensively revised during August and it is informative to examine its content. Students were divided into two groups: Group A – those with less than six hours of flying time, and Group B – those with more (of whom there are unlikely to have been very many). The course broke down broadly as follows:

First Week. Examination in basic signalling; the principles of electricity as related to W/T; theoretical and practical map-reading; the theory and practice of aerial reconnaissance and reporting, including some flying exercises; artillery co-operation, including use of the Artillery Code, i.e. ranging and spotting, using an Artillery Target and/or 'puff targets';[2] Morse practice; and an introduction to the general routine of the duties of an RFC squadron. Any Group B students with more than fifteen hours of flying experience were tested on the content of the first week of the syllabus on arrival and if they passed they were up-coursed and proceeded directly to Week Two;

Second Week. General principles of W/T, including the tuning of transmitters and receivers (although the standard in-service airborne installations were still transmit-only devices, it was necessary for an observer to be able to handle a ground receiver); lectures on photography; an introduction to the Lewis gun and progress tests on all work completed thus far;

Third Week. W/T practice; revision; practical artillery work – flash spotting, pre-arranged and opportunity targets (including some flying exercises) and final examinations.

This comprehensive syllabus, preceded by a sound theoretical indoctrination at one of the Schools of Instruction and reinforced by a practical gunnery course at Hythe, meant that all observers trained from the summer of 1916 onwards should have been far better prepared than any of their predecessors had ever been. This would only be true, of course, if all observers were permitted to attend the full sequence of courses and if the various schools were all capable of handling the whole curriculum competently.

[1]The first commander of the joint school at Brooklands (it continued to train large numbers of wireless officers and operators) was Maj H.A. Oxenham.

[2]The use of 'puff targets' involved a full-scale simulation whereby puffs of smoke were released on the ground to represent shell bursts in the vicinity of a 'target', the observer flying in an aeroplane being required to estimate the range and bearing of the error and pass an appropriate encrypted correction to the 'battery'.

Unfortunately, these conditions could not always be met. For instance, it was part of the stated aim of the course that all observers passing through Brooklands were to spend fifteen hours in the air. A routine weekly return for 17 January 1917 reported that there were 104 officers under instruction there on that date. Although there was no indication of how many of them were observers (rather than W/T officers), the names of at least seventy-seven appear on a nominal role dated 29 January[3] so by this stage they clearly represented the bulk of the student body. Since the unit could field only five aeroplanes, however (one BE2d, one AW FK3 and three BE2cs), it is extremely doubtful whether any observers had been acquiring anything like the intended fifteen hours of airborne time during 1916.

The overall situation did improve slowly over the next two years but, in order to maintain the strength of the front line, substantial numbers of observers continued to be sent to France, part-trained and very short of airborne time for much of 1917. Indeed, it is known that some observers were still reaching their first squadrons with less than fifteen hours in their log books as late as the summer of 1918.[4]

Nevertheless, despite the training machine's persistent inadequacies, its limitations were gradually being overcome and there was a perceptible and continuing improvement

The location is unknown but this picture appears to show a qualified observer instructing with the aid of a Lewis-based camera-gun. The trades of the students are not known but, because he is wearing full RFC rig, the man actually handling the gun is more likely to have been a prospective pilot than an observer. (J.M. Bruce/G.S. Leslie collection)

[3]AIR1/1009/204/5/1290.

[4]2/Lt John Blanford provides a case in point. Having begun his training in March 1918, he joined No 206 Sqn as a probationary observer on 9 May. At that time he had just six hours of airborne time recorded in his log book. His flying badge was formally bestowed on 5 July by which time he had accumulated some fifty additional hours, representing about twenty operational sorties. A first-hand account of Blanford's wartime experiences was published in *The Cross & Cockade Journal*, Vol 7, No 4 and Vol 8, No 1 (1976–77).

in the competence of observers from mid-1916 onwards. To reflect this, the qualification standard was redefined in November. In their essentials the new requirements did not differ greatly from those which had been laid down in the summer of 1915 (see pages 15/16) but they were now expressed with greater precision.[5] Furthermore, an increased degree of formality was introduced. Rather than simply being certified on what amounted to the subjective assessment of his CO, an observer now had to be examined in the field by specialist officers at brigade or wing level. The subjects in which he was to be tested were: co-operation with artillery; the use and care of wireless equipment; photography and the care of the RFC camera; and the use and care of machine-guns. A clear indication of what would be required to satisfy the examiners was laid down in each case.

Late 1916. The status of the RFC's observers is further enhanced

With hindsight it is hardly surprising that the 'improvements' to their conditions of service which had been announced in November 1915 had failed to dispel, indeed they may well have added to, the widespread perception that observers were held in little esteem and that they had very limited career prospects. Whether the first of these impressions was justified may be a moot point, but there can be no doubt that the second reflected a fair appreciation of the situation. As a result, while HQ RFC had been able to reassure the War Office that it had ample numbers of prospective observers on its waiting list in April 1916, by the autumn this was no longer the case.

Between June and September the number of squadrons authorised for the RFC had been more than doubled and the establishment of qualified observers/gunners on each of the two-seater units had been raised from seven to eighteen. This meant that in round figures the projected requirement for operational back-seaters had grown from about 200 to something like 1000 in just four months. In the meantime General Haig's edict, that *all* applications from officers volunteering to fly were to be forwarded to GHQ, had been repeated at least twice.[6] Since the CinC's wishes were quite unambiguous and widely known, it could be safely assumed that COs were not blocking applications. It had to be concluded, therefore, that there was some other reason for what was now an inadequate response.

The RFC was finally beginning to discover that there was a price to pay for its discriminatory attitude towards observers. Officers were simply not prepared to volunteer to be treated as second-class citizens, not, at least, in the numbers that were now required, hence the introduction of non-commissioned gunners. There is no doubt that the War Office understood the nature of the problem. As Lt-Col W.W. Warner[7] put it, 'In view of the difficulty in obtaining observers for the Royal Flying Corps, the question of their prospects and status in the Corps has again been under consideration.' Nevertheless, despite its having correctly diagnosed the cause of the problem, the RFC's reluctance to accept the unavoidable implications of the fact that it required two men to operate a two-seat aeroplane successfully, prevented it from applying the obvious cure.

Since the members of a two-seater crew were mutually interdependent, it followed that they deserved to be treated with equal consideration and respect. This was still too much for the RFC's generals to swallow, however, and the only concession that they were prepared to grant was the abolition of the intermediate 'grade' of Qualified Observer from November 1916.[8] Thereafter any observer serving in the field, up to a maximum of twelve per squadron, *and* holding the necessary certificates would be immediately and automatically gazetted to the RFC as a Flying Officer (Observer).

While this was obviously intended to improve the observer's lot, it turned out to have little immediate impact at the coal face. In fact the new regulation served only to entrench even more deeply the unfair principle that had first been laid down in July 1915. All newly trained observers (all of whom lacked their certificates, since these could be obtained *only* 'in the field') still reached their squadrons on probation and, unlike pilots, they still had to undergo a baptism of fire before they were permitted to put up their badges. Note that the 'in the field' provision also meant that, again unlike pilots, it was impossible for a newly trained observer posted directly to a Home Defence Squadron (or any other UK-based flying unit) to qualify for his flying 'O'.

It is quite clear that the changes to the observer's terms of service of November 1916 had been no more than cosmetic; there was still no career structure for them. The attitude of the RFC's 'establishment' had not really changed and the 'Poor Bloody Observers' knew it. Writing only a few months after leaving No 70 Sqn, with whom he had flown as an observer during the latter half of 1916, 2/Lt A.J. Bott summed up the situation as follows:[9]

> 'The only two of our then flight-commanders still on the active list are now commanding squadrons, while all the subaltern pilots have become flight-commanders. The observers, members of a tribe akin to Kipling's Sergeant Whatisname, are as they were in the matter of rank, needless to say.'

1917. Complications arising from the new regulations

While they represented only a small concession, the revised terms of service of November 1916 did produce one tangible benefit. Observers had not previously been formally acknowledged by the RFC *until* they were graded, putting them at a significant (typically four to six months) disadvantage in terms of seniority compared to pilots of similar experience. Under the new rules, once an observer was certified as being fully qualified (and until he was he still did not receive full flying pay), his seniority was backdated to his embarkation for France (or elsewhere), in the case of those trained in England, or from the effective date of his

[5]AIR1/997/204/5/1241. HQ RFC letter CRFC 2047G dated 29 November 1916.

[6]AIR1/522/16/12/8. General Haig's directive, to the effect that all applications were to be forwarded to GHQ 'without fail', was republished, as AG/D1936, on 12 June and 4 September 1916; these may not have been the only occasions. The wording of this directive was somewhat misleading, incidentally, as it clearly stated that observers graded as Flying Officers would be eligible to become Flight Commanders and for promotion to captain. This was true, of course, but it presupposed qualification as a pilot and the text failed to make this point.

[7]Lt-Col Warner was AAG at the DMA.

[8]AIR1/406/15/231/47. The details of this decision were announced in War Office letter 100/FC/95(AO2) dated 15 November 1916. The message was disseminated to units in France by HQ RFC letter CRFC 1701(A) dated 26 November and more generally by Army Order 403 of December 1916.

[9]'Contact', *An Airman's Outings With the RFC, June-December 1916* (1917). 'Contact' was 2/Lt Alan John Bott, who was credited with three victories while serving his RFC 'apprenticeship' as an observer. Thereafter, he followed a well-beaten path by training as a pilot. Only by taking this step was he able to realise his full potential and before being taken prisoner in April 1918 he had shot down two further aeroplanes while gaining his captaincy as a Flight Commander with No 111 Sqn.

initial attachment to the RFC for those who were still being recruited and trained in the field. Furthermore, if an observer subsequently retrained as a pilot, as many of them did, he retained all of the seniority he had built up during his service as a back-seater, which put him well ahead of a newly-trained 'straight through' pilot.

Presumably in association with this change in policy, the practice of recording back-seaters separately in the Army List under the heading of Flying Officer (Observer) ceased. From the November 1916 edition onwards a combined Flying Officer list was reinstated, observers once again being distinguished by an '(O)', but this time after, rather than before, their names. Prior to this, in accordance with the previous regulations, the earliest seniority held by any graded observer had been 21 October 1915 (see Chapter 5, Note 2) but subsequent Army Lists incorporated extensive amendments to reflect the revised conditions and some observers eventually had their seniority considerably backdated.[10]

It will be appreciated that within less than two years of the observers badge having been introduced, the rules associated with its award and with the status of the wearer *and* those governing his seniority within the RFC *and* with the way in which this was reflected in the Army List had changed three times – and there were further amendments to come. As was only to be expected, this extremely fluid situation had caused some confusion, prompting a number of requests for retrospective recognition, antedates of seniority and so on. Some of the decisions handed down in these cases were almost certainly incorrect.

The case of Lt R.C. Morgan provides a good example of the arbitrary way in which the regulations were sometimes interpreted. A Canadian, who had been attached to the RFC on 4 August 1915, Morgan had been rated as a qualified observer and authorised to wear a flying 'O' with effect from 21 September. Having completed a stint of active service with No 6 Sqn, Morgan was eventually posted to Home Establishment to train as a pilot. For some reason he was unsuccessful in this endeavour but he remained with his unit, by now No 45 Sqn, in an administrative capacity. This arrangement was formally recognised when, on 15 November 1916 (by which time he was back in France), Morgan was gazetted to the RFC as a Recording Officer.

Wishing to have his earlier service properly acknowledged, Morgan subsequently applied to be retrospectively gazetted as a Flying Officer (Observer) with his seniority antedated to that of his original attachment to the RFC. Under the recently revised regulations, this was a perfectly valid request but it was ruled, quite incorrectly, that, an observer's seniority within the RFC could not be back-dated prior to 15 October 1915. Although he was still entitled to wear his observers badge, it was finally decided that Morgan's formal transfer to the RFC as a Recording Officer in November 1916 would have to stand.

The pattern became even more confused when Morgan ceased to be employed as a Recording Officer a few months later. It was eventually agreed that he could now be belatedly recognised as a Flying Officer (Observer) after all, although the effective date would have to be that of his return to Home Establishment for the second time, i.e. 28 May 1917. Thus, although it could have been done within the rules, Morgan's first fifteen months of service with the RFC never was formally acknowledged.[11]

Probably because the junior officers who were submitting their cases for review were quite lost in the confusing jumble of regulations, they were unable to detect when the authorities were having similar trouble in finding their way through the maze. Like Morgan, most people were simply obliged to accept whatever decision was handed down. It is not suggested that any of those who were doing their best to interpret the rules were in any way malicious, merely that they were sometimes mistaken. Indeed there is ample evidence to show that most of their decisions were perfectly fair and sometimes even generous.

A typical early case is provided by that of 1/AM H. Woodcock (4258) who, having had no formal training whatsoever, had accumulated over fifty hours of operational flying time in the course of thirty-one sorties flown with No 4 Sqn between December 1915 and July 1916. On the strength of this record, he subsequently sought permission to wear an observers badge. His CO supported his case and forwarded the submission to the War Office, accompanied by a certified copy of Woodcock's flying log book. On 14 November the application was approved by the DMA.[12]

An example of a particularly generous ruling is provided by the case of Lt D.R. Smith who, although he had spent some time flying with No 43 Sqn, had never completed his qualification as an observer. By 1917 Smith was serving as a machine-gun instructor with No 61 (Home Defence) Sqn. Since it would enhance his credibility if he could show some evidence of having seen active service, he sought permission to wear a flying 'O'. His CO backed his submission and appropriate authority was granted in September, although, since he was technically unqualified, Smith was never actually gazetted as a Flying Officer (Observer).[13]

Although the RFC was at pains to ensure that there were adequate regulations to govern the conditions of service of observers, they only worked if they were efficiently implemented. Unfortunately, this was not always the case and many of the problems experienced by individuals were caused by maladministration. For example, a recommendation for Lt J.W. Barnes to be gazetted was raised by No 42 Sqn in January 1918 and sent to 51st Wg who forwarded it to HQ VII Bde. In the meantime Barnes had been shot down and taken prisoner. Several months later his status was queried.[14] By this time all three units concerned were in France, whereas they had been in Italy when Barnes had been lost, which had muddied the waters considerably. In the event HQ VII Bde claimed never to have received 51st Wg's recommendation, but the latter were considered to share the blame as they should have taken some sort of follow-up action after a suitable interval. That they failed to do so was

[10]To take a random example, 2/Lt H.A.T. Trier had his seniority backdated from 21 October to 23 August 1915, the date on which he had first been attached to the RFC. It is interesting to note, however, that very few of the RFC's earliest observers still appeared as such in the Army Lists of 1916. Some of them had been killed; some had returned to the trenches but many more had become pilots and were therefore listed without the (O) annotation. 2/Lt A.J. Capel, for instance, had been accredited as an observer as early as 30 November 1914 but he subsequently retrained, his seniority as a pilot dating from 3 November 1915. As a result, despite his having been one for a year, Capel never appeared as an observer in *any* Army List.

[11]AIR1/1026/204/5/1415 contains the correspondence related to Lt Morgan's case.

[12]AIR1/406/15/231/47 contains the correspondence relating to 1/AM Woodcock's case.

[13]AIR1/1026/204/5/1415 contains the correspondence related to Lt Smith's case.

[14]It is quite possible that the investigation into Barnes' status was prompted by his bank, as some banks adopted a very positive attitude towards protecting their clients' interests under such circumstances.

probably because they had been packing up and moving back to France at the appropriate time. Nevertheless, 51st Wg did have some record of the correspondence and on 9 June 1918 Barnes was belatedly confirmed as having been a Flying Officer (Observer) with effect from 17 January.[15]

While there may have been some justification for papers being lost in Barnes' case, some errors were simply due to inefficiency. On more than one occasion Lt-Col H.P. Van Ryneveld's 11th Wg was found to have been at fault for not following the correct procedures. For instance, 2/Lts A. Leach, H.S. Gros and A.S. White of No 57 Sqn were all authorised to wear a flying 'O' in II Bde's Orders for 31 January 1918. HQ 11th Wg should then have initiated formal gazetting action, but they never did. A couple of months later Leach wrote to the War Office to enquire why his name still had not appeared in the *London Gazette*. Needless to say, No 57 Sqn had since moved and its new sponsors, 13th Wg, were unable to offer any explanation. Despite II Bde's Orders eventually being produced to support Leach's claim, the War Office was not prepared to backdate his case and he was made a Flying Officer (Observer) with effect from 31 March, effectively robbing him of two month's seniority. On 18 June Gros joined in to complain that he still had not been gazetted – and so it went on.[16]

While these cases, and others like them, may well have been of little significance in the context of a World War, from the point of view of the individual, they could loom large. The reason for citing such examples here, however, is to provide further evidence of the way in which observers could be ill-served by the RFC's complex rules and regulations. Although, there may have been one or two cases of pilots having to argue the toss to gain the right to wear their 'wings' (although this writer has not actually come across any), they generally put them up on completion of their training and that was that, even if they never flew again, let alone in combat.[16A]

Early 1917. A formal case for observers to be granted virtual equality with pilots is fought and lost

When the RFC's observers had first been granted a degree of formal recognition in November 1915, the regulations had clearly been framed on the basis that observers were primarily regarded as a source of additional pilots. In short, they were seen as a means to an end, not an end in themselves. The prevailing argument was that, since the majority of observers were expected to become pilots, it could be safely assumed that those who showed the necessary promise would then be promoted. Since observers were, in effect, therefore, serving on relatively short-term engagements, it followed that there was no need to provide a career structure for them as such. When the implications of the amended regulations of November 1916 had been digested at unit level it became quite clear that there had been no change in the RFC's basic philosophy. The only substantial innovation had been to make service as an observer accountable when it became necessary to calculate his seniority within the corps after, in the natural course of events, he had become a pilot.

By this time, however, there was at least one senior officer who, like (or perhaps because of) the Bailhache Committee, had begun to appreciate the advantages to be gained from having permanent professional observers, rather than a transient group waiting for places at flying schools. He was Brig-Gen W.G.H. Salmond, then commanding the RFC's Middle East Brigade. Noting that the failure rate at his flying schools in Egypt was running at 15–20%, Salmond was concerned that current RFC practice failed to take account of the fact that some people simply lacked the degree of hand and eye co-ordination that was necessary to fly an aeroplane satisfactorily. Furthermore, he believed that there were others who did not even want to be pilots. Experience had clearly shown, however, that an individual's inability, or disinclination, to be a pilot did not necessarily degrade his performance as an observer. In fact, since they were committed to being long-term back-seaters, such men were likely to be better motivated than the majority of their colleagues and, since their longevity involved their accumulating a substantial amount of experience, they also tended to be more accomplished.

Salmond thought it manifestly unfair to deny such valuable officers any prospect of advancement and he knew that this same lack of prospects made it difficult to persuade some unsuccessful pilots to remain in the RFC as observers, their services thus being lost to the corps altogether. In January 1917 he wrote to the Director of Air Organisation (DAO)[17] at the War Office to point out that 'an officer whose aim and object is to become an efficient permanent observer is as valuable to the Royal Flying Corps as a pilot.' He recommended that the bar to the promotion of observers should, therefore, be lifted. This would permit them to advance to Flight Commander grade and thus to become captains.[18]

The DAO's staff did not like this idea at all. Lt-Col Warner's reply pointed out that it was RFC policy to encourage all observers to become pilots and expressed the fear that if they were allowed to become captains many of them might never make the effort to learn to fly.[19] Undeterred, Salmond tried again, explaining his proposal in greater detail.[20] Without changing his basic argument, this time, like Bailhache, he stressed the value to the RFC of having a 'cadre of highly trained observers'. Salmond proposed that an observer ranked as a captain should be established at flight level, not to command but to supervise the activities of its back-seaters, and that each squadron should also have a major to co-ordinate the efforts of the captains.[21] He further suggested that it

[15]AIR1/1028/204/5/1416 contains the correspondence relating to Lt Barnes' case.

[16]*Ibid.* Correspondence on 2/Lts Leach, Gros and White.

[16A]Strictly speaking, the regulation which had introduced the pilots flying badge, Army Order 40 of 1 February 1913, had stated that it could be worn only by those who 'remain efficient aeroplane pilots'. This was a little inconvenient as it clearly ruled out a lot of people, including most senior officers. Needless to say, the rules were changed in 1916 to permit any pilot to wear his wings permanently, regardless of his competence, so long as he continued to serve with the RFC. The correspondence relating to the refinement of the regulation governing the wearing of 'wings' in 1916 is filed under AIR1/818/204/4/1308.

[17]At the time the DAO's responsibilities included specifying the tasks of RFC units, laying down their establishments (which made him very influential in the context of determining terms and conditions of service) and authorising their formation and disbandment. The first incumbent of the post was Brig-Gen W.S. Brancker who took up his appointment on 27 March 1916. His successors were Brig-Gen L.E.O. Charlton from 28 February 1917, Brig-Gen G. Livingstone from 18 October 1917 and Brig-Gen B.C.H. Drew from 18 February 1918. Drew remained in post until relieved by Brig-Gen P.W. Game on 8 March 1919 at which point the responsibilities of the appointment were merged with those of the Director of Training.

[18]AIR1/2362/226/7/28. HQ ME Bde letter AG172 dated 1 January 1917.

[19]*Ibid.* War Office letter 100/FC/95(AO2) dated 22 January 1917.

[20]*Ibid.* HQ ME Bde letter AG172 dated 12 February 1917.

[21]It would take many years for Salmond's ideas to catch on but, in effect, he had predicted the creation of the Squadron Navigation Officer, an appointment introduced in the mid-1930s. The original Squadron Navigation Officers were pilots but in 1942 the task was taken over by observers (later navigators) and the post of 'Navigation Leader', survives to this day.

would be appropriate for an observer major to command an observers training school, that a captain would make an ideal Wing Adjutant and that observers of either rank would be suitable to fill a variety of graded staff appointments.

The revised proposal still amounted to heresy, however, as it continued to challenge the RFC's doctrinaire belief in the absolute supremacy of the pilot. The War Office was quite unmoved by the justice and logic of Salmond's argument. Indeed it is probable that it was only his unique status as the commander of an independent overseas brigade that had enabled Salmond to submit his case to the DAO at all. Had he been stationed in France, there can be little doubt that the other Brigade Commanders, and certainly Trenchard, would have seen to it that his proposals never reached London.

Warner's second response was another flat dismissal.[22] While this was certainly authoritative, it was sorely lacking in substance. In the absence of any coherent counter-argument London simply resorted to a tired re-statement of dogma to justify its rejection. Most significantly, the War Office failed to offer any alternative solution to the very real plight of the 'permanent' observer which Salmond had highlighted. Instead, Warner merely admonished that 'it must be realised that an observer cannot be promoted to command a flight.' Sadly, he failed to explain *why* an observer could not command a flight, but, since Salmond had specifically not suggested that he should, perhaps 'Willie' Warner had simply felt it advisable to remind the General of one of the pillars of RFC wisdom. Presumably as a concession, his letter went on to state that the War Office had no objection to observers serving as Wing Adjutants or as Staff Officers. It failed to explain, however, how, under the existing regulations, they were supposed to attain the ranks associated with such appointments – which had been Salmond's point all along.

With the benefit of hindsight we can see that the War Office's flat refusal to grant observers any form of executive authority was extremely short-sighted. It was also illogical, embracing, as it did, a fundamental contradiction. After all, what was the point of having *commissioned* observers at all if they were not to be allowed to command? Underpinning the RFC's rigid policy was a belief that, for some indefinable reason, only pilots were capable of exercising authority. This assumption was plainly confounded by the fact that none of the RFC's senior generals had any substantial experience as aviators. This was hardly their fault, of course, but that is not the point. The point is that, despite their lack of flying hours and, in some cases, their marginal abilities as pilots, they were able to function as leaders. Why? Because the ability to lead and to command has very little to do with being a skilled pilot.

At the highest levels an air commander needed (and still needs) to be a planner and organiser, and a competent tactician who could manage his resources and inspire his men. His degree of flying skill was quite immaterial. In this context, it is interesting to note that while the RFC's senior generals were (at least notionally) pilots, their German counterparts were not. Unlike Trenchard and Brancker, neither von Hoeppner nor Leith-Thomsen, his very able Chief of Staff, wore a flying badge.

On a much smaller scale, the tasks of a Squadron Commander were much the same as those of a general. His main preoccupations, in addition to supervising (not necessarily participating in) flying activities, were to do with serviceability, supply, accommodation, welfare, messing and the like.

[22] AIR1/2362/226/7/28. War Office letter 100/FC/95(AO2) dated 23 March 1917.

In fact a CO's primary responsibility was to see that his unit ran efficiently, not to take it into combat. Tactical leadership in the air was the responsibility of his Flight Commanders. Indeed, for much of 1917 Squadron Commanders were specifically forbidden to cross the lines, making their ability as pilots of somewhat marginal interest.

Under these circumstances, any competent officer with some practical experience of aviation should have been capable of commanding a squadron, or even a wing, irrespective of what kind of flying badge he wore. In fact many such units were commanded by officers who had begun their careers as observers.[23] Had they remained in the back-seat they would have been the same men but they would never have progressed beyond lieutenant rank. Yet, simply by becoming pilots, they were considered to have undergone some mysterious transformation which enabled them to function as majors and lieutenant-colonels. It was nonsense, of course, but the longer this myth was sustained, the more it came to be believed.

Of its generals, only Geoffrey Salmond seems to have appreciated that the RFC's policy was misguided but, having been turned down twice he was obliged to abandon his one-man campaign on behalf of back-seaters. Nevertheless, while his ideas had failed to generate enough lift to permit his kite to fly, they did at least represent a straw in the wind.

Early 1917. The beginning of the end of the RFC's squadron-based observer training system

Despite its reluctance to grant observers their due, the War Office had clearly been devoting considerable thought to the RFC's back-seaters during 1916. If nothing else, this showed that they were aware of observers and had some idea of what they expected of them. But restating what observers needed to know and tinkering with the regulations governing their seniority and the wearing of badges were all relatively superficial measures. Much more attention needed to be paid to the underlying problem – the inadequacy of the training being provided, especially for the observers who were still being recruited in France.

By this time the staffs at St André-aux-Bois were changing their tune. In April 1916 HQ RFC had politely declined to have anything to do with Brooklands, maintaining that it was perfectly capable of training its own observers. Two months later their attitude had softened to the extent that they were prepared to make some tentative use of Hythe. By the autumn, however, the magnitude of the field training task had forced them to acknowledge that they needed help. It was easy for them to accept this, since they were now able to recognise the increasing effectiveness of the training machine which

[23] Among the ex-observers who commanded wartime operational units after becoming pilots were Lt-Cols E.W. Powell, A.W.H. James, A.G.R. Garrod, T.A.E. Cairnes, A.V. Holt and C.T. Maclean and Majs J.O. Andrews, A.M. Vaucour, C.G. Burge, G.W. Murlis Green, A.J. Capel, R.W. Gow, W.S. Douglas, E.L. Foot, L.T.N. Gould, C.E.M. Pickthorn, R.StC. McClintock, J.A. McKelvie, C.F.A. Portal and J.H.S. Tyssen. Wartime units commanded at one time or another by erstwhile back-seaters included: Nos 1, 3, 4, 6, 7, 11, 12, 13, 15, 16, 21, 22, 27, 30, 32, 33, 35, 36, 43, 44, 45, 52, 56, 58, 63, 66, 70, 82, 84, 92, 94, 100, 112, 148, 202, 207, 209 and 220 Sqns and 9th, 10th, 22nd, 69th and 81st Wgs. Both of these lists are far from being exhaustive, but both are quite long enough to show that ex-observers were perfectly capable of exercising command. It is hardly reasonable to suppose that all these men, some of whom would eventually attain very senior ranks in the RAF, would have been incompetent had they not changed their flying badges.

Brig-Gen J.M. Salmond had been building since March. In December, Maj-Gen Trenchard finally requested assistance, writing to the DAO as follows:[24]

> 'At present the elementary instructional work of observers in a squadron is very considerable, and time is taken up in teaching such work which should be used in raising the standard of qualified observers.
>
> Further, new observers often arrive in a squadron after a long spell in the trenches, without any leave, in an unfit condition to take up work demanding absolute freshness mentally and physically.
>
> I therefore propose, if you can make the necessary arrangements, to send home officers on their joining the RFC on probation for a course of training as observers. I would suggest that the course should last at least a month.'

The GOC's letter went on to forecast that 'about one hundred officers a month would be sent home once the scheme was in full working order' and to include a detailed list of the topics that he thought ought to be covered. This produced a very rapid response, Brig-Gen Brancker promptly setting in hand appropriate arrangements which were to become effective on 1 January 1917;[25] 70% of those sent home were expected to go to the Schools of Military Aeronautics (SoMA)[26] while the remainder were to go to the School of Aerial Gunnery at Hythe.

The main function of the SoMAs was to provide aircrew recruits who had completed their basic military training with a broad-based academic introduction to the business of being an aviator.[27] The content of the syllabus at Reading/Oxford has already been discussed but it is significant, especially for the men being sent home from France, that it included no practical flying experience. The course at Hythe was very different, being concerned solely with the technicalities of the Lewis gun and providing an introduction to its use. By this time the full Hythe syllabus involved two weeks in the classroom and on the range and a fortnight's flying but most of the men sent back from France in the early days of the scheme attended abbreviated courses, very few of them gaining much airborne time.

Sending men back to England to attend these, often truncated, courses did serve to lighten the load on the hard-pressed squadrons a little, but it was hardly a complete answer to the training problem. A survey conducted in France during March 1917 revealed this all too clearly. Squadrons were asked to report how long their detached observers had spent at the School of Aerial Gunnery, how long they had spent at other schools and how much flying time they had accumulated. Within II Bde, for instance, Nos 20 and 45 Sqns had released a total of seven officers; on average each of them had spent fourteen days at Hythe, one day somewhere else and had logged just twelve minutes in the air.[28] The reports from the other four brigades were similarly disappointing, adverse comments including: 'require more practice in shooting from the air' (I Bde); 'one month at Hythe considered essential' (III Bde); 'general knowledge poor' (IV Bde) and 'insufficient practice in co-operation with the pilot' (V Bde). Despite these generally negative reactions, something had been gained and Trenchard wrote to the DAO to acknowledge that the UK courses had provided some 'relief from elementary instructional work in squadrons', although his letter went on to include an extensive list of suggestions as to where improvements needed to be made.[29]

Mid-1917. Trenchard insists that all observers complete their qualification

In the early summer of 1917 the quality of observers, and of their training, remained a topic of particular interest to Trenchard. The GOC was in the habit of making frequent visits to front-line units in order to keep his finger on the RFC's pulse. On one such occasion he ascertained that a particular probationary observer had been with his squadron for ten weeks. The General asked him why he was not yet a Flying Officer (Observer) to be told that he had not yet accumulated sufficient flying hours to make him eligible. In point of fact this could only have been his CO's personal opinion, since qualification had never actually been defined in terms of airborne time. Having made further enquiries, however, the GOC was disturbed to discover that this was no isolated case. It transpired that there were significant numbers of observers who had been in France for periods in excess of two months without having qualified. Furthermore, many of them had done a substantial amount of war flying, in addition to any airborne time which they might have accumulated in the UK. As a result, although most squadrons had ample numbers of observers on strength, very few were manned to establishment, i.e. they did not have twelve *qualified* Flying Officer (Observers).

Trenchard decided that responsibility for this unsatisfactory situation had to lie with Squadron Commanders, rather than with individual junior officers. On 30 June Lt-Col Festing wrote to all five Brigade Commanders and Lt-Col Newall, commander of the autonomous 11th Wg, to inform them of the General's concern. There was still no attempt to define what was required in terms of flying hours but the letter made it quite clear that it was the GOC's view that 'if an observer is not recommended for grading as Flying

[24] AIR1/997/204/5/1241. HQ RFC letter CRFC 2047G dated 8 December 1916.

[25] *Ibid.* These arrangements were announced by AO 266 dated 14 December 1916.

[26] At this time there were two SoMAs in the UK, these having been created on 27 October 1916 by redesignating Nos 1 and 2 RFC Schools of Instruction, at Reading and Oxford respectively, on the authority of AO 234. The 'Military' was dropped from the title following the establishment of the RAF in 1918 and by the Armistice seven such units were functioning in the UK and two more abroad. Two of the former (Nos 7 and 9) dealt exclusively with observers.

[27] The basic military training of direct entrant potential officers, and the commissioning of RFC NCOs and other ranks, was originally undertaken by the RFC Cadet Battalion which had been established at Denham during 1915. Redesignated for a few days as the RFC Cadet School, it became the RFC Cadet Wing on 31 October 1916. In anticipation of a second wing being set up at Blenheim, the original unit became No 1 Cadet Wing on 14 April 1917. The second wing actually came into being at Winchester (Hursley Park), others being formed later to keep up with the RFC expansion programme. By the autumn of 1917 all initial training had been concentrated at Hastings under the auspices of the Cadet Brigade which had been formed on 3 September. Shortly afterwards the 27-year-old Brig-Gen A. C. Critchley was appointed to command, his HQ being established at 13 Eversfield Place.

Thereafter Hastings/St Leonards functioned as the main induction centre for RFC/RAF officers until the entire brigade (by then comprising Nos 1, 2, 5, 6 and 8 Cadet Wings) moved to Shorncliffe (Folkestone) shortly before the end of the war. Overseas, No 3 Cadet Wing was at Aboukir and there was another at Long Branch in Canada (although confirmation is lacking, logic suggests that this should have been No 4, to account for the absence of a No 4 Cadet Wing elsewhere). The other 'missing' unit, No 7 Cadet Wing, had been set up in July 1918 to deal solely with observers but, since it closed in September, it is doubtful whether it ever completed the training of any cadets.

[28] AIR1/1135/204/5/2224. This information was reported in HQ II Bde's A26/1206 of 19 March 1917.

[29] *Ibid.* HQ RFC letter CRFC 2047G dated 29 March 1917.

Officer at the end of, say, two months in addition to his course in England, he is not worth keeping unless there are special reasons to the contrary.'[30]

This very pointed piece of advice produced a flood of recommendations for probationers to be gazetted and action on such applications was soon having to be postponed because some squadron establishments were becoming oversubscribed. Thus, for example, when 2/Lt R.F.W. Sheraton's name was put forward for gazetting on 7 August, HQ RFC rejected the recommendation on the grounds that No 59 Sqn's entitlement had already been filled.[31] Sheraton had to bide his time until a vacancy became available, his second recommendation being approved on 24 August.

The delay in such cases rarely amounted to more than a few weeks but, apart from generating unnecessary correspondence and denying the individual concerned an increase in pay, it achieved nothing of any substance. It simply represented yet another unfortunate consequence of the RFC's apparent inability (or its stubborn refusal) to treat observers fairly. It hardly seems reasonable for the staffs to have withheld formal acknowledgement of an observer's having successfully cleared all the hurdles associated with qualification, while flying in combat, simply to satisfy a numerical target set by some official in London. There can be little doubt that the RFC would have considered this practice to be quite intolerable had anyone tried to impose such a policy on its pilots.

A unit's official establishment represents no more than an ideal manning level but, especially in wartime, it is a target which tends to be missed far more often than it is hit. Since a squadron was expected to continue to operate while it was in deficit, however, it would surely have done no more than help to balance the books to allow it to have the odd surplus observer from time to time. It was certainly a common occurrence for units to have one or two 'spare' pilots on strength. Until they could be slotted into an established post they were simply attached to the HQ Flight and carried on the books as supernumeraries. Why could this paper exercise not have been extended to embrace observers? The evidence suggests that it was because they were still held in such low esteem that, in the eyes of the staffs, the interests of a flesh-and-blood back-seater counted for less than a neat balance sheet.

1917. A bid for observers to be granted a greater degree of equality with respect to pilots leads to a dispute over the award of 'wings'

Despite the inadequacies of the top-up training being provided for observers temporarily sent back from France, that being provided for recruits trained entirely in the UK was considered to be of quite a high standard by the summer of 1917. In view of this, on 10 July the DAO, Brig-Gen Charlton, proposed that all observers should be awarded their 'wings' on graduation, dispensing with the four-to-eight weeks of probationary service in France and permitting those observers assigned to home defence squadrons and other UK-based units to qualify for their badges. This provoked a rapid response from Maj-Gen Trenchard who, claiming the support of his Brigade Commanders, contended that while '90% of a pilot's work can be learnt in England', an essential element of an observer's education still had to be acquired over the lines. Brig-Gen J.M. Salmond joined the fray on 30 July, writing to the DGMA to support the DAO's view by confirming that, in his opinion, the sequence of courses now being offered by his Training Brigade was sufficiently comprehensive to warrant the immediate award of an observers badge on their completion, i.e. at much the same stage as pilots were entitled to put up their 'wings'.[32]

The award of flying badges was proving to be a sensitive issue. In view of the GOC's adverse reaction, the staffs in the Hotel Cecil were having second thoughts and on 9 August they proposed a compromise – only the best two students from each of the courses graduating from Hythe and Brooklands would be given their badges immediately, the remainder having to complete their probationary period in France as before.[33] Trenchard did not like this one either and on 18 August he wrote to London, objecting strongly to this approach on the grounds that an observers wing was awarded for 'war service' and expressing (with a deft touch of tautology) the view that it should not therefore be given away as a 'prize won at a competitive competition.'[34]

This raised an interesting question – was a flying 'O' a 'war service badge' or was it a 'qualification badge'? Precedent, and the GOC's contention that an observer could only really learn his trade in action, certainly suggested that the flying 'O' was, in effect, awarded for war service. On the other hand, there was a growing body of opinion that favoured the latter interpretation, to bring the award in line with that of a pilots 'wings' which were indisputably awarded on qualification. The argument begged a very obvious question. Why not standardise in the reverse sense? That is, why not make pilots serve a probationary period on active service? The question was never asked. Could this have been because it might have invalidated the 'wings' worn by many of the RFC's most senior officers? After all, few of them had actually logged many operational flying hours.

Still doggedly fighting his corner, Charlton minuted the Director General to remind him that in 1915 virtually untrained observers were being awarded their badges on the recommendation of their CO after about six weeks of active service. He went on to point out that dogmatic adherence to this procedure two years later amounted to a condemnation both of the efforts of those who had striven in the meantime to create a formal training system and of the system itself. He suggested that the GOC be asked how many new observers he was being obliged to send home on the grounds of incompetence. If the figure compared favourably with that for pilots, significant numbers of whom were being rejected by squadrons at the time, it was argued that the General should be obliged to accept the inevitable conclusion. Although the argument rumbled on into the autumn, this very sensible proposal was not acted upon and Lt-Gen Henderson eventually put an end to further discussion by acceding to the wishes of his field commander. On 10 November 1917 the 'prize' option was finally rejected and it was ruled that all observers would still have to complete their qualification in the field.

Thus, despite the notional abolition of the interim period of service as a 'Qualified Observer' in November 1916 and further lengthy consideration of the situation over the next twelve months, very little actually changed at squadron level.

[30] AIR1/1025/204/5/1415. HQ RFC letter CRFC 1701/1 (A) dated 30 June 1917.

[31] AIR1/1026/204/5/1415. HQ RFC letter CRFC 1701/1(A) dated 10 August 1917 rejected HQ III Bde's initial request for 2/Lt Sheraton to be recognised as Flying Officer (Observer).

[32] *Ibid.* Training Brigade letter TB/1135/16 dated 30 July 1917.

[33] *Ibid.* DAO letter 87/685(O.2) dated 9 August 1917.

[34] *Ibid.* HQ RFC letter CRFC 1701(A) dated 18 August 1917.

Throughout 1917 observers continued to embark on their operational flying careers underpaid and without their badges until they had collected all the necessary certificates and had been assessed as being fully competent. This interval was variable in length and largely at the discretion of Squadron Commanders. Typically, it involved four to eight weeks during which the probationer accumulated a substantial amount of operational experience – provided, of course, that he survived. Even if he did, he still had very limited career prospects. Despite the recommendations of the Bailhache Report, an observer still could not be given an executive appointment or even be promoted to captain.

Nevertheless, by this time, despite the disadvantages which the system persisted in imposing upon them, observers no longer saw themselves as the objects of derision of 1915, as described by 2/Lt Money (see page 17). By 1917 the flying 'O' was worn with considerable pride and regarded with great respect in informed circles, for, unlike a pilot's 'wings', it had been won the hard way – under fire. In fact some observers became so attached to their badges that they were reluctant to give them up when they subsequently qualified as pilots. This led to a very naughty practice which was firmly suppressed in March 1917 when the DAO's staff circulated a memorandum which read as follows:[35]

> 'Instances having occurred of pilots wearing wings with an O underneath, it is notified that no badge of this pattern has been sanctioned. Disciplinary action will be taken in the event of any pilot or observer wearing an unauthorised badge.'

Denied the right to advertise the fact that they had once been observers, which implied that they had seen a substantial amount of active service, some pilots took to sewing their old badge under the lapel of their tunic as a memento of what they had been through.[36]

Despite the evident pride felt by some back-seaters, there were others who still felt undervalued. For example, writing home to his family in Canada in the summer of 1917, Lt G.W. Blaiklock complained that he was 'not appreciated; none of us observers are' – and this was from a man who took part in seven successful combats while flying 1½ Strutters with No 45 Sqn, at least four of the victims being driven down by his Lewis gun.

While the 'establishment' was arguing about the timing of the award of the observers badge, it did little to police its style. Lt Eric Lubbock (left) qualified for his flying 'O' with No 5 Sqn on 29 October 1915. Since the badge had been introduced only eight weeks before, it is quite possible that Lubbock's was one of the initial batch of 100 that had been ordered in July; it certainly bore an acceptably close resemblance to the design approved by Col Brancker (see page 18). Thereafter, however, artistic licence was allowed to go unchecked, resulting in distinctly distorted interpretations, such as that apparently being worn by Lt Archibald Streeter of No 82 Sqn in 1918. 'Apparently' because a studio would sometimes paint a badge onto an existing image. The author has an indentical photograph of Lubbock sporting a very convincing set of pilots 'wings' in place of his observers badge and it is suspected that the picture of Streeter may well reflect this practice; nevertheless, it is known that non-standard badges were in circulation. (Author and M. O'Connor respectively)

[35] AIR1/2433/305/33/1. AO 387 of 22 March 1917.

[36] This practice was attested to by Col T.G. Greenwell (MP for the Hartlepools) during a Parliamentary debate on the wearing of observers badges by Army personnel, see *Hansard* for 18 January 1945.

Chapter 9

1917. The RFC refines its Brooklands/Hythe training sequence

Although substantial progress had been made, the RFC was still not entirely satisfied with the training of its observers and further refinements were constantly being introduced. As a first step the syllabus taught by the Wireless and Observers School was reviewed and revised in the spring of 1917. Under the guidance of a new CO, Maj J.A. Chamier,[1] the course was extended by a further week. The last fortnight was to concentrate on practical work which was supposed to include ten hours in the air. Some of these changes were inspired by the fact that, in addition to observers, (as explained later) pilots were about to start attending the Brooklands course as well.

To support the flying phase, the Netheravon-based Artillery Co-operation Flight of the Central Flying School had already absorbed the Artillery Co-operation Flight at Lydd on 13 January to form the Artillery Co-operation Squadron (although the element in Kent remained *in situ*).[2] In effect this squadron served as a remote extension of the Wireless and Observers School, providing students from Brooklands with practical experience of simulated and/or live artillery shoots in co-operation with the guns on Salisbury Plain. It was also intended to provide opportunities for live machine-gun firing, the aim being for each student to fire 1000 rounds. Partly to be closer to the action and partly to provide space for expanded aircraft production at Brooklands, the school moved to Winchester in October 1917.

In the meantime experience had shown that, while the facilities on Salisbury Plain were satisfactory for artillery work, live machine-gun firing could be carried out from Netheravon only with some difficulty. Since there were dedicated air firing ranges available at Hythe, all responsibility for this aspect of training was transferred to No 1 (Auxiliary) School of Aerial Gunnery in the autumn of 1917. The standard training sequence for observers destined to work with the guns thus became four weeks at Winchester followed by a fortnight at Hythe.

1917. Role specialisation is formally acknowledged within the RFC

By early 1917 the days of underpowered, inadequately armed, general purpose aeroplanes, flown by crews prepared to have a go at anything, were virtually over. By the end of June the BE2's day was almost done and no fewer than twenty-three squadrons were flying RE8s, FK8s, DH 4s or Bristol Fighters. Each of these much more capable two-seaters had been designed in the light of combat experience. Furthermore, each had been introduced to carry out a specific function and it was inevitable that this would lead to a demand for increasingly specialised role-related training. An early indication that the RFC's bureaucracy had recognised this trend came in February 1917 when, at the same time as the trade of Aerial Gunner was formally identified, observers were categorised as Corps or Army Observers, depending upon the nature of their employment.[3]

Like the demand for increased output, the advent of 'second-generation' aeroplanes was to have a significant impact on the training system. For instance, despite its disappointing initial showing in combat, much was expected of the Bristol Fighter and it soon became apparent that traditional two-seater fighter tactics (based on flying in formation) would have to be discarded if the new aeroplane was going to realise its full potential. Furthermore, as early as March 1917 III Bde's Brig-Gen J.F.A. Higgins was writing to HQ RFC to point out that much of the content of the Brooklands course was superfluous for observers destined to fly Bristols.[4] In fact this was equally true of all Army Observers, since those flying FE2bs, DH 4s and 1½ Strutters were not expected to work with the guns either, nor did their aeroplanes often carry wireless equipment.[5]

Things were also changing in the corps reconnaissance world. The previously noted tendency for pilots to assume responsibility for conducting artillery shoots had been gaining in popularity ever since the summer of 1916 and was now a fairly widespread practice. While there was some tactical logic behind this development, it is likely that a considerable degree of pragmatism may also have been involved. By this time many of the earliest observers were back in France flying as pilots. They were, therefore, already at home in the air and very familiar with artillery co-operation procedures. It seems likely that, having the capacity to do so, some of these pilots may well have preferred to deal with the guns themselves rather than put up with the initially poor judgement and bad Morse of their inexperienced companions, especially those who had come straight from the trenches.

Whether this had been a significant factor or not, it was being argued, notably by OC 3rd Wg, Lt-Col E.R. Ludlow-Hewitt, that the best way to exploit the new RE8s and FK8s was for the pilot to manoeuvre his aeroplane on his own initiative, keeping the target or the friendly battery in sight

[1]Maj Chamier, previously OC No 34 Sqn, arrived at Brooklands on 31 March 1917, taking up his appointment as Commandant of the school a month later. The unit was subsequently expanded and redesignated (see Chapter 12, Note 3), Chamier being promoted to lieutenant-colonel to reflect its increase in size. He was succeeded on 26 May 1918 by the unit's last wartime CO, Lt-Col C.H.B. Blount, who remained in command until 22 November.

[2]The first CO of the Artillery Co-operation Squadron was Maj K.T. Dowding.

[3]AIR1/997/204/5/1241. AO 336 of 13 February 1917, which had introduced the term aerial gunner (see Chapter 6, Note 5), had also formally categorised Corps Observers as being those employed on corps reconnaissance squadrons, while those on fighter, fighter reconnaissance and bomber squadrons were to be identified as Army Observers.

[4]AIR1/1135/204/5/2224. HQ III Bde letter 3B/55A dated 19 March 1917.

[5]AIR1/1001/204/5/1260. A week after a meeting of the RFC Wireless Telegraph Committee held at Woolwich on 2 November 1916, all fighter and bomber squadrons had been established to hold airborne receivers on the authority of AO 241. In practice, however, since they generally operated beyond the limited range of the available equipment, these units made little (if any) use of these facilities.

as required, and handle W/T transmissions himself. This approach, it was argued, had the advantage of leaving the observer free to concentrate on general intelligence gathering and, more importantly, on rear defence.

It should be understood that the pilot-based approach to artillery work being advocated by Ludlow-Hewitt was not actually all that new. For example, J.T.B. McCudden recorded an example of a pilot successfully directing the fire of an artillery battery by using a lamp to transmit Morse signals as early as December 1914. He was No 3 Sqn's Capt A.S. Barratt who spent some forty hours on this task, all of them flown solo in a Blériot. Perhaps even more to the point, McCudden later describes a flight he made with Ludlow-Hewitt himself on 27 November 1915. During this sortie 'the pilot ranged on his target while I kept a look out for enemy gun flashes and noted their time and place, above all I kept myself awake for two damnable Fokkers who were always present in this vicinity.'[6]

Eighteen months later, Ludlow-Hewitt was convinced that this was what all observers should do all the time. His opinion was underpinned by the knowledge, gained both by observation and from personal experience, that it was perfectly feasible for a competent pilot to conduct a shoot while simultaneously flying his aeroplane. The only weakness in his argument was that it assumed that all pilots were as capable as he was himself. Sadly, this was not the case, especially in the spring of 1917.

As we shall see, some twenty years later Ludlow-Hewitt was still disposed to overrate the competence of the average pilot, which was to have some repercussions in the context of the second generation of air observers. In the meantime, however, if the prospective corps reconnaissance pilots of 1917 were going to assume many of the duties performed by the RFC's back-seaters, it would be necessary to ensure that they were all provided with a thorough grounding in artillery co-operation techniques.

Eventually, on 23 May, Ludlow-Hewitt committed his views to paper in a letter to HQ IV Bde. In this he outlined his concept of operations and formally requested that his pilots be more appropriately trained in the future. A week later Maj-Gen Trenchard wrote to the War Office, seeking its assistance in improving the training of corps pilots.[7] In fact, the need for pilots to attend the Wireless and Observers School had been anticipated at home as early as March. The combined throughput of pilots and observers was expected to be at a rate of 300 per month, however, and before this proposal could be implemented it would be necessary both to expand the available accommodation and to find additional instructional staff. Appropriate measures had already been put in hand so that by early June, in response to the GOC's request, the DAO was able to inform him that some fifty pilots were already in residence at Brooklands.[8]

The initial results of this development appear to have been somewhat disappointing. It is clear, for instance, that there was no apparent improvement in the competence of the replacement pilots reaching V Bde. In September its GOC, Brig-Gen C.A.H. Longcroft, wrote to HQ RFC to suggest that there would be considerable advantage in sending corps pilots to Brooklands for a similar course to that given to observers.[9] It is not clear whether Longcroft was subtly 'making a point' or whether he had simply not been paying attention, but HQ RFC's reply assured him that 85% of corps pilots were already passing through Brooklands and that it was hoped that 100% soon would be.[10]

Since Longcroft had complained in his letter that a number of his new pilots displayed little awareness of what they were supposed to do, this would appear to indicate either that V Bde was getting the 'other' 15% or that the training being provided was less than adequate. It was almost certainly the latter, the reason being an intolerable additional burden which circumstances had temporarily imposed on the training machine. Already finding it extremely difficult to produce sufficient aircrew to man the ever-expanding front line, its problems had been considerably exacerbated by an urgent need to replace the heavy losses which had been experienced in the spring. This circle could only be squared by cutting corners and many pilots had to be sent to France in the spring and summer of 1917 without having been fully or properly trained. The same was true of observers, Longcroft having reported that some of his replacement back-seaters were arriving with less than four hours' total flying experience.[11]

Because of the time it takes to train aircrew there is always a significant lag in the system. The people who were causing V Bde concern in September would have begun their training several months earlier, when the crisis had been at its height. By the late summer, however, several remedial measures had been implemented and the system was already recovering. Recruiting had been stepped up yet again and the introduction of professional flying instructors, employing the techniques advocated by Maj Smith-Barry (see page 71), was producing a marked increase in the effectiveness of pilot training. Thereafter the competence of new arrivals began to improve significantly, a trend that was to continue for the remainder of the war.

It had also been possible to relieve the pressure on the Wireless and Observers School where a bottleneck had begun to develop as a result of the decision to send corps reconnaissance pilots there. This was partially achieved by a further expansion to permit the school to handle up to 500 students per month. The other factor was the decision to act on the earlier observations of field commanders, like those of Brig-Gen Higgins. Since it was now clearly inappropriate for observers earmarked for bomber and fighter squadrons to go to Brooklands, they ceased to do so from the late summer of 1917. The role training of all Army Observers was subsequently carried out entirely at Nos 1 and/or 3 (Auxiliary) Schools of Aerial Gunnery at Hythe/New Romney.

1917. Aerial gunners are granted their 'wings'

In addition to the two types of observer, there had been a third category of aviator in the RFC since February 1917, the non-commissioned aerial gunner. By the summer, so far as RFC personnel were concerned, Hythe-trained gunners probably outnumbered squadron-trained volunteer air mechanics but the overall balance between RFC personnel and soldiers drawn from other organisations had changed little. In March 1917

[6]James McCudden, *op cit*.
[7]AIR1/1135/204/5/2224. HQ RFC letter 2047G dated 30 May 1917.
[8]*Ibid*. War Office letter 87/Instruction/235(O.2) dated 7 June 1917.
[9]*Ibid*. HQ V Bde letter 5B/3/3 dated 4 September 1917.
[10]*Ibid*. HQ RFC letter 2047G dated 15 September 1917.
[11]Trevor Henshaw, *The Sky Their Battlefield* (1995). Henshaw's work indicates that something in excess of 160 observers were killed, wounded, injured or taken prisoner during 'Bloody April'. The distribution of these losses varied widely but the brunt was borne by Nos 11, 16, 20, 48, 57 and 59 Sqns, each of which lost ten or more (a total of seventy-nine between them), which meant that all of these units had to be virtually rebuilt from scratch.

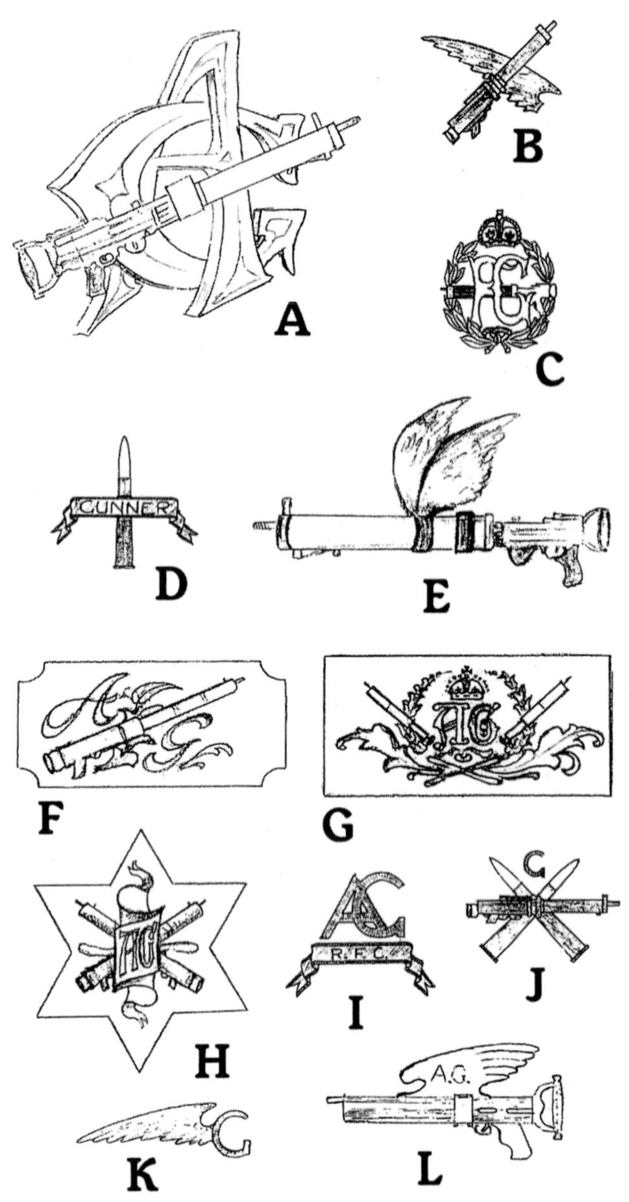

The original bid for gunners to wear a flying badge was accompanied by some suggested designs sketched by the following: ***A*** *– 1/AM F.W. Turner (20346):* ***B, D, I, J*** *&* ***K*** *– 2/AM E.D. Collinson (64091);* ***C*** *– 2/AM C.A. Jones (63571);* ***E*** *– 2/AM A.H. Brown (52708);* ***F, G*** *&* ***H*** *– 2/AM E. Harper (30822) and* ***L*** *– 2/AM A.G. Matthews (17081).*

60% of the available gunners had been RFC men and, although the numbers involved had virtually doubled by late August, the proportions remained the same. Of the 202 gunners on the strength of the forty-seven squadrons serving with the BEF by then (thirteen of them equipped single-seaters), 121 were enlisted members of the RFC, the remainder having come from elsewhere.

In June it had been proposed that a distinguishing badge should be introduced for these men, several designs being submitted for consideration.[12] As previously noted, HQ RFC had sanctioned the wearing of a standard observers badge by its squadron-trained gunners as early as March and the War Office declined to complicate the issue by introducing a different emblem for those who had undergone a more formal course of instruction. It chose instead to endorse HQ RFC's initiative and in July authority was granted for any gunner who had passed the Hythe course and who had 'performed eight trips overseas' to wear an observers wing.[13] Unfortunately, this automatically excluded gunners who were flying with Home Defence Squadrons, Aircraft Acceptance Parks and other UK-based formations and steps had to be taken to have these men posted abroad, their places being taken by combat veterans who already had their badges. Interestingly, the use of the flying 'O' meant that an RFC gunner was superficially indistinguishable from an NCO who was actually an accredited observer.

As with all military regulations, if there is a way round them, someone will find it. In this case the rules had been expressed with insufficient precision and by October the 'eight trips overseas' condition was being interpreted as eight cross-Channel ferry flights. By November gunners who had yet to leave the country at all were to be found wearing the flying 'O'. This caused the DAO's staff to amplify the rules, the revised regulations making it quite clear that only those aerial gunners who had 'qualified for them by service overseas' were entitled to wear observers badges.[14]

As always, observers and gunners of all ranks, aspired to become pilots and many of those who were lucky enough to have survived a period of operations eventually returned to England for cross-training. Not surprisingly, their familiarity with the airborne environment (the common rule of thumb being that a back-seater should have flown at least 100 hours in France before being recommended for retraining[15]) made them excellent prospects and most of them passed through the instructional sequence with relative ease.

1917. Night bombing focuses attention on the practical problems of weapons delivery and air navigation

During 1916 the RFC had begun to make increasing use of its FE2bs in the bomber role and by November some of them had begun to fly offensive missions by night. The 'Fee' had adapted easily to this nocturnal activity and, since it could deliver a respectable bomb load (about 350 lb) and was about to be superseded by later types for daylight operations, it was decided to employ them as dedicated night bombers.

The night-flying expertise of No 51 (Home Defence) Sqn was exploited by using it to foster the first dedicated unit of the new Light Night Bomber Force, No 100 Sqn, which was raised in February 1917. The training provided was initially aimed solely at pilots and dealt purely with the art of flying in the dark. Once No 100 Sqn went into action, however, its crews rapidly discovered that there was much more to it than that. Within weeks Maj-Gen Trenchard was requesting that future night bomber crews be provided with a substantial amount of tactical training, including night reconnaissance techniques, night bombing and flying in the face of searchlight beams.[16] This was beyond No 51 Sqn's limited resources

[12]AIR1/818/204/4/1306. This proposal was originated by 2/Lt W.T. Douglas of the Aerial Gunners Office in Lympne in letter 3/AG/4 dated 10 June 1917.

[13]*Ibid.* Immediate authority for qualified gunners to wear the observers badge was granted by War Office letter 87/RFC/600(OG) dated 12 July 1917.

[14]*Ibid.* The revised regulations were promulgated by AO 663 dated 19 November 1917.

[15]AIR1/1169/204/5/2591. It is unlikely that this rule was ever dignified by formal legislation but it had long been the standard yardstick. A relatively early written reference to it crops up in a letter of 12 December 1915 in which OC 3rd Wg, Lt-Col W.S. Brancker, advised the COs of Nos 4, 8 and 11 Sqns that '... 100 hours in the air after qualification should be the minimum amount for which an observer can be considered for training in flying ... '

[16]AIR1/1135/204/5/2224. HQ RFC letter CRFC 2047G dated 19 April 1917.

and the demand for additional night bomber crews led to the creation of several dedicated FE-equipped Depot Squadrons (later restyled Night Training Squadrons).

In August Trenchard submitted to the Director General a secret memorandum on No 100 Sqn, which had by then been in France for five months.[17] Among other topics, this report included an assessment of the capabilities of the unit's aircrews. The numbers involved were rather too small to constitute a statistically valid sample but, since they were all he had to go on, the GOC had little option but to use them as the basis for his appraisal. Of the forty-three pilots who had flown with the unit thus far Trenchard considered that 'roughly one-third proved excellent night pilots, capable of finding their way remarkably well, even on moonless nights if clear. Another third, though less reliable, have done consistently useful work, whilst the remainder have been more or less of a failure.' He went on to say that, 'of the officer observers who have been on strength, only about 50 per cent have proved themselves really suitable, while of the aerial gunners less than 20 per cent have proved efficient.'

Trenchard went on to recommend (again) that his night bomber crews should be given more night flying training before being posted to France. He also noted that experience had 'proved beyond doubt that in night-bombing the aiming, if not the actual releasing, of the bombs should be carried out by the observer.' This, he explained, was because a pilot had quite enough to do avoiding searchlights and gunfire and judging when to make the attack run. Once committed, the most useful contribution that the pilot could make was in keeping his aeroplane 'on a level keel and at a previously agreed height.' Since the observer had much the better view from an FE2, he was best placed both to assess what corrections needed to be made to minimise line error and when to release the bombs.

For this reason Trenchard expressed a marked preference for commissioned observers for night work, noting that, while gunners were not lacking in courage, it had been found that they could 'seldom follow a pilot's course or assist him to get his correct line over the target.' It was hardly surprising that gunners tended to display relatively limited abilities in this respect, as they had received little (if any) formal training in either navigation or bomb-aiming. It is also possible that, depending upon the individuals concerned, this problem may have been compounded in cases where pilots found it difficult to accept what amounted to orders from non-commissioned personnel, although there is no specific evidence to support this conjecture.

Early experience of night bombing operations conducted by No 100 Sqn indicated that aerial gunners were no substitute for officer observers, which was hardly surprising in view of the limited scope of their training and their inferior status compared to commissioned pilots. This is one of No 100 Sqn's FE2bs, A5428, toting a 230 lb bomb. (J.M. Bruce/G.S. Leslie collection)

[17]AIR1/393/15/231/34. HQ RFC letter CRFC 1957/1G dated 14 August 1917.

It is quite clear from Trenchard's report that, because it was the best way to do the job, the observers of the night bombing force had actually begun to assume direct responsibility for bomb-aiming as early as the summer of 1917. Although the same rationale could have been applied to the day bomber force, however, its pilots seem to have been less enthusiastic about adopting the procedure. Predictably, while the RFC's policymakers were content to condone the practice, their aversion to allowing non-pilots to wield any measure of executive authority prevented them from formally endorsing it. Nevertheless, the GOC's observations had opened up the possibility and before the end of the war responsibility for bomb aiming would have been formally assigned to observers. Furthermore, the observer's potential for improving the overall efficiency of a crew in other respects, notably in the field of navigation, would also have been acknowledged.

As Trenchard's report had also pointed out, navigation had become a rather more demanding business at night and additional training was considered to be necessary, specifically including cross-country exercises covering distances in excess of 100 miles. Although the GOC had actually recommended 'more' training, it was decided that the training provided should also be better and from October 1917 units directly involved in night flying training were each established to have an EO3 to act as a specialist instructor. Most of these men had been electrical engineers in civilian life and they all attended a course at the Admiralty Compass Observatory at Slough before taking up their appointments as Compass Officers.[18]

The academic syllabus they taught included: compass theory; the triangle of velocities; basic astronomy, e.g. the identification of *Polaris* and its use as a northerly datum; and maps and map-reading, stressing those features of particular significance at night and the exploitation of moonlight as an aid to nocturnal map-reading. Practical exercises for prospective night bomber crews included: being tested in day and night air-to-ground gunnery and bomb dropping; flying in searchlight beams; the use of W/T; day and night cross-country flying and simulated exercises flown, in daylight, while wearing dark goggles, making allowance for the forecast wind in all cases. In all a pilot had to log ten hours of night flying prior to graduation, an observer requiring only five hours. Although the navigational content of the syllabus was being aimed primarily at pilots, observers received the same instruction, were tested in navigation and, where practical, all flying exercises were conducted as crews.

The initial establishment provided for one Compass Officer to be shared between two Night Training Squadrons. In view of the increasing emphasis being placed on navigation, however, this was raised to one per squadron in January 1918, their designation being changed to that of Air Navigation Officer. At the same time the War Office suggested that each operational Night Flying Squadron (i.e. those flying FE2s in the bomber role) should also have its own Air Navigation Officer to co-ordinate raid planning and to calibrate the unit's compasses. Evidently regarding this as excessive, the GOC declined the offer but he did agree to one being added to the staff of Bombing Wings, of which the RFC had only one at that time, the 41st.[19]

[18]Slough had begun training selected RFC and RNAS aircrew as Compass Officers several months earlier.

[19]AIR1/398/15/231/39. War Office letter 87/RFC/1115 (O1a) dated 4 January 1918 contained the offer of an Air Navigation Officer for each Night Flying Squadron. A second letter of 14 January agreed to the GOC's request for one per wing which had been counter proposed by HQ RFC's CRFC 1957/1G of the 11th.

1917–18. The state of the art of air navigation

It may have been noted that, although the timeframe of this narrative has reached 1917, there has been little previous mention of navigational techniques. This has been not so much an oversight as a reflection of the fact that, having been almost entirely a question of fair weather map-reading, in daylight, over relatively short distances, navigation in the RFC was a very straightforward, and thus unremarkable, business. Nevertheless, due to the efforts of a number of individual RNAS officers, who had been adapting well-understood maritime procedures and applying them to the air environment, a variety of useful navigational calculators and instruments had been developed.

Army aviators showed little interest in these devices at first, although the increasing intensity of night operations throughout 1917 (defence against German intruders at home, as well as bombing in France) did make them increasingly aware of the problems inherent in air navigation. For all practical purposes, however, since the RFC's nocturnal activities continued to consist almost entirely of short-range, tactical operations over familiar terrain, simple map-reading still sufficed. Prompted by the onset of long winter nights and the creation of the nucleus of a long-range strategic bombing force, the RFC finally began to acknowledge the need for more sophisticated methods of navigation in the autumn of 1917.[20] In effect, it had begun to adopt the tools and techniques which had been devised by the RNAS.

The recollections of Lt R. Shillinglaw, who flew on night operations with No 100 Sqn from June 1918 until the end of the war, provide a succinct first-hand impression of the evolution of contemporary RAF practice:[21]

> 'On the FE2b, we flew to targets by map-reading, using a flashlight consisting of a battery strapped to a belt and a loose flex to the light itself. We knew the ground so well that maps were hardly necessary except in finding a new target. Later, in Handley Pages, it was a different matter. I only did about a dozen raids on these. Again, open cockpits and we used to fly on a course by dead reckoning of a landmark every half hour or so [*i.e. 30–40 miles apart – CGJ*]. I used to draw out the course beforehand in our mapping room using triangles and parallelograms for track, course, forecast wind and speeds, etc. En route sometimes we could have an angle of drift of 45°, so on the side of the fuselage we had a drift indicator and, with two points on a track, obtained a drift angle [*and, presumably, groundspeed by using a stopwatch to measure the time taken to fly between them – CGJ*] and so calculated the change of direction and speed of wind.'

Although the RNAS had certainly made considerable progress in developing navigational techniques, it should not be assumed that all naval aviators were prepared to put their entire faith in them. In an account of his wartime experiences, Obs Lt P. Bewsher recalled a special mission flown on 29 September 1917, the target being the Luxembourg Bridge at Namur.[22] The sortie involved a round trip, at night, of some 250 miles, requiring about four hours in the air. He was briefed by the very experienced OC 7(N) Sqn, Sqn Cdr J.T. Babington, who advised him to 'fly by compass and only use landmarks as a check.' Bewsher goes on to provide a detailed description of the subsequent planning and successful execution of the mission. After debriefing, while congratulating him on his navigational skill, Babington remarked, 'I suppose you did it by compass!' To which Bewsher responded, 'No, sir! By landmarks!'

Reading between the lines of these anecdotes provides us with some insight into the theory and practice of air navigation during the last year of the war. Paul Bewsher's tale, for instance, clearly shows that by the summer of 1917 primary responsibility, for both flight planning and the conduct of navigation, was considered to lie with the observer, at least for long-range operations (then still the exclusive preserve of naval aviation).

Unfortunately (as will become clear later), the RNAS never managed to train sufficient professional observers to satisfy its needs. Since all naval pilots continued to receive comprehensive instruction in navigational techniques, however, the shortfall could be made up by misemploying some of them. It became quite common, therefore, for RNAS Handley Pages to carry two pilots, one of them acting as observer, with responsibility for both navigation and bomb-aiming. When the RFC finally began to establish a strategic bombing force of its own, the division of responsibility between the members of its crews broadly reflected naval practice. In contrast to the RNAS, however, the Army had sufficient trained observers both to avoid having to misemploy pilots and to redress the unbalanced manning situation in naval bomber squadrons when these were absorbed into the RAF.[23]

From late 1917 onwards the content of navigational training, both theoretical and practical, was progressively expanded. As a result, as Roy Shillinglaw's account tells us, the aircrews of 1918 were familiar with the devices which had been developed by the RNAS and knew how to employ them to complement simple dead reckoning. The complexity involved in actually using these tools and methods made them unattractive propositions, however, and the unreliability of contemporary instrumentation meant that, in reality, the results which could be achieved were of doubtful accuracy. Furthermore, since the only means of fixing position was by reference to a map, it is hardly surprising that, once they were airborne, like Bewsher, many observers preferred to rely entirely on traditional map-reading.

Map-reading was only practical with good visibility, of course, and it had long been appreciated that in the future aeroplanes would be required to operate routinely by night, as well as by day, and in all weathers. Work had been going on globally to develop practical solutions to the more intractable problems associated with air navigation since before the war. An interesting paper on this subject, translated

[20]Commanded by Lt-Col C.L.N. Newall, HQ 41st Wg was set up on 11 October 1917 to control three bomber squadrons, two RFC and one RNAS. Against a background of prolonged politico-military debate over the desirability of establishing an Anglo-Franco-Italo-US strategic bombing force, the British expanded their own organisation. In anticipation of the establishment of a second wing, Newall's command became HQ VIII Bde on 1 February 1918 and with effect from 6 June this was subordinated to Maj-Gen Trenchard's HQ Independent Force, RAF. By the end of the war, the IF was controlling one fighter and nine bomber squadrons in France with others on the point of becoming operational at home. Trenchard was eventually appointed to be CinC of an Inter-Allied Independent Air Force, but not until October 1918 – too late for it to have had any impact on the outcome of the war.

[21]Taken from an account of the wartime experiences of Lt Roy Shillinglaw, as told to Marvin L. Skelton and published in 1979 in *The Cross & Cockade Journal*, Vol 10, No 3.

[22]Paul Bewsher, *Green Balls* (1919).

[23]This process had actually begun before the formation of the RAF. There were, for instance, three RFC observers flying Handley Pages with A Sqn RNAS as early as November 1917 (Lts H.A. Samson, A.H. Thompson and L. Harper), although the Army's primary objective at this stage was probably to gain first-hand experience of heavy bomber operations, rather than to relieve the shortage of qualified naval observers.

from the original German, was circulating at the Admiralty as early as February 1914.[24]

This document made reference to such remarkably advanced concepts as celestial navigation, gyro-compasses and the use of airborne W/T, including the measurement of radio bearings in the air and the possibility of assessing position relative to two radio transmitters by measuring the difference between the strengths of their received signals.[25]

None of these was a practical proposition at the time but their potential had clearly been recognised. Of more immediate practical use was a network of light beacons which had been established in pre-war Germany to identify aerodromes and to act as navigational aids; twenty such facilities were already operating at the time the paper was written. By the end of the war substantial progress had been made in all the fields discussed in the paper but the only one to have had any direct impact on operations was the deployment of lighthouses as an aid to nocturnal navigation. Development of the other applications continued but it would take another twenty-five years or so for most of them to become familiar practices at squadron level. (A summary of the development of navigational tools and techniques during WW I is at Annex D.)

1917. The RFC quantifies the scale of its observer training task

It is informative to consider what the numerical requirement for observers was expected to be in mid-1917. The major influence here was a series of policy decisions taken during the latter part of the previous year. In the light of the experience of aerial fighting gained during the long drawn-out Battle of the Somme, approval had been given for a succession of increases in the front-line strength of the RFC. This culminated in an Air Board decision of 16 December which endorsed a plan for a total of 106 Service Squadrons, two more FE2 night bomber squadrons being added shortly afterwards. This would give the RFC more than four times as many operational units as it had had at the beginning of the summer. Since an air force's operational squadrons are comparable to the tip of a metaphorical iceberg, this implied an even greater expansion of the RFC as a whole. The requirement for additional manpower was enormous and in the early part of 1917 the training system was hard pressed to meet the seemingly insatiable demand, especially where aircrew were concerned.

Another factor which served to increase the pressure was yet another increase in the size of corps reconnaissance squadrons. This derived from a technical innovation, the 'clapper break', which, by altering the pitch of the tone produced by each transmitter, permitted a ground station to distinguish between the Morse signals received from different aeroplanes working on the same frequency. It now became possible to allocate a crew responsibility for each 2000 yards of trench line without mutual interference. To maintain permanent coverage while operating at this density, however, required more resources and in preparation for the Battle of Arras in the spring of 1917 it was decided to build up some units to twenty-one, and in some cases twenty-four, aircraft.[26] Neither the aeroplanes nor the manpower were available to permit the strength of all units to be raised to this level at the time but in the summer this temporary measure was made permanent, all corps reconnaissance squadrons being established to have twenty-four aircraft and twenty observer officers.[27]

On 21 June 1917 the War Office recommended that the size of the RFC, which had still to reach its presently authorised total of 108 squadrons, should be virtually doubled yet again. On 2 July the Cabinet sanctioned this increase, the aim now being to field a force of no fewer than 200 squadrons, forty of them to be equipped with long-range bombers. Following this decision, a study was carried out to assess its implications in terms of manpower. It forecast that to sustain the expansion of the RFC, while simultaneously replacing wastage, it would be necessary to provide 782 new observers during the remaining six months of the year. The monthly requirement for 1918 was expected to increase progressively to reach an annual total of 4691 (these figures were exclusive of those needed to man kite balloons. See Chapter 10). The corresponding demands for pilots were expected to be 3252 and 13 387.[28] By January 1918, however, the enlarged establishment of aircraft and crews previously authorised for corps squadrons had been extended to cover the two-seater squadrons of the (Army) Wings as well. This will have further increased the demand for personnel and partially invalidated the manpower forecasts made only six months before.

These estimates had been based on the loss rates being experienced (from all causes) in mid-1917, which gave an observer (and a pilot) an expected availability of four months on artillery co-operation and night bomber units and two weeks less on fighter reconnaissance and day bombing squadrons.[29] Apart from being very depressing, these predictions were statistically significant in two ways. First, they were considerably shorter than the duration of a typical tour of duty, indicating that the front line might need to be replaced at something like double the rate suggested by the size of its

[24]Papers published in foreign journals were (and are) routinely translated and studied by Intelligence staffs to keep abreast of technological developments. The article in question is believed first to have appeared in *Marine Rundschau* in November 1913.

[25]This approach was not really practical as it stood, since it envisaged the measurement of too imprecise a parameter; nevertheless it contained the germ of the differential principles which underlay later hyperbolic navigation aids, such as GEE, LORAN, DECCA and OMEGA.

[26]Nos 2, 7, 9 and 59 Sqns were to have twenty-one aircraft while Nos 8, 12, 13 and 16 Sqns were to have twenty-four. Apart from No 59 Sqn, which had RE8s, all these units were still operating, mostly late model, BE2s.

[27]AIR1/2434/305/33/1. The amendment to the establishment of a corps reconnaissance squadron, raising its strength to twenty-four aircraft with a proportional increase in personnel, was announced by AO 527 dated 16 August 1917. The resources were still not available to meet this requirement in full, however, so the build up was to be progressive at a planned rate of three squadrons per month. It would seem that this target had still not been achieved by the end of the year, however, as a revised unit establishment published on 29 January 1918 stated that new squadrons were to deploy to France with their full complement of personnel but with only eighteen aeroplanes, the balance to be provided in-theatre.

[28]AIR1/676/21/13/1773. All these figures had been calculated on the basis of the 'estimated life' of an individual. This term was a little misleading, however, as it suggests that all aircrew eventually perished. This was not the case; they were far more likely to become non-effective through wounds, injuries, sickness or posting.

[29]*Ibid.* The outlook was even bleaker for single-seat fighter pilots who had a statistical life expectancy of a mere ten weeks.

numerical establishment.[30] Secondly, this problem was much more acute in the case of pilots since they took some eight months to train, two or three times as long as they were likely to survive on operations.

To address this situation, direct recruiting would obviously have to be considerably stepped up. Even so, it would take many months for the enlarged input to pass through the system to provide a corresponding increase in output. So far as observers were concerned, this meant that the RFC was obliged to continue drawing a substantial number of prospective observers from the trenches. By early 1917, however, air warfare had become far more complex and intense than it had been only a year before. It was quite clear that the 1915-style, informal, squadron-based approach to the training of locally recruited observers was no longer viable. Furthermore, as noted previously, the attempt to prolong the system by introducing top-up courses in the UK had yielded disappointing results (see page 49). From the spring of 1917 onwards therefore, all serving personnel transferring to the RFC in the Field were posted to Home Establishment where, prior to formal specialist training as observers or aerial gunners, they were to attend aviation indoctrination courses alongside new recruits.

It is interesting to note that by May 1918 the output of observers from Winchester, i.e. those earmarked for corps duties alone, had risen to some 220 per month.[31] Bearing in mind that training had stopped before the end of 1918, the numbers of qualified aircrew actually available to the RAF in the following January (see page 101) would suggest that the targets set in mid-1917 had been substantially achieved.

Once it had become standard practice for all observers to attend a sequence of formal training courses it became apparent that there was a flaw in the revised conditions under which observers were now serving. It will be recalled that since November 1916 they had begun to accrue seniority once they became notionally available for operations, i.e. either from the date of their posting *to* France or from that on which they were initially attached to the RFC *in* France. Since the latter group were now promptly being shipped home, they were accumulating several month's seniority without actually seeing any action.

This anomaly was removed at the end of August 1917, the amended rules now stating that the date from which all observers would accumulate seniority was to be that on which they 'report overseas for duty', having completed all requisite training courses at home.[32] This change was to be implemented immediately, but it was not to be applied retrospectively. In general, the key date was considered to be that on which a trained observer was taken on strength by HQ RFC, but there were certainly some instances where it was the date on which an individual was allocated to a squadron. The difference was usually only a matter of a few days but in some cases, when an individual had been taken ill for instance, it could be several weeks.

While the DMA was content that its latest ruling had solved a parochial RFC problem, it had reckoned without the assistance of the rest of the War Office's bureaucrats. The revised terms of service introduced in late 1916 had been reflected in Army Order 403 of that year. Unfortunately an amendment (Army Order 367) was published in December 1917 which served only to confuse the issue as it reverted to the original date, i.e. that of *leaving* the UK, and reinstated authority for an immediate nominal transfer to the RFC for observers who were recruited in the field.[33]

It would be charitable to credit the War Office with having made these changes to cater for the more remote theatres. In these cases there could be a gap of several weeks between a formally trained observer's departure from the UK and his reporting for duty and it was still the normal practice in the Middle East and elsewhere for observers to be recruited and trained in the field. On the other hand, on-the-job training had ceased in France, where the overwhelming majority of observers were employed, and one suspects that the drafter of the amended Army Order 367 was simply unaware of this. In theory, since it had been published by a higher authority and carried a later date, the Army Order should have overridden the instructions issued by the DAO in August 1917 and thus confounded his intentions.

It is difficult to be certain whether this confusion actually had any direct impact on RFC procedures and it seems likely that the latest change in regulations may well have been tacitly ignored, at least in France. Nevertheless, this incident provides yet another example of the seemingly careless way in which the kaleidoscope of regulations governing the lives of observers would be periodically picked up and given an unnecessary shake. Why unnecessary? Because, by mid-1917 observers really ought to have been serving under the same stable and comparatively generous terms as pilots.

1917. Flying pay and its significance in the case of observers who had become prisoners of war

Several references have already been made to the fact that observers were entitled to draw flying pay but the implications of this have not been examined in any detail. It will come as no surprise to learn that, as with practically all of its regulations, the RFC had managed to ensure that those governing the issue of flying pay meant that observers were badly treated when compared to pilots. The most obvious difference was that qualified pilots received flying pay at eight

[30]The length of a tour of flying duty does not appear ever to have been rigidly laid down by statute and its duration could be extended or shortened as required. Personal factors, such as battle fatigue, were taken into consideration when circumstances permitted but the 'exigencies of the Service' always had an overriding priority. Despite these variables, it is generally true to say that a notional tour lasted about six or seven months, including one or two leave breaks, although ten months was not unusual. What this meant in airborne time was dependent upon the role of a particular squadron, the intensity of the ground operations it was supporting and the prevailing weather conditions but a typical corps observer might expect to accumulate 150–200 flying hours, possibly more, *if* he stayed the course. His chances of surviving that long were not good, but for the first three years of the war his prospects were improved by the likelihood of his being short-toured after three or four months so that he could be retrained as a pilot. The RAF sustained the traditional RFC practice of recycling its observers as pilots right up to the Armistice but by mid-1918 there was a growing tendency for this to follow completion of a relatively lengthy period as a back-seater.

[31]AIR1/161/15/123/15. This figure has been extracted from a brief, undated (but certainly post-war), account of his involvement in observer training rendered by Wg Cdr Chamier.

[32]AIR1/2434/305/33/1. AO 548 of 31 August 1917. Notwithstanding the publication of this memorandum, it should be understood that seniority was not publicly acknowledged until an observer had been formally gazetted to the RFC which still did not occur until he had completed his probationary service, this process frequently taking three months or more. Only then was an observer's name added to the RFC section of the Army List, the entry being appropriately backdated, and only then did he receive full flying pay.

[33]AIR1/835/204/5/255. The amendment to Army Order 403 was reproduced in HQ RFC's Routine Orders for 23 December 1917.

shillings per day while observers were paid only five (these sums being additional to regimental pay in both cases). There may have been some justification for this in the early days, on the grounds that observers were neither formally trained nor members of the RFC, but for those who were subsequently both certified as competent and gazetted as Flying Officer (Observers) it is arguable that the differential should no longer have applied.

This differential was not simply confined to rates of pay, however. While pilots drew their daily eight shillings continuously, so long as they were filling an established post, observers were entitled to their five shillings only on those days on which they flew. As noted earlier, authorisation for non-commissioned back-seaters to draw flying pay continuously had been published in December 1916 (see page 19), but this provision was not officially extended to include officers until 2 April 1917.[34]

While it was a trifle late, this concession was certainly worthwhile, but it failed to resolve another major anomaly. The regulations governing the payment of allowances to prisoners of war and internees, had been promulgated in June 1915.[35] These permitted the continuous issue of flying pay but only to officers entitled to the eight-shilling rate. This meant, of course, that the pilot of a downed crew would have his accumulated allowances to look forward to once he was released. His observer, always the poor relation, would not.

In view of the relentless consistency with which War Office regulations managed to operate to the disadvantage of observers, it is difficult to avoid the conclusion that this was just one more manifestation of a sustained policy of deliberate discrimination. On the other hand, one should not perhaps ascribe to malice decisions which may have been taken on the basis of incompetence. It is conceivable that the unfortunate circumstances of captured back-seaters had actually been created through an oversight.

It is possible that, to ensure that allowances would continue to be paid only to those who were fully qualified, the drafter of the regulations had chosen to define entitled pilots by reference to the eight-shilling rate. If this was the case, apart from being rather cumbersome, such a definition was actually quite superfluous. After all, it was hardly likely that an *un*qualified pilot, drawing the instructional rate of flying pay, would be taken prisoner. Furthermore, this definition had had the unfortunate effect of excluding all observers, none of whom were entitled to draw the princely sum of eight shillings. This was of little consequence, however, as, not being entitled to continuous flying pay until April 1917, any observer shot down on an earlier date had forfeited his allowance in any case.

Then again, it is possible that, since it was to do with the outlay of public funds, the man who drafted this particular regulation was a paymaster, rather than an aviator. When he was writing his rules in mid-1915, observers had not even been authorised to wear a distinguishing badge, let alone been formally admitted into the exclusive ranks of the RFC. It is quite possible, therefore, that the rule writer was quite unaware that there were such creatures. Under the circumstances, while still unforgivable, his exclusion of them would at least be understandable.

Once published, however, the rules remained in force. Perhaps because they rarely received bank statements, there are unlikely to have been many complaints from observers who had been incarcerated in Germany and it was more than two years before this particular injustice was legislated away. In September 1917 the regulations were revised, Army Order 277 permitting Flying Officer (Observers) to draw flying pay under the same conditions as those applying to pilots.[36] The daily rate for back-seaters was still only five shillings, however, and entitlements could be antedated to no earlier than the introduction of continuous flying pay, i.e. 2 April 1917.

While this measure was obviously well-intentioned, the complex web of regulations which had accompanied the evolution of observers still left many outside the system. The residual problem was that, in order to retain their entitlement to flying pay as prisoners, back-seaters had to be both 'on the authorised establishment of observers and graded as flying officer (observers).'[37] Technically, this automatically excluded two groups of prisoners: those who had fallen into enemy hands prior to the introduction of formal grading, i.e. before November 1915, even though they may have been recognised as 'qualified observers'; and those who had been shot down while still on probation, i.e. before they had been formally graded.

By this time, however, there was sufficient awareness of observers for someone to feel concerned about those who were languishing at Holzminden, Karlsruhe, Ingolstadt and elsewhere but whose flying pay was still being withheld. An uncharacteristically magnanimous War Office appears to have decided that, despite the clear intent of Army Order 277, it might be possible to bend the rules. This would involve exploiting a subsidiary phrase to the effect that flying pay could *not* be drawn by officers 'who were not within the authorised establishment of observers on the date of their capture'. By stretching a point, it could be argued that the converse must also be true, i.e. that anyone who *was* filling an established post could continue to be paid. This interpretation would serve to cover most of the more than one hundred back-seaters who had been taken prisoner prior to the introduction of continuous flying pay and who had not been gazetted as Flying Officer (Observers) but who had been held against their unit's official entitlement to observers, the first such establishment having been published in December 1914 (see Chapter 2, Note 19).

A list of the observers who had been taken prisoner prior to the spring of 1917 was compiled by the War Office and forwarded to HQ RFC who were asked to indicate which of these men, regardless of their status and degree of qualification, were being carried against the official establishment of their units at the time they were shot down.[38] Confirmation is lacking, but it is suspected that those who were identified as having fallen into this category will subsequently have been paid five shillings per day.

These change in the rules were certainly positive, especially as the War Office seemed to be applying them generously. Nevertheless, compared to captured pilots whose flying pay had never been withheld, the regulations still managed to short-change a lot of captured observers because there was no provision for any of them to receive an antedate of pay to any date earlier than 2 April 1917.

[34]Reference to the introduction of continuous flying pay for established Flying Officer (Observers) is made in Army Order 277 of September 1917.
[35]Army Order 198 of June 1915.

[36]Army Order 277 of September 1917.
[37]*Ibid.*
[38]AIR1/1026/204/5/1415. War Office letter 48/Misc/1479(O3a) dated 20 September 1917.

Chapter 10

Balloon observers in the RFC

Apart from observers and gunners there was another distinct group of aviators who wore the flying 'O', those who flew in lighter-than-air craft. To complete the non-pilot aircrew picture it is appropriate to consider the wartime evolution of the military balloonist. Balloon observers had originally been introduced to carry out much the same tasks as the earliest aeroplane observers. As the war progressed, however, the contrast between their very different operating environments, and the differing perspectives of the battlefield which these provided, meant that they had increasingly little in common.

The most obvious reason for these differences was that, although its location could be changed, a tethered balloon operated from what amounted to a fixed site and thus offered a very restricted field of view, compared to that available to an aeroplane observer. On the other hand, this permitted a balloon observer to become extremely familiar with the terrain he surveyed, enabling him to detect the smallest sign of unusual activity, whereas aeroplane observers tended to gain a more general impression. Another major difference was that balloonists worked exclusively with the guns, communicating with the batteries under their control via telephone landlines. Since they had comparatively little involvement in photography, used voice rather than Morse to communicate, never dropped bombs and had no Lewis gun to look after, a balloon observer was able to devote all of his energies to the task in hand and they became expert in dealing with the more esoteric implications of ballistics, trajectories, times of flight and so on.

The introduction of observation balloons to support land operations in France was complicated by the fact that the RN had been given sole responsibility for *all* lighter-than-air affairs in January 1914. Satisfying the Army's demands, therefore, required an extensive exercise in inter-Service co-operation. As a first step, the Admiralty made available to the War Office the facilities of its balloon training ground at Roehampton, which had been formally established under the overall command of Wg Cdr E.M. Maitland on 21 March 1915, following the first successful flight of a kite balloon in the UK from there on the 15th.[1] The first lighter-than-air unit assigned to work with the army, No 2 Kite Balloon Section (KBS) of the RNAS, arrived in France on 8 May.

At a conference convened by the Admiralty on 19 July, Sir David Henderson proposed that responsibility for all aspects of military ballooning should be transferred to the War Office. Whether they liked it or not, it would have been difficult for the admirals to have resisted Henderson's approach, as the War Cabinet was already of the opinion that the navy had become far too deeply involved in land warfare. Shortly afterwards it was decided that control of most of the quasi-military naval units operating in France (including, in addition to the balloon sections, armoured cars and trains and a variety of infantry and artillery formations) was to be transferred to the Army.

Since the navy currently controlled all lighter-than-air affairs, hardware as well as manpower, it was inevitably going to take some time to implement the new arrangements. Nevertheless, a start was made in August 1915 when the RFC's Capt J.D. Boyle was authorised to begin internal recruiting with the aim of raising further balloon units which were to be entirely army-manned. Training soon gathered pace at Roehampton under the overall supervision of a naval officer, Flt Cdr H. Delacombe, with the parochial interests of the attached soldiery being looked after by Boyle. By the end of the month three more RNAS balloon units had been despatched to France (Nos 4, 6 and 8 KBSs).

In the meantime, the generals having effectively recovered their balloons from the admirals, there had been a dispute as to which of them should exercise control over them: the end-users – the gunners? or the operators – the flyers? The RFC contended that the logistic requirements, of what were indisputably 'air' assets, could be adequately met only by the RFC's dedicated supply channels. Furthermore, while the balloons were plainly only there to serve the guns, the aviators argued that any form of flying was a highly specialised business which only they could conduct efficiently, the implication being that they probably already knew how to do it. Both of these arguments would prove to be deeply flawed but this was not apparent at the time and the air lobby

Following their acquisition of two French examples, the British began to deploy observation balloons in the late spring of 1915. At first the RFC used Spencer-built copies of the German Drachen *design, like this one, which was photographed at Fricourt in the Somme sector, where it was being operated by one of the sections controlled by Maj C. Bovill's No 1 Kite Balloon Squadron.* (T. Treadwell)

[1]All balloons used previously by the army and navy, whether for observation or to train airship pilots, had had relatively simple spherical envelopes. A kite balloon had an elongated shape, stabilising fins and a much more complicated rigging system.

won the debate. Control of the four naval balloon sections was assumed by the RFC on 16 October 1915.[2]

The RFC's claim that its specialised logistic system was bound to be best suited to supporting lighter-than-air operations had helped to carry the day, but the argument was ill-founded. After all, the flyers had had no more experience of handling the equipment associated with ballooning than the gunners when the issue was being debated in 1915. Kite balloons were virtually an unknown quantity at the time and the RFC could not, therefore, have known whether its specialised supply train was really any better placed to deal with them than the Royal Artillery's would have been. In the event, despite the army's increasing involvement in lighter-than-air operations, it continued to be wholly dependent upon naval sources for the supply of balloons, gas-making plant, winches and other ancillary technical equipment for many months, the War Office not beginning to place its own orders until as late as July 1916.

The RFC's other key claim, that its familiarity with air operations made it the natural choice to control ballooning, was equally insubstantial. Balloons were an innovation. No one really knew how to organise them operationally and whoever gained control was going to have to find out by trial and error. To begin with, the RFC tried grouping its lighter-than-air assets into Kite Balloon Squadrons, each having an established strength of two KBSs (four from March 1916). These operated under the auspices of the existing (Corps) Wings. While the activities of the aeroplane and balloon units certainly complemented each other, however, their operating procedures, lines of communication and logistic requirements proved to be very different. The scale of the problems caused by these differences increased with the proliferation of KBSs (there were twenty-two in France by the autumn of 1916) and a greater degree of autonomy became appropriate. From December 1916, therefore, the Kite Balloon Squadrons were redesignated as Companies and reorganised into newly established (Balloon) Wings, one of which was allocated to each Brigade to operate alongside its (Corps) Wing and its (Army) Wing.[3]

Early operational experience in France had shown that it was essential for balloonists to have an intimate knowledge of field gunnery procedures and several army officers were attached to the (still RNAS) balloon units to provide the necessary expertise. Thus, as early as October 1915, ten of the total of thirty-two officers carried on the books of Nos 2, 4, 6 and 8 KBSs were soldiers (seven artillerymen and three from the RFC). All the remainder were naval officers, including the four COs, then Flt Lts W.F. McNeece (but see Note 5), G. StC. Rollo and J. Ogilvie-Davis and FSLt A.S. Byng.[4] The first army-manned balloon units (Nos 5, 7, 9 and 10 KBSs) crossed the Channel during March 1916, along with sufficient additional trained soldiers to make a start on

This cartoon (by Bernard Hugh and reproduced in Air Pie *of 1919) graphically sums up all that needs to be said about the most important characteristic of a 'balloon hand'. The date is unknown but the fact that the artist has made a point of illustrating both RFC and RNAS uniforms suggests that it might have been drawn in the spring of 1916 when kite balloon sections were still being manned jointly.*

replacing the sailors still serving with Nos 2 and 4 KBSs. There were problems with finding enough RFC men to complete the process with Nos 6 and 8 KBSs but these were eased by the Admiralty's granting a dispensation permitting RN balloon personnel to remuster to the Army.[5] By the end

[2]AIR1/832/204/5/226. A Royal Warrant of 4 November 1915 amended that of 1 December 1914 (which laid down conditions of service and pay for the wartime Army) by recognising the addition of 'a Kite Balloon Section to our Royal Flying Corps (Military Wing)' with effect from 16 October 1915. The Warrant was promulgated by Army Order II of 10 November and published in HQ RFC's Routine Orders of the 25th.

[3]*Ibid.* The restructuring of its lighter-than-air organisation was announced in HQ RFC's Routine Orders for 5 December 1916. Like that of an aeroplane wing, the establishment of a (Balloon) Wing was not fixed but the usual strength ran to one Balloon Company (normally of two Sections) for each Corps served by the parent RFC Brigade.

[4]AIR1/377/15/231/18. This information was extracted from a nominal roll of all officers serving with the RFC as at 15 October 1915, covered by War Office letter 114/Returns/1869(MA1) dated six days later.

[5]AIR1/373/15/231/14. As early as 27 August 1915 War Office letter 87/5808(MA1) had proposed that the Admiralty should permit RNAS balloon personnel serving in France to transfer to the RFC, albeit only for the duration of the war. This was agreed in principle but the arrangement was not implemented until 9 March 1916 when another letter, carrying the same reference, announced the details. Ratings wishing to remain in France were to be locally discharged from the RNAS and immediately re-engaged by the RFC. RN officers would be lent to the Army while officers of the RNAS, RNR and RNVR were to resign their commissions and join the RFC, this being a purely administrative procedure. In all cases personnel were to be taken on by the RFC at an equivalent rank/grade to that held previously and with the same seniority. It is not known to what extent people actually exercised this option.

Despite the *de facto* independence of the RNAS, the more conservative elements of the bureaucracy had ignored this reality. The Army and Navy Lists, for instance, both continued to reflect the *de jure* situation whereby the RFC was still supposedly divided into Military and Naval Wings. This adherence to the letter of the law probably made inter-Service transfers by officers relatively straightforward. It was never a common practice but several prominent personalities did 'switch sides'. For instance, when of June fourteen sections were in action in France, all of them manned by the RFC, apart from two which were located on the coast to co-operate with naval batteries.

By this time the demand for balloon personnel had outstripped the capacity of the existing naval training facilities so the army expanded its own training organisation. Having already set up its own Kite Balloon Training Depot at Roehampton,[6] the RFC opened Balloon Training Schools at Rollestone Camp (Larkhill) and Lydd in July 1916.[7] Thenceforth balloon pilots and EOs were trained at Roehampton/Richmond Park, the two new schools providing tactical training in artillery observation and handling the technical instruction of NCOs and men. The Depot was tasked with being able to form (up to) two new kite balloon sections per week; each of the schools could also form new sections if required, but at a much lower rate. Although the Army was now ostensibly carrying out its own training, the RFC was not in a position to dispense completely with the assistance being provided by the RNAS at Roehampton until as late as June 1917 when it was able to offer a reciprocal arrangement under which naval free balloons could be launched from a military facility at the Kennington Oval if and when required.

As with aeroplane observers, it became necessary to supplement the output of the home-based training organisation by recruiting and training additional balloon observers in France. This practice became increasingly widespread from late 1916 onwards. Most of these 'do-it-yourself' balloonists were drawn from the Royal Artillery and they proved to be ideally suited to the task. Inevitably, however, questions soon began to be asked about the precise standing of these attached 'gunners' within the increasingly complex hierarchy of aviators. These questions proved to be difficult to answer and it took several months for the problems to be resolved (see below).

In action, kite balloons (initially Spencer-built copies of the German *Drachen*, but standardising on the French-designed Caquot Type M from late 1916) would frequently remain aloft for ten hours or more at a stretch. Suspended above the lines, typically at about 3000 feet, beneath some 30 000 cu ft of highly inflammable hydrogen in what amounted to a wickerwork laundry hamper that swung wildly in windy conditions, the balloon observer's occupation was not an enviable one. Furthermore, balloons were very vulnerable to marauding German fighters, at considerable risk from the friendly anti-aircraft guns that were supposed to ward off these attackers and occasionally in the direct line of fire in an artillery duel. Many were shot down and damage to cables caused others to slip their moorings and drift away over the battlefield, usually towards the enemy lines as a result of the prevailing westerly winds (although at least one finished up in Derbyshire). To cater for these situations balloon observers were unique among RFC aviators in that they were provided with parachutes, and while these were far from perfect, they did save many lives.[8]

In the summer of 1916 the British adopted the French-designed Cacquot Type M as its standard observation balloon. (T. Treadwell)

Col F.H. Sykes was posted to command naval air units in the Aegean in 1915, following (what might be diplomatically described as) a clash of personalities within the upper echelons of the RFC in France, he adopted the rank of wing captain RNAS. In the specific context of ballooning the most significant figure to transfer was Lt-Col E.M. Maitland, the doyen of the lighter-than-air community and the original CO of No 1 Airship Company RE (later No 1 Sqn RFC). He changed his army uniform for that of a RNAS wing commander in July 1914 after his field of expertise had become an entirely nautical affair.

Another example is provided by the Hon C.M.P. Brabazon who, as a major serving with the RFC, was appointed to command No 2 KBS, the first to go to France. Since this was a naval unit, it was presumably considered politic for him to hold RNAS rank and he duly became a squadron commander with effect from 19 April 1915. He continued to function as a lighter-than-air 'sailor' until April 1918 when he was transferred again, this time to the RAF as a lieutenant-colonel Dirigible Officer. Needless to say, despite these transfers, he continued to be carried on the books of his original tribe, the Irish Guards, who regarded him as a major with seniority dating from 19 April 1913. Somewhat anachronistically, however, as late as May 1919 his entry in the Army List still had him serving 'on attachment to the RNAS', an organisation which had by then been defunct for more than a year.

Brabazon's successor as OC No 2 KBS, Flt Lt W.F. McNeece, was, incidentally, another RFC pilot (originally of the Royal West Kents) who became a naval balloonist while 'on loan' to the RNAS, although he returned to the khaki fold when manning of the KBSs in France was taken over by the Army.

[6]Originally set up with its Headquarters at 331 Upper Richmond Rd, Putney, the RFC's Kite Balloon Training Depot was restyled the Balloon Training Wing on 21 October 1916 by which time it was operating from the Pole Pavilion of the Roehampton Club.

[7]The initial manpower establishments of Nos 1 and 2 Balloon Training Schools, at Larkhill and Lydd respectively, were published on 28 July 1916, which will have been close to, possibly their actual, date of formation.

[8]Alan Morris notes, in *The Balloonatics* (1970), that 106 parachute descents were made between June 1916 and June 1917 within 2nd (Balloon) Wing alone, 2/Lt S. Jolley making five (of an eventual total of seven) jumps in the course of a mere 97 hours of airborne time in May/June 1917.

1916–17. Another dispute over 'wings' and status

Since the RFC's balloonists were plainly aviators, it was deemed necessary to recognise them as specialists but, since they were not pilots in the conventional sense, it was decided to introduce a new category. The grade of Balloon Officer was introduced in October 1915, the first two, 2/Lts L.E. Brown-Greaves and E.B. Broughton, appearing in that month's Army List.[9] By the following January they had been joined by a further seventeen.

The formal recognition of Balloon Officers inevitably created a demand for them to have some form of distinguishing badge – predating by more than a year the (previously discussed) requirement for aerial gunners to wear some kind of distinctive emblem. Needless to say, there could be no question of balloonists wearing pilots 'wings' and as early as October 1915 (then Brig-Gen) Trenchard had opposed the use of the observers flying 'O' on the grounds that it might 'cheapen' it.[10] For its part, London had vetoed the idea of a special badge, leaving the balloonists in France totally unadorned.

In February 1916, Roehampton's Maj Boyle made a second attempt to gain authority for his *protégés* to wear a badge and this time the War Office acceded to his request. Overruling Trenchard's views, the DMA announced that qualified balloon *pilots*, who were *also* certified as being observers by the Commandant at Roehampton, would be entitled to wear the same badge as aeroplane observers.[11] Trenchard, as GOC (and, not unreasonably, in view of the precedent represented by the case of aeroplane observers), immediately claimed the right to certify those 'balloonatics' who were being recruited and trained in the field. London denied him this right. Boyle promptly stepped in to point out that the General had already been doing it, citing Maj C. Bovill and Lt J.A.G. Swaine as examples of badge-wearing balloonists whose qualifications had not been endorsed by Roehampton.[12]

The crux of the problem was that, although they actually functioned as observers and wore an observers single wing, to be *fully* qualified, Balloon Officers were also required to be able to 'pilot' a free balloon. There were no facilities (or time) for free ballooning in France, however, which meant that, at Roehampton's insistence, locally-trained balloon observers, however experienced they might be, could not be regarded as being fully qualified. The wrangling dragged on, reflecting to some degree the differences in opinion which were to surface in 1917 as to whether a flying 'O' was a 'war service' or a 'qualification' badge (see pages 50–51).

A compromise was arrived at in April whereby the GOC was empowered to license a balloon observer to go aloft operationally and, once satisfied as to his competence, to authorise him to wear an observers badge.[13] These men could *not*, however, be graded as Flying Officer (Observers); *nor* could they be graded as Balloon Officers without first being additionally trained as free balloon pilots, which still required an unacceptably lengthy detachment to the UK. Since they continued to be ungraded (and thus unrecognised as members of the RFC) this still left locally-trained balloonists in France at something of a disadvantage, but these arrangements had to suffice for the time being. Just as these negotiations were drawing to a close, Trenchard wrote to the DAO to complain that 'several balloon officers have lately been posted to the Expeditionary Force who have had little, or no, experience in a kite balloon before proceeding overseas. One officer had never been up in a kite balloon and one only once.'[14] In view of Roehampton's earlier pious protestations, this must surely have provided the GOC with a degree of mischievous satisfaction.

The situation was rationalised in June by the introduction, again at Maj Boyle's urging, of the grade of Balloon Officer (Observer) to cater for those balloonists who had not been trained as 'pilots'.[15] This finally permitted the RFC to acknowledge the many officers who had previously been on active service in a kind of bureaucratic limbo – much like the aeroplane observers of 1914–15 had been. Despite this acknowledgement, however, no provision appears to have been made for distinguishing these men in the Army List before the realities of the supply and demand equation prompted a further revision of the rules.

In February 1917 Trenchard returned to the fray. Arguing that free ballooning was of little practical value, he went on to point out that the pay of officers who had not qualified as balloon pilots was adversely affected, compared to those who had. Since he could ill afford to send these men home to acquire what amounted to a useless certificate, Trenchard asked that this situation be rationalised.[16] This time he won his case. The mandatory requirement for free ballooning was promptly dropped and, although some of the men being trained at home continued to qualify as balloon pilots, the previous distinction was abandoned and thereafter all 'certified balloonatics' were graded as Balloon Officers and all were listed as such.[17]

This decision was accompanied by confirmation of the GOC's standing authority to award a flying 'O' to any field-trained balloon observer whose competence had been assessed on the basis of local examination, this milestone generally being passed after the accumulation of about 100 hours of airborne time. The significance of this was that the wearer of a badge awarded in the field could now be graded, and thus paid, under the same terms as applied to a balloonist who had passed through the formal training system at home.

It would seem that some uncertainty still lingered, however, and a year later the War Office was still having occasionally to advise units that Balloon Officers could be authorised to wear a flying 'O' on 'the recommendation of the General Officer Commanding, RFC, under whom they are serving.'[18] This form of words made it quite clear, incidentally, that authority to grade balloonists had not been vested in Trenchard alone and that similar provisions applied to, for instance, the air commander in the Middle East.

The more realistic attitude being shown towards balloonists brought with it a discrete hierarchy. Until January 1917

[9]Balloon Officers were effectively introduced with effect from 15 October 1915, when the RFC had been given formal authority to operate balloons (see Note 2).

[10]AIR1/404/15/231/45. HQ RFC letter CRFC 1701(A) dated 30 October 1915.

[11]*Ibid*. War Office letter 87/6912(MA1) dated 26 February 1916.

[12]In point of fact, although he had evidently not passed through Roehampton, Bovill would actually have been entitled to wear his flying 'O' as he had been rated as a qualified aeroplane observer with effect from 10 February 1915.

[13]AIR1/404/15/231/45. War Office letter 87/6912(MA1) dated 17 April 1916.

[14]AIR1/861/204/5/472. HQ RFC letter CRFC 934/21(A) dated 18 April 1916.

[15]AIR1/404/15/231/45. DAO letter 87/6912(AO1) dated 17 June 1916.

[16]AIR2/8/87/6912/D155. HQ RFC letter CRFC 1706/13G dated 10 February 1917.

[17]*Ibid*. DAO letter 87/(Inst)/104(AO1a) dated 16 February 1917.

[18]*Ibid*. DAO letter 87/6912(O.2) dated 9 January 1918.

only Balloon Officers, i.e. the lieutenant and subaltern 'drones', had been specifically identified as such in the Army List. Officers filling executive appointments within the lighter-than-air organisation as Section, Company and Wing Commanders were embedded among the Aeroplane Officers of equivalent grades. In the February edition, however, they were listed separately under the generic heading of Balloon Officers; there were six lieutenant-colonels, seven majors, twenty-seven captains and 174 junior officers. This exercise, incidentally, provides yet more evidence to support the contention that the RFC discriminated against its aeroplane observers. After all, if observers who flew in balloons could be lieutenant-colonels, why were those who flew in aeroplanes still prevented from progressing beyond the rank of lieutenant?

It should perhaps be pointed out that the numerical requirement for balloon observers was quite substantial and perhaps much larger than is generally appreciated. In early 1917, for instance, it was forecast that another forty men were needed to meet the then current expansion programme, after which it would be necessary to train a further 150 every six months to cater for wastage across the deployed force. Allowing for the constraints of training capacity, this equated to an intake of thirty men every three weeks. There were actually ninety-four trainee RFC Balloon Officers in residence at Roehampton as at 2 March 1917. The course at this time was of some seven weeks duration, this being followed by a similar stint at Larkhill or Lydd, although the periodic need to replace losses and/or form new sections as a matter of urgency meant that training had sometimes to be considerably shortened. As with its aeroplane observers, the RFC maintained a strong preference for balloonists to be commissioned but a few NCOs managed to qualify from as early as 1916 and for a period in late 1917/early 1918 they appear to have been trained in relatively large numbers.

In the context of recruiting, it is worth recording that, possibly in anticipation of a shortage of volunteers, the Standing Medical Board was prevailed upon to lower the minimum standards for employment as a balloon observer.[19] From September 1917 onwards it was deemed to be acceptable to train men who had lost one or even both legs, so long as they had been cut off below the knee. It is not known, however, whether it ever became necessary to employ amputees.

Balloon observers in the RNAS

While much of the navy's initial ballooning effort had been shore-based, supporting army operations in France, it had not neglected its own requirements. With No 1 KBS on board, the 3500 ton *Manica* (the first vessel to be converted into a balloon carrier) had sailed for the Aegean before the end of March 1915. Within a month its *Drachen* had seen action, directing naval gunfire in the Dardanelles. In July another RNAS balloon, carried by the *Menelaus*, began working with naval guns bombarding the Belgian coast. The experience accumulated during these early deployments laid the foundations for subsequent shipborne balloon operations for, despite its being obliged to relinquish control of military ballooning over the next twelve months, the navy continued to deploy its own balloons at sea until 1918.

To begin with, the naval programme was entirely supported by courses run at Roehampton but further training grounds

[19]AIR1/123/15/40/138. War Office letter 87/9384(O.2) dated 25 September 1917.

A naval Cacquot keeps watch over the Grand Fleet's 2nd Light Cruiser Squadron in 1918: HMS Birmingham *on the right, flying the balloon, and* Melbourne *on the left.* (J.M. Bruce/G.S. Leslie collection)

were set up later at Wormwood Scrubs, Hurlingham[20] and Sheerness. Shipborne ballooning really began to get into its stride from mid-1917 onwards, a notable difference from army practice being that the RNAS never dispensed with the requirement for all of its balloonists to qualify as free balloon pilots. Furthermore, the RN saw no reason to differentiate between its landplane, seaplane, airship and balloon pilots. They were all regarded as being birds of an only slightly different feather and, as aviators in control of some kind of airborne craft, they were all graded generically as Flight Officers. This, of course, was in marked contrast to the RFC whose balloonists were regarded as a form of observer. As discussed below, this fundamental difference of opinion was to cause a degree of friction when the two air arms were merged in 1918 (see page 81–82).

Scores of ships were eventually equipped to handle a balloon and by November 1918 the RAF was operating from some twenty-one naval Balloon Bases, fifteen of them in the UK and the remainder at Mediterranean ports, individual holdings varying from two to twelve balloons per Base. While they had considerable potential as observation platforms in Fleet actions, these never materialised so many naval balloons were actually employed on anti-submarine work. Being unable to engage the enemy himself, the idea was for the balloonist to look out for periscopes and then direct destroyers into the attack. Unfortunately, a balloon, which could be seen from miles away, betrayed the presence of surface ships at a much greater range than the observer could hope to spot a periscope. Nevertheless, the mere presence of a balloon obliged U-boat captains to remain submerged and passive. As a result there was only one successful engagement.[21]

Because of their effectiveness in countering the submarine threat, balloons were also extensively employed for convoy protection. For convoy work a balloon, complete with its flight crew and a handling party, would be attached to a ship at its home base and accompany a convoy to its destination. From

[20]As part of the rationalisation of training facilities, following the creation of the RAF, the ex-RFC facility at the Kennington Oval closed down on 11 May 1918. The ex-RNAS unit at Hurlingham became No 1 Free Balloon School, providing experience of free ballooning for the remainder of the war for all Airship Officers and those Kite Balloon Officers who needed it. see Air Ministry Weekly Order (AMWO) 265 of 15 May 1918.

[21]Directed from aloft by Flt Lt C.A. Butcher, the destroyer HMS *Patriot* sank the U69 on 12 July 1917.

there it would repeat the exercise on the homebound run, being transferred, if necessary, to a returning vessel.

Compared to military operations, there was little risk of a naval balloon's being shot down but that did not mean that ballooning at sea was a sinecure. Typically, the watch system while afloat would involve four hours aloft, followed by eight hours off duty, although, since an observer was also a ship's officer, the demands of shipboard routine would have absorbed much of his nominally 'off duty' time. Like their counterparts in the RFC, the navy's balloon observers were provided with parachutes to cater for the unforeseen, and changing crews in a balloon tethered to the heaving deck of a destroyer steering a zigzag course at up to 25 knots in a Force Six gale meant that the unforeseen could occur quite frequently. The provision of a parachute may have provided a fillip for morale, but in reality the U-boat threat was such that it was highly unlikely that a commodore would risk any of the ships in his convoy stopping to effect a rescue. Despite the hazards, however, casualties were very few and the shipborne balloon proved to be a very cost-effective deterrent to the captains of enemy submarines.

Airships

Although the Army had cracked the RN's lighter-than-air monopoly by regaining control of its own balloons before the end of 1915, this did not include dirigibles. The operation of airships remained an exclusively naval preserve until the creation of the RAF, and even then the Admiralty retained a controlling interest.[22] Airship training was conducted at Kingsnorth (Nore) and/or Wormwood Scrubs until the RNAS Central Training Establishment opened at Cranwell on 1 April 1916.[23] Thereafter HMS *Daedalus* became an increasingly important centre for naval aircrew training for the remainder of the war, continuing its lighter-than-air association after the formation of the RAF under the new title of the Airship Training Wing. It should be noted, however, that, while powered lighter-than-air craft required crews of between two and thirty men, very few (if any) true 'observers' were directly involved in maritime airship operations. Interestingly, however, when the RNAS deployed a Sea Scout and crew to France in July 1916, so that the Army could assess the value of airships for inserting and extracting secret agents, the RFC assigned a fully accredited observer, 2/Lt C.R. Robbins, to participate in the project.[24]

While naval airships, like this North Sea Class, had ten-man crews they included few (if any) Observer Officers, although substantial numbers of enlisted ex-RNAS W/T operators were beginning to sport flying 'O's by late-1918 (see pages 82–83). Having been retained in service to train American crews for the R.38, NS-7 was the last non-rigid airship to be operated by the RAF, making its final flight in October 1921. (P.H.T. Green)

[22]In January 1918 it was agreed that the Air Ministry would assume responsibility for the provision of airship personnel following the formation of the RAF. In view of the exclusively maritime application of these craft and the fact that operational policy was still evolving, however, the Admiralty was to continue to direct employment, retain control over procurement and provide the operating bases. While operations continued to be conducted successfully for the remainder of the war and some progress was made with the development of a new generation of large rigid airships, the division of responsibility proved to be unrealistic, as it created administrative and organisational problems and fostered divided loyalties. The situation was finally resolved in 1919 at an Air Ministry meeting held on 22 August. It was decided that the Air Council would assume full responsibility for airship policy with immediate effect, responsibility for construction and staff following in October. Thereafter the Admiralty was to retain only a marginal involvement in that it continued to be responsible for paying any RN personnel still associated with airship activities; all other costs were to be billed against the Air Ministry Vote. These arrangements were publicised by AO 1435 which announced that all lighter-than-air affairs had been taken over by the Air Council with effect from 22 October.

The RAF had little enthusiasm (or funding) for lighter-than-air activities, however, and, although the Air Ministry retained overall responsibility for all airships, its military branch began to close down in January 1921. This turned out to be a prolonged process, however, largely because of contractual obligations concerning the delivery of the ill-fated R.38 to the US Navy.

[23]Although training did not start until April 1916, the RNAS unit at Cranwell had been commissioned as an independent entity as early as 10 December 1915 when Capt G.M. Paine had been appointed as commodore; see Admiralty Monthly Order 146 of 1 March 1916.

[24]In the event this airship, the uniquely black-painted SS 40, does not appear to have undertaken any espionage missions but it did carry out numerous nocturnal reconnaissance sorties throughout the period of the Battle of the Somme. A first-hand account of the activities of SS 40 by one of its pilots FSLt V. Goddard, was published in 1981 in *The Cross and Cockade Journal*, Vol 12, No 4.

Chapter 11

1917. The navy finally recognises its observers and introduces a distinctive badge for them

Having considered the navy's lighter-than-air activities, it is convenient to review here some of the remarkable changes in the fortunes of the RNAS's aeroplane observers which occurred during 1917. As noted previously, the Admiralty had been relatively slow to acknowledge the need for professional observers and thus to provide them with adequate instruction or any tangible status. As the RFC had already discovered, however, there was an inexorability about this development. The question was not whether to recognise the observer but when? – and to what extent?

A major factor in persuading the navy to accept that it really did need competent professional back-seaters was the experience gained during its pioneering attempt to establish a strategic bombing force in 1916–17. Although this enterprise was terminated before it had been permitted to realise its full potential, it taught many lessons. The type which had been selected to equip the majority of the force had been the Sopwith 1½ Strutter. Probably better known as an RFC two-seat reconnaissance-fighter, many of those operated by No 3 Wg RNAS at Luxeuil were single-seaters with an internal bomb bay.

On his return to England, Wg Cdr R.B. Davies, No 3 Wg's erstwhile senior pilot, wrote a paper in January 1917 in which he noted that, despite their success, the Sopwiths had not been ideally suited to their appointed task.[1] This was partly because their 'pilots all have great difficulty in working any kind of sight while flying the machine' and partly because the lack of a gunner made them extremely vulnerable. Davies recommended that future bombers should be two-seaters with the 'passenger' (*sic*) having responsibility for both bomb-aiming and defence. It was recognised that there would have to be a trade-off in terms of the bomb load which could be carried but, it was argued, the reduced weight of bombs would be more than offset by the increased accuracy with which they could be delivered. Furthermore, the provision of a self-defence capability, the effectiveness of which would be multiplied by flying in formation, would avoid the very expensive alternative of having to provide escort fighters.

If this advice was going to be acted upon, it was clear that the RNAS would require many more back-seaters and, since they were to have a clearly identified and crucial function, that they would have to be taken far more seriously. It is not known to what extent Davies' report served as a catalyst in provoking action along these lines, but what is certain is that a comprehensive career structure for naval observers was introduced shortly after it was written. At a single stroke, with effect from 2 April 1917, the navy introduced: direct recruiting into the RNAS (in place of the previous use of RNVR officers); distinctive rank titles (up to Captain RN equivalent); continuous rates of pay; and a realistic prospect of advancement, since Observer Officers were to be 'eligible for command of Air Stations in the same way as Flight Officers.'[2] Having previously been even less enlightened than the Army in its attitude towards its back-seaters, the RN had suddenly raised the inter-Service stakes significantly, as the rank of RFC observers was still constrained to that of lieutenant and they continued to be ineligible for executive appointments.

[1]AIR1/113/15/39/35. *Remarks on Experience Gained in Air Raids and on Probable Requirements as to Types of Machines in the Future* by Wg Cdr R.B. Davies, dated 4 January 1917.

[2]Admiralty Monthly Order 1648, which published the details of the observers rank and career structure, was not actually promulgated until 5 May 1917 so its effective date of 2 April was retrospective. It was superseded on 6 December by Monthly Order 4359 which provided further amplification of the arrangements.

The accompanying table lists RNAS observer ranks and shows how these equated to those of the RN and their approximate relationships with those of the Army. Note that military and naval ranks did not always relate directly. For instance, differences of opinion as to whether an Observer (or Flight) Lieutenant in the RNAS corresponded to a Captain or a Lieutenant in the RFC were to cause complications when the air services were merged. Another example is provided by a naval aviator under training in early 1918 who, although on the very bottom rung of the ladder, appeared in the Navy List. As a mere Flight Cadet, his opposite number in the RFC did not yet figure in the Army List (see Chapter 7, Note 18).

RNAS Observer	RN	Army
Observer Captain also holding Captain RN rank	Captain	Colonel
Observer Captain not ranked as a Captain RN Wing Observer	Commander	Lt-Colonel
Squadron Observer (of eight years' total seniority or when in command)	Lt Commander	Major
Squadron Observer (of less than eight years' seniority)	Lieutenant of four years' seniority (but senior to all Flight Observers)	Captain
Flight Observer	Lieutenant of four years' seniority	
Observer Lieutenant	Lieutenant	
Observer Sub-Lieutenant	Sub-Lieutenant	Lieutenant and/or 2nd Lieutenant
Probationary Observer Officer	Midshipman	2nd Lieutenant; later Flight Cadet

All Observer Officers (including those under training) wore the winged 'O' once these had been introduced (see Note 3), but the complex pattern of rank equivalence necessitated modifications to the badge to permit the status of certain RNAS officers to be distinguished so that their precedence compared to other naval officers would be apparent. Thus, for instance, an Observer Captain who was not ranked as a Captain RN, and who therefore wore Commander's rank lace, had a single gold star above his flying badge to differentiate him from a Wing Observer, who wore the same rank lace but who did not sport a gold star. The comparative status of the three RNAS ranks equating to Lieutenants RN was indicated by the addition of two gold stars for a junior Squadron Observer and one for a Flight Observer while an Observer Lieutenant simply wore an unadorned badge. Similar refinements were applicable to the eagles worn by naval pilots of equivalent seniority and rank.

In June the enhanced status of the naval observer was further endorsed by the introduction of a distinctive badge – a gilt winged 'O'. The navy's badge was to have two wings, in contrast to the RFC's idiosyncratically asymmetric design, and be worn in the same fashion as the RNAS eagle, the wearing of which was thenceforth confined to pilots.[3] It is also significant that the RNAS continued to permit its badges to be worn by any officers who were routinely obliged to undergo the risks attendant upon flying, including those who were still under training. This was in marked contrast to the RFC where an observer might have to risk his neck for six months or more before being permitted to wear a flying 'O'.

The introduction of observer ranks applied equally to new RNAS recruits and to those (mostly RNVR) officers already serving as observers under the original arrangements. It should be appreciated, however, that the application of an (O) annotation had not previously been considered to imply a permanent commitment to being an aviator, whereas the adoption of RNAS rank would. In the event, the majority of pre-existing observers did elect to transfer to the RNAS but a significant number did not. In fact, although they may well still have been associated with aeroplanes, several erstwhile observers had already traded in their (O)s for some other annotation, e.g. (E) for Engineers or (W/T) for wireless specialists.

Of the original naval observers of early 1915, for instance, Lt D'Albiac was attached to the Headquarters staff of No 8(N) Sqn, but he was now working in an administrative capacity and his (O) annotation had already been replaced by an (R) – for Records. Another veteran of 1915, Lt O.G.G. Villiers was with the RNAS Headquarters at Dunkirk but his original Observer specialisation had been superseded by that of Intelligence. Then again, Lt L.H. Strain, who had been serving in and around Mesopotamia and the Eastern Mediterranean since late 1915, kept his (O) annotation but remained with the RNVR. Thus, although all three continued to work *with* the RNAS, none of these men adopted observer ranks. Needless to say, it took several months to resolve the individual circumstances of each of the old hands, but the first two men to be publicly associated with the new titles appear to have been ObsrSLt M.O.F. England and PObsrOr M.W. Moffat, whose new ranks were announced by the Admiralty as early as 17 May.[4]

The first fourteen observer sub-lieutenants to graduate from training under the new system materialised in August. Most if not all of these men (and the output of the next few courses) had been internally remustered to observer duties, as opposed to having been directly recruited. By January 1918 the Navy List recorded 256 officers bearing observer ranks. The three most senior of these were squadron observers, but more than half of the remainder were very junior probationary observer officers still under training.[5]

1917–18. The RNAS refines its observer training system

It will be recalled that Capt Swann[6] had first complained about the inadequacy, indeed the lack, of naval observers in 1915. Almost two years later, despite a gradual increase in output from Eastchurch, the numbers being trained had been largely offset by the growth of the Service. Furthermore, many of the additional observers who were becoming available were proving to be of indifferent quality. On balance, therefore, very little seemed to have changed. Swann was moved to write to London again in August 1917.[7] His comments were directed primarily at the shortcomings of replacement pilots, but his letter made it quite clear that he was equally dissatisfied with the abilities of observers. Swann considered that all aircrew arriving fresh from training were far too inexperienced to be committed to operations without extensive additional instruction and practice. Specifically, new pilots and observers were reported to be unfamiliar with the airborne environment, insufficiently practised in navigation, the taking of bearings, the use of W/T and in handling the few other instruments and tools which were available; furthermore, none of them had any grasp of the implications of working as a crew or of the need for mutual co-operation.

In fact, the failings of the system were already well understood by this time and, in association with the enhanced status of the naval observer, a determined effort had been made to introduce a more structured approach to aircrew training. In particular, the establishment of the Observers School at Eastchurch at the beginning of 1917 had made it possible to dispense with the previous series of makeshift courses. The RN schools in Portsmouth ceased to be involved in observer training from January 1917 onwards and the last course to pass through Roehampton left there in February.

Even the RNAS Depot found itself excluded from the system. The last group of prospective RNVR observers at Crystal Palace was transferred to the Observers School on 14 February and all subsequent intakes reported directly to Eastchurch. For the next twelve months Eastchurch was to have sole responsibility for all aspects of naval observer training, from initial military indoctrination right through to final graduation as professional aviators.

[3]The wearing of the RNAS observers badge was authorised with effect from 1 July 1917 by Admiralty Monthly Order 2322 which was promulgated on 22 June. The regulations specifically included the wearing of the badge by Probationary Observer Officers, i.e. it could be worn by any observer, trained or otherwise. Instead of being confined to the left sleeve and shoulder, as in the past, however, the new badge was to be worn on *both* sleeves, above the rank lace, and, when appropriate, on *both* epaulettes. This 'doubling up' reflected a recent change to the regulations governing the wearing of the RNAS eagle which had been announced by Weekly Order 2106 of 8 June. Although this Order had made no provision for flying badges to be worn on the left breast by naval officers, as observed at Chapter 4, Note 7, it is known that this is how they were generally worn on khaki uniforms. Since this practice seems never to have been sanctified by formal legislation, however, it appears that officialdom must simply have regarded it with a Nelsonian eye.

[4]Previously a probationary flight officer and a petty officer, respectively, England and Moffat had both recently been recategorised as observers after having been suspended from pilot training at Vendôme. In the former case this was actually a reversion to a previous grade. England had been a member of one of the earliest cohorts of RNAS observers to pass through the original school at the Clement Talbot Works in 1915. He had subsequently seen active service at Dunkirk before embarking on his unsuccessful attempt to become a pilot, hence his rank of observer sub-lieutenant, which indicated that he was already qualified.

[5]Prior to the introduction of the rank of Probationary Flight Officer (by Admiralty Weekly Order 2027 of 25 August 1916) directly recruited RNAS aircrew, i.e. pilots, had been commissioned on entry as Flight Sub-Lieutenants. Thereafter, however, although they were specifically authorised to wear the RNAS eagle on their sleeves, they had the effective status of midshipmen while under training, confirmation of their commissions in the rank of Flight Sub-Lieutenant being conditional upon their successful graduation from Cranwell. Up to three month's antedated seniority could be granted on commissioning, depending upon the standards achieved while under instruction.

Until May 1917 naval observers had also been commissioned before commencing their professional training, in their case as RNVR Sub-Lieutenants, but the introduction of a career structure for them as full members of the RNAS brought with it the rank of Probationary Observer Officer. From then on, all directly recruited naval aircrew, pilots and observers, were trained as quasi-midshipman.

[6]Oliver Schwann anglicised his name in April 1917.

[7]AIR1/663. Letter 7/B, dated 9 August 1917, from Capt Swann to the Director of Air Services.

A significant advantage gained from concentrating all training at one unit was a considerable saving in time. Compared to the seven or eight months (sometimes as long as a year) required by the original scheme, observers were now being trained in four to five months. Their course embraced seamanship, Fleet tactics and ship recognition, aircraft construction, electricity, signals, photography, bombing, the machine-gun, intelligence, W/T, navigation and meteorology, and plenty of 'naval discipline'.[8] As Oliver Swann's letter suggested, however, the effectiveness of the training being provided may have left much to be desired – but then it always had so, in this respect, the new, streamlined approach was no worse than the old one and, being much shorter, it was at least cheaper.

Apart from producing observers, and continuing to function as a basic flying training school, by mid-1917 Eastchurch had become the recognised instructional centre for naval aircrew of all other trades. Aerial gunlayers, mostly destined for DH 4s or Handley Pages, spent two months there being introduced to air armaments, the syllabus covering the use and maintenance of machine-guns, both Lewis and Vickers, and bombs and bomb-aiming. Following their technical training at Cranwell, W/T operators spent three weeks at Eastchurch to be checked out on the Lewis gun. 'E' Ratings, the qualified engine fitters who doubled as gunners in large flying boats, made do with a fortnight's Lewis gun course. Practical armament training for all students at Eastchurch took place at nearby Leysdown where there were facilities for ground training and a small aerodrome to support air-to-air and air-to-ground live firing and practice bombing.

Having adopted a particularly aggressive stance from the outset, the RN had become directly involved in land-based air operations on the Continent (and elsewhere), had pioneered strategic bombing and had led the way in the development of heavy bombers. By late 1917 the RNAS had a substantial force of bomber squadrons stationed in France and these had become the major employer of naval observers and gunners. Before joining their operational units, these men spent some time at Manston flying O/400s and/or DH 4s with the Handley Page Training Squadron.[9] Most of the remainder found their way into the maritime world of anti-submarine patrols, using both landplanes and seaplanes operating from coastal bases, while a few will have flown in shipborne floatplanes involved in Fleet reconnaissance and gunnery support work.

The navy preferred to use two pilots on its large flying boats, so the number of observers directly involved in maritime operations was relatively small. Perhaps for this very reason, the RNAS never made much effort to provide them with a worthwhile introduction to their very specialised operating environment. Until 1918, therefore, observers earmarked to fly in floatplanes carried aboard naval vessels tended to be far less well prepared for active service than their pilots. For instance, on the grounds that they would become an integral part of their ship's company, as early as 1915 the Admiralty had directed that, whenever possible, shipborne pilots were to be given some time at sea before being assigned to their first vessel. It was equally important that observers should be given the same sort of preliminary experience, of course, but it would be 1917 before anyone saw fit to provide any back-seaters with preparatory sea time.[10]

Similarly, it was not uncommon for shore-based seaplane observers to report directly to their first operational units on graduation from Eastchurch without ever having flown off water. With the steady proliferation of coastal anti-submarine flights, however, it eventually became possible to send some newly qualified observer sub-lieutenants to operational units for a few weeks of preliminary experience before taking up their first appointments. This innovation began to be introduced on a limited scale in August/September 1917, the units involved being the seaplane pilot training schools at Calshot and Lee-on-Solent and the patrol station at Cattewater.

From December onwards the programme was expanded with Yarmouth, Felixstowe and Killingholme taking over the bulk of the task. By early 1918 this procedure had come to be regarded as an integral part of the basic curriculum, rather than a post-graduate phase, and most of those who participated did so in the rank of probationary observer officer. An examination of the later careers of these officers indicates, a little surprisingly, that being sent to a seaplane station for the final phase of his course did not necessarily mean that an individual was destined for maritime operations. Many were, but a significant proportion were subsequently diverted to fly DH 4s or Handley Pages with the bomber squadrons in France.

Meanwhile there had been a significant change in the training sequence followed by naval pilots. Until the summer of 1917 they had been inducted into the Service via the RNAS Depot at Crystal Palace where the so-called 'Disciplinary Course' prepared them for commissioned service. Apart from the inevitable drill and PT, this course dealt almost exclusively with 'OQ's'[11] and was broadly comparable to that provided by the RFC's Cadet Brigade. On passing-out the students proceeded directly to preliminary flying training which embraced all aviation-related topics, both academic and practical. In August 1917 responsibility for initial officer training was transferred to the Royal Naval College at Greenwich (the first draft arriving there on the 27th), leaving Crystal Palace to concentrate on ratings.[12]

[8]Details of the training syllabus to be completed by a W/T Observer were published in Admiralty Weekly Order 2416 of 29 June 1917. The 'W/T' annotation was regarded as being particularly significant (not least because it attracted an additional allowance of three shillings per day) and arrangements were made to ensure that all pre-existing observers were adequately qualified.

[9]With the transfer of the Handley Page, Training Squadron to Stonehenge on 19 January 1918, an independent DH 4 School, commanded by Sqn Cdr E.T. Newton Clare, was set up at Manston on 11 February.

[10]The first observers to be given some preliminary sea time appear to have been Sub-Lts G.H. Elliott, A.A.N. Haywood and R.StH. Clarke who were attached to the battleship HMS *Orion* on 3 March 1917. The next was Sub-Lt F.L. Morrison who joined HMS *Renown* in June. Such instances continued to be rare, however, and most observers reported to *Manxman, Vindex, Riviera, Pegasus, Ark Royal* and the other seaplane carriers without the benefit of having had any previous time afloat.

[11]OQs – Officer Qualities, a catch-all title, covering responsibilities towards subordinates, leadership, discipline, protocol, military law and naval lore, general deportment and social conduct, and so on.

[12]RNAS ratings had originally been inducted into the Service via the Sheerness Training Establishment, which is believed to have been set up for this purpose in the autumn of 1914. Established to provide similar facilities for prospective officers, the RNAS Depot opened for business at Crystal Palace on 1 May 1916. Shortly afterwards the training of non-commissioned personnel was transferred to the Depot, the only RNAS unit at Sheerness by the end of the year being a kite balloon facility. Although officer training subsequently moved to Greenwich, Crystal Palace continued to function as the 'boot camp' for non-commissioned RNAS recruits until the system began to change following the creation of the RAF. Apart from disciplinary training, it is believed that the RNAS Depot also provided mechanic ratings with some technical instruction on airframes and aero-engines.

To conform with naval book-keeping procedures, incidentally, personnel assigned to Greenwich and Crystal Palace were carried on the notional strength of HMS *President II*. This was standard practice for most naval personnel serving ashore in the Greater London area, including those who had previously passed through the original observer and W/T operator schools at the Clement Talbot Works.

In November the Greenwich curriculum was considerably expanded to include a substantial aviation content. In addition to generous helpings of drill, it now covered the theory of flight, W/T, aircraft construction, aero-engines, armament, meteorology and navigation.[13] The induction course for naval pilots now bore a close resemblance to that provided by the RFC's Cadet Wing-SoMA sequence, although further academic training continued to be provided at the elementary flying schools run by the RNAS at Vendôme, Redcar, Eastbourne and Eastchurch.

Although the navy had formally recognised its observers in May, for a time the bulk of its intake continued to consist of RNAS personnel who had been unsuccessful in pilot training and serving officers who were transferring from other branches of the Service. Since these men would have already completed their initial training, Eastchurch was still able to cope with the relatively small numbers of *ab initio* students involved. As a result, no observers were sent to Greenwich during 1917, despite the advantage which they might have gained from being exposed to the recently enhanced aviation content of its syllabus. By the end of the year, however, direct recruiting of observers into the RNAS had begun in earnest and these freshmen did need to pass through Greenwich, the first intake arriving there on 17 February 1918.[14]

1917–18. Persistent problems with both quality and quantity in the RNAS

Despite a gradual increase in numbers, the RN was still very short of qualified observers throughout 1917 and, to make matters worse, the quality of the intake into training was considered to be generally unsatisfactory. By November the Commandant at Eastchurch, Capt J.M. Steel, had become so concerned about this situation that he wrote to the Director of Air Services to let him know of his misgivings.[15] Despairing that 'the number of Observers will ever meet the requirement,' he pointed out that the practice of selecting all the most promising candidates for training as pilots meant that those who did become observers inevitably tended to be 'second best'. That Steel had a very poor opinion of these leftovers is clear from his comment that 'to be a passenger in the air requires a standard of courage which the majority do not possess' (this observation invoking echoes of the Bailhache Committee's comments on the stress of flying as a back-seater). Furthermore, many of the trainee observers who were not unhappy about flying wanted to be pilots and the apparent ease with which they could remuster siphoned off the best of what was available. Steel advocated a more robust, RFC-style approach – once selected as an observer, to satisfy the needs of the Service rather than the aspirations of the individual, there should be no prospect of retraining as a pilot until a substantial period of active service had been completed.

To overcome the shortage of suitable officers Steel proposed that consideration should be given to substituting gunlayer and/or wireless ratings where possible and examining the feasibility of training ratings for employment as observers with warrant officer rank. The RFC had long since taken similar steps, of course, but it was unlikely that such measures could solve the RNAS' problem, because Eastchurch was experiencing considerable difficulty in obtaining suitable men to be trained as gunlayers. As Steel wrote of recent intakes,

> 'a large number are perfectly useless and in many cases do not want to go in the air again after their first flight. The material for this important work is slowly getting worse and I have already pointed out that unless steps are taken to get young, healthy and active ratings from the Navy or some other source the situation will become very serious.'

So far as the allocation of manpower resources was concerned, however, national policy dictated that the majority of young men fit enough to serve in the trenches should be directed towards the army, which, to some extent, enabled the RFC to take its pick. The RNAS was obliged to make do with what was left, but only after the RN had made its selection. So much for quality.

So far as quantity was concerned, some idea of the scale of the naval training programme can be gauged from the fact that there were 127 trainee observers at Eastchurch on 17 December 1917. Of these, three were observer lieutenants and five were observer sub-lieutenants, the remainder being probationary observer officers. These numbers represented some improvement on the situation of a year before, but they were still not nearly enough. The RNAS was hopeful that its shortage of competent observers would be overcome by the formation of the RAF, since this was expected to provide access to a much larger pool of manpower. This proved not to be the case, however, and the fact that the problem persisted provoked strong suspicions that the new Service regarded maritime affairs as a secondary consideration.

This impression arose in part from the RAF's failing to satisfy a naval request of April 1918 for no fewer than 200 qualified observers to be made immediately available for hydrophone training at Portland. This initial batch was required to be supplemented at a rate of fifty per month thereafter. There were other problems (to do with the training and availability of maritime pilots and the provision of aeroplanes, particularly torpedo carriers) and in August the Admiralty lodged a formal complaint with the Air Ministry over the RAF's apparent neglect of naval interests.[16] In the meantime the RN had been reassessing its air needs and by July it had calculated that the RAF would need to earmark no fewer than 1600 of its observers in order to meet its maritime obligations.

It is not known how the Admiralty actually arrived at this remarkable figure but two possible explanations are offered. First, there were the demands created by the formation of the

[13]RNAS aviators had always been required to know rather more about navigation and the weather than their RFC counterparts. From September 1916 (as laid down in Admiralty Weekly Order No 2337), and probably even earlier, navigational topics specifically addressed during *basic* training included: great and small circles, the rhumb line and the Mercators chart, the triangle of velocities, radius of action, interception of a moving target, e.g. a ship, the uses of the compass, its errors and the means of correcting them, variation and deviation, and so on. The RNAS meteorology syllabus considered: the composition of the atmosphere; radiation, conduction and convection; the vertical temperature gradient; the circulation of the atmosphere and the effect of the Earth's rotation on the wind; the variation of wind with height; the measurement of barometric pressure and its implications in weather forecasting; precipitation – dew, fog and clouds; the synoptic chart and its interpretation; etc. Although the RFC paid some attention to these matters they were not really studied in much depth by army flyers until late 1917 when, during the run-up to the creation of the RAF, naval practice began to have a significant influence on military thinking.

[14]Following the formation of the RAF, the indoctrination of prospective naval aviators became the responsibility of the Cadet Brigade at Hastings. Greenwich received its last RNAS intake in March 1918 and by August the aviation training facility had closed down.

[15]AIR1/663/17/122/692. Unreferenced letter from Commandant, Eastchurch to the Director of Air Services, Cdre G.M. Paine, dated 30 November 1917.

[16]AIR1/643/17/122/257. Admiralty letter M.022313 dated 8 August 1918.

numerous land-based 'special duties', i.e. anti-submarine patrol, flights which were being set up during 1918 to supplement the ex-RNAS floatplane units already engaged on similar tasks, this force also being substantially expanded. To begin with most of the shore-based units were equipped with redundant DH 6 trainers, but it was intended to replace these in the medium term with DH 9s, possibly supplemented by some DH 4s and FE2s.[17] Long-term planning envisaged the eventual use of DH 10s and Vimys. All of these aeroplanes were bigger, more powerful and more capable than the interim DH 6s and would eventually have required properly constituted and qualified two- or three-man crews.[18]

The second area of expansion was in seagoing air power. During 1918 most of the Grand Fleet's capital ships were modified to permit them to launch aeroplanes from turret-mounted platforms. Most of the aircraft involved were fighters but some were two-seaters, initially 1½ Strutters, and these would all have required observers. Furthermore, it was anticipated that two-seaters would be operated from aircraft carriers. The Parnall Panther had been specifically ordered for this purpose but, had the war continued into 1919, it is reasonable to suppose that established types such as the Bristol Fighter and DH 9A would also have been adapted for use at sea.[19]

While some of the above is conjecture, it is clear that maritime aviation was becoming a growth industry in 1918 and that it would require substantial numbers of back-seaters. Regardless of how the Admiralty had actually done its sums, however, its projected requirement was for 1600 observers and it looked to the Air Ministry to provide them – and promptly.

Since the Admiralty had spectacularly failed to produce adequate numbers of observers while it had had responsibility for the RNAS, this was all a bit rich. In April 1918 the RNAS had been able to deposit only 181 qualified observers in the RAF's newly opened joint manpower account, a mere 10% of the total. All of them were already committed, of course, and therefore non-negotiable. For the Admiralty to expect to be able to make an immediate withdrawal of an additional 200 men was stretching its credit to the utmost. Furthermore, since they clearly expected instant satisfaction, the admirals' demands revealed how little they understood of the complexity of aircrew training or of how long it took.

The Air Ministry's response to the Admiralty's complaint acknowledged that there had been unavoidable delays, but it reassured the navy that its requirements had all been receiving appropriate attention.[20] In the specific case of the 200 observers required for hydrophone training, for instance, although the Admiralty had lodged its initial request in April, as claimed, it transpired that it had not actually provided specific details until as late as the middle of June. Not surprisingly, the RAF simply did not have 200 spare trained observers immediately to hand. Nevertheless, it had taken immediate steps to increase the numbers being sent to Eastchurch (by now an RAF station but specialising in the training of maritime observers) and had established a dedicated hydrophone training facility by opening a new air school for this purpose at Aldeburgh. Twenty-two observers were actually made available for maritime duties during August; a further seventy-two were expected to graduate in September and thereafter it was anticipated that the requirement for fifty per month would be met. (Some notes on the development of hydrophones are at Annex E.)

Despite further increases in recruiting, however, the RAF was already overstretched, since it was now obliged to fill the cockpits of all of the multi-seat naval aeroplanes which it had inherited. This problem was exacerbated by the imposition of an RFC-style manning policy in place of that of the RNAS. As previously noted, for instance, it had been a widespread naval practice to use two pilots, rather then a pilot and observer, in heavy aircraft like Handley Pages. The RAF generally preferred to use only one pilot per aeroplane which inevitably created an increased demand for observers.

It was also necessary to readjust the significant imbalance between observers and gunners on ex-RNAS two-seat bomber squadrons to conform to RAF establishments. While rationalising the manning of the naval two-seater squadrons based in France was a relatively straightforward exercise, incidentally, it turned out to be a fairly protracted business among the ex-RNAS formations based in southern Italy (No 6 Wg) and around the Aegean (No 2 Wg).[21]

All of this aside, the RAF was still well short of providing the manpower required for the 200 squadrons which had been authorised (for the RFC) a year before, so the Admiralty's demand for 1600 fully-trained maritime observers was obviously going to take a long time to satisfy (but see page 96).

[17]When these nominally operational units were first being established, apart from being equipped with obsolete training aircraft, some of the pilots assigned to fly them were only part-qualified. This is borne out by AMWO 585 of 3 July 1918, which required COs of Special Duties Flights to recommend, three weeks after the arrival of each new pilot, whether he should be authorised to wear his 'wings'. This provision was subsequently endorsed by AMWO 794 of 8 August which effectively made provision for any pilot flying on active service to wear a flying badge and draw full flying pay, similar arrangements being made for observers at the same time (see Chapter 13, Note 12).

On gaining his CO's approval, a pilot who had graduated 'B' (see page 41 for an explanation of the graduation categories), and was thus already a 2nd lieutenant, was to be authorised to draw full flying pay. What was surprising, however, is that pilots who had graduated only 'A', and who were thus still mere flight cadets, were also addressed by the regulations. If sanctioned by their CO, they too were to be promptly gazetted as 2nd lieutenants and authorised to draw full flying pay.

[18]Establishments AF/H/76, for a six-aircraft flight of float seaplanes, and AF/H/123, for a six-aircraft flight of anti-submarine light bombers, provided for six Observer Officers in each case. AF/H/77 had, incidentally, initially established five observers for a three-aircraft flying boat flight but these had been deleted before the end of May 1918. Thereafter, presumably to accommodate the previous habits of ex-RNAS folk, flying boats were crewed by two pilots and such gunner/mechanics and/or W/T operators as were considered necessary.

Excluding flying boat units, by November 1918 about one hundred semi-autonomous flights had been formed for maritime duties, some of them overseas and most of them by that time grouped into squadrons. At six per flight, this force alone could account for some 600 of the Admiralty's total demand for 1600 observers.

[19]At the time of the Armistice, No 133 Sqn was expected to join the Grand Fleet in about February 1919; it was to have been equipped with DH 9As.

[20]AIR1/643/17/122/258. Air Ministry letter B3158/D/CAS dated 16 September 1918.

[21]It is not known why it took so long to bring these comparatively isolated and rather loosely structured units into line. It may have been a direct result of their remoteness, or of the instability arising from their sometimes frequent changes of base and/or of their being afforded a low priority. Furthermore, unlike the RNAS units in France, all of which had worked alongside (many of them under the direct control of) RFC formations, those operating in the 'side-show' theatres had had little experience of army-style organisation. This unfamiliarity may well have caused some of the more insular naval personnel involved to be less than enthusiastic about toeing the RAF line and, if so, this could also have contributed to the delay. All of this is conjectural but, whatever the reason, it is known that, despite their having been assigned RAF squadron numbers within the 200-series reserved for ex-RNAS units as early as 9 March 1918 (by AO 800 – AIR1/913/204/5/856), it was as late as September before these identities gained much currency around the Mediterranean, especially among the Aegean-based units.

Chapter 12

1917–18. Smith-Barry's instructional methods begin to influence attitudes towards all aircrew training

While the RNAS had been refining its overall flying training sequence, the RFC had been introducing a far more methodical approach to the specific business of teaching pilots to fly. Concerned at the lack of ability displayed by many of the replacement pilots he was being sent while commanding No 60 Sqn in the autumn of 1916, Maj R. Smith-Barry had analysed their failings. He used his conclusions to develop a training philosophy predicated on the use of an aeroplane with appropriate handling qualities and fitted with dual control, the Avro 504, and a comprehensive syllabus to be taught by experienced pilots who had themselves first been taught how to teach. While the need for such an approach may seem self-evident today, it was a revolutionary development at the time.

The so-called 'Gosport system', was initially applied on a limited scale, producing an immediate and remarkable improvement in both the competence and the confidence of newly qualified pilots. The success of Smith-Barry's methods led to a major restructuring of the RFC's pilot training organisation, a project which had been under active consideration since February 1917. In July these deliberations were concluded by the granting of approval for the establishment of seven new flying training schools on a trial basis. These Training Depot Stations (TDS) proved to be a great success and between March and August 1918 the remainder of the pilot training system was converted wholesale.

The necessary resources for forming new TDSs were obtained by disbanding the existing Training Squadrons and abandoning the long-established expedient of employing Service Squadrons as makeshift training units prior to their mobilisation, many of the latter also being disbanded.[1] Thereafter most TDSs provided all-through flying training, the initial phase on Avro 504s and the advanced phase on a current operational type, thus combining the functions of latter day basic and advanced flying training schools with the addition of some aspects of an operational conversion course.[2]

The introduction of TDSs was accompanied by corresponding improvements in the instruction of rear crews. Four factors drove the changes to this element of the system. First, as a spin-off from Smith-Barry's philosophy, there was an increased awareness of the need to improve the quality of the instruction being provided for *all* aircrew, which led to a reappraisal of some elements of the observer training sequence. Secondly, there was the need to cater for the range of skills required which broadened at an accelerating rate during 1918, leading to the establishment of a series of new schools to deal with new specialisations and tactics. Thirdly, as the nature of the air war changed, due to the introduction of more advanced aeroplanes and more sophisticated equipment, it was necessary constantly to revise the length and content of courses in response to feedback from the front line squadrons. Finally, the merging of the RFC and RNAS meant that the use of the separate, and in some instances duplicated, schools inherited by the new Service on 1 April had to be rationalised to produce an integrated RAF system.

It was envisaged that once the reorganisation of the training system was complete new operational squadrons would be formed two months before they were scheduled to be deployed overseas. The pilots for a headquarters element and three flights were to be contributed by four different TDSs and transferred to a designated Mobilisation Station. There they would be joined by any necessary rear crew members and a draft of ground tradesmen, issued with their operational equipment and commence their work-up programme.

The changes outlined above were very extensive and they could not be implemented overnight. Moreover, the process was prolonged by the fact that a change to the syllabus of one school often had a knock-on effect on that of another. Some idea of the instability within the system may be gauged from the rather bewildering series of redesignations to which some units were subjected, not to mention the cumbersome titles which they acquired.[3] The reorganisation of the training system may be considered to have begun as early as the

[1]AIR1/31/15/1/156. Because of the considerable disturbance and a number of misunderstandings caused by the adoption of the new approach to pilot training, the Master General of Personnel, Maj-Gen G.M. Paine, summarised the arrangements and the impact that these would have on existing and future units and circulated this information in Air Ministry letter C.4519 dated 4 July 1918.

[2]Despite the universal acceptance of Smith-Barry's approach, the restructuring of the training system and the widespread availability of the Avro 504, problems persisted within the pilot training system, not least the provision of adequate numbers of instructors. Louis Strange (*op. cit.*) recalls that when he assumed command of 23rd (Training) Wing in March 1918 he found, among other difficulties, that he had only twenty instructors to handle 185 students. His solution was to 'turn the next ten most promising pupils into instructors.' In other words, to reinstate the discredited practice of 1915–16 (see Chapter 7, Note 9). Since the pupils of 1918 were being properly taught, however, 'creaming off' some of the more capable graduates was now a far more practical proposition. It certainly seemed to work, as Strange claims to have succeeded in significantly increasing the output of pilots while simultaneously reducing both the workload on the staff and the accident rate. It is sobering to note, however, that he also admits that, notwithstanding his improvements, aeroplanes were still being written off at a rate of one every 140 flying hours. In a unit the size of 23rd Wg (which at the time comprised No 81 Sqn and Nos 11, 39, 45, 60 and 61 Training Squadrons located variously at South Carlton and Scampton) equated to 'between thirty and forty machines a month, in addition to some seventy or eighty minor crashes.'

Unfortunately, while the confidence with which these fairly precise statistics are presented tends to persuade us that they must be accurate, they should be treated with some caution, as Strange may have been prone to exaggeration. For instance, he also claims, with equally convincing precision, that his wing suffered sixteen fatalities in May 1918 alone. According to Chris Hobson's authoritative *Airmen Died in the Great War 1914–1918* (1995), the actual figure was eight.

[3]Reference has already been made to the frequent reorganisation and redesignation to which all the RFC's training units were subjected but it may be of

summer of 1917 but, despite gathering pace markedly following the establishment of the RAF, it was still not really complete when the Armistice brought the process to an abrupt stop. Nevertheless, by that time the system had more or less achieved its overall objective in that the deployment of the first of a new generation of freshly formed operational squadrons manned by comprehensively trained personnel was about to begin.[4] At least, the crews *should* have been comprehensively trained, but some doubt must remain as to the extent to which this aim was actually being achieved (see page 97).

1916–18. The contribution of the RFC's overseas training organisations

The changes which affected the training system were not confined to UK-based units. As early as April 1916 it had been decided to set up a training organisation in Egypt, primarily to produce additional pilots for the war in Europe, and this began to function in July. The schools in Egypt were originally provided with drafts of trainees from home but the expansion of the UK-based system during 1917 rendered it less necessary to sustain the time-consuming practice of shipping people to and from the Middle East. Thereafter the training units in Egypt began to draw the bulk of their intake from local internal recruiting and from South Africa, much of their output being absorbed by the growing number of in-theatre squadrons. Policy changed again in 1918, however, and before the war ended the training facilities in Egypt, which had been considerably expanded, and reorganised to resemble the late-war UK system, was once again being provided with large batches of cadets from home.

The first training unit in Egypt to have any potential relevance to observers was No 3 SoMA which opened at Aboukir in November 1916, this being supplemented in December by the nucleus of a School of Aerial Gunnery. By the time that the latter was formally established in the following April it was already turning out some fifteen officers per week. Most of these were pilots and EOs specialising in armaments, however, and very little real effort was devoted to the formal instruction of observers until 1918.

Operational units arriving from the UK, e.g. Nos 14, 17 and 47 Sqns, had generally brought a full complement of observers with them, these reflecting a variety of levels of skill and experience. Most of the observers who succeeded those in the original drafts, and those required for locally raised units, were trained in-house at squadron level, using similar methods to those employed in France in 1915–16. Very few trained replacements were sent out from home, indeed, from late 1917 onwards, the net flow was in the opposite direction, with observers trained in the Middle East being posted home for assignment to squadrons in France.

Serious consideration was not given to the needs of back-seaters in the Middle East until as late as November 1917 when an Artillery Observation School was set up at Almaza. This unit inducted its first course of pilots in January 1918 and its first batch of observers in February. By the time of the Armistice it had turned out 200 observers and 321 pilots, plus 115 W/T Operators and six EOs qualified as Wireless Officers.

Paralleling developments at home (see below) an Armament School had been established at Abassia and in May 1918 a flight of four DH 6s of the Artillery Observation School was hived off to form the nucleus of No 3 School of Navigation and Bomb Dropping (SNBD). It was not until August that this school came into its own, however, moving to Helwan on the 19th where it was expanded to have a fleet of twenty-three aircraft, BE2es, BE12s, AW FK3s (and/or FK8s?) and the DH 6s. With Maj G. Merton in command, training began in September and by the end of the following month No 3 SNBD had graduated a total of twenty-four students and had a further forty-six pilots and thirteen observers in residence. In September, again mirroring the UK-based training organisation, the School of Aerial Gunnery was merged with the Aerial Fighting School at Heliopolis to form No 5 Fighting School. Some idea of the size of this unit's throughput can be gauged from its turnover during October in which month alone it took in 155 students and graduated forty-nine pilots and forty-eight observers.

Despite the considerable expansion and increasing sophistication of the training system in Egypt, the regional requirement for observers remained relatively small and, so far as two-seater units were concerned, the RFC's overseas Order of Battle had more or less stabilised by early 1918. Furthermore, since there were few combat losses the rate of turnover was also low, compared to that in France. Once a unit was up to strength therefore, it needed relatively few replacements. Some idea of the numbers of back-seaters required in the 'side-show' theatres can be gained from the routine strength return for the week ending 14 March 1918.[5]

some interest to summarise here the progressive changes in nomenclature associated with the two longest-established observer training schools.

On 1 October 1917 the Wireless and Observers School moved from Brooklands to Hursley Park, Winchester, the dual functions of the school being separated shortly after its arrival. The training of wireless personnel was concentrated at the existing School for Wireless Operators at Farnborough, which reverted to its original designation of the Wireless School, RFC on 10 October. This title was to survive only for a month, however, as the division of responsibility was taken a stage further on 8 November when the unit at Farnborough became No 1 (Training) Wireless School, thenceforth dealing only with non-commissioned wireless mechanics and operators, No 2 Wireless School being set up at Penshurst at the same time to cater for W/T Officers, i.e. Equipment Officers specialising in wireless work. Now dealing solely with aircrew, the unit at Winchester needed to be renamed in any case, as its old title had failed to reflect the fact that it had been training large numbers of pilots for several months. On 12 October 1917 it became the Artillery and Infantry Co-operation School. Having moved to Worthy Down on 31 May 1918, it was renamed yet again on 19 September to become the RAF and Army Co-operation School.

Having taken up residence at Hythe on 27 November 1915, the RFC Machine-Gun School became the School of Aerial Gunnery with effect from 13 September 1916. In January 1917 the unit was redesignated as No 1 (Auxiliary) School of Aerial Gunnery. On 9 March 1918 it merged with No 3 (Auxiliary) School of Aerial Gunnery (which had formed at New Romney on 1 August 1917) to form No 1 (Observers) School of Aerial Gunnery, both aerodromes remaining in use.

[4]Largely as a result of the major upheaval within the training system, there had been an hiatus in the deployment of new two-seater squadrons. The last of the units formed under the old scheme to become operational had been No 110 Sqn which had crossed the Channel as long ago as the end of August 1918. None of the new-style squadrons were to see active service before the Armistice was signed but at that time the first of them, No 155 Sqn, was expected to take its DH 9As to France on 21 November with the similarly equipped No 156 Sqn following three weeks later.

[5]A consolidated strength return, reflecting the numbers and availability of pilots in all overseas theatres (other than France) had been routinely compiled on a weekly basis since mid-1916. Balloon Observers were included from October but it was not until 1918 that anyone bothered to count the aeroplane observers on strength on a regular basis (although their numbers could be divined from individual squadron returns). The requirement for the numbers of effective and non-effective observers to be reported to London was contained in War Office telegram 49666 of 1 January 1918 (AIR1/398/15/231/39). The first return in which they actually featured was that rendered for the week ending 10 January by which time there were a

Theatre	Balloon Officers	Observers	
		Unit	Number
Egypt and Palestine	39	No 14 Sqn	19
		No 111 Sqn	3
		No 113 Sqn	19
		No 142 Sqn	1
		No 1 Sqn AFC	10
Salonika	17	No 17 Sqn	12
		No 47 Sqn	14
Mesopotamia	11	No 30 Sqn	13
		No 63 Sqn	12
India & Aden	4 (Aden)	Nos 31 & 114 Sqns	14
Totals	**71**	–	**117**

Fig. 8. Distribution of Balloon Officers and Observers in overseas theatres (excluding France and Italy) as at 14 March 1918.

This reported on the availability of a total of 119 observers and seventy-one Balloon Officers.[6] Two of the former were with the Artillery Observation School; the distribution of the remainder is shown at Fig. 8. No 26 Sqn had been withdrawn at the beginning of February but it is worth noting that, until then, there had been several additional observers serving in East Africa. To give some scale to these figures, the 14 March return had also reported that there were 447 qualified pilots serving in these theatres with another 1031 in transit to Egypt, already undergoing training there or awaiting disposal after having gained their 'wings'.

Anticipating in many respects the Empire Air Training Scheme of WW II, another extensive network of schools had been set up in Canada early in 1917.[7] The system in Canada differed from the one in Egypt in that it was not provided with trainees from the UK, all students being locally recruited in North America. The training organisation in Canada was chiefly intended to produce pilots but it did eventually turn its hand to observers and 137 had graduated before training ceased.[8] By that time the units dealing with back-seaters were a Cadet Wing at Long Branch, No 4 School of Aeronautics (SoA) in Toronto, an Armament School at Hamilton, the School of Aerial Gunnery at Camp Borden and the Schools of Aerial Fighting and of Artillery Co-operation at Beamsville.[9]

1918. The impact of the capabilities of second-generation aeroplanes on the functions of the corps observer

While the home-based training machine had been undergoing a major overhaul and expansion there had been significant feedback from the two-seater squadrons operating in France. By the spring of 1918 the RFC had accumulated a year's operating experience with its RE8s and FK8s and Ludlow-Hewitt's earlier contention, that pilots were best suited to handle fire control, had gained widespread acceptance throughout the corps reconnaissance community. Although many units had already put this philosophy into practice, however, it had not yet been endorsed by officialdom as being *the* preferred operating procedure. Nevertheless, all pilots destined for corps squadrons had been passing through the Artillery and Infantry Co-operation School at Winchester since the autumn of 1917 and, since they attended the full course alongside observers, it was clear that there was considerable duplication of effort.

Furthermore, it had been decided as early as the previous July that the Bristol Fighter would be introduced for corps work from April 1918. The anticipated imminent arrival of these much more capable aeroplanes prompted the operators to review the way in which they conducted their business. There was a growing consensus (at middle management level at least) that if the responsibilities of crew members were not clearly redefined and assigned, much of the Bristol's considerable potential would be wasted on artillery work.

Lt-Col I.A.E. Edwards, OC 15th Wg, submitted his thoughts on the matter to HQ V Bde in March 1918.[10] He went so far as to claim that recent experience had shown that it was actually 'a danger for the observer to carry out a shoot,' maintaining that it was essential for him to concentrate on rear defence. It followed that observers therefore needed to be expert gunners and, while acknowledging that they 'had shot down a few (Huns)', Edwards considered that many opportunities for combat victories were being missed. Although he did not actually make the (surely even more important) point, an extension of his argument would suggest that many aeroplanes were also being unnecessarily lost. In short, Edwards, like Ludlow-Hewitt, believed that pilots were actually better than observers at gunnery direction, but he accepted that they could do it properly only if they were totally confident that their rear defence was in safe hands.

The nub of the problem was that corps observers were currently being trained to carry out those aspects of the job which pilots now wanted to do, indeed were doing, at the expense of developing their gunnery skills which were sadly lacking – or so the pilot fraternity maintained. The latest thinking was that the occupants of rear cockpits needed to be trained to look up, rather than down, and to be able to shoot straight when

total of 107 of them. The data in Fig. 8 was taken from the return for the week ending 14 March which was dated the 15th and bore the reference E.4506 (AIR1/2364/226/7/3C).

[6]On 31 October 1918, when the signing of an Armistice ended the fighting in the Near East, the RAF's strength in qualified observers, including those who had been inherited with the ex-RNAS squadrons in the Aegean, amounted to 129 (of whom twelve were NCOs), plus seventy-six Kite Balloon Officers. On that date there were a further ninety cadet/officer and five NCO observers under training in Egypt.

[7]While they were superficially similar, the flying training organisations established in Canada during the two world wars were fundamentally different. The WW I scheme was an entirely British undertaking, albeit lodged in Canada and provided with extensive facilities by the local administration. The constitution of the system set up during WW II became almost a mirror image of the original arrangement. Although it was given extensive material support by the British, especially in its early days, the Empire Air Training Scheme, of WW II was a Canadian responsibility from the outset.

[8]It is appropriate to note here that, because Canada had not established an air force of her own, all Canadian (and British-trained American) aircrew flew with the RFC/RAF, back-seaters wearing the standard single-winged flying 'O'. By contrast, Australia had set up the Australian Flying Corps (AFC) and Military Order 801/1915 announced that any back-seaters qualifying (in Australia) after January 1916 would wear a badge with *twin*-wings flanking the letter 'O', the latter being embroidered in pale blue within a white laurel wreath. This does not appear to have been a very common emblem, however, most Australian observers wearing the British pattern badge, presumably because they had been trained in the UK, or because they were flying with RFC/RAF units.

[9]Published references to some of the training units in Canada are conflicting. One has the School of Aerial Gunnery still functioning at Camp Borden at the end of the war, while another maintains that it had been absorbed into the School of Aerial Fighting at Beamsville. There is also some doubt as to the location of the Artillery Co-operation School, although Beamsville seems logical.

[10]AIR1/1135/204/5/2224. HQ 15th Wg letter GS.39 dated 15 March 1918.

necessary. On the other hand, while they still needed to have some understanding of the business of fire control and be able to handle a camera, they no longer required an exhaustive knowledge of artillery procedures nor did they need to be quite so handy with 'the buzzer'. Edwards' letter had included specific suggestions as to how he thought the training of corps observers should be tailored in the future.

Having gained the immediate approval of V Bde, Edwards' ideas were promptly forwarded to HQ RFC and thence to the Air Ministry with the endorsement of the GOC, by now Maj-Gen J.M. Salmond. A revised training sequence was introduced in April. Thenceforth, following their indoctrination course at a School of Aeronautics, corps observers were to undergo a fortnight of academic gunnery instruction at the Armament School at Uxbridge,[11] followed by three weeks of practical air-to-air and air-to-ground gunnery at Hythe and/or New Romney before spending just two weeks at Winchester. The planned intake into this system was to be at an initial rate of twenty-five per week.

In the event, problems with the supply of engines seriously disrupted production of the Bristol Fighter. Apart from a handful operated by autonomous Long Range Artillery Flights, one of which was allocated to each brigade towards the end of the war, only a few Bristols were made available for corps reconnaissance work, leaving the 'Harry Tates' and 'Big Acks' to fly doggedly on until the Armistice.[12] In the increasingly hostile air combat environment of 1918, however, the corps observer's enhanced ability to fight off attackers became an invaluable asset. It is true that a handful of artillery pilots did manage to score some victories, but they were exceptions to the rule. The more usual situation was neatly summarised by No 6 Sqn's Sgt Eddington (see Chapter 6, Note 17):

> 'The pilot (*of an RE8*) had a Vickers gun which synchronised through the propeller. But nine times out of ten it didn't – it hit the propeller. They were wooden propellers and the result was tremendous vibration because of the imbalance. You never used your gun – you relied on the observer who had a Lewis.'

1918. The increasing importance of the rear gun

The need for back-seaters to be expert gunners was equally important within the growing force of day bomber squadrons where many rear cockpits were occupied by non-commissioned personnel, in contrast to corps squadrons where, at the turn of 1918, there were not *supposed* to be any at all (although they were being tolerated again by the spring). Apart from tactical work in direct support of a ground offensive, daylight raids by DH 4s and DH 9s were usually carried out in formation. This tactic served to focus the effects of the attack but it also denied any freedom of manoeuvre and thus rendered the fixed forward-firing Vickers guns of the pilots virtually useless. On the other hand, flying in formation concentrated the defensive crossfire which could be delivered from the rear cockpits, the survival of bombers being, therefore, almost entirely in the hands of observers and gunners.

The situation was very different for the crews of fighter reconnaissance squadrons who were obliged to look after themselves once a fight developed.[13] As early as April 1917 the CFS had carried out a series of trials involving a Bristol Scout and a Sopwith 1½ Strutter (sometimes flown solo), each attacking and being attacked in turn. Analysis of the camera-gun film demonstrated quite conclusively that in all cases it was a mistake for the pilot of the two-seater to concentrate on trying to bring his own gun to bear, since 'infinitely superior results' were obtained if he manoeuvred to give his observer the best possible firing opportunity.[14]

Similar work had been going on at the RFC's Experimental Station at Orfordness, using, in addition to the Bristol Scout and the Sopwith, examples of the more capable RE8, Bristol Fighter, DH 4 and AW FK8, engaging with a Sopwith Triplane and a BE12. While not stated in quite such extreme terms, the report on the Orfordness project had also acknowledged the need for a two-seater pilot to fly with a view to providing his observer with a clear shot.[15] The trial had also convincingly demonstrated (if this were still necessary) that, regardless of the type of aircraft and/or its role, mutual co-operation between the crew members was the key to success in any two-seater. In view of this, it is a little surprising to find that, according to 2/Lt V. Voss, replacement Bristol Fighter pilots were still being sent to France as late as February 1918 without ever having flown with a passenger, let alone an observer.[16]

To operate the Bristol Fighter successfully in air combat obviously demanded a team effort between co-equal partners, regardless of their individual ranks and status. Some idea of the scale of the contribution made by back-seaters can be gained from the record of No 20 Sqn. The official early post-war accounting credited this squadron with a total of 613 successful claims, although much later research raised this to 619. Leaving aside the nuances of whether the enemy aircraft had been destroyed, captured, driven down out of control or merely damaged, an analysis of the records of these engagements suggested that only 138 of the victories claimed had been attributable to pilots, the remaining 481 (78%) having fallen to the guns of observers or gunners.[17]

[11]Commanded by Maj A.C. Bishop, the RFC's Armament School had originally been established at Perivale in June 1917 to provide training for technical personnel dealing with bombs, guns and synchronising gears. This unit was notionally disbanded on 18 December, its resources being used to establish a 'new' Armament School at Uxbridge on the same date.

[12]This did not change the intention, however, and at the time of the Armistice current planning envisaged squadrons of RE8s and/or FK8s being re-equipped at a rate of one in November, one in December, five in January and eight in February. The remaining two, which were not to be re-equipped, were to 'die out' during March 1919.

[13]AIR1/1001/204/5/1260. Units flying the Bristol Fighter (and the earlier FE2 and 1½ Strutter) were (and still are) often identified as 'two-seat fighter squadrons'. While this was a reasonably accurate description of their role it was not the officially approved terminology. The term 'Army Fighter Squadron' had been used in the summer of 1916 but AO 241 of 8 November 1916 proposed that the designations of all operational units should be standardised. HQ RFC agreed to the proposed new terminology which was formally introduced by AO 277 dated 21 December 1916. For the remainder of the war units operating two-seat fighters were always referred to as Fighter Reconnaissance Squadrons in official papers.

[14]AIR1/920/204/5/885. The pilots engaged on this work included Capt A.M. Vaucour, Capt N. Kemsley and 2/Lt T.P.H. Bayetto. A summary of the content of the trial, including the conclusions drawn, was submitted to the War Office in Training Brigade letter TB/1067/2 of 26 April 1917. This was subsequently forwarded to HQ RFC who circulated its contents among its subordinate formations under letter CRFC 1708G dated 4 May 1917.

[15]*Ibid.* Report A/39 published by the RFC Experimental Station on 30 April 1917. A number of notable pilots had participated in the Orfordness programme, including Capts R.H.M.S. Saundby, E.L. Foot and H. Meintjis and Lt J.T.B. McCudden.

[16]Vivian Voss, *Flying Minnows* (1935).

[17]The revised figure of 619 victories (and the apportioning of this total between pilots and observers/gunners) appeared in 'Top Scorers – The Record of No 20 Sqn RFC/RAF', an article by N. Franks and F. Bailey which was published in 1973 in *The Cross and Cockade Journal*, Vol 4, No 1.

A DH 4 of No 27 Sqn (top) and an anonymous Bristol Fighter (bottom). Note that in the DH 4 the crew stations are some six feet apart, making communication, let alone co-operation, very difficult. In the Bristol the pilot and observer/gunner sat back-to-back, which made for much greater efficiency as a fighting team. (J.M. Bruce/G.S. Leslie collection)

Folk knowledge tends to associate success in the field of air combat with squadrons which flew single-seat Camels and SE5as. It may come a surprise to some, therefore, to learn that the most successful, i.e. the top-scoring, British fighter unit of the war was the exclusively two-seater equipped No 20 Sqn and that it was not the only two-seater squadron to establish a remarkable combat record. Despite the level of damage which they inflicted on the enemy, however, the activities of the relatively pedestrian two-seaters have never excited the same level of public interest as have the exploits of the Camel drivers and others of their kind. Furthermore, such attention as they have attracted has, by association with their more glamorous colleagues, tended to focus on their pilots. Sadly, those who flew and fought with them are often treated as little more than footnotes. Thus, while the names of a handful of two-seater pilots, like McKeever, Latimer, Thompson and Atkey, still have some limited currency, those of notably successful back-seaters, like Powell, Noel, Fletcher and Gass, are virtually unknown.

While the annals of the RFC have little to say about observer officers the deeds of its non-commissioned gunners were afforded even less attention. Arch Whitehouse summed up the overall situation as follows:[18]

> 'You will not find any non-commissioned man listed among Great Britain's aces of World War I. Furthermore, few commissioned officers were considered important enough to be included in the glorious company of aerial aces. The two-seater fighter squadrons had many such heroes, but they sported the winged-O of the Poor Bloody Observers and were not fit company for the full-winged heroes.'

As a back-seater himself, Whitehouse was clearly biased (and it must also be acknowledged that his writings do tend to contain inaccuracies and exaggerations), but in this instance it is difficult to take issue with him. It was not until as late as March 1918 that the RFC bothered to revise its method of recognising victories to acknowledge formally the part being played by back-seaters. The new rules made it clear that, 'When an enemy machine is brought down by a two-seater both the pilot and the observer are credited with 1 EA.'[19]

1918. Changes in the employment of non-commissioned back-seaters

Oddly enough, in view of the crucial importance of aerial gunnery, the RFC had stopped producing aerial gunners by February 1918, possibly a few weeks earlier.[20] This paradox was more apparent than real, however, as it reflected only a change in nomenclature, not a reduction in output. The category of aerial gunner had been introduced to distinguish these men from observers at a time when all of the latter were additionally qualified in airborne photography and trained to work with the artillery and to use wireless equipment. This was no longer the case, however, because army observers had not been required to pass the Brooklands/Winchester course for several months, their professional training now being undertaken entirely by Hythe/New Romney. Since, apart from their ranks, there was now no significant difference between an army observer and an aerial gunner, there was no longer any need to maintain the previous distinction.

It remained to decide which of the two labels should be applied. While it might have been more appropriate to have regarded all of these men as gunners, 'the Brass' would no doubt have wished to avoid the presentational difficulties that were bound to have arisen had they tried to 'downgrade' officers to work at what was by now widely perceived to be a non-commissioned trade. This approach would also have caused significant administrative complications by introducing yet another RFC grade – that of the commissioned aerial gunner.

Subsequent research has indicated that No 20 Sqn's total may actually have been as high as 630, this figure being published in *Above the Trenches* (1990), jointly compiled by C. Shores, N. Franks and R. Guest.

[18]Arch Whitehouse, *op. cit.*

[19]AIR1/400/15/231/41. Air Ministry letter 87/RFC/1106 (M5 A/122) dated 16 March 1918. Although it was not British policy to encourage the cult of the 'ace', in the course of ratifying combat claims it was necessary to assign victories to individual pilots and it was inevitable that the identities of those who were particularly successful would become known and that their reputations would be established. In the two-seater world prior to March 1918, however, although combat reports (usually) make it clear whose gun had actually done the damage, and individual back-seaters will undoubtedly have kept their own tallies, officialdom automatically assigned victories to the pilot.

[20]AIR1/1078/204/5/1678. A precise date for the termination of aerial gunner training has not (yet) been traced but HQ RFC was notified of the decision to dispense with them by War Office letter 87/RFC/1018(SD2) dated 31 December 1917. Nevertheless, the employment of aerial gunners was still being provided for in unit establishments published on 29 January 1918, for squadrons stationed in France, and on 16 February for those in the Middle East. These documents specified the requirements for back-seaters as officer and NCO observers but included footnotes indicating where it was acceptable to substitute gunners in the event that insufficient observers were available. An amendment was published on 20 February (AIR1/399/15/231/40), which deleted any reference to aerial gunners from all unit establishments.

The line of least resistance was to opt for the alternative solution and 'upgrade' gunners to become NCO army observers.

Although current unit establishments provided for up to six sergeant gunners per squadron (see page 34), until now most of them had actually flown as air mechanics or corporals. To underline the increased status of non-commissioned aircrew, however, they were in future all to graduate in the rank of sergeant. The six aerial gunners serving with each army squadron were to be replaced on a one-for-one basis by sergeant observers, some of whom will have been provided by remustering and promoting experienced gunners. The gunners on the strength of corps squadrons, however, were to be withdrawn and replaced by commissioned observers.

As with all amendments to personnel policy, it took time for these changes to percolate down through the system and the term 'aerial gunner' took several months to fade away. In fact, because their qualifications and/or experience did not permit all of them to be automatically remustered as sergeant observers, a few gunners lingered on the books until the end of the war. Fig. 9 provides a summary of the actual manning levels within the force of two-seater squadrons based in France in January 1918.[21] In addition to those tabulated there were a further three qualified RFC observers flying Handley Pages with A Sqn, RNAS at Ochey and five probationary gunners on the strength of the Aerial Range at Cormont. Oddly enough, although they were equipped with single-seaters, Nos 43 and 60 Sqns were each carrying a solitary gunner on their books at this time.[22]

As part of the run-up to the formation of the RAF, the Air Ministry reviewed the establishments of all RFC squadrons and these were republished with an effective date of 1 April 1918.[23] The extracts at Fig. 10 illustrate the notional ratio of officer to NCO observers at this stage of the war. It is interesting to note, however, that the trend towards specialisation became increasingly marked over the next few months and by October it had been decided to reintroduce dedicated NCO gunners, although this intention was to be frustrated by the Armistice.

Unit	Type	Qual Obs	Prob Obs	Qual AG	Prob AG
No 2 Sqn	FK8	11	7	2	4
No 4 Sqn	RE8	9	11	1	7
No 5 Sqn	RE8	10	11	1	5
No 6 Sqn	RE8	0	0	3	1
No 7 Sqn	RE8	10	11	3	3
No 8 Sqn	FK8	6	11	3	4
No 9 Sqn	RE8	11	11	3	5
No 10 Sqn	FK8	9	12	5	2
No 11 Sqn	F2b	11	10	6	6
No 12 Sqn	RE8	10	7	5	2
No 13 Sqn	RE8	12	8	6	2
No 15 Sqn	RE8	10	8	4	2
No 16 Sqn	RE8	11	10	3	4
No 18 Sqn	DH 4	8	12	4	9
No 20 Sqn	F2b	8	11	1	8
No 21 Sqn	RE8	11	10	3	3
No 22 Sqn	F2b	9	12	6	5
No 25 Sqn	DH 4	8	14	6	4
No 27 Sqn	DH 4	4	14	4	6
No 35 Sqn	FK8	4	16	5	1
No 48 Sqn	F2b	6	16	2	8
No 49 Sqn	DH 4	0	22	5	4
No 52 Sqn	RE8	9	10	2	4
No 53 Sqn	RE8	12	11	4	3
No 55 Sqn	DH 4	11	6	6	2
No 57 Sqn	DH 4	9	14	1	7
No 59 Sqn	RE8	12	8	4	4
No 69 Sqn	RE8	2	18	1	0
No 82 Sqn	FK8	0	21	6	1
No 100 Sqn	FE2b	9	12	1	1
No 101 Sqn	FE2b	5	13	1	7
No 102 Sqn	FE2b	13	5	0	0
	Totals	**260**	**362**	**107**	**124**

Fig. 9. The distribution of non-pilot aircrew serving with RFC squadrons in France in January 1918. At this stage practically all observers were officers; aerial gunners could hold ranks up to sergeant-major but the vast majority were corporals or below.

Role	No & Type of Aircraft	Organisation	Observers	
			Officers	NCOs
Fighter Reconnaissance*	18 × Bristol F2b	HQ + 3 Flts	14	6
Night Flying	18 × FE2b	HQ + 3 Flts	20	–
Day Bomber*	18 × DH 4/9	HQ + 3 Flts	14	6
Corps Reconnaissance	24 × RE8/FK8	HQ + 3 Flts	20	6
Night Bomber	10 × HP O/400	HQ + 2 Flts	5	11

Fig. 10. The officially approved establishments of officer and NCO observers for RAF squadrons in France as at 1 April 1918, an asterisk indicating those roles in which it was considered acceptable to employ additional NCOs if insufficient officers were available.

1918. The RFC reconsiders its policy towards NCO pilots

While this book is intended to focus on non-pilot aircrew, in order to maintain some sort of perspective, it has been necessary to pay some attention to pilots and, in particular, to the way in which they were trained. Since space has already been devoted to non-commissioned gunners and observers, in order to maintain the balance, it is appropriate to consider the RFC's attitude towards the employment of sergeant pilots.

Provision for non-commissioned pilots had been made from the very outset. As early as 12 April 1912, the White Paper which had published the detailed arrangements for the formation of the RFC had noted that each of the planned seven squadrons was to have twelve aeroplanes and twenty-six pilots; only half of these pilots were to be officers. The first non-commissioned pilot (Cpl Frank Ridd) gained his RAeC Certificate on 4 June 1912. Others were to follow but their numbers never actually kept pace with those of officers so that

[21]AIR1/1214/204/5/2630. The data used to compile Fig. 9 has been drawn from a nominal roll of all officers and non-commissioned aircrew serving with the RFC in France in January 1918. It is thought that this return probably reported the presence of all personnel who had been on strength at any time during the month but it is possible that it reflected the position on one particular (but unspecified) day.

[22]*Ibid.* 2/AM A Moult was with No 43 Sqn and 1/AM E.R. Perrett with No 60 Sqn.

[23]AIR1/400/15/231/41. Updating editions which had been effective since 29 January 1918, the following revised establishments (for units based in France) were published at the end of March 1918: AF/F/17 for corps reconnaissance squadrons, AF/F/18 for day bomber squadrons, AF/F/19 for night flying squadrons and AF/F/20 for fighter reconnaissance squadrons.

AF/F/16, as reflected at Fig. 10, covered RAF night bomber squadrons but it is worth noting that the RNAS, the original sponsors of the O/400, had its own views on the manning of big bombers. By the spring of 1918 the establishment of a naval bomber squadron provided for a crew of two pilots plus two gunlayers per aeroplane with five commissioned observers being held on the strength of the HQ.

by the time that war was declared officer pilots outnumbered those without commissions by almost five to one.[24] Furthermore, in the light of experience, the RFC had refined its requirements by mid-1913 so that it now employed what were known as First and Second Class pilots, the qualification standards being published in September.[25] In practice, the majority of non-commissioned personnel progressed no further than becoming Second Class pilots, which meant, in essence, that they had passed the tests associated with the RAeC Certificate (although it is uncertain whether all of them actually obtained their 'ticket') and had demonstrated an awareness of only some of the technical aspects of aviation. First Class pilots had, in addition, to have accumulated an 'adequate' number of flying hours and passed examinations in a much broader range of topics at the CFS.

Even so there were marked distinctions within the First Class classification, in that officers had to pass in all eight subjects examined at Upavon, whereas non-commissioned pilots were not tested on the theory of flight or on meteorology. Furthermore they were not required to demonstrate a knowledge of troop formations or an ability to identify warships, nor, beyond an ability to map-read and use a compass, were they required to be familiar with aerial reconnaissance procedures and techniques. It is quite clear, therefore, that the RFC can have had no serious intention of using its non-commissioned pilots operationally and, although there were a few exceptions, this policy remained essentially unchanged throughout the war. There was never an embargo on the training of non-commissioned pilots but the majority of those who did qualify were assigned to second-line units where they served as, for instance, ferry pilots at Aircraft Parks or staff pilots at the School of Aerial Gunnery.

A return of all officers and aircrew serving with the RFC shows that in February 1916 just over thirty non-commissioned personnel were carried on the strength of UK-based units as pilots, most of them still undergoing training. There were, however, only three NCO pilots flying with operational units in France at that time – one each with Nos 1, 3 and 5 Sqns.[26] Despite the considerable expansion of the corps over the next two years, although more NCOs were trained, they continued to represent only a tiny proportion of the total number of pilots available.[27]

The employment of sergeant pilots on operations peaked during 1917. There were, for instance, a total of twenty-seven of them on the strength of the squadrons serving with the BEF in March,[28] twenty-four in May[29] and twenty-eight in August.[30] All the NCOs were overborne against each unit's current establishment which provided at that time for a total of twenty-one pilots per squadron, *all* of whom were to be commissioned – one Squadron Commander and two (presumably 'spare') Flying Officers with the headquarters and a Flight Commander and five Flying Officers for each of three flights). By August 1917 there were forty-seven squadrons in France, reflecting an overall requirement for 987 officer pilots. There were actually 970 on strength, representing a ratio of officers to NCOs of the order of 35:1.[31]

Since there was no official establishment for sergeant pilots, it would seem likely that the primary function of the handful serving in France may have been to provide a cushion to ensure that a squadron would remain fully operational if there were any delay in providing replacement officers. This is not to say that NCO pilots were used only as makeweights and those squadrons who had sergeants on strength certainly made full of use of them. It is worth noting, however, that they flew only with two-seater units; few (if any) NCO pilots were carried on the books of single-seat fighter squadrons until (as discussed below) the summer of 1918. Sergeants never represented more than 3 per cent of the available pilots in France and from the autumn of 1917, despite the continued expansion of the RFC, their numbers actually began to decline. By January 1918, there were only fourteen of them, this figure contrasting markedly with that for non-commissioned back-seaters of whom there were no fewer than 231 (see Fig. 9).[32]

There were signs, however, that the situation might be about to change. By the early summer of 1917 the War Office had become concerned at the difficulty that the training system was experiencing in finding sufficient suitable candidates to meet the RFC's apparently insatiable demand for officer pilots. Substituting NCOs was an obvious solution to the problem, but this was evidently regarded as being a decision of such gravity as to require endorsement at the highest level. In August the War Office submitted an outline proposal to the CinC BEF and sought his opinion on it.[33]

Recognising the inevitable, Field Marshal Haig agreed to the introduction of significant numbers of NCO pilots with the proviso that the measure should be tried 'purely as an experiment, subject to a further recommendation at some future date as to its permanent adoption.' The CinC went on to indicate that he was prepared to accept one complete flight of NCO pilots in each of the enlarged 24-aircraft corps reconnaissance squadrons and up to 50% of all pilots in day bomber squadrons. He was less enthusiastic about NCOs flying fighters but, on a trial basis, he was prepared to have one flight of sergeants in one two-seater squadron and one flight in each of six single-seater squadrons. For night bombing duties, however, Haig considered that all pilots 'must be officers.' He imposed two other conditions. First, that the influx of NCOs was to be provided in a single group, not

[24]R. Dallas Brett, *History of British Aviation 1908–1914* (1933). When war was declared there were 305 military and 101 naval officers holding RAeC Certificates. By comparison only forty-seven non-commissioned army personnel and thirty-nine naval petty officers had qualified as pilots.

[25]WO123/55. A pamphlet laying down the qualification tests for first and second class pilots certificates for officers and men was published with Army Orders for 1 September 1913.

[26]AIR1/1290/204/11/70. Nominal role of officers and non-commissioned aircrew serving with the RFC, dated February 1916. The three NCOs concerned were F/Sgt T. Carlisle (351), Sgt T. Bayetto (4808) and Sgt J. Noakes (4469) respectively.

[27]Comprehensive records of the number of officers and NCO pilots trained during WW I do not appear to have survived but sufficient documentary evidence exists to provide a reasonable impression of the balance between them. On qualifying for their flying badges the CFS issued all commissioned pilots with an RFC Graduation Certificate, NCO pilots receiving a very similar document called a Flying Certificate, each series being numbered independently. It is known, for instance, that Sgt E.A. Cook's Flying Certificate No 175 was dated 7 April 1917 while 2/Lt H.D. Arkell's Graduation Certificate No 5321 was issued on 26 June. While the dates of these documents differ by several weeks, they are close enough to show that officer pilots outnumbered NCOs by more than thirty to one, this ratio remaining more or less constant throughout the war.

[28]AIR1/1297/204/5/139. Nominal roles of officers and non-commissioned aircrew serving with the RFC overseas, dated January–April 1917.

[29]AIR1/1297/204/5/140. Nominal role of officers and non-commissioned aircrew serving with the RFC overseas, dated June 1917.

[30]AIR1/1301/204/5/158. Nominal role of officers and non-commissioned aircrew serving with the RFC overseas, dated August 1917.

[31]*Ibid.*

[32]AIR1/1214/204/5/2630. Nominal role of officers and non-commissioned aircrew serving with the RFC overseas, dated January 1918.

[33]AIR1/1078/204/5/1678. War Office letter 79/9962 dated 18 August 1917.

piecemeal, and, secondly, that separate messing facilities for sergeant pilots were to be provided on units associated with the trial.[34]

With hindsight, and in the context of this book, the second of Haig's conditions is of particular interest – more for what it implied than for what it actually said. While it was obviously impractical for sergeant pilots to share a mess with their officers, the idea that their introduction in relatively small numbers made it necessary to provide discrete accommodation for them was very odd, since every unit already had appropriate messing facilities for NCOs.

Was this curious decision the ultimate expression of the divisiveness which had been created by three years of treating pilots as an élite? After all, more than 200 non-commissioned back-seaters were already serving in France and no one had ever thought it necessary to make any special provision for them. Yet the prospect of half-a-dozen sergeants turning up to fly Sopwith Camels prompted the immediate establishment of a mess for their exclusive use. To the paranoid, this decision could be interpreted as yet another manifestation of prejudice against back-seaters. Even to those who are not emotionally disturbed, however, it must surely be seen to illustrate the army's sadly blinkered approach to the realities of being an aviator. If three years of war had proved nothing else, it had surely shown that pilots and observers were two of a kind – two halves of a whole. It is arguable that neither of them needed to be segregated from their groundcrew colleagues, but if one did, surely both did.

London signalled its acceptance of the CinC's constraints in November but declined the offer of using sergeants for corps work.[35] In effect, therefore, it had been agreed that the number of NCO day bomber pilots could be increased as required up to a maximum of 50% of establishment and that the use of a proportion of sergeants in selected fighter squadrons would be tried on an experimental basis. In practice, although a few sergeants did fly with bomber squadrons they never represented anything like half the overall strength and the aim of the trial began to focus increasingly on the single-seat fighter pilots who were expected to become available on 15 March 1918.

By that time the trial had been more clearly defined. It now embraced twenty-four pilots who had been trained on SE5as and twelve trained on Camels; they were due to reach France on 25 March. In anticipation of their arrival HQ RFC issued instructions that Nos 1, 24, 41, 43, 60 and 70 Sqns were to prepare the necessary accommodation (two Nissen huts per unit) and arrangements were made to provide the additional domestic staff (one cook and one steward per unit).[36] This directive was promptly short-circuited by receipt of a letter from the Directorate of Training announcing that 'the training of NCOs on other than 2-seater machines has not proved to be an unqualified success and there is no doubt that they have proved slow in taking to Scouts.'[37] The upshot was that the trial was postponed indefinitely. It had not been abandoned, however, and the training staffs persevered throughout the summer.

In the event it would be September before the trial commenced. By then it had evidently been decided not to concentrate on single-seaters and only two fighter units (Nos 84 and 203 Sqns) were nominated to participate in the experiment. The other units involved flew two-seaters in the fighter reconnaissance role (Nos 11 and 48 Sqns) and as day bombers (Nos 103 and 206 Sqns). The orders concerning the provision of separate accommodation were reissued and, since two-seater units were now involved, the instructions noted that any NCO observers on strength were also to be accommodated in the messes being provided for sergeant pilots – needless to say, no mention was made of the many NCO observers flying with other squadrons.

The new arrivals were initially to be held supernumerary to the nominal strength of each unit, being progressively absorbed against the establishment as replacements for officers who were lost or posted. Apart from stipulating that these NCOs were not to be transferred to other squadrons, HQ RAF deliberately laid down no policy as to how they should be employed. It was specifically left to the discretion of Brigade Commanders to decide whether to integrate them into their existing squadron organisations, or whether to concentrate them within all-NCO flights commanded by an officer.[38]

Had the anticipated shortage of pilots actually materialised there can be little doubt that the delays experienced in mounting the trial would not have been tolerated and that many sergeant pilots would have been sent to France, regardless of their capabilities. In practice the manpower problem had been solved, largely by the Dominions. An initial trickle of (mostly) South African and Australian cadets, arriving to be trained as pilots during 1917, had become a flood by mid-1918 and by that time substantial numbers of pilots were also beginning to graduate from the flying schools which the RFC had set up in Canada. When the output of the considerably expanded facilities in Egypt was added to the total, it seems possible that the number of officer pilots being turned out by the RAF's global training organisation might even have begun to exceed its requirements by the summer of 1918 (much as it was to do in 1944 (see page 178).

Against this background, little real urgency appears to have been attached to the NCO trial and, the original dynamic underpinning it having evaporated, the main reason for sustaining the experiment was probably scientific curiosity. The suspense date for reports on the experience gained from the trial was 10 November 1918 and at least five of those submitted have survived.[39] Although the comments they contain are specifically concerned with pilots, there is much that can be read across to back-seaters so it is worth noting the gist of what was said.

There was almost universal agreement that the separate messes had been a serious mistake. It was considered essential that all pilots should share the same domestic facilities, partly because that was where flying was constantly discussed, allowing newcomers to soak up the experience of the older hands, and partly because it was where *esprit de corps* was consolidated. Needless to say, no one actually made the point, but these arguments were equally applicable to back-seaters.

Opinions as to the overall capabilities of the sergeants involved in the trial varied considerably. For instance, Lt-Col T.A.E. Cairnes, OC 22nd Wg, had considered that all six of No 84 Sqn's NCOs had been 'good pilots' and Brig-Gen C.A.H. Longcroft, GOC III Bde, seems to have

[34] *Ibid.* GHQ letter OB/1826/E/1 dated 6 September 1917.
[35] *Ibid.* War Office telegram 45677 dated 14 November 1917.
[36] *Ibid.* HQ RFC letter CRFC 2022/1G dated 6 March 1918.
[37] *Ibid.* Brig-Gen H.D. Briggs informed HQ RFC of the problems being experienced in training NCO pilots on single-seaters in Air Ministry letter 79/9962 dated 5 March 1918.
[38] *Ibid.* HQ RAF letter 2567(A) dated 30 August 1918.
[39] *Ibid.* Reports to HQ RAF, submitted either directly or via Brigade HQs, representing the views of Nos 11, 48, 84, 103 and 206 Sqns are on file.

been equally content with those flying with No 11 Sqn who had 'proved themselves to be quite as good as the average officer pilot.' Brig-Gen Ludlow-Hewitt, GOC X Bde, was rather less enthusiastic about the experience of No 103 Sqn whose NCOs had been 'thoroughly satisfactory when working in formations led by experienced Officers' but lacking in 'initiative and enterprise when flying alone on Reconnaissance or Photography.'

On the other hand, although No 206 Sqn's style of operation will have been very similar to No 103 Sqn's, its CO, Maj C.T. Maclaren, had considerable reservations about the performance of his sergeants, even on bombing raids, since 'they do not keep good formation and when attacked are inclined to split up rather than packing together.' While acknowledging that two of his sergeants had been satisfactory, in general he was of the opinion that 'there is a marked difference between the NCO pilot and the Flying Officer, particularly with regard to reconnaissance and photographic work.' Maclaren had tried his men with both commissioned and non-commissioned back-seaters and had concluded that the two-NCOs combination did not 'possess the necessary intelligence and initiative for the carrying out of their work successfully' and he had no doubt that 'the absence of the spirit of the officer in command of the machine is largely felt.' While the provision of a commissioned observer did improve matters, such mixed crews still tended to perform indifferently, because of a lack of mutual understanding between its members.

The most damning report came from OC No 48 Sqn, Maj K.R. Park, who had received a total of nine sergeant pilots. He had had four of them posted home for further training and had recommended that a fifth be consigned to the trenches! Of the remainder, he considered only three to have been satisfactory. Park's assessment led him to draw a very interesting conclusion. He was of the opinion that his three good NCOs had been the equal of officer pilots and he recommended that if a man is 'of the right type and good enough to be a fighting pilot in a fighting unit, he should be commissioned.' Much the same view had been reflected by both Cairnes and Maclaren. The latter, noting that his two satisfactory NCOs had both been educated at Public Schools, failed to 'understand how they came out as NCOs as their flying is beyond reproach.'

With little else to go on, the RFC's preference for commissioned pilots had always been based largely on instinct. The feedback from the formal attempt to assess the capabilities of NCO pilots had provided positive, if unscientific, evidence that the corps had been right to trust its judgement. While their assessments had been entirely subjective, three very experienced unit commanders had independently drawn the same conclusion, that a good pilot needed to possess much the same personal qualities as those traditionally associated with a commission. This tended to confirm the long-standing assumption that the terms officer and pilot were, in many respects, synonymous. The same was true of back-seaters, apart, perhaps, from those whose duties were confined solely to gunnery in those day bomber squadrons which usually operated in formation.

The Armistice had been signed four days before the last report on the NCO trial had been rendered, so it is quite likely that none of them attracted much attention at the time. Nevertheless, anyone who did read them (and who was also able to read *between* the lines) might have been able to predict that the close correlation between commissions and, at least some, aircrew trades might well present a difficulty in the future. The problem was that if one were to commission almost anyone who flew, most of them would actually have no one to command, which would make their being officers a little pointless and thus devalue the whole business of commissions. As will become clear in later chapters, this peculiarly 'air force' problem was to crop up again and again and, despite several attempts, it has never really been satisfactorily solved.

The ratio of casualties between pilots and observers

Previous discussion of aerial gunnery, and of the observer's role in air combat, raises the closely related question of casualties. There was (and still is) a widely held perception that observers tended to be more vulnerable than pilots, although this writer is not aware that any specific evidence has ever been offered to prove this. The publication in 1995 of Trevor Henshaw's work on casualties has provided a readily accessible and reliable database, however, and this permits us to attempt some sort of analysis.[40] The results are presented at Fig. 11, which examines selected incidents which occurred during three separate months in which air fighting was particularly intense.

Only the relatively personal nature of close quarter air-to-air engagements could have revealed any bias one way or the other, since ground fire was far too inaccurate to have been aimed at an individual crew member. For this reason casualties known, or likely, to have been caused by 'Archie' or by machine-gun or small arms fire from the trenches have been excluded. Since fighting in the dark was not a significant factor either, incidents which occurred during night bombing missions have also been discounted, as have casualties sustained by two-seater pilots flying solo bombing sorties. It is acknowledged that the causes of some of the remaining incidents might be open to dispute but it is thought unlikely that there would be enough of these to alter the overall balance significantly. The tabulated figures are therefore believed to reflect, with tolerable accuracy, only those losses (killed or wounded in action or died of wounds) sustained as a result of air-to-air combat.

Since 55% of the sample were observers, compared to only 45% pilots, it seems quite clear that the observer/gunner of a two-seater operating in daylight was indeed statistically more likely to be killed or wounded than his companion. Why should this have been the case? One obvious explanation is that, since most attacks were delivered from a rear quarter, the attacker's priority was to neutralise the return fire from the gunner. On the other hand there may merely have been a tendency to aim at the most obvious target, the occupant of the rear cockpit. There is some evidence to support the second of these notions as it would explain the only significant anomaly which appears in the table, that of corps crews during 'Bloody April'. At that time the majority of the aeroplanes being used in this role were still BE2s, in which the pilot sat in the back, and this appears to have been the only case in which he was more likely to become a casualty than his companion.

There is another anomaly which should be pointed out, as it is not apparent from the tabulated figures, and this one tends to contradict the conclusion that he who occupied the back seat was invariably most at risk. The pilot of an FE2 also occupied the rear cockpit but in this case the 'normal' pattern

[40] Trevor Henshaw, *op. cit.*

Month	Role	Aircraft Types Involved	Pilots	Observers	Total
April 1917	Fighter Recce	FE2b/d, Bristol F2a, 1½ Strutter	47	66	113
	Day Bomber	DH 4, 1½ Strutter (RNAS)	3	6	9
	Corps Recce	BE2c/d/e/f/g, RE8, Morane P	51	42	93
		Totals	101	114	215
March 1918	Fighter Recce	Bristol F2b Fighter	12	16	28
	Day Bomber	DH 4	18	20	38
	Corps Recce	RE8, FK8	20	30	50
		Totals	50	66	116
September 1918	Fighter Recce	Bristol F2b Fighter	21	30	51
	Day Bomber	DH 4, DH 9, DH 9A	65	85	150
	Corps Recce	RE8, FK8	25	29	54
		Totals	111	144	255
		Grand Totals	**262**	**324**	**586**

Fig. 11. *Casualties sustained during air-to-air engagements over France at selected periods.*

of casualties was sustained, only (about) thirty-five pilots of the FE2s included within the April 1917 sample becoming casualties, compared to (about) forty-five *front* seat observers.

It could be that the inconsistency demonstrated by the FE2 is merely a result of the sample's being too small to be statistically significant and thus too small to permit any definitive conclusions to be drawn. Indeed it could reasonably be argued that the samples used are too small to substantiate any worthwhile findings in every case, and that the whole argument therefore lacks rigour. Nevertheless, the overall pattern which emerges is remarkably uniform, indicating very similar percentile differences in almost every case, both over time and regardless of role. It is acknowledged that the foregoing may be a little superficial but, even so, its consistency does make it rather persuasive.

There were, of course, many instances of pilots returning to base with a dead or wounded observer on board, whereas there were relatively few cases of this occurring in the reverse sense. This might appear to be a significant factor but it does not really alter the overall picture; it serves only to underline the disproportionate risk run by observers. As the Bailhache Committee had suggested in 1916, death through the incapacitation of their comrade in arms was a hazard virtually unique to back-seaters. For the purposes of this analysis, however, it is not necessary to establish how each individual observer died, only to demonstrate that they did so in greater numbers than pilots.

A case in point. This DH 4 of No 5(N) Sqn crashed after having been shot up while attacking troops near Villers Bretonneux. Although the damage sustained is believed to have been due to gunfire from the ground, rather than from an enemy aircraft, the injuries sustained by the crew conformed to the statistical pattern; the pilot, FSLt C.J. Haywood, was unhurt while Aerial Gunlayer T. W. Jones was categorised as wounded in action. Interestingly, since this incident occurred on 30 March 1918, N5992 was probably the last RNAS aeroplane to be lost in action. (J.M. Bruce/G.S. Leslie collection)

Chapter 13

1918. The creation of the RAF – complications arising from differences between RNAS and RFC grading policies and ranks

A major administrative task stemming from the formation of the RAF was the need to identify all of its personnel and transfer them to the books of the new Service. So far as officers were concerned, this eventually resulted in the publication of an Air Force List, broadly similar in style and content to the long-established Army and Navy Lists. This led to yet another change in the way in which observers were recorded. The new Service adopted the RNAS term Observer Officer to identify its back-seaters and reinstated segregated lists. This was not simply a reflection of an *apartheid* philosophy, however, and pilots would shortly also be subjected to division, being listed separately as Aeroplane Officers, Seaplane Officers and Airship (originally Dirigible) Officers. Balloon Officers (restyled as *Kite* Balloon Officers by the RAF) represented yet another discrete category of aviators – as they always had done in the RFC, but *not* in the RNAS.

On 1 April 1918 the RAF's strength in gazetted observers stood at 1764,[1] the RNAS having contributed 181 towards this total.[2] There were also 670 Kite Balloon Officers. In addition there were large numbers of ex-RFC flight cadets and ex-RNAS probationary observer officers undergoing training, the result of the much enlarged intakes which had begun the previous year. These trainees began to graduate over the next few months and the Air Force List for August indicates that by then the totals had grown to 2783 commissioned observers and 828 Kite Balloon Officers, both of these figures being supplemented by substantial, but undetermined, numbers of qualified NCOs.

Transferring these personnel to the RAF's books highlighted an example of misaligned military and naval practice – ranks, always a potential source of confusion. For instance, while an RNAS observer (or flight) lieutenant had ostensibly been equivalent to an RFC captain (see Chapter 11, Note 2), he was actually of much lower *status*, since the granting of a captaincy in the RFC had implied recognition of an officer's suitability to command a flight, i.e. like an RNAS flight observer (or commander).

To avoid the inevitable discontent that would have accompanied the RAF's effectively 'demoting' substantial numbers of its ex-naval brethren, it was eventually decided to accept all RNAS observer lieutenants into the new Service as nominal captains and to permit them to wear the appropriate rank insignia. Pending their selection for Flight Commander duties, however, they were actually graded as Observer Officers and generally regarded (and paid) as if they held RAF lieutenant rank. This distinction was indicated by an asterisk alongside their names in the Air Force List.[3] The August List contained three observers ranked as majors and fifty-four as captains, forty-seven of the latter being 'starred'. The ten observers whose executive status had been formally acknowledged by the RAF were all ex-naval officers who had held a variety of junior command appointments in the RNAS. Because of its policy, the RFC was, of course, unable to field a single observer with comparable experience.

1918. The various categories of RFC and RNAS observer inherited by the RAF are rationalised

In May 1918 regulations were published laying down that an RFC-style badge was to be worn by all qualified observers and balloonists.[4] This seemed to be straightforward enough but it would appear that an appeal may have been lodged on behalf of ex-naval balloonists, who had been regarded as pilots by the RNAS. If there was such a protest, however, it fell on deaf ears. In June the Air Ministry reaffirmed that the RAF would follow the precedent established by the RFC. This meant that *all* qualified balloonists, regardless of their

[1]Since it is potentially very misleading, the figure of 1764 gazetted observers deserves some amplification. Although it will have been a reasonably accurate reflection of the number of qualified observers carried on the RAF's books, in practice nothing like this total would have been available for operations. For instance, substantial numbers were being employed on administrative or experimental duties. Others, still technically graded as observers, were undergoing training as pilots. Yet another sizeable group was ineffective, having sustained wounds or injuries, while others had been imprisoned in Germany and Turkey or interned in Holland. Finally, it should be appreciated that a substantial proportion of the observers who had been shot down had been posted 'Missing in Action' and these men remained on the active list until their deaths had been confirmed or were presumed.

Based on the notional establishments of the squadrons constituting the RAF's Order of Battle on 1 April 1918, it is possible to make a reasonable guess at the broad distribution of the observers available at the time. If some allowance is made for significant variations in the manning of squadrons in the 'side-show' theatres and among those originating within the RNAS, and if the demands of units working up to operational status are included, this calculation suggests an overall requirement for something like 1000 qualified 'front-line' observers, leaving about 750 in the non-operational margins.

[2]The Navy List for 18 March 1918 (the last to be published prior to the formation of the RAF) indicates that the RNAS actually had 306 observers on its books at that time. The RAF acknowledged only those who were fully qualified, however, and 125 of the naval contingent were probationary observer officers, the new Service affording them the same interim status as RFC flight cadets. Interestingly, even allowing for a handful who may have fallen by the wayside (e.g. those who had been regraded as pilots, had switched to some other trade or had become casualties) it would seem unlikely that many more than 350 sets of RNAS observers badges were ever issued, which would account for their comparative rarity today.

[3]Details of these arrangements were first announced in AMWO 432 of 12 June 1918. Almost inevitably, because the new Service's RFC-dominated administration was conditioned to paying little heed to back-seaters, the language used had made AMWO 432 applicable exclusively to ex-RNAS pilots. The situation had to be redressed by publication of a separate Order (AMWO 579 of 3 July), extending the provisions of AMWO 432 to cover erstwhile naval observers.

[4]AMWO 330 of 22 May 1918 authorised all RAF officers qualified as Aeroplane, Seaplane or Kite Balloon Observers, or as Free Balloon Pilots, to wear a single-winged flying 'O', the retention of the RFC-style badge having been announced on 1 May (see Note 11).

background and degree of expertise, were now graded as RAF Kite Balloon Officers and that the appropriate badge for them was, therefore, the flying 'O'.[5]

This 'balloon debate' was not the only legislative hangover to which a cure needed to be found, however. In their customarily cavalier fashion the drafters of regulations had confined their efforts to officers. No one had given any thought to the hundreds of NCO observers whose circumstances had also to be catered for, resulting in yet another Weekly Order.[6]

But the problems did not end there. The language used in all Orders published thus far had specifically endorsed the wearing of the flying 'O' by 'observers', thus technically excluding the remaining ex-RFC aerial gunners. There were similar difficulties with ex-RNAS aerial gunlayers. Furthermore, the system had been complicated by the fact that some elements of the ex-RNAS faction had been very quick to take advantage of the creation of the RAF by formally remustering a number of technical ratings who would not have been recognised as aircrew by the RFC. This led the Air Ministry to issue an edict, specifically in the context of flying boat crews, imposing a moratorium on the promotion of any more W/T and/or engineering personnel as sergeant observers.[7] This prohibition remained in force until October (see below).

Because the RFC had ceased to train, or never had trained, aircrew in all of these categories, the RAF's personnel organisation was evidently experiencing some difficulty in framing regulations to acknowledge their continued presence. Nevertheless, despite the absence of any specific provision for these odds and ends, it is highly unlikely that the Air Ministry meant to deprive them of their badges and only a pedant would have attempted to enforce rules containing what were plainly unintentional errors of omission.

In the fullness of time, the new Service would come to accept that, particularly for maritime operations, there was a continuing need to employ aircrew in the specialisations previously sponsored by the RNAS, and it would also reinstate a requirement for NCO gunners. As discussed below, however, it was envisaged that all of these men would eventually be classified as sub-specialisations within the overall trade of the observer, although this concept did not begin to crystallise until the last few weeks of the war and it was never formally introduced.

In the meantime, there remained a rump of 'left over' non-commissioned ex-RFC and ex-RNAS personnel who were not actually observers but who would still have been wearing the flying 'O'. The interim policy was that, wherever possible, these men were to be remustered as sergeant observers.[8] Unfortunately, without a degree of top-up training, this was not feasible in every case and demobilisation will probably have intervened before the circumstances of some of these men had been finally resolved.

The ex-RNAS lighter-than-air fraternity, some of whom considered that they had been particularly badly treated, represented yet another outstanding problem. Apart from their pilots (including some non-commissioned coxswains), who were fully qualified, and a few appropriately trained fitters and wireless operators who might have been regarded as being professional aircrew, naval airships had tended to be manned on a relatively casual basis. Many of their crewmen were technical and wireless ratings drawn from the establishment of their operating bases with a nominal amount of gunnery training being organised from local resources. Another oddity (in army eyes) was that the RNAS had treated its airships rather like seagoing vessels with a crew being assigned to a particular craft. While this approach had served the navy well enough in the past, it did not sit very comfortably with the RAF's manning policy which, since the Army had been far and away the majority shareholder, usually tended to reflect RFC practices.

This is not to say that those ex-RNAS ratings who flew were not competent, but neither were many of them aircrew *per se*, that is to say that they had not attended an aviation indoctrination course at a SoMA or at the Crystal Palace. The RAF was not prepared to grant these men full blown observer status, which would have involved making them *all* sergeants, particularly as the trend was towards bigger and better craft. A typical rigid airship had a crew of four officers and up to twenty-six men; if the RN had had its way all the latter would have had to become NCOs.

Nevertheless, the advocates of the airship maintained that there was a case for awarding a flying badge to mechanics who flew, if only to distinguish them from those who did not. The Admiralty still had some influence within the Airship Branch and it sponsored a proposal which would have permitted any airship personnel certified as being competent to fly, but not actually rated as aircrew, to wear an observers badge and to draw flying pay in their existing rank, the latter only while assigned to a specific crew. This cut little ice with the Air Ministry, who considered that these ex-RNAS ratings equated to the ex-RFC mechanics serving with heavier-than-air units who frequently flew on air tests and delivery flights without having to be recognised as aircrew and devoid of flying badges of any description. Some further consideration was given to extending the existing arrangements for the granting of flying pay at casual rates to cater for 'unqualified' members of airship crews, but this did not meet with approval either, as experience had shown that such regulations were all too easily abused.

Although the navy never managed to gain recognition for all its lighter-than-air veterans, it did eventually succeed in wringing one significant concession out of the Air Ministry. In October it was finally agreed that suitably qualified wireless operators who were 'employed on continuous flying duties' could be remustered as wireless operator observers (sergeant mechanics).[9] This was a universal ruling and would have applied to ex-soldiers just as much as to ex-sailors, but, since the RFC had made relatively little use of airborne wireless operators, the regulation had clearly been designed to cater for the maritime case. The new ruling would certainly have permitted many ex-RNAS flying boat crewmen to be upgraded and to wear a flying 'O', thus bringing them in line

[5]AMWO 524 of 26 June 1918 amplified the position regarding ex-naval balloonists. It confirmed that, notwithstanding the fact that they may have been graded as Flying Officers, i.e. pilots, in the RNAS, they were now to wear the RFC-style observers badge.

[6]AMWO 525 of 26 June 1918 extended the provisions of Order 330 (see Note 4) to embrace similarly qualified non-commissioned personnel.

[7]AIR/1/401/15/231/42. Amendment, dated 30 April 1918, to establishment AF/H/77.

[8]AMWO 916 of 29 August 1918 required that, wherever possible, any remaining aerial gunlayers and/or aerial gunners should be remustered as observers.

[9]AMWO 1199 of 10 October 1918. In this connection it may be worth pointing out that the 'hand and thunderbolt' arm badge, previously associated with wireless mechanics, had been reassigned exclusively to wireless operators by AMWO 1066 of 19 September 1918. This did not make it an 'aircrew' badge, however (as has sometimes been suggested), as it was worn mostly by ground personnel. Wireless operators who succeeded in persuading the authorities that they were *bona fide* aircrew wore the flying 'O'.

Personnel associated with the airship NS-12, probably at Longside. The date is not known but it must have been between October 1918, when NS-12 was delivered, and February 1919, when she was deleted. Since she was quite capable of carrying out 24-hour patrols (NS-11 held the record at a little over 100 hours) she normally flew with a complement of ten, two five-man watches. The captain, Capt P.E. Maitland (seated front and centre) and the two officers to his left are wearing the interim khaki uniform, to his right, Capt Chambers sports the short-lived pale blue one; five of the ostensibly RAF airmen are still wearing RNAS cap badges. Taking full advantage of the October 1918 concession which had permitted suitably qualified personnel employed full time on flying duties to be remustered as wireless observers, no fewer than eight of the eleven non-commissioned personnel in this picture are wearing a flying 'O'. Curiously, anyone entitled to wear this badge should have been ranked as at least a sergeant, but only two of these men are (Wagstaff, seated on the left, and Betteday, on the right) and four of them do not appear even to be corporals. These anomalies would suggest that the ex-RNAS lighter-than-air brigade was still having trouble adjusting to the RFC-derived RAF regime. (J.M. Bruce/G.S. Leslie collection)

with current RAF policy which, by this time (see below), required that anyone wearing an observers badge should hold the minimum rank of sergeant.

Nevertheless, this appears not to have covered every case. By October 1918, the *ground* trade of the wireless operator had been sub-divided into three specialisations, one of which was specially trained to handle the direction finding equipment which was about to be fitted to Handley Pages. (For a summary of the progress that had been made in wireless direction finding techniques during WW I, see Annex F.) After a total of twenty-four weeks of technical training these personnel became available for posting to units as air mechanics 3rd class. A proportion of these men would be earmarked for flying duties, however, and these were required to be additionally qualified as W/T observers. This involved a further month of gunnery and bombing at Eastchurch (or possibly Leysdown) on completion of which they became fully-fledged, flying 'O'-wearing sergeants.

In contrast to this, while it was recognised that some of these *ground* wireless operators would also be required fly in airships, and the training system made provision for them to spend twelve days on airships at Cranwell in addition to the Eastchurch course, the rules did *not* state that they were to become W/T observers. This implied that the airship men would not be made up to sergeant; nor would they be permitted to wear the observers badge.[10] These rules seem to have been interpreted with a degree of flexibility, however, and photographic evidence suggests that substantial numbers of late-war airship crewmen sported flying 'O's as corporals or below, the ex-naval contingent presumably being content to turn a blind eye when it felt so inclined. The RN lobby continued to campaign on behalf of its remaining unrecognised 'aviators' but these negotiations were effectively terminated in 1919 when the Admiralty finally relinquished its residual grip on airship affairs (see Chapter 10, Note 22).

[10]AIR10/64. Pages 30/31 of FS 39, *Training Courses in the RAF for Commissioned and Non-commissioned Personnel, showing Status and Pay*, published in October 1918.

1918. The disputes over the significance of the observers badge are finally resolved

The creation of the RAF had meant, almost inevitably, that the oft-reviewed question of the significance of the observers badge had had to be aired yet again. The first change was relatively straightforward. With effect from 1 May the RNAS winged 'O' was withdrawn in favour of an RFC-pattern flying 'O' to be worn on the left breast of the interim army-style uniform adopted by the RAF.[11] As discussed above, however, because the implications of this decision do not appear to have been considered very deeply, it had subsequently been necessary to publish a series of amplifying regulations to establish precisely *who* could (and should) wear the badge. It

[11]AM Monthly Order 162 of 1 May 1918 advised that the form of dress for RAF officers for the rest of the war was to be an army-style khaki uniform, essentially a military Service Dress tunic, less the epaulettes, with RNAS pattern buttons and with a fabric belt in place of the Sam Browne. Rank was to be denoted by RN-style rings in khaki braid on the sleeves, surmounted by an RNAS-pattern eagle and a crown. Flying badges, new RAF 'wings' adapted from the RFC pattern for pilots and an unmodified RFC-style flying 'O' for all other recognised aviators, were to be worn on the left breast.

A light blue uniform embellished with gold braid had already been approved but this was optional and only to be worn as Mess Dress. On 10 July AMWO 617 introduced changes to some details of the blue uniform, including the deletion of the eagle and crown at the cuffs, and authorised its routine use for daily wear as a replacement for the interim khaki pattern.

No timeframe was laid down for the adoption of either the interim khaki or the permanent blue uniforms beyond the fact that they were to be used to replace existing outfits when these wore out. In the meantime AMWO 99 of 17 April had sustained the use of RFC and RNAS badges, pending the introduction of RAF equivalents, and authorised all personnel to continue to wear their current uniforms. These included the distinctive RFC 'maternity jacket', a variety of naval rigs and virtually the entire range of regimental outfits with their differently cut tunics and their associated bonnets, trews, riding breeches

'Say George Old Bean, what d'ye think of this month's RAF?' The RAF's inevitably mongrel appearance in the early days was not helped by changes to dress regulations which tended to make the whole business of 'uniformity' something of a joke, as suggested by this cartoon drawn by Cadet Alan Murray and reproduced in Air Pie *of 1919.*

remained to determine exactly *when* they would become entitled to wear it. The new rules were published in August.[12] An observer could now be awarded his badge:

a. on completion of all courses;
b. on passing all HQ VI Bde[13] tests (for night flyers);
c. on posting to a mobilising unit;
d. on posting to a mobilised unit; or
e. on posting to serve with any Expeditionary Force.

In this respect at least parity with pilots had finally been achieved and a long-running argument had been settled. An observer was *not* awarded his badge for 'war service'. From now on a flying 'O' was, like a pilots 'wings', quite definitely intended to be a 'qualification' badge. Furthermore, the Order specifically stated that on gaining his badge, under any of the above circumstances, an observer was deemed to be qualified and was to be gazetted as such with effect from that date.

Most observers, proceeding through the formal training system as flight cadets, will have fallen into one of the first two categories. On passing the final milestone they were immediately required to obtain and wear officers uniform, complete with flying 'O' and subalterns 'pips', although they were not paid as such until they had been formally gazetted.[14] Reference to the drawing of pay serves to highlight another significant clause which had been included in the August regulations as any qualified observer was now entitled not only to wear a badge; he could also draw full flying pay.

1918. Confusion over the effective date of an observer's seniority

The confusing succession of regulations under which RAF observers could be gazetted are summarised at Fig. 12 which, for convenience, also includes the rules which had previously applied within the RFC and RNAS. Before considering some of the specific problems which were caused by this endless chopping and changing, however, it would be as well to note some of the ground rules underpinning the creation of the RAF.

a. The constitution of the RAF was necessarily complicated but, in essence, on 1 April 1918 all officers of the RN, RNVR, RNR, RM, British Army and Indian Army previously serving as members of, or on attachment to, the RFC and RNAS were automatically and immediately transferred to the RAF. Their terms of engagement were to be similar to those under which they had previously been serving, with the proviso that anyone who applied within three months would, without prejudice, be permitted to return to his original Service. Officers who had been directly recruited into the RFC or RNAS as flying personnel and who declined to be transferred to the RAF had no original Branch of Service or unit to which they could revert. It would seem unlikely, therefore, that the War Office or Admiralty would have been under any legal obligation to take them back as officers.[15]
b. Although allowance was made for previous service, in the context of time promotion, seniority *within the RAF* could not be counted from any date earlier than 1 April 1918.[16] In general, qualified observers already on active service as RFC lieutenants or 2nd lieutenants, or as RNAS observer lieutenants or observer sub-lieutenants, were given the RAF rank of lieutenant (these rules applied equally to pilots and to officers of ground branches). It was recognised, however, that some errors might have been made and officers who considered that they had been ill-served were invited to bring their cases to the attention of the authorities.[17]
c. Whatever their notional date of seniority, officers qualifying as observers in the field after the formation of the RAF would not be entitled to draw flying pay at the full rate from a date earlier than 22 May, when the relevant regulations were considered to have come into effect (i.e. from the publication of AMWO 330 – see Note 4). Note, however, that observers were now (at last) entitled to the same rate of flying pay as pilots, i.e. four shillings per day while under training and eight when graded.

When the RAF had first come into being it had continued to apply the old RFC rules with regard to an observer's seniority in that it was antedated on qualification to, more or less, the date on which he had joined his squadron in the field. This policy was changed at the end of May, however, seniority thenceforth being counted from the date on which an observer's recommendation for confirmation was accepted, i.e. the end, rather than the beginning, of his period of probationary service.[18] In view of its significance to the individuals concerned, it is

and so on. The possession of any of these automatically marked the wearer as being an 'old hand' and (perhaps for that very reason) some officers continued to wear their original kit for many months. As a result, the RAF presented a distinctly mongrel appearance at first, although a modicum of drab khaki uniformity, relieved by the occasional splash of slightly Ruritanian blue and gold, was apparent by the summer of 1918.

On 3 October 1918 AMWO 1140 laid down that the only uniforms permitted to be worn in public were the adapted army-style khaki and the RAF blue. Other patterns could still be worn, but only as working dress, i.e. within the confines of a camp, barracks or aerodrome. On 1 January 1919 the Air Council ruled that no further army-style uniforms were to be purchased, although this never appears to have been promulgated as a regulation. The implementation of demobilisation on a massive scale soon after this meant that the pale blue uniform was to gain little currency before being superseded by the familiar RAF blue-grey with effect from 1 October 1919, on the authority of AMWO 1049 of 15 September.

[12]AMWO 795 of 8 August 1918.

[13]Note that earlier references to HQ VI Bde have related to the organisation which had become HQ Training Brigade in July 1916. The dormant VI Bde number plate was reactivated on 12 October 1917 when it was applied to HQ Home Defence Brigade. Although it had no direct association with its predecessor, the new VI Bde did have a permanent training commitment as it was responsible for instruction in night flying, both for its own crews and for those earmarked for night bombers.

[14]AMWO 1091 of 26 September 1918.

[15]AIR1/1995/204/273/222. The original three-month grace period was subsequently extended to six months by AMWO 426, HQ RAF DRO 815 of 3 October 1918 declaring 6 October to be the final cut-off date.

[16]Within a rigidly hierarchical organisation, such a casual approach to a matter as fundamental as seniority simply could not suffice. AMWO 370 of 1 June 1918 provided further advice to the effect that relative seniority among officers of the same permanent rank would be decided by their date of appointment to that rank. All officers holding temporary rank, i.e. the vast majority, would be junior to those holding corresponding permanent rank and were to take precedence among themselves according to their date of appointment to their temporary rank.

[17]AMWO 195 of 2 May 1918 noted that the Air Ministry had received a number of enquiries from officers regarding their seniority in the initial RAF Gradation List, i.e. as at 1 April. It is evident that the List had contained some errors and, until these could be corrected, it was ruled that it should be regarded as being merely a nominal roll of officers serving with the RAF who were, for the time being, to take seniority in accordance with their previous seniority within the RN or Army. When the next List appeared in August it contained numerous detailed changes, e.g. among the observers, the relative positions of Lts V.D. Fernald, P.E.H. Van Baerle and V.O. Lonsdale, who had been listed in that order in April, had been reversed.

[18]AIR1/1078/204/5/1677. HQ RAF appears to have been notified of this change in policy by Air Ministry letter 47921 (P4b) dated 25 May 1918. This writer has failed to find a copy of this letter but specific references to it in related correspondence, e.g. HQ RAF's AL/R/8 of 16 July, leave no doubt as to its content.

Service	Period	Qualification	Seniority
RFC	August 1914 to November 1915	Certified as competent after 4–6 weeks on CO's recommendation, signified by the award of an observers badge from August 1915.	Not applicable, as observers were only attached to (and not members of) the RFC.
RFC	November 1915 to November 1916	As above to become a 'Qualified Observer', subsequent advancement to Flying Officer (Observer) being conditional upon a vacancy in a squadron's establishment (of seven, later twelve, per unit) and requiring the CO's further recommendation.	Interim attached status as a 'Qualified Observer' still not recognised by the RFC, but grading as a Flying Officer (Observer) was formally acknowledged; seniority recognised from date of recommendation, except that this could be no earlier than 15 October 1915.
RFC	November 1916 to August 1917	Interim grade of 'Qualified Observer' abolished. Observers badge still awarded on CO's recommendation but now requiring successful completion of written and practical tests administered at brigade and/or wing level in addition to a satisfactory period of probationary active service – typically 4–8 weeks. Still subject to a vacancy within the twelve-man unit establishment.	Nominally regarded as a Flying Officer (Observer) from date either of posting to France* (for UK-trained personnel) or of initial attachment to the RFC (for those trained in the field). Initial probationary service was still on *de facto* attached basis but on qualification and formal gazetting to the RFC seniority was antedated to one of the above dates. N.B. Observers who had qualified before 15 October 1915 (see above) could now claim antedates of seniority to arrival in France* or date of original attachment in the field.
RFC (and ex-RFC)	August 1917 to late May 1918	As above, although total establishment progressively increased to as many as twenty per unit.	Similar to above but key date now that of reporting for duty overseas after completing all necessary courses at home.
RNAS	pre April 1917	RNAS eagle badge worn from initial direct assignment as an observer or from entry into training. First group regarded as qualified on appointment, the others on completion of necessary course(s).	Identified by (O) annotation in RNAS Disposition Lists, although practically all naval observers were actually RNVR personnel. N.B. The (O) implied neither membership of the RNAS nor permanent assignment to aircrew duties, only a current specialist qualification.
RNAS (and ex-RNAS)	April 1917 to late May 1918	As above, except that the eagle was superseded by a discrete observers badge from June 1917.	Observer Officers treated as full members of the RNAS from entry into training with seniority accruing from date of graduation.
RAF	1 April 1918	All graded Observer Officers and Flying Officer (Observers) serving with the RNAS and RFC were automatically acknowledged by the RAF (which adopted the former term) as lieutenants.	N.B. A few ex-RNAS officers were accepted as majors and captains; others were granted honorary rank as captains. In ***all*** cases seniority *within the RAF* dated from 1 April 1918.
Ex-RFC and RNAS personnel on probation	late May to August 1918	Observers badge still awarded on CO's recommendation after successful completion of written and practical tests administered at brigade and/or wing level and satisfactory period of active service – typically 4–8 weeks.	Gazetted as Observer Officers in rank of subaltern on qualification, seniority *within the RAF* being antedated to 1 April 1918 for those on probation prior to that date and to the date of qualification for those who arrived later.
Ex-regimental personnel on probation	late May to August 1918	As above.	Still regarded as being on attachment until gazetted to the RAF as Observer Officers with seniority from date of qualification. Normally ranked as subalterns but, where appropriate, previous service was acknowledged by honorary rank as a lieutenant or captain.
RAF	August to November 1918	Observers badge awarded on completion of training but, where appropriate, earlier probationary regulations still applied. (Intention to permit immediate award of badges on exceptional basis on posting to a mobilising or operational squadron or overseas withdrawn.)	Automatically gazetted as an Observer Officer on completion of training with seniority from that date. Any remaining probationers were to be gazetted on qualification with seniority effective from the date they joined their unit.
RAF	3 October 1918	Probationary arrangements terminated in France (and probably elsewhere).	

* Although the regulations specifically stated (on more than one occasion) that seniority was to accrue from the date of leaving the UK, it became a common practice to use the date on which an observer was taken on strength by HQ RFC, whether as an individual or as a member of a newly arrived squadron.

Fig. 12. *Summary of conditions of service for commissioned observers, 1914–18. Note that examination of the service records of individuals reveals that there was considerable inconsistency in the application of these 'rules', particularly in France during the legislatively confused months of May–October 1918. It seems likely that anomalies would have been even more prevalent in the more remote theatres.*

surprising that no public announcement of the new policy seems to have been made, the first indications of its having been implemented being the appearance of apparently incorrect dates of seniority in the *London Gazette*.

This caused some consternation, the situation soon being aggravated by the spirit of the regulations published in August and September. These made it quite clear that it was the Air Ministry's intention that any observer actually serving in the field should be entitled to wear a flying badge and to draw full flying pay. This implied that any observer ought to be fully qualified before he was sent into action. It followed, therefore, that there would be no probationary period in the future so, following the publication of AMWO 795 in August, seniority was made effective from the date of gazetting, which was expected to be more or less that of qualification on completion of the sequence of formal training courses. This could not apply in every case, however, as there were still substantial numbers of old-style probationers on active service and, until the system could actually provide 100 per cent qualified men, more of them might well be needed.

The new rules caused considerable confusion within the bureaucracy, not to say some discontent among disadvantaged probationers. Did not the regulations proclaimed by AMWO 795 mean that seniority should now accrue from at least the beginning of a probationary period, and possibly even earlier? If so, what of the observers who had been short-changed for the previous three months? These and other questions led to a prolonged exchange of correspondence between St André-aux-Bois and London.[19]

In point of fact, AMWO 795 had clearly stated that an observer could be regarded as qualified, and was to be gazetted as such, from as early as the date on which he joined a 'mobilising' squadron, i.e. even before his unit had left England. It would seem that, on reflection, the Air Ministry had had second thoughts over this and had decided that this was too much of a concession. On 9 August, therefore, (only one day after publication of the AMWO!) it was agreed that the old RFC procedure should be reinstated, that is to say that seniority was to be backdated, on qualification, to the date of joining an operational squadron. Because there were a number of other grey areas which HQ RAF wished to have clarified first, however, this ruling was not announced in France until 3 October.[20] When it was finally published, the same order effectively terminated the probationary procedure by stating that any remaining observers who had not been recommended for gazetting were to be returned to Home Establishment for further training or disposal.

While their circumstances were slightly different, there had been similar uncertainty over the recognition of Kite Balloon Officers. There was no problem with those who were arriving from home fully-qualified, but some were still being recruited and trained in the field and, since it was anticipated that this practice might have to continue, a slightly amended version of the old procedure had to remain in force. As with Observer Officers, it was early October before the fine detail had been sorted out but thereafter a probationary regimental balloonist, attached to the RAF to be trained in the field, was immediately permitted to draw flying pay at the (by now universal) instructional rate of four shillings per day. He was authorised to draw the full eight-shilling rate, and to put up his badge, on formal gazetting as a qualified Kite Balloon Officer. The effective date of his transfer to the RAF would, assuming that it was ratified by the GOC, be regarded as that on which the original recommendation had been forwarded by the officer commanding his Balloon Wing.[21]

It is worth noting, incidentally, that by this time, although, as non-pilots, they were still classed as observers in the broadest sense, in practice the Air Ministry had come to regard Kite Balloon Officers as a quite distinct category. While it does not seem to have been pressed to the point of formal legislation, as a matter of policy London now avoided using the term 'observer' when referring to balloonists in official correspondence.[22]

1918. The inappropriate use of the term 'probationer'

Following the establishment of the RAF, although it was applied only selectively, it became fairly common for the term 'probationer' to be used as a rank for unqualified observers. There were other examples, but this malpractice was particularly prevalent within II Bde, where Nos 4, 7, 10, 20 and 53 Sqns all did it for several months in 1918.

It is not known for certain why this occurred or why it was so common in units under the command of Brig-Gen T.I. Webb-Bowen, but it is suspected that the explanation had its roots in Army General Order 1520.[23] Originally issued in April 1916, and republished from time to time, this had ruled that 'all appointments to temporary commissions in the field will, in the first instance, be made on probation,' eventual confirmation being dependent upon the subsequent recommendation of the subject's CO. General Order 1520 had been framed primarily to cater for soldiers being commissioned from the ranks but it seems possible that in some quarters its provisions may have been extrapolated to cover the case of unqualified observers.

The *London Gazette* provides numerous examples of the sense in which the term 'probationer' was supposed to have been employed, a typical entry within the RAF Section reading as follows: 'The undermentioned temp 2nd Lieutenants (late General List, RFC, on probation) to be confirmed in their rank as 2nd Lieutenants, Observer Officers.' Note, incidentally, and crucially, that these provisions did not apply solely to observers, the *Gazette* containing many similar entries confirming the RAF commissions of pilots 'late General List, RFC, on probation'.

The 'on probation' tag was plainly intended to refer to the status of an officer's commission, not to his professional standing. It was an unfortunate coincidence that, although the context was different, the same term also happened to be applied to observers who had yet to complete their formal professional qualification. Even so, it was quite inappropri-

[19] *Ibid.* Most of the questions were raised Lt-Col Adrian Clark in France, seeking the resolution of apparent inconsistencies between certain recent AMWOs. Most of the answers were contained in Air Ministry letters 47921/1918(P4b) of 9 August and C.23632(P4b) of 7 September 1918, written by Maj S.C. Raffles and Capt C.F. Apthorp on behalf of Col R.H. More, the Deputy Director of Personal Air Services in London.

[20] AIR1/1995/204/273/222. HQ RAF DRO 815 of 3 October 1918.

[21] *Ibid.* The definitive regulations governing the appointment of Kite Balloon Officers were published in HQ RAF DRO 819 of 10 October.

[22] AIR1/1078/204/5/1677. In commenting on the forms of expression used in a draft HQ RAF Order concerning Kite Balloon Officers, which Lt-Col Clark had submitted to London for vetting, Maj Raffles noted that the term 'observer' was considered to be inappropriate in connection with balloonists and that it was no longer used by the Air Ministry in this context. This advice was offered in Air Ministry letter C.23632 (P4b) dated 3 October 1918.

[23] AIR1/872/204/5/552. HQ RFC reproduced the relevant paragraph from Army Order 1520 in its Routine Orders for 21 April 1916; it was subsequently repeated on, for instance, 20 October 1916.

ate, under any circumstances, to apply the 'probationer' label as if it were a rank but, if it were going to be done at all, then it should have been done to pilots as much as to observers. Needless to say, it was not. It is possible that this selective misapplication of 'probationer' was simply a misunderstanding but, in view of the RFC's track record in such matters, it is difficult to dismiss the possibility that it was yet another exhibit from the range of subtle humiliations that were reserved for back-seaters. Whatever the explanation, HQ RAF finally outlawed the misuse of the term 'probationer' in September 1918.[24]

1918. Real and perceived problems over seniority

The misuse of nomenclature was not the only way in which observers appeared to have been disadvantaged by RAF regulations in the summer of 1918. For instance, because the RAF had been created on 1 April this date had been given a legislative significance which seemed to have unfortunate consequences for some observers, although this did not become apparent until June when unexpected dates began to appear in the *Gazette*. Once the problem had been identified, however, it provoked a protest from Maj A.G.R. Garrod. By then Garrod was commanding No 13 Sqn as a pilot, but he had originally been an observer, which may have made him unusually sensitive to the RFC's customary disregard for the interests of back-seaters. Perhaps hoping that the RAF would prove to be more enlightened, he was moved to put pen to paper in June.[25]

Writing to OC 1st Wg, Lt-Col E.L. Gossage, Garrod's letter cited (in essence) the hypothetical case of two ex-regimental, 2nd lieutenant probationary observers who might have joined his squadron on the same day in, let us say, January 1918, but who qualified a few days apart on (say) 28 March and 2 April. On the evidence of recent *Gazettes*, it appeared that anyone who qualified before 1 April 1918 would have his seniority antedated, RFC-style, to the date that he joined his squadron. By contrast, anyone qualifying after 1 April would accrue seniority only from the date on which they qualified. In Garrod's example, therefore, it seemed that his two men could have three months' difference in seniority which, apart from anything else, because it would influence the date of their subsequent promotion, would have some financial implications for the individuals concerned. He furnished the names of five officers who were directly affected by this problem and requested that the seniority of all of them be back-dated to their initial assignment to his squadron.

HQ 1st Wg was not prepared to make an issue of Garrod's complaint, its reply simply acknowledging that, while they might seem a little unfair, rules were rules. In effect, and somewhat predictably, Gossage and his staff appear to have taken the fairly robust view that one could not make an air force omelette without breaking some eggs – and, so long as they were observer eggs, this was of no real consequence. It might have been a different matter if they had been pilot eggs, of course, but there was no question of there being a 'seniority gap' for them. Pilots continued, as they always had done, to accrue seniority from the date on which they gained their 'wings', irrespective of their level of competence, or even whether they were on active service.

With hindsight we now know that this exchange of correspondence had been prompted by a misconception, the confusion having arisen because the associated regulations were still ill-defined and, as a result, poorly understood. Fortunately, while Lt-Col Gossage appears to have been insufficiently moved by the plight of observers to raise the matter with his brigadier, similar complaints must have been raised by units within V Bde and these had been forwarded up the chain. In responding to V Bde's letter, HQ RAF was able to put everyone's mind at rest. While seniority *within the RAF* could not, under any circumstances, date from earlier than 1 April 1918, officers could be 'recommended for promotion to Lieutenant after 12 month's commissioned service whether in the Army, Navy or Air Force.' Clearly, therefore, Garrod's misgivings had been groundless. The first of his men to qualify would have had his seniority in the Air Force List noted as 1 April while his colleague's would have dated from the 2nd. This difference was of little practical significance, however, as both would still have been eligible for promotion to full lieutenant one year from the dates on which they had first been commissioned.[26]

1918. The resolution of unusual cases

While it was relatively unusual for commanders to take up the cases of observers with any enthusiasm, as Maj Garrod had done, he was not alone. For instance, when HQ RAF eventually publicised the final version of the regulations governing the qualification of observers in October 1918, Maj J.F. Jones submitted an appeal on behalf of the ten original observers of No 215 Sqn, all of whom had been gazetted with effect from 16 August. Since they had all joined the squadron before it left the UK, he invoked AMWO 795 to request that their seniority be amended to reflect either the dates on which each individual had joined the squadron (the earliest of which was 27 May) or that on which they had all flown to France, which was 2 July. HQ Independent Force backed the case, requesting the Air Ministry to action the earlier date.[27] Probably because the war was effectively over by the time the appeal reached London, from an examination of the personal records of these officers, no remedial action ever appears to have been taken.

While there were a few other instances of such formal complaints being given official backing, most were submitted by individual officers. As previously noted (see pages 45–47), since early 1917 the constantly changing pattern of regulations had prompted a steady stream of appeals from observers who suspected that their cases might have been mishandled or who considered that their peculiar circumstances warranted special consideration. The confusion of contradictory arrangements which had been implemented

[24]AIR1/983/204/5/1169. HQ RAF drew attention to the inappropriate use of the term 'probationer' in its Routine Orders for 10 September 1918.
[25]AIR1/1028/204/5/1416 contains the related correspondence.

[26]AIR1/1078/204/5/1677. This advice was provided by HQ RAF in its letter AL/R/8 of 27 June 1918. In fact, however, it would seem that the Air Ministry had probably acted unilaterally in introducing a twelve-month interval before promotion to lieutenant, this having been announced by AMWO 304 of 22 May 1918, as eighteen months was usual in the Army, certainly since the publication of Army Council Instruction 1253 of 12 August 1917. Since there were clearly financial implications here, the Treasury stepped in to object to the RAF's procedure. An appeal, on the rather dubious grounds that it was more dangerous to be a flyer than an infantryman, was rejected on the basis that aviators were already amply compensated for the risks they ran by the issue of flying pay. The RAF was eventually obliged to come to heel and it adopted an eighteen-month rule in October 1918.

during 1918 had served only to increase the incidence of such submissions. Most of these sought either antedates of seniority or permission to wear an observers badge where this had previously been withheld. In many cases the applicants were not even asking to be formally gazetted as Observer Officers; they simply felt that, having done a modicum of operational flying, and often having been wounded or injured for their pains, they ought to have more to show for it than a limp.

The ultimate decision in such cases was (usually) taken by the Director of Air Personal Services (DAPS) at the Air Ministry, acting on advice received. In practice this meant that the matter was referred to HQ RAF who handed it down, via Brigade and Wing Headquarters, to the squadron on which the applicant had served. After examining the unit's records, amplified by his personal impressions (if he could recall the subject of the enquiry), the CO would express his opinion and the file would wend its way back up the chain to London. Since they rarely knew anything about a particular case, it was unusual for any of the intermediate formations to add more than a token comment, so the final judgement eventually handed down by the Air Ministry almost always reflected the recommendation made at squadron level.

In most cases DAPS' pronouncement was accepted as being final but, very occasionally, an applicant would appeal. For instance, in the spring of 1918 a Stores Officer, Lt Hugh Jones, requested permission to wear a flying 'O' on the grounds that he had done a substantial amount of flying with No 2 Sqn.[28] His claim was rejected because OC 2 Sqn could find no record of Jones ever having served with the unit. This provoked a second, more detailed submission and on further investigation it transpired that Jones had indeed served with No 2 Sqn (July 1912 to November 1914) and with No 7 Sqn (April 1915 to January 1916) and that he had flown with both units. At the time, however, he had been Air Mechanic, Jones, H. (229); it had simply never occurred to anyone that the applicant might not have been an officer.

Most cases were much easier to settle. For example, although Capt R.G. Lucena had flown with No 1 Sqn in 1915, he had never been authorised to wear an observers badge and he eventually sought permission to do so.[29] On investigation, this turned out to have been a simple bureaucratic oversight, as Lucena had been formally categorised as a qualified observer as early as 16 July 1915; authority for him to wear his flying 'O' was granted on 11 July 1918.

On the other hand, 2/Lt F.C. Wallis was less successful when he tried his luck.[30] His submission was based on his claim that, having joined No 20 Sqn in late October 1917, he had made three non-operational and eight operational flights, one of which had involved an aerial combat, before being wounded in action on 17 November. Although he never flew again, and had not completed his certification, Wallis considered that this record ought to be sufficient to earn him at least the right to wear an observers badge. OC No 20 Sqn disagreed, however, and Wallis' request was denied.

The Wallis case did not reflect a definitive policy, however, and in very similar circumstances the authorities sometimes took a more generous view. For instance, by September 1917 2/Lt A.L. Sutcliffe of No 21 Sqn had flown about forty hours and passed the tests in artillery observation and signalling. When he was shot down on the wrong side of the lines on the 26th he was still unqualified, as he had yet to be certified in gunnery and photography. His right leg having been amputated six inches from the top, he was eventually repatriated in February 1918. His subsequent request that he be permitted to wear an observers badge was granted, although he was never formally gazetted.[31]

A similar case was submitted by Lt J.E. Cross on 25 July 1918.[32] Slightly edited, his letter read as follows:

> 'I joined No 11 Sqn on 24th October 1917. I passed all the specified tests and did several hours over the lines and 4½ hours on an Aerial Gunnery Course at Berck Plage, but crashed badly on 26th November during the Cambrai offensive – my pilot going temporarily insane in the air. I was in hospital for 7 weeks after that, but returned subsequently to the same squadron. My Squadron Commander recommended me for my "wing" after the crash but I understand it was refused as I had not done sufficient flying.
>
> After returning to the squadron I did several hours more, but was brought down, I understand by enemy anti-aircraft guns on 13th January.[33] I sustained a compound and depressed fracture of the skull and was taken unconscious to hospital. I understand that I was again recommended for my "wing" after that – and while I was in hospital the Wing Adjutant came to see me, and when I questioned him about it he said that it would go through all right. Whether he meant it or whether he said it to prevent me from worrying I do not know.
>
> I have now been 6 months in hospital and my name has not yet appeared in the London Gazette as a Flying Officer. I understand also that I am unfit for further flying.'

If nothing else, this tale of woe provides a classic illustration of Sir Clement Bailhache's point about the observer's lack of autonomy. After all, while the presence of a mentally deranged observer might have been something of an inconvenience to a pilot, it was unlikely to cost him seven weeks in hospital. Sadly, however, it was decided that, despite his considerable misfortunes, Cross had not suffered enough. Permission for him to wear an observers badge was denied.

Although the authorities tended to take a fairly hard line in such matters, they did make exceptions where appropriate. For instance, No 35 Sqn's Intelligence Officer, 2/Lt G.A. Morris, frequently flew over the lines to verify reconnaissance reports and to develop his ability to interpret photographs. In recognition of his having spent more than fifty hazardous hours in the air on such activities HQ V Bde sought permission for him to wear an observers badge.[34] This request was granted by the GOC on 16 May 1918. Thus, although he never actually qualified as an observer and he does not appear as such in the Air Force List, 2/Lt Morris was officially authorised to wear a flying 'O'.

This was not a unique case, another example being provided by Lt T.L.M. Meares, an Armament Officer, who had flown several night raids in No 83 Sqn's FE2bs.[35] The GOC gave permission for him to wear a flying 'O' on 29 June. HQ V

[27] AIR1/1989/204/273/147. No 215 Sqn letter 215/1805 of 5 October 1918 and HQ Independent Force letter IFA 1/6 dated 12 November.
[28] AIR1/1028/204/5/1416 contains the correspondence relating to this case.
[29] *Ibid.*
[30] *Ibid.*

[31] AIR1/1027/204/5/1415 contains the correspondence relating to this case.
[32] AIR1/1028/204/5/1416 contains the correspondence relating to this case.
[33] AIR1/2011/204/305/11. No 11 Sqn's Casualty Returns do not indicate whom Cross's mad companion might have been on 26 November but his pilot on 13 January was probably 2/Lt J.H. Hartley. Interestingly, despite the verbal reassurances which Cross claimed to have been given, the entries against his name on both Casualty Returns submitted by his squadron specifically did *not* recommend that he should be confirmed as an observer.
[34] AIR1/1028/204/5/1416 contains the correspondence relating to this case.
[35] *Ibid.*

Bde's submission concerning Meares had, incidentally, included the rather interesting statement that he 'desires to remain an Armament Officer, as the chances of his becoming a pilot are very small, as he was severely wounded and lost an eye when serving with his Regiment.' This would seem to indicate that, even as late as the summer of 1918, service as an observer was still regarded by some as being no more than a half-way stage to becoming a pilot. If, like Meares, there was little likelihood of realising such an ambition, it followed that there was little point in bothering to become an observer – even if it was nice to be able to wear one of their badges.

Since the resolution of each case generally reflected the opinion of just one man, usually the erstwhile Squadron Commander, as the foregoing examples suggest, there was almost bound to be some inconsistency in the decisions that were handed down. All of this could have been avoided, of course, if the RFC could only have overcome its reluctance to acknowledge the fact that, qualified or not, any observer flying in France, or anywhere else for that matter, was risking life and limb and that this really did deserve some small token of recognition. As noted above, in August 1918 the RAF did finally rule that all observers on active service would be entitled to wear a flying 'O'. It had taken four years to prise this concession out of the authorities, however, and in the meantime many observers had died, denied even the right to wear a simple cloth badge.

Until the summer of 1917 there had rarely been any question that any observer who fell by the wayside while still on probation, including those who had been careless enough to be wounded or killed in action, had forfeited his right to wear a badge. By June of that year, however, some cursory consideration was being given to such cases via a routine monthly return of all observers struck off charge by each brigade. Instigated by HQ RFC, this requirement was later sustained by HQ RAF.

The return covered all deletions, including, apart from operational losses, those arising from accidents, sickness, postings and detachments. In each case a recommendation was made as to whether the individual concerned should be considered for any form of advancement. This provided, for instance, an opportunity to gazette a missing probationer as a Flying Officer (Observer) so that, in the event that he had been taken prisoner, he would be entitled to the (then full) five shilling rate of flying pay, or to promote to lieutenant someone who had been killed flying as a subaltern, or to suggest that a particularly capable observer should be made up to Flight Commander (which would still involve his having to retrain as a pilot). The returns were submitted via the Headquarters of each Brigade to St André-aux-Bois where they were consolidated and forwarded to the War Office/Air Ministry for any appropriate action with regard to the *Gazette*.

Since the August 1918 regulations had been drafted on the assumption that virtually *all* observers would be fully qualified on arrival, the requirement for this return had lapsed by October. There were, however, a number of unresolved instances of observers who had been killed or taken prisoner while still on probation during the transitional period immediately following the formation of the Service. The Air Ministry's advice as to the disposal of these cases was subsequently sought by HQ RAF. As the status of these men had financial implications for their estates, the Ministry decided that, in view of the fact that they had become casualties, and to reflect the more generous spirit of the August regulations, they all deserved to be gazetted.

This involved HQ RAF's having to conduct a lengthy trawl through its personnel records to identify all the individuals involved. This exercise took six weeks and it was a fortnight after the Armistice before a list of 152 names could be despatched to London. The Air Ministry was able to take appropriate gazetting action for most of these men but, somewhat surprisingly (or perhaps not?), it was unable to trace any record of no fewer than thirty-four of them. In January 1919 HQ RAF was asked to provide any additional information which might help to identify these individuals.[36] By this time the personnel staffs at all the agencies concerned would have had little spare capacity to undertake such a task, as they would have been heavily involved in preparing for and then overseeing a massive programme of repatriation and demobilisation. By the end of that month entire units were disbanding or being reduced to cadre status at a rate of one per day, many of their records being destroyed in the process. Nevertheless, all the lost sheep were eventually tracked down, permitting the loose ends to be neatly tied off.

Before moving on, there is one last aspect of the wearing of flying badges which is worth mentioning. Although anyone actually serving with the RFC or RNAS on 1 April 1918 had been automatically transferred to the RAF, anyone who elected not to remain in the new Service was able to return to his parent organisation during the next three (later changed to six) months. Furthermore, some erstwhile aviators had already returned to their original folds before the RAF had been established. This raised the question of whether these people should still be permitted to wear their 'wings'. The Air Ministry was content that they should. The War Office, however, took the view that all flying badges were now air force business and that it was no longer appropriate for soldiers to wear them. The RN adopted a similar line and in May 1918 it was ruled that flying badges were to be worn only by RAF personnel.[37] As will become clear later, this ruling was to have unfortunate consequences during WW II (see pages 193–194).

1918. The RAF grants its observers (apparently) equal status with that of its pilots

While most of the complications associated with their ranks and with the wearing of the flying 'O' had been overcome without too much animosity, the merging of the two air services had thrown up another problem to do with observers, and this one was rather more contentious. It will be recalled that the Admiralty, once it had taken the plunge and accepted that observers were people too, had decided that they would be eligible to hold executive appointments and had set their notional rank ceiling as high as Captain RN. The RFC had never taken either of these steps, however, and it was now necessary to bring these mismatched policies into line. The Air Council deliberated and elected to round up, rather than down. At a meeting held on 1 May 1918 it was decided that, possibly subject to their having to undergo a brief pilot's course, all RAF observers should be eligible to hold appointments as Flight, Squadron or Wing Commanders.

[36]AIR1/1078/204/5/1677. The list of 152 ungazetted probationary observers, most of whom had become casualties of one kind or another, was covered by HQ RAF letter AL/R/8 dated 26 November 1918. Air Ministry letter C.56065(P4b) contained London's request for additional information on thirty-four of these men.
[37]AMWO 168 of 2 May 1918.

The senior air commanders in France were appalled at this prospect, Trenchard and Salmond both protesting to the Air Ministry on the grounds that any such appointments would seriously damage the efficiency and morale of the RAF in the Field. The Air Council dismissed these objections, evidently taking the view that, as a matter of principle, ex-RNAS observers ought not to have their prospects blighted as a result of their having been transferred to the RAF. Conversely, it followed that ex-RFC observers could not be seen to be disadvantaged by comparison with their ex-naval colleagues. At a meeting held on 5 June the original decision was confirmed; furthermore, it was decided not to pursue the tentative requirement for a nominal amount of pilot training.[38]

Had they reflected a little more deeply, the two outraged generals would probably have realised that they need not have been quite so concerned. It would soon become apparent that the system had a built-in bias so strong that (apart from the handful of ex-RNAS men who had slipped through the net on the strength of their previous record) it proved to be virtually impossible for any observer to gain even a footing on the RAF's promotion ladder.

This was an inevitable consequence of the RFC's long-standing aircrew employment policy which had ensured that all senior RAF appointments were held by pilots. Pilots, therefore, both made and approved all recommendations for promotions and appointments. The record plainly shows that, regardless of the Air Council's enlightened ruling that the RAF was to be an 'equal opportunities employer', those in positions of influence and authority were quite capable of keeping the back-seater very firmly in his place. It was to be another half-century before navigators (or officers of any other trade for that matter) began to break through the 'glass ceiling' in any significant numbers.

Despite the ingrained reluctance of the upper echelons of the hierarchy to give observers their due, there had been a distinct change in attitude at the working level and many junior pilots had come to appreciate their comrades-in-arms. This was to little avail, however, as the prominence that officialdom had accorded solely to pilots meant that their companions often failed to gain the credit which they sometimes felt they deserved. To judge from (ex-2/Lt) George Fuller's recollection of his time with No 9 Sqn in 1918, this still rankled sixty years later.[39]

> 'On every flight the reports of duties carried out ... were written by the pilot and handed in to the Squadron Office ... some of them certainly needed no press agents ... If the observers had been given the same opportunity they might have picked up a few more mentions (*in despatches*) or perhaps the odd decoration for their part in a joint effort.'

Nevertheless, despite the deep-rooted opposition to the idea of an observer's being allowed to attain any sort of standing, there were signs that, had the war continued, this situation just might have been about to change. If such a breakthrough was ever going to happen anywhere, it would probably have occurred in the very long-range squadrons of the Independent Force. On 29 August 1918 Lt-Col R.H. Mulock, commander of the prospective, élite V/1500-equipped No 27 Group, wrote that '... the Observer will in all probability be the Captain of the machine.' In view of his earlier opposition to observers being given any executive responsibility, it seems improbable that Trenchard would have endorsed Mulock's proposals. On the other hand, the GOC was well aware of the vital role that the observer was expected to play in long-range navigation in the future and he did agree to the appointment of one observer per V/1500 squadron in the rank of captain, which suggests that he may have begun to moderate his view.[40]

This concession was eventually reflected in an amendment to the official establishment of a V/1500 squadron. It is interesting to note that, uniquely, each V/1500 was established to have its own crew, there being four crews/aircraft per squadron.[41] A crew consisted of nineteen men in all, eight of them for flying duties. There were to be four pilots, one of them a captain, two engine fitters and two W/T operators, all four of the mechanics being dual qualified as aerial gunners. Oddly enough, however, an observer was not provided, although there were to be six of them on the strength of the HQ Flight, these presumably being assigned as required on a mission-by-mission basis.

A precedent for observers ranked as captains had actually been created a month before Trenchard agreed to their provision on V/1500 squadrons. As early as 27 August the following footnote had been added to the official establishment of O/400 squadrons of the Independent Force:[42] 'Of the total 10 Observers, 1 may be a Captain Observer for duty as Navigation Officer.' Note that the man filling the post did not *have* to be a captain; it was merely permissible for him to be one. In practice, of course, captain observers were such rare animals that few (if any) bomber squadrons were able to take immediate advantage of this amendment.[43] So far as V/1500s were concerned, the Armistice precluded their being committed to operations, so Mulock's remarkably advanced ideas on captaincy were never put to the test.[44]

The status of the observer in the German air service

It is actually somewhat misleading to describe 'Red' Mulock's ideas as 'remarkably advanced', as this was true only within the blinkered society of the RFC/RAF. After all, the RNAS

[38]AMWO 577 of 3 July 1918 proclaimed the policy that RAF Observer Officers, specifically including those not qualified as pilots, would be eligible for consideration for appointments as Flight, Squadron and Wing Commanders. Original documents relating to the discussions leading to this decision have proved elusive but a copy of the relevant extract from the minutes of the 1 May meeting is contained in AIR2/91/C.49935. A summary of the discussions of 5 June is in Air Historical Branch précis AM/C1025 which may be found in AIR1/683/21/13/2234.

[39]This extract is drawn from G.S.B. Fuller's personal account of his wartime experiences published in 1978 in *The Cross & Cockade Journal*, Vol 9, No 3.

[40]AIR1/462/15/312/121. Trenchard's agreement to the establishment of one captain observer per squadron was recorded in the Minutes of a conference held, under his personal chairmanship, on 30 September 1918 to discuss a variety of topics relating to the Independent Force.

[41]AIR1/1988/204/273/138. This file contains copies of the original establishment for a V/1500 squadron (AF/F/39 dated 6 June 1918), of the final version (AF/IF/6 dated 28 August) and of the amendment of 10 October reflecting the post of a captain observer.

[42]Note that, by this time, there were two establishments extant for O/400 units, AF/F/46 [in succession to the original AF/F/16 (see Fig. 10) and the later AF/F/38] for squadrons serving under HQ RAF, and AF/IF/5 for squadrons of the Independent Force.

[43]Possibly prompted by the anticipated early introduction of directional wireless equipment, on 29 October 1918 HQ Independent Force nominated three experienced observers for acting captaincies. They were Lt E.D. Harding, 2/Lt R.P. Keely and 2/Lt (Hon. Lt) J.F.D. Tanqueray.

[44]Remarkably, considering that he was a pilot, 'Red' Mulock's willingness to recognise the capabilities of observers indicates that he did not feel at all threatened by them. This may well have been accounted for by the fact that he was an ex-RNAS man and thus reflected the positive attitude towards back-seaters which characterised that Service by 1918 but which was still sorely lacking within the RFC.

had accepted, at least the possibility of, observer captains in 1917. Because the navy had so few qualified observers, however, it is doubtful whether many (any?) of them were ever formally nominated as aircraft captains or commanded operational units before April 1918. Once the RNAS had been absorbed into the ultra-conservative RAF, of course, its back-seaters were consigned to the anonymous obscurity that was so familiar to their RFC colleagues.

While the RFC/RAF was not alone in confining executive authority exclusively to pilots, there were air forces which took a more liberal view. This was particularly true within Germany's *Luftstreitkräfte*, where:

> 'The observer, invariably an officer, was as a rule the person actually responsible in an aeroplane. This was not only the case in giant aeroplanes, of which the Commander was generally an observer, but also in smaller types where the pilots were frequently of non-commissioned rank.'[45]

Why did the Germans take such a different view? Perhaps, their *Junker* tradition permitted them to associate leadership with the officer class, without being distracted by the largely irrelevant issue of which seat a man occupied in an aeroplane. Whatever the reason, there were many instances of German observers (*Beobachter*) commanding operational units, one such being *Hauptmann* Hermann Köhl, *Gruppenkommandeur* of the AEG G.IV-equipped *Bogohl 7* in 1918. Because the Germans were able to recognise that command of a unit involved its management and the direction of operations, which did not necessarily involve flying, they could even accept the appointment of observers as executives within their fighter force. This was never a common practice but a notable example was *Hauptmann* Erhard Milch, who, despite his 'objections that he could not fly himself', was given command of *Jagdgruppe Nr 6*, a formation which controlled four squadrons of single-seat fighters.[46]

The award of decorations was another field in which German practice contrasted sharply with that of the British. There were, of course, differences in the national criteria used to decide whose gallantry or service should be recognised but the fact remains that all nineteen airmen decorated with the Victoria Cross during WW I were pilots. Why were there no observers among them? It cannot have been because they never did anything very brave, because there were, for example, several instances of back-seaters saving the lives of wounded and incapacitated pilots, sometimes by climbing out of their cockpits to stand on the wing so that they could reach the controls. Such actions might win an observer an MC, but never a VC.

Unlike the RAF, the German air services were quite content to recognise the efforts of their observers. For instance, of the eleven aviators awarded Bavaria's highest military honour, the *Militar-Max-Joseph Orden*, four were observers. Allowing for the numerical preponderance of pilots (every aeroplane has, at least, one, whereas only some need an observer) this would appear to have been a reasonable statistical outcome. Within the German armed services, a special cachet attached to the Prussian *Orden Pour le Mérite*, the 'Blue Max', of which eighty-one were awarded to aviators. Predictably, the lion's share of these, sixty-two, went to the glamorous coterie of single-seat fighter pilots, leaving nineteen for the rest. Of these, six were awarded to observers (Brandenburg, Horn, von Grone, Müller-Kahle, Nielebock and Schreiber), two went to pilots who flew as, and were specifically decorated for their services as, observers (Griebsch and von Pechmann) and one went to a balloon observer (Rieper).[47]

In the context of this book, one of these *Pour le Mérite* holders is of particular significance. He was *Hauptmann* Ernst Brandenburg, *Gruppenkommandeur* of *Kagohl* 3 in 1917. He led, and flew in, his unit's Gotha G.IVs during the opening phase of the German air assault on the UK which began in May. The shock caused by the 162 fatalities inflicted by a daylight raid on London on 13 June was the greatest single factor leading, via the Smuts Report, to the establishment of an Air Ministry and the amalgamation of the RFC and RNAS. Since the RAF, which was so consistently dismissive of back-seaters, could be said to owe its very existence to the men who bombed London in 1917, there is an exquisite irony in the fact that they had been led by an observer.

Hauptmann Ernst Brandenburg, Gruppenkommandeur *of* Kagohl *3, wearing his observers badge (below the Iron Cross 1st Class) and the emblem of the Blue Max. No British observer was ever decorated with his country's highest award and it was inconceivable that any would have been permitted to command a squadron, yet, in a sense, it was this German observer who was responsible for the creation of the RAF.* (T. Treadwell)

[45]Georg Paul Neumann, *The German Air Force in the Great War* (1920).
[46]David Irving, *The Rise and Fall of the Luftwaffe* (1973). Milch, who had qualified as an observer in 1915, was later Managing Director of *Deutsche Lufthansa* before becoming a founder-member of the *Luftwaffe* and, in 1940, a *Generalfeldmarschall.*

[47]See, for instance, Peter Kilduff, *Germany's First Air Force* (1991) and Terry Treadwell and Alan Wood, *German Knights of the Air* (1997).

Chapter 14

1918. The observer's involvement in bomb-aiming grows as the air weapon matures

The increasing reliance being placed on the observer in aerial combat suggests that by early 1918 his functions had been largely reduced to those of an air gunner. This was only partially true, however, and in other respects his responsibilities were growing significantly to deal with the increasing sophistication of role equipment. In the early days, for instance, there had never been any doubt that it was the pilot's prerogative to squint over the side and judge when to drop bombs, with or without the aid of a primitive bomb sight. A recollection of the 'technique' being employed by No 18 Sqn's FE2b crews during the Battle of the Somme, for instance, is provided by Flt Lt P.S. Jackson-Taylor:[1]

> 'Usually two or four 20 lb bombs were carried on each patrol and dropped whenever and wherever the pilot wished. I do not remember any form of standard bomb sighting being used. Consequently the bombing was of a very elementary character and the absence of individual knowledge of the principles of Bomb Dropping made the process of pulling the release toggle a delightful game of chance. I shall never forget peering over the side to watch the effects of a salvo of two bombs on the German trenches at Martinpuich (*or*) my consternation on seeing the bombs fall and burst quite half a mile away to the west in front of our own front line.'

By 1918, the development of increasingly efficient aiming devices was rendering such haphazard methods redundant. Furthermore, since these devices tended to be operated by the observer, there had been a detectable, if still slight, shift in the balance of power within a crew.

In July of that year the Air Ministry convened a conference to review the situation regarding bomb-aiming, the outcome effectively endorsing what was already tending to become common practice.[2] It was recognised that pilots needed to handle bombing in ground support operations and, for attacks delivered from below 1000 feet, they were to continue to do so. Above that height, however, a more scientific approach to bomb-aiming was to be adopted.

It had been noted from observation of practice sorties carried out on academic ranges that when pilots carried out their own bomb-aiming they often did so with as much as 6° of bank applied. This was probably a result of their having to lean to one side (sometimes right out of the cockpit) to use the sight, but whatever the reason, it did nothing to improve accuracy, which was bound to be further degraded under the stress of a combat situation. It was decided that in future 'high' altitude bomb aiming should become the business of the observer, the pilot's contribution being confined to endeavouring to maintain his aeroplane in balanced, level flight at a constant airspeed. The only proviso was that, for attacks delivered from above 10 000 feet by formations of day bombers, the preferred tactic would be for one crew to act as the 'master bomber' with the others releasing their weapons on a given signal. Maj-Gen Salmond required each bomber squadron to nominate two such crews within each flight – two to allow for attrition.[3]

So far as the provision of equipment was concerned, O/400s, DH 9s, DH 10s and Vimys were all to have a Negative Lens Sight to provide their pilots with a downwards view and to enable them to assist in lining up on the target. It was intended, however, that this sight should cease to be used for bomb-aiming. O/400s, DH 9s and DH 10s were to have a High Altitude Drift Sight installed, along with the release system, at the observer's station. A duplicate release system was provided in the DH 9 to permit the pilot to drop bombs in formation attacks. The Vimy, and large flying boats, were to have the Low Height Drift Sight as standard but it was anticipated that these would eventually be replaced by a Course Setting Sight. Whichever model was provided, it was to be installed in the nose of the aircraft and operated by the observer. The only other bomber being used in substantial numbers was the night flying FE2b but by this time their normal delivery mode was a shallow dive attack, releasing at about 500 feet, and this tended to be done by the pilot without the aid of a sight.

It is interesting to note that during the conference some consideration had been given to providing the observer with a means of controlling the rudder so that fine adjustments could be made during the bomb run. This was an attempt to overcome the long-standing problem of how best to pass steering signals from the bomb-aimer, who could always see the target, to the pilot who often could not.

Depending upon the type of aeroplane involved and whether he was located behind, beneath or in front of the pilot, observers employed a variety of methods to do this, e.g. tapping on the appropriate shoulder or flying boot, or using hand signals. On its big Handley Pages the RNAS had tried a system of signal lights. Controlled by switches at the bomb-aimer's station, the observer could direct the aircraft to turn left or right or fly straight ahead by illuminating a red, green or white light on the pilot's instrument panel.[4] Since all of these approaches lacked responsiveness and precision, it seemed a logical idea to cut the pilot out of the loop altogether and allow the bomb-aimer to fly the bombing run himself. It was a very far-sighted proposal but one which was at least one war too early. It would happen eventually, but it

[1]AIR1/2388/228/11/84. Taken from an account of his previous Service experience, written by Flt Lt P.S. Jackson-Taylor at the RAF Staff College in 1926. Before training as a pilot, Jackson-Taylor had spent August 1916 to March 1917 flying as an observer with No 18 Sqn.

[2]AIR2/84 B.5386. A summary of the conference's conclusions was circulated under cover of Air Ministry letter 11224/1918/DAE dated 11 July 1918.

[3]*Ibid.* Salmond's stipulation was contained in his letter AF1821/QB2 dated 31 July 1918.

[4]For a first-hand description of the problems involved in bomb-aiming from Handley-Pages, see P. Bewsher, *op. cit.*

Photographs of wartime two-seaters with a bomb sight rigged for use by the observer are extremely rare. This one, of a DH 9A, F1001, of No 205 Sqn, actually dates from shortly after the Armistice but it does feature an aeroplane fitted with a High Altitude Drift Sight (presumably a Mk Ia, which was calibrated in mph, as distinct from the Mk I, which was calibrated in knots for maritime use) mounted alongside the rear cockpit. The crew were Lts W.B. Esplen (pilot) and C.H. Latimer-Needham. (J.M. Bruce/G.S. Leslie collection)

was to be many years before pilots would be content to tolerate such a degree of overt interference in their domain.

While the July 1918 discussions had effectively laid down the officially approved bombing policy for the future, the degree to which it could actually be implemented would depend upon the extent to which the appropriate sights could be supplied and fitted. Observers certainly tended to look after bombing in Handley Pages in the summer of 1918, but then they always had. On the other hand it would seem unlikely that much change occurred in the DH 9 squadrons. The Drift Sight was designed for external mounting and it should, therefore, be readily visible in photographs. In practice, pictures of DH 9s with a bomb sight rigged for use by the observer, or by the pilot for that matter, are extremely rare which suggests that the Negative Lens Sight may well have remained in use with pilots continuing to do the aiming. (Some notes on bomb sight development during WW I are at Annex G.)

1918. The introduction of a comprehensive system of air armament training

The availability of purpose-built bomber aircraft, bigger bombs and more sophisticated sighting devices had created a need for yet more training and this began to be arranged in the months immediately preceding the creation of the RAF. To provide specialist instructors in this field a School of Bombing was set up in London (at 14 Langham Place) on 1 October 1917.[5] This school moved to Uxbridge on 22 March 1918 to join the Bombing Squadron which was then being organised within the existing Armament School (see Chapter 12, Note 11). Commanded by Capt W.H.J. Eldridge (previously a lieutenant RNVR – most of the officers assigned to the original directing staff at Uxbridge were contributed by the navy), the Bombing Squadron was staffed mainly by NCO instructors drawn from the infantry who had themselves only recently been trained by their own officers, using RNAS facilities at Eastchurch.

Following the merging of the two air arms in April, the Armament School began running a variety of courses on bombs and bomb gear tailored to the needs of prospective observers (and others). At the same time instruction on bombing was deleted from the syllabuses of the SoAs, responsibility for this aspect of basic training passing initially to the ex-RNAS School of Armament at Eastchurch. Over the next few months the facilities at Uxbridge were considerably expanded and it gradually took over most of the courses being run by Eastchurch so that the Armament School eventually became the main RAF training centre for the technical aspects of offensive weapons. The ex-RNAS school was not entirely eclipsed, however, and it continued to operate, under its RAF name of the Ground Armament School, until the end of the war. Despite its name, Eastchurch still catered for aircrew, especially those destined for maritime units, most of whom continued to learn about bombs the navy way.

On 1 August 1918 the rapidly expanding Armament School was reorganised, being internally sub-divided into a Bombing Wing and a Gunnery and Gears Wing. Two weeks later instruction in gunnery was finally deleted from the curriculum of the SoAs, where it had been in steady decline

[5]The CO of this school, Lt W. Moulding, took up his post with effect from 16 October.

By the time that this picture was taken on 28 September 1918, No 1 School of Navigation and Bomb Dropping at Stonehenge had become quite a substantial unit. In this picture it is possible to make out thirteen DH 4s, three O/400s and a stray Sopwith single-seater (Snipe?). (J.M. Bruce/G.S. Leslie collection)

since April. Responsibility for this element of the syllabus was largely assumed by Uxbridge, although, as with bombing training, Eastchurch continued to run gunnery courses for maritime aviators.

While Eastchurch still had a role to play, Uxbridge handled the lion's share of the overall RAF task for the remainder of the war, turning out ever-increasing numbers of Armament Officers, armourers and flight cadets, as well as its own officer and NCO instructors. Some idea of the scale of this operation can be gauged from a head count taken on 11 November when the Gunnery and Gears Wing alone had forty-nine officers on its staff along with 301 NCO instructors; there were 2089 students (of all types) in residence, some of them in overspill accommodation in Ealing. By this time, leaving aside technical personnel, the aircrew throughput of the whole school was reported to have been running at a remarkable 1200 flight cadets (pilots *and* observers) per month.[6]

1918. Navigation training is placed on a firm footing

While the RFC had been establishing a training system dedicated to air armaments, the associated need to improve navigational standards had been receiving similar attention.

[6]Ironically, in view of the way in which the wartime pattern of armament training had evolved, it was the school at Uxbridge which closed down after the war, leaving Eastchurch to become the RAF's peacetime 'centre of excellence' for air weapons training, a function which it discharged until 1938.

The initiative in this case came from the RNAS whose Director of Air Services, Cdre G.M. Paine, sought the advice of the Admiralty Compass Observatory in the autumn of 1917. The observatory's director, Frank Creagh-Osborne (a retired captain RN), responded on 2 October. He recommended a four-week course, three of compass theory to be held at Slough and one of practical air pilotage (a combination of map-reading and rule of thumb dead reckoning) at Manston. Joint army/navy participation was anticipated with suggested intakes of twelve at weekly intervals. Academic instruction was to be handled by the navy, Slough's Lt L.H. Pelly being offered up as a suitable chief instructor. In addition, one RFC and one RNAS staff pilot would be needed to supervise the flying phase.

This proposal was passed to the War Office for its consideration. Maj-Gen Brancker's immediate response was positive and, recognising the navy's expertise in this field, he readily acknowledged that the RNAS was best placed to handle instruction in the theory and practice of air navigation. On the other hand, while Creagh-Osborne's concept might have satisfied the relatively modest needs of the RNAS, it would have been quite incapable of dealing with those of the RFC. Thinking on a military scale, Brancker envisaged courses of fifty students each, so that there would be something like 200 pupils in residence at any one time, and he considered that the whole business ought to be conducted at an aerodrome.

The eventual outcome of these deliberations was the first unit dedicated to the provision of academic and practical training in both navigation and bombing. From the resources made available by disbanding the RFC's No 2 TDS and the transfer of the RNAS' Handley Page Training Squadron from Manston, No 1 School of Navigation and Bomb Dropping came into being at Stonehenge on 5 January 1918. Although the school was nominally an RFC unit, its joint-Service constitution was underlined by the fact that its first CO was Wg Cdr J.T. Babington, one of the most experienced naval Handley Page pilots. By the end of the war the school's planned output amounted to some 120 aircrew per month, half of them qualified by day and half by night. The notional aircraft establishment stood at forty-eight DH 4/9s for prospective day bomber crews, ten Handley Pages for heavy night work and forty FE2bs for crews destined for light night bombers. When the Armistice was signed a second such school was operating at Andover; there was a third in Egypt and a fourth had recently been opened at Thetford.

1918. The establishment of a comprehensive training sequence for observers

It will have become apparent from earlier chapters that until the summer of 1917 the various schemes devised to train observers had never really lived up to expectations. Since recruiting had consistently failed to keep pace with the demands of the expanding air services, the system had frequently had to resort to sending men into action before they had been adequately trained. This situation was exacerbated from time to time by the need to replace substantial combat losses as a matter of urgency and further complicated by the changing requirements of the front line squadrons. As a result there had always been a degree of dissatisfaction with the quantity, the quality and/or the nature of the training being provided. Major advances were made thereafter, however, and the situation had been completely transformed by the time of the Armistice. During 1917 the RNAS and the RFC had both stepped up direct recruiting considerably and the latter's 'do-it-yourself' squadron-based training system had finally been abandoned. It was still possible for an officer to request a transfer from the trenches to flying duties, of course, but this now invariably involved a posting home for a series of formal courses.

So far as directly-recruited observers were concerned, along with prospective pilots and officers of ground branches, they continued to be inducted into the RFC/RAF via the Cadet Brigade at Hastings. From there some (but certainly not all) went to No 7 (Observers) School of Military Aeronautics [(O)SoMA] which had been set up at Bath on 14 January 1918 to provide a dedicated ground-based aviation course specifically tailored to the needs of back-seaters. Over the next few months the SoMA's syllabus was gradually amended to emphasise basic military topics (drill, PT, deportment, organisation, messing arrangements and rations, law, pay, etc.) at the expense of its more technical content. Much of the latter was progressively deferred to later stages of training when it could be dealt with in greater depth at appropriate specialist schools after a cadet had been selected for a particular role.

The first topic to be deleted was artillery co-operation in January, followed by bombing in April and eventually gunnery. A substantial aviation content still remained, however, Bath continuing to deal with subjects which were common to all roles, e.g. elementary airframe rigging, signalling, instruments, the principles of aero-engines (including the ability to start one by swinging the propeller) and navigation; in fact the emphasis on aerial navigation was significantly increased.[7] This process was not unique to observers, incidentally. The curriculum at the SoMAs/SoAs attended by cadet pilots underwent similar changes during the early part of 1918, instruction in role-related matters and tactical skills being progressively deferred to later stages of training, permitting more time to be devoted to basic subjects at the initial stage.

While the initial training of pilots remained substantially unchanged thereafter, a further rationalisation of that for observers took place in mid-1918. Precise details are obscure but it would appear that it had been decided to separate the induction training of pilots, observers and administrative and technical officers. The closing down of the Officers Technical Training Wings[8] in July released sufficient instructional staff to permit the formation of No 7 (Observers) Cadet Wing at Hastings. On 8 August the nucleus of this unit moved to Reading. In the meantime, however, a revised syllabus had been introduced at Bath, this now incorporating much of the Cadet Wing curriculum. Thereafter (probably from July[9]) prospective observers bypassed the Cadet Wing phase and reported directly to No 7 (O)SoA which now offered twelve- (and later eight-) week courses.

Based on their performance at Bath, the Commandant (Lt-Col C.P. Rooke DSO, Middlesex Regt) determined whether his cadets would graduate as flight cadets, i.e. potential officers, or as NCOs (Non-Technical).[10] He was also required to select them for a particular role, the most promising students being earmarked for corps, fleet or anti-submarine work. By May 1918 there were considered to be five roles for 'proper' observers: corps; fighter reconnaissance; day bomber; night bomber and maritime, i.e. for shipboard and anti-submarine duties. The first three of these could be undertaken by officers or NCOs, night bombers and floatplanes being the exclusive preserve of officers. In addition there were NCO W/T and engineer observers to satisfy the special requirements of flying boats and airships.

Two examples will give some idea of the length of training at this stage.[11] A fighter reconnaissance observer was expected to spend twelve weeks at Bath, followed by three

[7]AIR1/396/15/231/37. DAO letter 87/Inst/378(O.2) dated 27 November 1917 directed that increased emphasis was to be given to navigation at the SoMAs and that selected officers from their instructional staffs were to be attached to the Royal Naval College at Greenwich to attend an appropriate specialist course in aerial navigation.

[8]The Officers Technical Training Corps (later restyled No 1 Officers Technical Training Wing) had been set up at Hursley Park, Winchester, in mid-1917. Its function was to permit the RFC to engage promising young men, who had been members of the Officers Training Corps (OTC) while at school, some three months before they actually became eligible for military service at the age of eighteen. The scheme was considered to be a success and in the autumn No 2 OTTW was formed, both units being located at Hastings/St Leonards as part of the Cadet Brigade. By mid-1918 the need for the OTTWs had passed and they had effectively become a Brigade Pool, holding cadets, many of them by now from the Dominions, pending their entry into formal training with one of the Cadet Wings. In July the OTTWs were closed down, their redundant staffs being used to form three additional Cadet Wings, Nos 6, 7(O) and 8.

[9]One contemporary reference states that the 'first' course at No 7 (O)SoA began on 8 July 1918. It is known, however, that training had actually been under way at Bath since the unit had first opened in January. It is possible that the significance of the July course may have been that it was the first to be run against a combined syllabus, incorporating the curriculum previously handled by a Cadet Wing.

[10]In the RFC/RAF *patois* of the day Cadets were known as 'Fledglings' and Flight Cadets as 'Roosters'.

[11]Both examples are taken from a May 1918 edition of FS Form 224, the Training Transfer Card for Observers.

It is clear from this photograph that by mid-1918 observers were being trained on an industrial scale. Taken at Bath on Sports Day, 27 July, a rough count indicates that some 750 young men, clad in shorts-and-singlets, were involved in this representation of No 7 (O)SoA's title. The fact that there were still enough left over to form the sizeable parade in the background, suggests that there were at least 1000 cadets on the ration strength. (Reproduced from *Roosters and Fledglings*, the RAF Cadet Journal, October 1918)

weeks of ground armament training at Eastchurch and four of practical work at Hythe/New Romney, three at the School of Photography, a fortnight at one of the Schools of Aerial Fighting and Gunnery and a week's course at the Wireless Telephony School at Chattis Hill; a total of twenty-five weeks.

A corps observer did the same twelve weeks at Bath, plus another fortnight with No 1 SoA at Reading, two weeks of ground armament at Uxbridge plus three weeks practical at Hythe/New Romney and a fortnight at the Artillery and Infantry Co-operation School at Worthy Down; a total of twenty-one weeks. It is interesting to note, incidentally, that Reading was still employing much the same, by now well-tried, techniques as had been used at Gosport in 1915 (see page 13). As described by Frank Shire:[12]

> '... we had to climb trees where they had fixed seats and a sending key for Morse. On the ground below a miniature of the front line in France was mapped out, trenches, artillery positions, barbed wire, etc. A target was assigned to us, then a puff of smoke was ignited, this being a shell exploding near the target. We then had to send by Morse the "clock" position of the burst from the target. This was repeated until we had registered a direct hit.'

Since No 1 SoA was primarily concerned with pilots, it was decided to open another (O)SoA for the specific benefit of corps observers. To create this unit, the redundant No 7 (Observers) Cadet Wing at Reading was disbanded on 23 September to furnish the nucleus of the second (O)SoA, No 9, which moved to Cheltenham on 26 October, although it can have achieved very little before the Armistice.

In the meantime, the situation had been complicated by a revised forecast of the numbers of observers required which meant that output had to be more than trebled. In July 1918 the RAF was putting 120 corps and 400 army observers per month through its two-stage Uxbridge/Eastchurch and Hythe/New Romney sequence, plus an indeterminate number for maritime work at Eastchurch. The new requirement envisaged an output of no fewer than 1500 observers per *month*, 500 corps, 600 army and 400 maritime, the latter figure being of particular interest in view of the Admiralty's complaints over what it perceived to be the RAF's lack of interest in naval air requirements (see page 70). To handle this throughput it was decided: to exclude Uxbridge from the sequence; to provide expanded all-through air/ground facilities both at Eastchurch and at Hythe/New Romney and to establish a third such unit at Manston. It was estimated that a total of 328 aircraft would be needed to equip all of these units to the required scale.[13] Although some progress was made with implementing these proposals, notably the establishment of No 2 Observers School at Manston, the plan had not been fully implemented before the war ended.

While little increase in output had been achieved before the Armistice,[14] substantial headway had been made in other respects and by the late summer the two training systems which the RAF had taken over from the RFC and the RNAS had been

[12]F.J. Shire, *The Diary of a PBO* (1981).

[13]AIR6/17. Details of the current and proposed situations regarding the training of observers were contained in the minutes of a Training Expansion Committee meeting held on 12 July 1918. These were subsequently submitted to the Air Council in support of a request for authority to cease work on the underground hangars then under construction at Manston and to reallocate the airfield for use as an observers training school.

[14]No precise figures regarding the output from training during WW I appear to have been compiled but the Air Force List for March 1919 provides some indication. This can only be approximate, however, as this List does not reflect observers who had died, had left the Service or had been transferred to another branch; moreover it deals only with officers, there being no equivalent list for NCOs. Nevertheless, despite these reservations, it is interesting to note that at least 550 observers were commissioned during August 1918, 450 in September and 420 in October. While these figures may well be imprecise, they serve to indicate that the RAF was still a long way short of achieving the 1500 per month target that had been set in July.

Type	Status	Title	Entry
1	Officer/NCO	Corps Observer	Direct recruiting; entry as cadets via No 7 (Observers) School of Aeronautics at Bath
2a	Officer	Fighter Reconnaissance Observer	
2b	NCO	Fighter Reconnaissance Observer	
3a	Officer	Day Bomber Observer	
3b	NCO	Day Bomber Observer	
4	Officer	Night Bomber Observer	
5	Officer	Fleet Reconnaissance Observer	
6	Officer	Anti-submarine Patrol Observer	
7	Officer	Light Night Bombing Observer	
8	Officer	Home Defence Observer*	
9	Officer	Kite Balloon Observer (Sea)	Drawn from cadets and serving naval officers
10	Officer	Kite Balloon Observer (Land)	Drawn from cadets and serving army officers
11	NCO	W/T Observer	Civilian or internal recruits via No 1(T) Wireless School
12	NCO	Engineer Observer	Selected from trained fitters serving with units

*The precise nomenclature used in this case was 'Night Flying Bristol Fighter (Home Defence) Observer'

***Fig. 13.** The recognised categories of observer in September 1918.*

harmonised. Where possible, common ground between various specialisations had been identified and a dozen broad categories of non-pilot aircrew had been recognised; these are summarised at Fig. 13. For each of these 'trades' a logical training sequence had been developed; Fig. 14 represents the UK-based system circa October 1918, the 'Types' in the first column being the same as those in Fig. 13.

It is stressed that the arrangements reflected in Fig. 14 must be regarded as a snapshot and not a definitive picture, as the system was still evolving and subject to frequent changes.[15] Training units moved from time to time and, apart from a seemingly unending process of redesignating existing schools, new ones were constantly being opened. The changes to the initial training of observers, which have already been discussed, provide one example of this trend, but there were many others. For instance: No 3 Fighting School moved from Bircham Newton to Sedgeford in November; as previously noted, No 2 Observers School had opened at Manston before the end of the war, as had No 4 School of Navigation and Bomb Dropping at Thetford; and an Observers School of Reconnaissance and Aerial Photography had been set up at Shrewsbury on 19 October. Had the war continued these additional units, and others, would have been integrated into the training sequence but, in view of their formation dates, none of these latecomers can have made any significant contribution to wartime training.

While the late-war training sequence was extremely comprehensive, as Fig. 14 indicates, it was also lengthy. As a result, very few of the observers who had been exposed to this quite sophisticated system completed all of their courses in time to see any action. Consider, as a random example, the case of Lt F.L. Barlow, a Canadian infantry officer. He transferred to the RAF on 25 July 1918, beginning his indoctrination training at No 1 SoA on 23 August. Earmarked for fighter reconnaissance duties, he began a two-week armament course at Eastchurch on 14 September, moving on to No 1 (O)SAG for live firing on the 28th. A month later he was transferred to No 1 Fighting School for a final tactical polish before being put at the disposal of the Air Ministry on 9 November. Posted to Italy, he reported to No 139 Sqn on the 18th – a week after the shooting had stopped.

As previously noted (see Chapter 12, Note 4), the introduction of the new training system had caused an hiatus in the formation of new squadrons from July onwards. As Barlow's experience shows, it had caused a similar hiatus in the provision of aircrew, pilots as well as observers. Replacements were available, but many of these were products of the old RFC/RNAS schemes or of hybrid interim arrangements. As a result, the training of many of the observers being despatched to France still left much to be desired.

As late as September 1918, for instance, OC No 215 Sqn, Maj J.F. Jones, was obliged to complain about the abilities of some of his observers. One of them, 2/Lt W.J.N. Chalklin, had joined the RAF on 22 April 1918. He had spent a month with the Cadet Brigade at Hastings before moving to Reading where his instruction in navigation had comprised a single one-hour lecture. Following armament training at Eastchurch and Hythe/New Romney, he had been sent to No 33 Sqn for specific training in night work. The only instruction provided having any relevance to navigation had been a single lecture on the construction of the compass and several on compass swinging. Practical work had consisted of one 50-mile

[15]AIR10/64. The information used to create Figs 13 and 14 was derived from FS 39, *Training Courses in the RAF for Commissioned and Non-commissioned Personnel, showing Status and Pay*, which appeared in October 1918, and an earlier draft of the same document. FS 39 opens with a number of caveats, including notes to the effect that individuals would not all necessarily follow the standard pattern, that alterations to the specified courses could be expected and that the missing arrangements for airship pilots and technical officers would be included in a subsequent edition. Publication of the consolidated edition appears to have been pre-empted by the Armistice although details of the revised syllabus for airship pilots were announced in AMWO 1241 of 17 October and for administrative officers and technical officers specialising in stores, W/T, armament, photography and general engineering (aero-engines, rigging and MT) in AMWO 1387 of 7 November. It is symptomatic of the instability within the system that the first of these regulations was already out of date, as it stated that an airship pilot's career was to start with an eight-week course as a cadet at Hastings; in fact the Cadet Brigade had already moved to Shorncliffe by this time; see AMWO 1209 of 10 October.

One other point is worthy of comment. According to FS 39, W/T and Engineer Observers were expected to receive their gunnery training at 'No 3 Observers School'. To date this writer has failed to find any other references to this unit. The titles applied to the training units inherited from the RNAS, and to some of those subsequently set up by the RAF to support maritime activities, were often rather vague and there was a confusing tendency toward duplication. Towards the end of the war several of these schools were redesignated, in an apparent attempt to establish a logical pattern of individually numbered units. It is suspected that No 3 Observers School may have been the designation earmarked for the aerial gunnery training facilities at Leysdown which provided practical experience for students attending courses at Eastchurch.

<table>
<tr><th rowspan="2">Type of Obs</th><th colspan="17">Weeks of Training</th></tr>
<tr><th>1</th><th>2</th><th>3</th><th>4</th><th>5</th><th>6</th><th>7</th><th>8</th><th>9</th><th>10</th><th>11</th><th>12</th><th>13</th><th>14</th><th>15</th><th>16</th><th>17/18</th></tr>
<tr><td>1</td><td colspan="2">Reading[1]</td><td colspan="2">Uxbridge[2]</td><td colspan="4">Hythe/New Romney[3]</td><td colspan="2">Worthy Down[4]</td><td colspan="7"></td></tr>
<tr><td>2a</td><td colspan="2">Uxbridge[2]</td><td colspan="4">Hythe/New Romney[3]</td><td colspan="3">Farnborough[5]</td><td colspan="2">Turnberry (and Ayr), Marske or Bircham Newton[6]</td><td colspan="2">Chattis Hill[7]</td><td colspan="4"></td></tr>
<tr><td>2b</td><td colspan="2">Uxbridge[2]</td><td colspan="4">Hythe/New Romney[3]</td><td colspan="4">Turnberry (and Ayr), Marske or Bircham Newton[8]</td><td colspan="2">Chattis Hill[7]</td><td colspan="5"></td></tr>
<tr><td>3a</td><td colspan="2">Uxbridge[2]</td><td colspan="4">Hythe/New Romney[3]</td><td colspan="5">Stonehenge or Andover[9]</td><td colspan="2">Chattis Hill[7]</td><td colspan="4"></td></tr>
<tr><td>3b</td><td colspan="2">Uxbridge[2]</td><td colspan="4">Hythe/New Romney[3]</td><td colspan="4">Stonehenge or Andover[9]</td><td colspan="2">Chattis Hill[7]</td><td colspan="5"></td></tr>
<tr><td>4</td><td colspan="2">Uxbridge[2]</td><td colspan="4">Hythe/New Romney[3]</td><td colspan="5">Stonehenge or Andover[9]</td><td colspan="2">Chattis Hill[7]</td><td colspan="4"></td></tr>
<tr><td>5</td><td colspan="16">Eastchurch[10]</td><td></td></tr>
<tr><td>6</td><td colspan="10">Aldeburgh[11]</td><td colspan="7"></td></tr>
<tr><td>7</td><td colspan="2">Uxbridge[2]</td><td colspan="4">Hythe/New Romney[3]</td><td colspan="8">Newmarket, Harpswell or East Retford[12]</td><td colspan="3"></td></tr>
<tr><td>8</td><td colspan="2">Uxbridge[2]</td><td colspan="4">Hythe/New Romney[3]</td><td colspan="8">Newmarket, Harpswell or East Retford[12]</td><td colspan="3"></td></tr>
<tr><td>9</td><td colspan="12">Roehampton[13]</td><td colspan="4">Sheerness[14]</td><td></td></tr>
<tr><td>10</td><td colspan="6">Richmond Park[15]</td><td colspan="4">Larkhill or Lydd[16]</td><td colspan="7"></td></tr>
<tr><td>11</td><td colspan="4">Leysdown?[17]</td><td colspan="13"></td></tr>
<tr><td>12</td><td>Leysdown?[18]</td><td colspan="16"></td></tr>
</table>

Prior to embarking on the sequences tabulated above, all direct entrant Types 1-10 had spent eight weeks as cadets at No 7 (Observers) School of Aeronautics at Bath, leaving there (or, in the special case of Type 1, after leaving Reading) as Observer Flight Cadets or Sergeants (Non-technical). On completion of their training they graduated in the ranks of 2nd Lieutenant or Sergeant (Mechanic) and were awarded their observers badges. Trainees with previous service, remustering as observers, particularly Types 9, 10 and 12, attended their courses in their current ranks. W/T Observers (Type 11) had previously completed a five-month course at No 1(T) Wireless School at Flower Down, the syllabus content including wireless theory, spark and CW telegraphy, wireless telephony, directional wireless and signalling.

Notes:

1 No 1 [or *possibly* No 9 (Observers)] School of Aeronautics – map-reading, signalling, theory of artillery and infantry co-operation.
2 Armament School – the Lewis gun, ground firing, bombs, bomb gear. Some students destined for maritime operations may still have been attending equivalent courses run by the Ground Armament School at Eastchurch.
3 No 1 (Observers) School of Aerial Gunnery – the Lewis gun, air firing, reconnaissance, photography, map-reading.
4 RAF and Army Co-operation School – photography, map-reading, practical artillery and infantry co-operation.
5 School of Photography, Maps and Reconnaissance – photography, map-reading and reconnaissance.
6 Nos 1, 2 and 3 Fighting Schools, respectively – aerial fighting, gun-camera work.
7 Wireless Telephony School – voice telephony.
8 Nos 1, 2 and 3 Fighting Schools, respectively – aerial fighting, gun-camera work, map-reading, photography.
9 Nos 1 and 2 Schools of Navigation and Bomb Dropping, respectively – bombs, bomb gear and sights; practical map-reading, navigation, bombing and photography.
10 No 1 Observers School – high rate visual and W/T signalling, wireless theory, navigation, seamanship, Fleet tactics, ship recognition, photography, the Lewis gun, bombs and bombing.
11 Marine Observers School – similar to Note 10, plus hydrophone techniques. NB Some Anti-submarine Observers did the sixteen/eighteen-week Fleet Observers course at Eastchurch instead.
12 Nos 192, 199 and 200 Night Training Squadrons, respectively – day/night cross-country flying and bombing, night reconnaissance, navigation, gunnery, W/T; minimum of 5 hrs night flying to qualify.
13 No 1 Balloon Training Depot – winches, rigging, knotting and splicing, fabric, valves, balloon and parachute packing, signalling, ship recognition; seven ascents to qualify as a free balloon pilot.
14 No 1 Balloon Training Base – transfer of balloons shore-to-ship and ship-to-ship, handling with and without a winch, use of snatch blocks, flying leads, etc, repairs, meteorology, gunnery direction, Fleet tactics.
15 No 2 Balloon Training Depot – technical content similar to Note 13 plus maps, photography, compasses, artillery observation, flash spotting, dummy shoots; seven ascents to qualify as a free balloon pilot.
16 Nos 1 and 2 Balloon Schools, respectively – map-reading, artillery co-operation, advanced practical observation work.
17 'No 3 Observers School' (see Footnote 15 to this Chapter) – the Lewis gun, ground firing and aerial gunnery.
18 'No 3 Observers School' – as above.

***Fig. 14**. Training sequences in use for the various categories of observer (see Fig. 13) circa October 1918.*

reconnaissance sortie by day and one of 100 miles by night. On neither flight had there been a compass in the observers cockpit and the staff pilot had simply map-read his way around the route. Once committed to operations, it soon became apparent that Chalklin had no grasp of 'even the elementary principles of reaching an objective by means of a compass course' and no knowledge whatsoever of the Course and Distance calculator. Similar inadequacies were reported in the case of 2/Lt H. Davies. Maj Jones made it quite clear that the deficiencies exhibited by these two officers were not of their own making and it was noted that both were making good progress with remedial training under arrangements being provided by HQ 83rd Wg.[16]

[16]AIR1/1982/204/273/88. Letter 215/1555 dated 4 September 1918 from OC No 215 Sqn to HQ 83rd Wg whose CO, Lt-Col J.H.A. Landon, forwarded it to HQ VIII Bde with a covering note stressing the paramount need to ensure that all observers were properly trained.

Although questions remain as to the effectiveness of the late-wartime training system, this photograph of the bombing range at Lakenheath provides some indication of the level of sophistication that was becoming increasingly common. (P.G. Cooksley)

We have no specific observations on the abilities of Lt Barlow but, being an early product of what appears, at least on paper, to have been a very sophisticated training scheme, one would like to think that he had been provided with adequate instruction. Unfortunately, there is reason to believe that this may not have been the case. In October 1918, for example, the Air Ministry felt it necessary to urge the COs of maritime units to provide continuation training because 'the present pressure is such that the period of training is not sufficient to ensure that observers have complete knowledge of all subjects'.[17] Plainly, all was not well within the system and part of the problem may well have been a lack of appropriate instructors.

By 1918 the RFC/RAF bureaucracy appears to have been quite meticulous over the issue and subsequent amendment of unit establishments. These were based on a grid with (broadly speaking) trades down the left hand side and ranks across the top. By inserting a number in the appropriate boxes, it was possible to specify how many officers, NCOs and other ranks each unit was to have in each trade, running from major-generals to privates. The interesting thing is that, until as late as the end of June 1918, no training unit ever appears to have been provided with any observers whatsoever. Even a unit as dedicated to the production of back-seaters as No 1 (O)SAG at Hythe/New Romney failed to attract any, although it was entitled to no fewer than ninety-nine staff pilots![18] A similar total lack of observers was reflected in the establishments for such pivotal training units as Training Depot Stations, No 1 School of Navigation and Bomb Dropping, the Artillery and Infantry Co-operation School and so on.

If experienced observers were not being cycled back through the training organisation to pass on their knowledge, it would hardly be surprising if the output from the system turned out to be somewhat lacking. There is some evidence to suggest that this situation may have begun to change during the last months of the war.[19] Even if it had, however, it would have been too late to have had any impact at squadron level, because a cadet who entered training after July 1918 was unlikely to have become operational before the Armistice. As it happened, the reorganised training scheme, which was poised to start turning out very large numbers of observers in the autumn, was a case of too much, too late and many of its graduates simply cooled their heels until they could be demobilised.

'1919'. The observers who might have been

While the training system had been more or less rationalised by the summer of 1918, this was less true of the various types

[17]AMWO 1289 of 24 October 1918.
[18]AIR/1/403/15/231/44. Establishment AF/H/30 as at May 1918.

[19]It is known, for instance, that on 15 September 1918 six observers (Lts G.R. Thornley and A.O. Fraser, and 2/Lts A. McInnes, A.F. Pope, A. Outhwaite and J.A. Blythe), all of them experienced in night operations, had been posted from France to Andover. They were earmarked to join No 166 Sqn but, pending the availability of V/1500s, they were attached to No 2 School of Navigation and Bomb Dropping for instructional duties. This, of course, is hardly the same as providing a formal establishment of instructor posts.

Category	Expertise and Status
Observer	Corps reconnaissance; artillery work; photography – all officers
Marine Observer	Fleet reconnaissance; anti-submarine patrol; low-level bombing – all officers
Aerial Navigator	Advanced navigation, including directional wireless – all officers
Aerial Bomber	Basic navigation; precision bomb-aiming – all officers
Aerial Operator	W/T work – officers, NCOs or ORs
Aerial Engineer	Fitter and/or rigger skills – officers, NCOs or ORs
Aerial Gunner	Aerial fighting – officers, NCOs or ORs

***Fig. 15.** Proposed aircrew categories, autumn 1918.*

of observer which the RAF had inherited. The existing matrix of pigeon holes (see Fig. 13) had been created more by accident than by design and it was decided to revise the system with a view to creating a more logical subdivision of specialisations. Responsibility for this task fell to Maj-Gen Brancker, by now the Master General of Personnel. After some weeks of deliberation he came up with a suitable proposition and circulated the draft of a revised breakdown of trades to the RAF GOCs in France and Egypt and to Maj-Gen Trenchard, now commanding the autonomous Independent Force.[20] Brancker's ideas met with broad approval and after minor amendment it was intended to implement the system.

The new structure would have provided for seven recognised categories of aircrew (other than pilots and balloonists) which would have applied, irrespective of whether they flew in aeroplanes or airships. In essence, any aviators who were fully trained as such were to be regarded as graded aircrew, regardless of the nature of their subsequent employment. If they were not *fully* trained, they were to be regarded as 'walking freight', which, as discussed previously, caused some concern within the lighter-than-air community.

An Air Ministry Weekly Order explaining the new arrangements was drafted during October but it was still doing the rounds of the concerned staffs when the Armistice was signed. Within the Department of Air Personal Services the importance of refining wartime employment patterns was immediately eclipsed by the need to handle the problems associated with demobilisation, which had been receiving some attention since as early as June. Consequently, the ultimate wartime order concerning the categorisation and employment of observers was never published. Nevertheless, since it is of some historical interest to consider what these arrangements might have been, they are summarised at Fig. 15.

Among the new titles (some of which, had begun to acquire a limited degree of currency in advance of their official endorsement) could be discerned the navigators, wireless operators (air gunner), flight engineers, air bombers and the like of WW II, but Brancker did not go quite that far. Under his system all non-pilot aircrew would have been generically classified as 'observers' and all would have worn an observers badge, but there were to have been two major distinctions. First, only the first four categories would have

[20]AIR2/91/C.49935. Air Ministry letter 21322/1918 MGP dated 26 September 1918.

Role/Type	Rear Crew Manning
Corps Reconnaissance	25% Observers 75% Aerial Gunners
Day Bomber (single engine)	15% Observers 30% Aerial Bombers 55% Aerial Gunners
Night Bomber (single engine)	30% Observers 70% Aerial Bombers
Fighter Reconnaissance	25% Observers 75% Aerial Gunners
Fleet Reconnaissance	100% Marine Observers
Large Flying boats	50% Aerial Operators 50% Aerial Engineers
Anti-Submarine (two-seat day bombers and floatplanes)	100% Marine Observers
Vimy/DH 10 (maritime)	50% Marine Observers 50% Aerial Operators
HP O/400	Not specified
HP V/1500	40% Aerial Navigators 20% Aerial Operators 20% Aerial Gunners 20% Aerial Engineers

***Fig. 16.** Proposed rear crew allocations, late 1918.*

worn the single-winged *flying* 'O'; the other three would have had a simple 'O', without any embellishment. The second innovation related to ranks. While direct entrants for the first four categories would automatically have been commissioned on completion of their training, no specific status attached to the other three trades; promotion within these categories was to have been dependent upon seniority, merit and overall performance, both on the ground and in the air.

Another problem that needed to be addressed was that of estimating the numbers of each of the new trades that the system would be required to produce, these in turn dictating both the recruiting targets and the size of each specialised training unit. This calculation depended upon the eventual distribution of the various categories of observer, which would be determined by the role of each operational squadron and the composition of its crews. It was a complicated knot to unravel, as military aviation was maturing rapidly in late 1918 and the implications of the imminent introduction of very advanced aircraft types, such as V/1500s fitted with directional wireless equipment, could only really be guessed at.

Despite this uncertainty, some indication of the likely pattern is provided by Fig. 16, which represents Brancker's own thoughts at the end of September. Two points are of interest. First, while Brancker's list had included the O/400 he had declined to suggest what its future crew complement might be. It is thought that this may have been in deference to Trenchard whom Brancker might well have expected to have had firm views on the manning of 'his' aeroplanes.[21] Secondly, while the inclusion of maritime Vimys and DH 10s reflected contemporary planning, some doubts were already being expressed over the suitability of these types for this role.

All of this future planning was rendered redundant by the Armistice. Within a matter of days the whole system began

[21]*Ibid.* In commenting on Brancker's proposals in his RAF 1701A of 23 October 1918, Trenchard expressed an initial preference for his Handley Pages to be manned on a 50 : 50 basis with aerial gunners and aerial bombers. Somewhat surprisingly, he appears to have seen no need to employ specialist navigators.

to grind to a halt: the deployment of Nos 39 and 119 Sqns was suspended while they were actually *en route* to France; the mobilisation of the next ten squadrons was permitted to proceed, although their deployment was held in abeyance; all formed squadrons whose mobilisation was less advanced were to be disbanded and plans for the formation of other units were cancelled.[22]

1919. Peace and the balance sheet

With no further need for additional personnel, recruiting stopped and the training machine began to shut down. In numerical terms, the system had almost certainly been producing sufficient observers to match the targets set in mid-1917 (see page 57). This was still a long way short of providing the 18 000 newly qualified men per year which had been specified in mid-1918, of course, but this was no longer an issue and within three weeks of the guns falling silent the flow had completely dried up. Having processed their last intakes, the Cadet Wings and Schools of Aeronautics began to close down in the New Year, the suspension of instructional pay from 15 February 1919 effectively marking the end of the wartime flying training programme.[23]

Unfortunately, it has not been possible to ascertain precisely what the training system had achieved in numerical terms. We do not even know for certain how many observers there had actually been, although it is possible to speculate with reasonable confidence. Although references to individual back-seaters are widely scattered throughout surviving WW I documentation, it has been possible to establish that (trained, part-trained or untrained) at one time or another something in excess of 8500 officers flew as observers with the RFC/RNAS/RAF. Records relating to non-commissioned personnel are far more difficult to reconstruct but several thousand of them will have flown as back-seaters. In terms of formally qualified observers, gunners, W/T operators and the like, the numbers will have been relatively small, perhaps 1000 or so, certainly no more than 2000. These professionals were preceded and backed-up, however, by hundreds of virtually untrained air mechanics and naval ratings who flew as back-seaters and by the substantial numbers of soldiers who flew as probationary gunners with the RFC in 1917, albeit many of them only briefly.

The RAF's peak strength in Observer Officers is no easier to establish than the overall total but the largest numbers to be reflected in any Air Force List appeared in the January 1919 edition. Correct as at the 6th of that month, it identifies 4478 Observer Officers, plus another 1035 flying 'O'-wearing Kite Balloon Officers, for a grand total of 5513 commissioned non-pilot aircrew. By comparison, the RAF had 15 817 officer pilots (ranked as lieutenant-colonels or below) on strength in January 1919, also the maximum figure to be recorded in any List. They comprised 14 375 Aeroplane Officers, 695 Seaplane Officers, 413 dual-rated Aeroplane and Seaplane Officers, and 334 Airship Officers.[24]

As a matter of interest, it is informative to compare the situation of observers in January 1919 with that of August 1918, when there had been fifty-seven nominal captains and majors (see page 81). Since the number of qualified observers had risen by some 61% over the intervening period, it followed that, simply to maintain the same proportions, one could reasonably expect the total to have included at least ninety-two captains and majors. 'At least' because it would be equally reasonable to expect a rather larger number, since observers were supposed to have had the same (improved) promotion prospects as pilots since the previous June.

In fact, despite the substantial increase in overall numbers, there were *fewer* captains and majors. The RAF could now boast only two majors and forty-nine nominal captains among its back-seaters, thirty-two of the latter actually being graded as lieutenants. Predictably, with one exception, they were all ex-RNAS.[25] Thus, while the ranks had been swelled by an additional 1695 observers in the five months since August 1918, the proportion afforded any substantial degree of recognition had been virtually halved, from 2% down to 1.1%. This compared to the 13.4% of pilots who were ranked as captains or above. If that was 'equal opportunities' in action, it boded ill for the future.

Although the observer's involvement in, and responsibility for, bomb-aiming and navigation increased throughout 1918, aerial gunnery remained the primary function of most back-seaters until the Armistice. This picture shows observers (or aerial gunners) collecting their weapons. Most of the guns leaning against the wall have the light tubular casing (to protect the gas cylinder) of the Lewis Mk II. That being carried at the slope could be a stripped Mk I but is more likely to be a Mk II without its protective casing; it is fitted with a Norman vane sight and a Hazelton muzzle booster. The magazines are 97-round Type 5s. (T. Treadwell)

[22]AIR1/913/204/5/856. These curtailments were announced by Air Organisation Memoranda 1155 and 1156 dated 15 and 16 November 1918, respectively.

[23]AMWO 306 of 6 March 1919.

[24]The names of an additional 1418 Aeroplane and Seaplane Officers were recorded under a note to the effect that they would be incorporated into the List in a later edition. The reasons behind this are not understood. Subsequent Lists indicate that few (if any) of these men ever were relisted and demobilisation meant that, along with all of the other totals, their numbers began to decline from the February edition onwards. By November 1919, the last List to record pilots under sub-Branches, only 388 remained in this half-acknowledged category.

[25]There were several other acting and honorary captains scattered among the listed lieutenants but the only ex-soldier listed as a substantive captain was Capt A.D. Wright (ex-RFA and RFC) who had seen service as a Kite Balloon Officer prior to his becoming an Observer Officer.

Examples of the aeroplanes in which observers would have flown had the war continued into 1919. (All J.M. Bruce/G.S. Leslie collection)

The 'Berlin Bomber'; a Handley Page V/1500 at Bircham Newton.

A Felixstowe F.5, N4637, which flew with the Seaplane Training Squadron in the early 1920s.

An anonymous DH 10, one of those used by No 216 Sqn during the early days of the Cairo–Baghdad Air Mail.

An FE2b, A6562, of No 102 Sqn. Surprisingly enough, despite their antiquity, the RAF was still operating six squadrons of these light night bombers when the war ended and contemporary plans did not envisage the last of them being replaced by DH 10s or Vimys until April 1919 – and such plans usually ran late.

Part II

Fall and Rise Again 1919–42

Chapter 15

1919–21. Early indications that the post-war RAF would continue to employ observers prove to be illusory

In August 1919 the RAF introduced its own distinctive rank titles.[1] The familiar term Flying Officer, long used to describe the employment grade of a qualified pilot, now became a rank, as did the equivalent Observer Officer. This innovation appeared to acknowledge that observers had finally achieved the public recognition which they had surely earned. Furthermore, it suggested that they were to become a permanent feature of the *post bellum* air force.

This proved to be but a short-lived illusion. In fact little serious consideration had ever been given to retaining observers. Sir Frederick Sykes had been the Chief of the Air Staff (CAS) when the war ended, so it had fallen to him to formulate a plan for the future and he produced a quite detailed memorandum less than four weeks after the Armistice had been signed.[2] He had envisaged a rather grandiose scheme which assumed the maintenance of a substantial permanent air force with responsibilities embracing the whole of the Empire. Presumably accustomed to wartime rates of expenditure, Sykes appears to have anticipated that he would be equally free to spend in peacetime. As a result, his proposals were so ambitious as to be quite unrealistic. In the specific context of this book, however, it is interesting to note that, while he does devote a little space to the training of 'aviation personnel', Sykes makes no specific reference to observers. On the other hand, he does consider the provision of technical, administrative and staff officers, most of whom were to be aviators who, for whatever reason, were no longer suited for flying duties.

Sykes was succeeded as CAS by Sir Hugh Trenchard in March 1919 and he, in turn, began to consider the way ahead. The 'Trenchard Memorandum' of 25 November 1919 would turn out to be a far more practical proposition than Sykes' effort and, following its presentation to Parliament in December, it was to become the blueprint for the RAF of the 1920s.[3] Like Sykes, Trenchard made no mention of observers, but his paper was far more specific than that of his predecessor. It was quite clear that the only officers in Trenchard's air force, certainly the only officers of any consequence, were going to be pilots.

In fact, it would appear that the RAF had probably decided to do away with observers before Trenchard had even taken up his appointment.[4] By that time it was already busily restructuring itself to exclude them. To illustrate this point, consider the case of No 216 Sqn. The constitution of the crews flying its O/400s when the war ended, a pilot and two observers, had not been arrived at by chance. This arrangement represented the distilled experience of four years of aerial warfare; it was the most economical and efficient way to man and operate the aircraft.[5] Only six months later, when the squadron began its move from France to Egypt in May 1919, it took with it twenty-three pilots and only three observers. The lesson had been forgotten already.

While the future of the commissioned observer may have been, at best, precarious, there was no uncertainty whatsoever about NCO aircrew. They were quite definitely not wanted. While most wartime airmen were only too eager to resume, or in most cases to start, their civilian careers, a few had applied to extend their engagement by volunteering to serve with the Occupation Forces. There were, however, 'no vacancies for NCO Pilots, Observers and Aerial Gunners.' Applicants were to be advised that they could be considered for further service only if they were prepared to take up some other trade for which they might be considered suitable.[6]

After some uncertainty, the wartime RAF had eventually concluded that the ideal crew for an O/400 was a pilot and two observers. Yet when No 216 Sqn deployed to Egypt in 1919 it took twenty-three pilots and only three observers; the peacetime rot had already set in. This O/400, B8811, flew with Nos 58, 207 and 216 Sqns but it had been written off before the latter moved to the Near East. (J.M. Bruce/G.S. Leslie collection)

[1]AMWO 973 of 27 August 1919.

[2]AIR8/6. A copy of Sykes' *Memorandum by the Chief of the Air Staff on the Air-Power Requirements of the Empire* of 9 December 1918 is on this file and the text, less the Annexes, is reproduced as Appendix VII to his autobiography *From Many Angles* (1942).

[3]AIR1/17/15/1/84.

[4]On 18 March 1919 the Reconstruction Committee published a *Memorandum on the Post-War Air Force*, broadly outlining its likely organisation and the nature of its manpower requirements, both officers and men. In the former case it was assumed that they would all be pilots and details were provided of both the initial and the post-graduate professional training that they were expected to undergo in the course of their careers. No reference whatsoever was made to observers. A copy of this document is filed among Lord Trenchard's papers at the RAF Museum.

[5]Note that the establishment (AF/F/16) of five officer observers plus eleven NCOs recorded for an O/400 unit at Fig. 10 had been superseded by AF/F/38. This had omitted the commissioned observers, leaving each of the ten aeroplanes with a notional crew of two officer pilots and one NCO observer. The first unit to arrive in France manned to this establishment was expected to be No 215 Sqn. When Maj-Gen J.M. Salmond learned of this he protested to GHQ at the lack of observer officers (his letter CRAF 2022/1G dated 27 June 1918 is on AIR1/533/16/12/114). Field Marshal Haig promptly relayed the GOC's complaint to London. The result was the publication of establishments AF/F/46 and AF/IF/5 of 16 July, both of which provided for a total of twelve officer (including two with the HQ Flight) and four NCO observers. These provisions remained in effect for the remainder of the war, the most common practice being for Handley Pages to be flown by a crew of one pilot and two observers, both of the latter usually being commissioned.

[6]AIR1/1036/204/5/1455. Air Ministry letter C.85253/M4a dated 5 April 1919.

It may well be asked whether it had been wise to disrupt wartime manning practices and to dispose of so much expertise so hastily. In the light of subsequent events, it seems quite clear that it had been a mistake. This had plainly not been apparent, however, at a time when the dominant considerations would have been the clamour for demobilisation and budgetary constraint. Wise or not, what amounted to a pilots-only policy had been implemented and, since Sir Hugh Trenchard was to reign as CAS for the best part of eleven years, it was here to stay. By 1930 the concept of the omnipotent pilot would be so deeply etched into the air force psyche that nothing short of a World War would serve as grounds for questioning the logic which lay behind this perception.

Meanwhile, shortly after the Armistice, the appointment of Aerial Navigation Officer had been introduced.[7] As previously noted, by the summer of 1918 observers had become so closely associated with navigation that O/400 and V/1500 squadrons were entitled to have one on strength in the rank of captain to act as Navigation Officer. In view of this, one might have expected that observers would have been required to fill the new post-war appointments. In the event most, probably all, of them went to pilots. At headquarters these officers were expected to provide specialist advice to the various staffs. At squadron level they held the keys to the Map Store and were responsible for swinging all the compasses held on charge by the unit. It was originally anticipated that they would also establish the quadrantal errors on aircraft fitted with wireless direction finding equipment, indicating that it was expected that this technique would soon become commonplace.

Like the direction finding equipment, however, the early Aerial Navigation Officers soon faded away to be replaced, on units where a residen navigational expert was deemed to be necessary, by an establishment annotation reflecting a requirement for one officer to have formal responsibility for the supervision of air pilotage.[8] In the meantime, responsibility for compass swinging tended to be delegated to ground tradesmen, while some of the Navigation Officer's other chores were often farmed out to junior pilots as secondary duties.

In June 1919 the RAF published its plans for peacetime post-graduate training.[9] Two schools were to be set up to run courses in applied navigation – for pilots. Andover was to run a series of air pilotage courses, training up to fifty officers per year in practical day and night cross-country navigation. Another forty were expected to attend an annual long navigation course at Calshot. This, the so-called 'Long N', was to cover more advanced techniques, including wireless direction finding.

Both programmes proved to be wildly over-optimistic. In the event, Andover ran just one course which started in September 1919. It had thirty-eight students when it began but by the time it ended three months later priority postings and demobilisation had taken their toll and only sixteen were left – and four of these were assessed as failures. Calshot was a little more successful to begin with, running year-long courses in 1920, 1921 and 1922, albeit never with more than ten trainees, but subsequent intakes were reduced to one or two students per year until 1932. On the other hand, three-month air pilotage courses had been reinstated. Now run at Calshot, these provided post-graduate instruction in practical navigation for up to thirty officers per year, which was more than enough to satisfy the RAF's limited requirement for such specialists.

By this time, despite the introduction of the rank title of observer officer, it had long since been made quite clear that there was to be no place for observers in the exclusively 'pilots only' club which the peacetime RAF had become. Any lingering doubts on this score had been removed as early as January 1920 when the Air Ministry had published the following statement:[10]

> 'In view of the decision that practically all officers remaining in the Royal Air Force are to learn to fly, all pilots may in future be employed in any capacity as crew of an aircraft, i.e. as observers, gunners, photographers, etc. It should be noted, that as no provision has been made for observers in the permanent Air Force, all officers are to be considered available for the duties of observers, etc from the date of this Order.'

As this Order implied, any observer who was offered a permanent commission was required to undergo a flying training course, after which he would trade in his flying 'O' for a set of pilots 'wings'.[11] By mid-1921 the Air Force List contained only 152 commissioned observers.

1921–24. The RAF dispenses with its commissioned observers in favour of part-time, non-commissioned aerial gunners

By 1921 the effectiveness of air power in colonial peacekeeping situations had already been convincingly demonstrated during a brief and, more importantly, an impressively cheap campaign in Somaliland. As a result the RAF was given overall responsibility for the maintenance of stability in Iraq in 1922 and it was to be engaged in similar operations in Palestine, the Aden Protectorate and on the North West Frontier of India throughout the inter-war years. To begin with most of the aeroplanes used for these tasks were DH 9As and Bristol Fighters, these being progressively replaced by Wapitis, Fairey IIIFs, an assortment of Hart variants, Gordons and, finally, Vincents. All of these aircraft were two-seaters, as were many of the bombers flown by home-based squadrons. Rather than retaining some observers, however, the RAF decided simply to ignore the experience of 1914–18, electing instead to misemploy ground tradesmen as part-time aircrew.

[7]Aerial Navigation Officers were introduced by AMWO 104 of 23 January 1919. This appointment should not be confused with that of the wartime Air Navigation Officer most of whom had been technical specialists.

[8]AMWO 439 of 12 August 1926 introduced the symbol **p** in the Air Force List to distinguish officers serving with units as navigation specialists, this presumably implying previous attendance at an Air Pilotage Course, although this was not specifically stated to be a prerequisite. Similarly, an **a**, **e**, **s** or **ph** indicated that the pilot concerned was responsible for, and therefore had at least some acquaintance with, armaments, engineering, signals or photography. Advanced qualifications in these and other fields, acquired via courses lasting up to a year (later as long as two years) were indicated by a series of upper case annotations which had been introduced in 1923 (by AMWO 37 of 25 January), that associated with the Long Navigation Course, for instance, being an **N**.

[9]AIR1/616/16/15/329. AO 1338 of 21 June 1919.

[10]AMWO 19 of 8 January 1920.

[11]AMWO 866 of 31 July 1919 dealt with the award of permanent commissions. It included the statement that officers 'who are not flying officers will ... be required to qualify as pilots within 12 months from 1 August 1919.' The only exceptions were to be Stores Officers and certain Technical Officers. AMWO 1051 of 18 September 1919 published the specific rules governing the acquisition of pilots badges by observers and non-aircrew officers. In the event, the system was unable to cope with this task within the year allowed and some officers were still being retrained as pilots in the late 1920s. Technical Officers were to be another short-lived breed, incidentally; by 1922 they too had been dispensed with, their functions subsequently being discharged by pilots.

Following the uncertainties of the initial post-war period, interim arrangements for the provision of crewmen were announced at the end of 1919, as follows:[12]

a. *Single-engined landplane or seaplane squadrons.* Not more than one aerial gunner per aircraft.
b. *Twin-engined landplane squadrons.* DH 10s and Vimys – not more than two aerial gunners per aircraft; O/400s – not more than one aerial gunner, one fitter and one wireless operator per aircraft.
c. *Four-engined landplane squadrons,* i.e. *V/1500s.* Not more than three aerial gunners, two fitters and one wireless operator per aircraft.
d. *Flying boat squadrons.* Not more than one fitter and one wireless operator per aircraft.
e. *Airships.* Not specified, except that crewing was to be in accordance with the pattern established for aeroplanes and that crew pay would be allowed only for airmen constituting 'the actual flying crew of a ship.'

Notwithstanding the evident need for crewmen, as with most of its officer observers, the RAF proceeded to dispense with its professional NCO back-seaters. In this case, however, it was to wipe the slate completely by abolishing all the non-commissioned wartime aircrew trades other than that of the pilot, a handful of whom were retained.[13] Although they had been remustered to ground trades, a number of ex-aircrew continued to serve in the peacetime air force so it was possible, for a while, to misemploy them to fill the RAF's remaining back seats. This could be only a temporary measure, however, and it soon became necessary to start finding replacements.

To begin with, the Air Ministry restricted the internal recruiting of aerial gunners to non-technical personnel of Trade Group V, i.e. those required to meet only the minimum educational standard and who were on the lowest pay scale.[14] Could this have been an indication of a continuing lack of appreciation among the upper echelons of the Service of the level of competence actually required of a back-seater? Whatever the reason, this policy did not prevail for very long. Perhaps because too few aircrafthands proved to be of the necessary calibre, or because they failed to volunteer in sufficient numbers, or possibly because the Service wished to offer an interesting opportunity to other personnel, the selection field was soon broadened to permit airmen of any trade to fly as gunners.[15]

The definitive arrangements for providing peacetime aerial gunners, all of whom were to be employed on a part-time basis, were published in 1921.[16] Any airman who had logged 50 hours of combat flying during the war was accepted without further instruction, so long as he was able to pass the specified tests. There were not nearly enough of these veterans to meet the Service's need, however, so it was necessary to start training airmen volunteering from the ranks. Successful candidates serving in the UK were sent to the School of Aerial Armament and Gunnery at Eastchurch where they attended a six-week course. Thereafter they were expected to return to the school every three years to renew their qualification.

Unfortunately, there were no dedicated armament training facilities in overseas Commands and in these cases training had to be carried out at squadron level. Since much of the RAF was employed on colonial peacekeeping or garrison duties during the 1920s this meant that, in practice, the majority of aerial gunners were trained, somewhat informally, under local arrangements (shades of 1916). Despite the lack of proper schools, gunners trained abroad were supposed to qualify to the same standards as those demanded at home and to pass the same tests. Furthermore, gunners serving abroad were required to renew their qualifications annually. This proved to be easier said than done, however, and quality control tended to be variable.

The point should perhaps be made that, while the only recognised non-pilot aircrew trade was that of the aerial gunner, airmen acted in a variety of other airborne capacities as, for instance, wireless operators, photographers and bomb-aimers. There were no formal courses for these other activities, however, so it was necessary to employ suitably qualified tradesmen and/or to organise the appropriate instruction at squadron level. Apart from needing airmen to carry out specific tasks in the air, it was also customary for fitters, riggers and, to a lesser extent, armourers to be included within the 'aircrew' complement of a squadron. This was particularly so in the case of units flying relatively large aircraft and/or those which frequently operated away from base, especially flying boats. Many of these flying tradesmen were dual-qualified as gunners, but this was not an essential requirement.

All airmen employed on flying duties were entitled to draw crew pay at a rate of two shillings per day, those additionally qualified as gunners drawing a further sixpence as duty pay. While half-a-crown a day may not seem much, it actually represented a substantial supplement to an airman's pay at the time, the basic daily rate for a leading aircraftman of Trade Group V in 1921 being four shillings. The payment of both of the additional allowances was directly related to established posts. It was permissible, if undesirable, for duty pay to be drawn by gunners held surplus to establishment, so long as they maintained their currency by reclassifying annually, although their unit was also expected to take appropriate action to correct the anomalous manning situation. By contrast, the issue of crew pay was very strictly controlled and it could be issued *only* to airmen specifically held against a unit's establishment for flying duties.

The method used to calculate the numbers involved was adjusted from time to time but in 1924, for instance, crew pay

A DH 9A, E8673, of No 27 Sqn, typical of the late-wartime aeroplanes flown by the early permanent air force. In January 1920 the Air Ministry announced that pilots were to carry out the duties of observers but it subsequently failed to provide enough of them to fill both cockpits. This was probably just as well because most pilots were disinclined to take a back seat, so the second member of a crew usually turned out to be a volunteer airman. (P.H.T. Green)

[12]AMWO 1295 of 18 December 1919.
[13]AMWO 70 of 22 January 1920 abolished the trade of the Wireless Observer, those who remained in uniform being remustered as Wireless Operators (Mechanic) or Wireless Operators, depending upon their qualifications. Similarly, AMWO 187 of 26 February remustered all NCO Observers as Aircraft Hands (Aerial Gunner).
[14]AMWO 109 of 9 February 1921.
[15]AMWO 271 of 14 April 1921.
[16]AMWO 624 of 4 August 1921.

could be issued to one airman for every aircraft on a two-seater squadron, two per aircraft on a three-seater squadron and four per aircraft on larger types. Of these totals, twelve appropriately qualified airmen on two- and three-seater squadrons could draw gunner's pay and twenty-four on units operating larger aircraft. In all cases these totals were to be reduced by the number of officer observers on strength, although, conversely, establishment vacancies caused by the absence of observer officers could be filled by additional airmen.[17]

In 1923 the Air Ministry had granted its aerial gunners a degree of distinction by authorising an appropriate badge, a gilded winged bullet, to be worn on the upper right uniform sleeve.[18] Unfortunately, this gesture was somewhat devalued by the fact that the regulation that had authorised the gunners badge had simultaneously introduced an equivalent emblem for Physical Training Instructors (PTI). The implication was plain. In the eyes of the Air Ministry, the status of an airman who was prepared to risk life and limb by flying, and even, on occasion, being shot at, appeared to be on a par with those who pumped iron in the gymnasium. This impression was reinforced by the value of the PTI's badge, which turned out to be exactly twice that of a gunner's![19] If there were any lingering doubts as to who really counted in the RAF of the 1920s, these could be resolved by comparing allowances. A First Class PTI attracted qualification pay at a shilling-a-day, twice the rate for a gunner, and even a Second Class PTI drew eightpence.[20] In fact, the six penny scale for gunners was the lowest of the six rates of qualification pay then being issued.

Meanwhile, while the RAF had been adapting to making-do with part-time gunners, what of its remaining stock of commissioned observers? This had continued to waste away until, by June 1923, there were a mere seventy-three left, only about two dozen of whom might still be regarded as having been engaged (as observers) in activities directly associated with flying. Most of the others were either attending courses, serving on the staffs of specialist schools or filling a variety of staff, instructional or administrative appointments.[21]

By 1924 the flying 'O' had become such a rarity that Gp Capt J.D. Boyle was so surprised to come across someone wearing one that he wrote to the Air Ministry to ask whether this was still appropriate. It was confirmed that, although it was no longer awarded, the badge was still current and that it could be worn by any personnel whose records showed that they had been authorised so to do.[22]

While the professional observer was rapidly becoming extinct, a warning note had been sounded over the operational implications of their rapidly diminishing numbers. At a meeting held to discuss this problem in 1924, Gp Capt P.B. Joubert (the Deputy Director of Manning) pointed out that current war establishments already provided each squadron with three pilots to carry out observer duties[23] and that his department considered that this, along with airmen gunners, was sufficient. Speaking for the operations staff, Sqn Ldr R.M. Drummond disagreed, contending that the demands of long-range reconnaissance, advances in radio equipment and the complexity of the Course Setting Bomb Sight (CSBS) would call for more officer grade operators. Some very justifiable reservations were also expressed over the possibility of airman gunners having to be sent to liaise with Army staffs in the field and the acceptability of this at brigade and divisional level.

It was eventually agreed that, when operating at its wartime strength of eighteen-aircraft (versus twelve in peacetime), each single-engined bomber and army co-operation squadron would require at least six officers to act as observers. This was not considered to be necessary on twin-engined bomber squadrons, as these were already established to have two pilots per aeroplane, the second of whom could fulfil the functions of the observer. These decisions having been taken, it remained to find a means of providing the additional manpower, since the RAF no longer had the numbers of commissioned observers that it now required.[24] The provision of more pilots was considered to be an undesirably costly option. The reinstatement of observers was also seen to be uneconomic, as they were not regarded as being necessary in peacetime. The Army was a possible source of trained observers, but there were doubts as to whether their release could be guaranteed in an emergency. In the end, the favoured option was to create an Air Observers Section within the forthcoming Special Reserve.[25]

1925–33. Early indications that the RAF's policy of relying on part-time aircrew might have serious limitations

While the increases in wartime establishments decided in 1924 had been duly implemented, nothing had been done to recruit the proposed reserve of commissioned observer officers by 1926 when the Air Ministry next reviewed the situation. In essence, the 1926 meeting, which was chaired by AVM Sir Ivo Vesey,[26] had been convened to re-examine the assumptions which had previously led to the decision to sustain some commitment towards professional, albeit reservist, observers.

[17]AMWO 311 of 8 May 1924.

[18]AMWO 204 of 12 April 1923. There was uncertainty in some quarters as to whether the new badge had any impact on the old flying 'O'. AOC India, AVM Game, for instance, sought guidance in his 1753/1/Air dated 26 June 1923. The Air Ministry's response, 442529/23/P.2 of 24 August, confirmed that an airman gunner entitled to a flying 'O' could continue to wear it, in addition to a winged bullet (see Air 5/482).

[19]AP 809. Gunners badges (Section 22D/Ref 238) cost 2¼d each while those for PTIs (Section 22D/Ref 239) cost 4½d.

[20]AMWO 109 of 9 February 1921 provided details of current rates of pay and allowances for all non-commissioned personnel. Since inflation was not a significant factor at the time, there were few variations in these rates over the next twenty years.

[21]The Air Force List for June 1923 shows that twelve observers were serving with maritime air units (Nos 3, 230 and 267 Sqns and Nos 401, 440 and 441 Flts); five were assigned to HMS *Ark Royal;* one was with HMS *Argus* and each of Nos 2, 5, 6, 11, 47 and 216 Sqns still had one observer on strength. Thirteen were at flying training schools where most of them were being turned into pilots. There were three observers on the station staff at Calshot, two at Leuchars and one at Gosport. Fourteen were serving in various capacities at ground training units, including the Electrical and Wireless School, the Armament and Gunnery School, No 1 School of Technical Training (Boys), the Boys Wing at Cranwell and the Schools of Army Co-operation, of Photography, of Naval Co-operation and of Balloon Training. One was with No 1 Armoured Car Company; another was at the Air Ministry with most of the others being distributed between sundry Group and Wing Headquarters or at one of the RAF's several Depots.

[22]AIR5/498. Boyle's query was contained in HQ Inland Area letter IA/300/721/4/P1 dated 25 September 1924. The Air Ministry responded on 17 October 1924 with its 539294/24/S.7.

[23]These three officers were not specifically annotated as observers. Since all pilots were considered to be capable of carrying out the duties of an observer, a unit was simply provided with three more pilots than it needed to fill its front seats, each individual's subsequent employment being at the CO's discretion.

[24]AIR5/351. Minutes of an Air Ministry meeting held on 20 March 1924 to discuss the provision of officers for observer duties.

[25]Although reserve forces had been provided for in the Air Force Constitution Act of 1917, it was 1925 before the first Special Reserve and Auxiliary Air Force units, Nos 502 and 602 Sqns respectively, were formed.

[26]Sir Ivo Vesey was actually a soldier (a colonel who had held the temporary rank of major-general since 1918) who had been loaned to the Air Ministry where, as a temporary air vice-marshal, he filled the appointment of Director of Organisation and Staff Duties from 1923 to 1928.

One of the more significant contributors to the debate was OC No 39 Sqn, Sqn Ldr H.V. Champion de Crespigny, one of three Squadron Commanders who had been summoned to participate in the discussion. He argued that, if they were drawn from the higher trade groups, gunners were perfectly capable of handling the CSBS and of dealing with photography, wireless and so on. The problem was not one of competence, but of time, it being contended that 'the training of an individual for gunner duties in a bombing squadron was more difficult and lengthy than the training of a pilot.' De Crespigny went on to inform the meeting that, within a peacetime bomber squadron, it was normal for each flight to assign one of its wireless operators permanently to flying duties as a gunner. In effect, these men were being employed as full-time aviators and it was readily apparent that the 'air efficiency of (*these airmen*) was far superior to that of the other Air Gunners in the Squadron.'

This experience indicated that gunners could represent a workable solution to the problem of providing the manpower required to fill the posts established for observers. Furthermore, it was considered by many of those present that, provided that they were properly trained, because they would be in current practice, regular airmen were actually a better prospect than reserve officers. The ideal would be for the gunner to be recognised as a discrete trade and for these men to be employed on a full-time basis. That proposal was registered for later consideration but the meeting was primarily concerned with determining the future of the observer officer. Should any more effort be expended on attempting to breathe new life into this moribund category, or should it finally be allowed to expire? A great deal of weight will, no doubt, have been attached to the views of Air Mshl Sir John Salmond who, as AOCinC ADGB, was the RAF's senior field commander. His representative stated bluntly that in his master's opinion 'officer observers could be dispensed with'. The meeting concluded: [27]

> 'That officers for observation duties should be deleted from the Peace and War Establishments of Bombing Squadrons (single engine), and that they should be replaced by Air Gunners.'

This decision settled the fate of the professional observer for the next ten years, although the Air Ministry conveniently forgot to do anything about replacing them with the necessary *full-time* gunners. Despite this, however, there were still a few officers who thought that the RAF had made a mistake. One of them was Sqn Ldr J.O. Andrews who, while at Staff College in 1926, wrote:[28]

> 'I believe that efficient, experienced observers are necessary to any multi-seater squadron, and that it is worthwhile affording them the same treatment as pilots, particularly if the Royal Air Force is being rapidly expanded under stress of war. Why not Flight Lieutenant and Squadron Leader Observers on a scale commensurate with the relative observers strength in the Service?'

Students passing through Andover were perfectly entitled, perhaps even encouraged, to express views which were out of sympathy with mainstream thinking, but they were hardly likely to provoke a change in policy.

At much the same time the Air Ministry conducted a survey of the status and employment of its remaining commissioned observers. Since there were so few of them (and two were already flight lieutenants), it was decided to dispense with the unnecessary complication of the separate rank of observer officer. The King was asked to sanction this. He duly obliged and the rank was formally abolished in July 1926. The

Sqn Ldr George Elliot Godsave, proudly wearing the observers badge that he had earned in France in 1916. He was subsequently recategorised as an Equipment (later Technical) Officer, spending much of 1917–18 at the Admiralty Compass Observatory. Having gained a permanent commission in the peacetime air force, Godsave attended the first Long Navigation Course whence, still a Technical Officer, albeit now with an **N2** *category, he joined the cadre of the defunct School of Air Pilotage at Andover. Following a second stint at the Admiralty Compass Observatory, he was posted to Iraq where, after being promoted to squadron leader, he assumed command of No 4 Armoured Car Company in 1925 (which roughly dates this picture). The obligation to become a nominal pilot (which was implicit in the acceptance of a permanent commission) finally caught up with him when he returned to the UK and he gained his 'wings' at No 1 FTS in 1929, thus eclipsing one of the last remaining flying 'Os'. After further service at Calshot and the Air Ministry, Godsave retired in February 1935.*

As indicated by his very non-standard beret, a pragmatic approach was plainly taken to dress regulations while 'up country' and, while it is difficult to tell from a black and white picture, it is possible that, since he was clearly working under field conditions at the time, Godsave may actually have been wearing (out) an old example of the original pale-blue-with-gold-rank-braid uniforms. (RAF Regiment Museum)

[27]AIR5/351. Minutes of an Air Ministry meeting held on 18 March 1926 to discuss the establishment of observers in bombing squadrons.

[28]AIR1/2388/228/11/91. Taken from an account of his previous Service experience written by Sqn Ldr J.O. Andrews at the RAF Staff College in 1926. Andrews had spent nine months flying as an observer with No 5 Sqn before training as a pilot at the end of 1915.

handful who were left became flying officers, although they retained an **O** annotation in the Air Force List.[29]

Two years later the 1926 survey was updated. This exercise revealed that the air force now boasted only twenty-three annotated observers. Interestingly, all but two of these veterans of WW I were ex-RNAS, rather than ex-RFC, personnel. Most were serving on engagements which were due to terminate in 1932–33 but there were a few who had the option of serving to age 49 or 50 which, in theory, meant that the RAF might not dispose of the last of its commissioned wartime observers until as late as 1943.[30] The point should perhaps be made that, although the RAF may have had only twenty-three officers actually serving as *annotated* observers, as Gp Capt Boyle had discovered, there may have appeared to have been rather more because other veterans, now engaged in quite different activities, could still have been wearing their old flying 'O' badges.

Meanwhile, what of the airman gunners who were supposed to be filling the breach? On 1 February 1926 their rate of crew pay was cut by 50%, to just one shilling.[31] In the main, this will have been a consequence of the Churchillian Treasury's deflationary policies.[32] On the other hand, because corresponding cuts were not imposed on other specialist allowances, it is difficult not to see it also as a reflection of the RAF's lack of regard for its flying tradesmen. At the same time the regulations were tightened up so that an air gunner had to be currently in receipt of crew pay in order to draw his duty pay, effectively closing the loophole through which sympathetic COs had previously been able to continue to pay an overborne gunner his daily sixpence.[33]

There were other changes too. While the requirements governing their qualification had been laid down in some detail in 1921, it had subsequently proved necessary to grant considerable latitude in their interpretation. In principle, all gunners were still supposed to spend six weeks at Eastchurch but, apart from this being impractical for those recruited overseas, the school actually lacked the capacity to train all of the men required by home-based squadrons, let alone those returning from abroad. If a convenient course was not available, therefore, from 1927 it became permissible 'as a temporary measure' for Squadron Commanders to authorise duty pay for an airmen who had already been flying as a gunner for two months. In the fullness of time such men were still supposed to go to Eastchurch but they were to be tested shortly after their arrival and, if considered satisfactory, they would be immediately returned to their units without having to complete the full six weeks.[34]

As a result of this concession it became increasingly common for gunners to receive practically all of their training at unit level, formal certification being endorsed by a brief visit to Eastchurch when such an excursion was mutually convenient. With the passage of time the 'when' began to be construed as 'if' and this interpretation gained a degree of legitimacy in 1929 when gunners were added to the establishment of Special Reserve and Auxiliary Air Force (AAF) squadrons. In the case of reservists it was specifically stated that their training was to be an exclusively unit responsibility. There was no requirement for these men to attend the Armament and Gunnery School at all, although it was intended they should be tested on the ground by a visiting officer from Eastchurch. Practical qualification tests in air firing and bombing were to be completed under squadron arrangements during the annual practice camps held at one of the permanently established RAF stations.[35]

All of this may well have represented a pragmatic approach to the provision of part-time gunners but it also represented a perceptible lowering of standards. Although the RAF would not, at the time, have admitted (or probably even have recognised) that it was starting to paper over the cracks, that is precisely what it was doing. As part of this process, and notionally endorsing the practice reported by OC No 39 Sqn in 1926, full-time gunners were actually established on single-engined day bomber squadrons in 1927.[36] What had plainly been needed to take the place of observer officers had been several full-time airmen gunners per flight. The Air Ministry had successfully short-changed itself, however, as it had authorised only *one* full-time gunner per *squadron*, albeit in the rank of corporal. Two years later a full-time corporal gunner was added to the establishment of all twin-engined bomber squadrons.[37] By 1933 some units had been established to have as many as three full-timers, but this still fell a long way short of what de Crespigny and others had been angling for.

While these men were employed as gunners on a full-time basis, it should be appreciated that they were not career aviators. All of them were dual-qualified and, once a gunner had completed his stint as a flyer, he was expected to revert to his original trade. In the meantime he was temporarily mustered as, for instance, an air gunner (fitter) to distinguish him from a part-timer who would be a fitter (air gunner). The initial introduction of full-time gunners involved only a handful of men but it represented the first indication that the Service was beginning to appreciate that total reliance on part-time aircrew might not really be a viable proposition after all.

1927–33. The first cracks begin to appear in the pilots-only edifice which had been erected in 1919

By 1927 the RAF had had eight years' experience of relatively stable peacetime conditions which was enough to show that all was not well with its manning policy. While the provision of adequate numbers of air gunners had been achieved by some judicious corner cutting, other, and far more serious, difficulties were beginning to emerge. Most of these

[29]AIR30/191. Sir Samuel Hoare's submission to the palace of 28 June 1926 is on this file; it is annotated, by hand, 'App'd GRI'. The abolition of the rank of observer officer was subsequently promulgated by AMWO 394 of 15 July 1926.
[30]AIR2/291/666683/26.
[31]AMWO 59 of 28 January 1926.
[32]Winston Churchill's reign as Chancellor of the Exchequer (1924–29) was notable for a drive to return to the Gold Standard and to restore the pound to its pre-war value. What this meant in real terms is open to debate but it certainly imposed considerable strain on the national economy and was, arguably, a contributory cause of the General Strike of 1926. Despite the RAF's air gunners having previously been obliged to contribute to the sinking fund at a rate of a shilling a day, it had also increased the country's vulnerability to the recession which followed the Wall Street crash of 1929.
[33]The post-war RAF had initially sustained the use of the WW I term 'aerial gunner' but by 1925 this had been superseded, apparently without any formal notification of the change, by 'air gunner'.
[34]AMWO 347 of 26 May 1927 revised the terms under which a gunner was to qualify. While the regulations still appeared to be fairly rigorous, they actually contained provisions which made it relatively easy (and permissible) to short-circuit the system.
[35]AMWO 147 of 7 March 1929.
[36]AMWO 457 of 14 July 1927.
[37]AMWO 63 of 24 January 1929.

problems stemmed from the fact that the Service's officer corps was composed (almost) entirely of pilots.

Before examining a few of the issues which this raised, it may be helpful to outline the make-up of the RAF's three-element officer/pilot constitution. Less than half the RAF's pilots were career officers. Most of the rest were civilian entrants, serving on (initially four-year) short service commissions, supplemented by a few seconded RN and Army officers.[38]

In the autumn of 1921 the RAF had introduced a third category when it had also begun to train a limited number of its non-commissioned personnel as pilots.[39] These men were to be drawn from serving airmen, rather than being directly recruited, and preference was to be given to those who were already qualified as gunners. They were to receive two shillings per day instructional pay while under training. On gaining their 'wings' they were to be promoted to sergeant, their daily rates of pay being twelve shillings and sixpence for men drawn from Trade Group I, eleven shillings and sixpence from Trade Group II and ten shillings from Trade Group III. The remaining wartime NCO pilots were to be paid at the Trade Group II rate plus four shillings per day qualification pay.

An airmen pilot was expected to fly for at least five years after which he had the options of extending his service or re-engaging with a view to securing a pension. When he ceased flying he would revert to his ground trade but those who had been given accelerated promotion to sergeant would then have to wait at least two years before being considered for elevation to flight sergeant. This scheme proved to be both popular and successful and by 1928 it was envisaged that up to 15% of pilots would be NCOs in the future, thus reducing the overall requirement for (more expensive) officers.

Practically all the RAF's difficulties were associated with the first group, the Cranwell-trained career officers. Some of the more significant problems are outlined below.

a. The overall manning concept, which underpinned the peacetime Service, depended upon all career officers developing a secondary skill, but experience had shown that some were less enthusiastic about pursuing this aspect of service life than they were about flying.
b. Having been trained in an alternative discipline, career officers were not subsequently employed permanently in that field. It was necessary, therefore, to provide a constant flow of replacements. In effect, therefore, there was an expensive overprovision of underused specialists.
c. There were very few specialist appointments for officers above the rank of flight lieutenant. As a result, most of those who were promoted (and most Cranwell graduates were promoted) promptly ceased to practise in their secondary field which meant that their expensively acquired skills were wasted.
d. Following on from the above, since practically all specialist posts were filled by junior officers, they were able to exert little real influence on policy. Thus, while some of them may have been able to see defects in the system and/or find better ways to do things, their advice was rarely heeded.
e. In some fields, particularly engineering, there was some difficulty in providing the numbers of specialists required.

Although it had not been clearly identified by 1928, within two years another problem would have been registered. In order to provide Armament, Signals and Photographic Officers at unit level, it was proving to be necessary to withdraw young pilots for appropriate technical training within a year of their having joined their first squadrons. At this stage of their careers they were barely competent to handle their primary tasks, let alone to take on secondary responsibilities, especially as they were unlikely to return to their original units. The resultant instability did little to consolidate a pilot's flying skills and his youth and lack of seniority gave him little credibility as a specialist.

All these trends were manifesting themselves against the background of another serious problem. The RAF's officer corps was the wrong 'shape'. Ideally, it should have been a pyramid. Through an accident of history, it was actually pear-shaped, and steadily becoming more so. This situation had arisen because, when its foundations had been laid down in 1919, the peacetime Service had been officered by young wartime pilots and relatively young wartime generals. Over the ensuing years there had been an annual intake of fresh young officers into the bottom of the system but there had been comparatively few retirements from the top. By 1927 the earliest Cranwell graduates were reaching the stage at which they could reasonably expect to move into junior executive appointments while some of the wartime veterans were overdue for promotion to more senior ranks, but there were insufficient vacancies in both cases.

This was a complicated problem to solve and it is not necessary to discuss here all of the remedial measures implemented by the Air Council. Suffice to say that these amounted to a substantial restructuring of the officer corps and included a number of early retirements. There was, however, one innovation which is worthy of closer consideration. It was decided both to introduce (a few) specialist appointments at squadron leader and wing commander level and to reduce the overall requirement for career officers to become specialists by about 20%. Some of the surrendered posts were to be filled by civilians, but most were to go to warrant officers. Employing these men meant that, by exploiting their years of practical experience and their skilled craftsmanship, the Service was able to complement (or perhaps to compensate for) the purely academic knowledge of its pilot/technical officers. At the same time the creation of these additional posts had significantly improved the career prospects of non-commissioned personnel.

Despite this change in emphasis, in principle, the Air Council remained firmly wedded to the concept of a pilot-dominated air force. So long as pilots could be relied upon to do more or less everything, it was believed that 'the danger is avoided of developing technical branches out of touch with flying and fighting requirements, and out of sympathy with the officers who fly and fight.'[40] This may have been true in

[38]AMWO 781 of 7 July 1919 had published the details of the arrangements for short service commissions. The original scheme offered four-year engagements (strictly speaking three, plus the option of a year's extension) followed by four years of service on the reserve. Captains and below could, if they wished, extend their reserve service to age 30 and majors to age 35.

AMWO 427 of 21 June 1928 introduced a medium service scheme under which selected short service officers were given the option of extending their original, by now five-year, engagements to a total of ten years, such an undertaking attracting a preferential rate of gratuity. The demands of the expansion era led to further changes so that by the late 1930s short service officers were able to obtain extensions permitting them to serve a total of seven years on the active list, medium service being extended to eleven years, before transferring to the Reserve of Air Force Officers (RAFO) – see Air Ministry Order (AMO) A.225/37 of 15 July. The regulations were constantly amended during the later 1930s, the term 'medium service' finally being abandoned – see AMO A.228/39 of 22 June.

[39]AMWO 706 of 8 September 1921.

[40]AMWO 426 of 21 June 1928, from which the quotation is taken, contained an analysis of the RAF's personnel management problems and summarised the remedial steps that were to be implemented.

theory, but for this philosophy to have been valid the RAF's pilots needed to be capable of actually *doing* everything. In practice many of them could not, or did not want to.

While Fg Off (later Gp Capt) F.D. Tredrey was not one himself at the time, he has left us a contemporary impression of attitudes towards, what many regarded as being, the less desirable aspects of a career officer's lot in the mid-1930s:[41]

> '... if you've a permanent commission, away you go for real solid bookwork, to blossom forth as what KRs are pleased to call a specialist officer. If it's navigation you're selected for, a year of logarithms and nautical tables, spherical trig and astronomical theorising is your misfortune. Engineering means two awful years of toil in workshops mixed with dusty reading. Armament and signals are the other two left. They all give you grey hairs.'

While the lack of enthusiasm reflected here would not have been universal, of course, there can be no doubt that many young pilots would have much preferred to have stayed in the cockpit, rather than being obliged to return to the classroom. Furthermore, since their qualifications were gained through attendance at what were essentially academic courses, most specialist officers, particularly engineers, lacked much relevant practical ability. To keep an aeroplane flying one needed to be able to bend copper pipe, operate a lathe, panel-beat, sew fabric, splice and glue a timber joint, grind valves, tune a carburettor, balance a crankshaft or a propeller and so on. Although they would have been shown how to do such things during their courses, most of the RAF's middle and senior management were incapable of actually doing many of them adequately themselves.

The inter-war years were an era in which craft skills were still valued and those who possessed them were respected. Officers who lacked much practical ability were inevitably held in low esteem by the work force. Nevertheless, the officer in charge of engineering would always have been given the credit for the degree of technical efficiency attained by his squadron. In reality the achievement was generally more attributable to the flight-sergeants, than to the flight lieutenant – and the aircraftmen knew it. So, despite the Air Council's policy, there was (is and always has been) a divide between air and ground crews. The way to bridge this gap is by fostering professional excellence in both spheres, leading to mutual respect, not by amateurish interference in fields in which one lacks expertise.

The increasing reliance being placed on warrant officers as engineers from 1928 onwards represented the thin end of a wedge. Two years later, in order to relieve the burden being imposed on young pilots the principle was extended to permit warrant officers to fill appointments as Squadron Armament Officers on single-engine day bomber and army co-operation squadrons, both at home and in the Middle East.[42] This wedge was to be driven further home in 1933 when it was decided to grant permanent commissions to selected and suitably experienced warrant officers. They were to be given the rank of flying officer and serve as specialists in a variety of technical fields.[43] They were not to be dignified by the creation of their own branch, however, nor could they expect to be promoted. In the Air Force List they appeared on the pages immediately preceding warrant officers under the headings of 'Commissioned Engineer (or Signals or Armament or Photographic) Officers'.

During the later 1930s far more complicated aeroplanes began to enter service and in much larger numbers than before. This trend made the unsatisfactory nature of the RAF's management of its technical affairs increasingly apparent and pressure began to mount for the establishment of officers dedicated to such tasks. As one, clearly disgruntled, pilot, obliged to work as an engineer, put it:[44]

> 'The engineer in the Service *must* be a specialist. At present he is not. In fact he is scarcely an engineer at all! He is inadequately trained, and in some cases has but little stomach for the job. In spite of himself he is inefficient!'

Having identified what he perceived to be the drawbacks in the RAF's traditional approach, he went on to ask:

> 'How is this sorry state of things to be rectified? In the opinion of the writer the only solution lies in the formation of a separate Engineering Branch of the Service.'

The experience gained from employing specialist technical officers was so satisfactory that in July 1939 the Air Council did decide to re-establish a Technical Branch. This came into being in 1940, shortly after professional administrative officers had been reinstated. It would take just as long for commissioned non-pilot aircrew to reappear, but the way ahead was clear for those who could read the signs. Unfortunately, if understandably, when the mould first began to crack in 1927–28 there was no one who could.

1932–34. Increased attention begins to be paid to the neglected art of air navigation

It is interesting to observe that, in reviewing its requirements for technical officers in 1928, the Air Council had decided that the proportions of specialists required to work in the fields of engineering, signals, armament, photography and navigation would be 30 : 9 : 7 : 1 : 1.[45] These figures suggest that, despite the RAF's celebrated advocacy of the doctrine of

[41]Frank D. Tredrey, *Pilot's Summer* (1939).

[42]AMWO 676 of 23 October 1930.

[43]AMOs A.110/33 and A.111/33 of 13 April reintroduced specialist technical officers and defined their terms of service. It was then envisaged that about 60% of engineering posts would continue to be filled by officers of the General Duties Branch. When the scheme was introduced, of course, 100% of engineering posts were already filled by pilots so the initial requirement for professionals was relatively small. It was expected to be satisfied by the commissioning of seven engineer officers, one or two signals officers and one armament officer per year.

[44]The quotation is taken from an article which appeared in the *Royal Air Force Quarterly*, Vol VI, No 4 (1935). It was written by a flight lieutenant with an **E** annotation but published anonymously, as was the practice at the time. The selection of articles for publication was entirely at the discretion of the Editor and their appearance in print did not imply any form of Air Ministry endorsement. The Editor (C.G. Burge) had his finger firmly on the air force's pulse, however, and would have felt perfectly justified in using a piece which articulated the resentment felt by pilots who were obliged to give up flying to practice some other trade for which they often lacked much aptitude and in which they had little interest. While the original article was a trifle emotive, it served to prompt others, e.g. *RAF Quarterly* Vol VII, No 1 (1936) and Vol IX, No 4 (1938). While these later submissions tended to adopt a more measured style and took issue with some of the detail in the first offering, they still supported the idea of establishing a professional body of engineers.

[45]In view of the proportions envisaged in 1928, it is of some interest to consider the actual position ten years later. The Air Force List for June 1938 identifies a total of 190 miscellaneous commissioned officers, three of whom had managed to become flight lieutenants. The numbers specialising in engineering, signals, armament and photography were 123, 37, 22 and 3 respectively, which was tolerably close to the original forecast. Far more attention had been paid to navigation during the 1930s, however, and, in the event, responsibility for it had been wholly retained by the General Duties Branch. On the other hand, while the anticipated commissioned navigation specialists had failed to materialise, pilots were busily divesting themselves of another of their traditional chores and by June 1938 there were five specialist Physical Training Officers.

Since Calshot was unable to mount an Air Pilotage Course in 1931, and pending the establishment of the new Air Pilotage School at Andover, No 101 Sqn stepped into the breach to sponsor a navigation course in early 1932. The flying exercises were conducted on the squadron's Sidestrands; this one, J9178, was photographed at Catfoss during an Armament Practice Camp. (Museum of Army Flying)

strategic air power, it was actually devoting very little effort to fostering the technologies and techniques which would permit such a concept to be employed.

This was particularly true of navigation which had to be conducted accurately if aeroplanes were to be employed effectively. Unfortunately, the more esoteric aspects of navigation had never appealed very much to the majority of pilots. As a result, its development had been badly neglected and by the early 1930s it was acknowledged that the standards being achieved were far too low.

It is arguable that this was because the RAF had disposed of the people who should have become its professional navigators, its observers. By 1934, only twelve officers annotated as observers remained. Of these only two had managed to beat the system by attaining the most junior of senior ranks. They were Sqn Ldr L.J. Chandler, who had carved himself a niche as a signals expert, and Sqn Ldr C. Porri, who had become a specialist in photography.

No longer having any aircrew dedicated to its practice, the RAF had maintained only a token interest in air navigation during the 1920s and it had made virtually no attempt to exploit the potential represented by the tiny handful of career officers who had studied the subject in depth. There was some familiarity with navigational techniques in the specialised world of flying boat operations but even these relatively long-legged aircraft rarely ventured out of sight of land. On the whole, for the average squadron pilot, the navigation training being provided in 1930 was probably less comprehensive than it had been in 1918.

It should perhaps be recorded here that there was one worthwhile navigational development between the wars; the introduction of Route Books. The first of these was published in 1922 to support the Cairo-Baghdad Air Mail. Essentially a combined flight plan and strip map, supported by amplifying notes, it described and illustrated the entire 850 miles in considerable detail. This booklet was subsequently amended and updated and in 1930 it was joined by a set of similar documents covering the entire London–Singapore trunk route. From 1937 onwards, further books were published covering other imperial connections such as Kano–Port Sudan and Aden–Karachi. Separate editions were available to cater for landplanes and seaplanes. These enormously useful books were the ultimate in 'Bradshawing' but they were not really the answer to navigation; they were a substitute for it.[46]

Having finally begun to recognise the inadequacy of its navigational skills, the Service began to take training a little more seriously. As a first step, a temporary (Avro Tutor-equipped) 'Air Pilotage School' was established to operate as a third flight within No 24 Sqn at Northolt. Between November 1931 and February 1932 this unit ran a total of five two-week courses. There was then a pause, presumably while the results were evaluated.

In August 1932 the Air Council announced a new policy towards the provision of navigation training.[47] In September the four Tutors at Northolt were transferred to Andover where a new Air Pilotage School was to be opened in 1933. Initially, the new school was intended to provide two-week courses which were to be attended by all career officers between their fourth and sixth year of service, i.e. as they were becoming eligible for appointments as Flight Commanders. Once qualified, Flight Commanders were to be held responsible for consolidating the rather sketchy introduction to air pilotage that the junior pilots under their command had received during their Flying Training School (FTS) courses. At the same time all flying instructors were also required to qualify to the same 'two-week' standard as Flight Commanders with a view

[46]'Bradshawing', RAF *patois* for the practice of navigating by reference to railway lines and stations, was named for the contemporary guide to British railway timetables which was published by Messrs Bradshaw.

[47]AMO A.233/32 of 25 August.

[48]Formally established at Andover on 5 May 1933 as the Air Pilotage School, the unit was renamed the Air Navigation School on 25 January 1935. On 6 January 1936 it, and the Navigation School from Calshot, moved to Manston where, notionally on the same day, the two units were merged to create the School of Air Navigation (SAN). For the remaining years of peace (the school moved to St Athan on the outbreak of war) Manston became the RAF's centre of excellence for navigation training. The SAN ran the Specialist Navigation Course (by now further reduced to just six-months), the three-month 'sn' Course, another course of similar length specifically tailored to meet the needs of the increasingly land-based general (i.e. maritime) reconnaissance role and eventually offered specialist training in astro.

It is perhaps worth pointing out that in his book *The Paladins* (1990), John James states that the first course for commissioned 'navigators' began at the School of Air Navigation in June 1938. This is incorrect. Although they were attending a variety of courses *in* navigation, practically all pre-war students passing through Manston were pilots. A few observers did eventually begin to go there, to attend a specialist course in astro, but not until June 1939 and even then they were all NCOs. In point of fact the RAF had *no* commissioned observers until 1940 and the aircrew category of 'navigator' was not introduced until 1942.

to improving the overall quality of instruction being provided during basic training. Flying instructors were not required to go to Andover, however, their training in navigation being integrated into their CFS courses.

Increased attention was also given to the more advanced training still being provided by the Navigation School at Calshot. Although they now lasted for only eight months, the 'long' courses of 1932 and 1933 (known since 1929 as the Specialist Navigation Course) had three students each, instead of the more usual two, and later peacetime intakes were progressively increased to as many as fourteen (up to two places on each of the larger courses being made available to students from foreign or Commonwealth air forces).

The Navigation School was also still offering its three-month Air Pilotage Course but an increase in flying boat conversion work had meant that it had been unable to run a course during 1931. To fill the gap, a somewhat *ad hoc* thirteen-week course was conducted at Andover between January and April 1932, the flying exercises being carried out in Sidestrands of No 101 Sqn. This temporary arrangement, which may well have served to highlight the degree to which Calshot's course had become biased towards maritime operations, would prove to be the last Air Pilotage Course conducted under that name. While the substance of the original syllabus was to be retained for pilots attending Calshot's lengthy flying boat conversion courses, its content was reviewed and revised to form the basis of a more broadly-based curriculum. This became the syllabus of a new thirteen-week Squadron Navigation Course (soon to be colloquially known as the 'sn' Course) responsibility for which was transferred to the new Air Pilotage School at Andover.[48] All the graduates of this new course were to be known as Squadron Navigation Officers. Some of them would be recycled to become instructors within the training system but most were destined to join bomber squadrons where they were to relieve the Flight Commanders of their responsibility for improving the generally low standard of navigation.

Had they been introduced several years earlier, these changes might have done the trick but by 1933 it was already too late. The RAF was about to embark on a series of massive expansion programmes which would consistently outrun its ability to provide adequate training in air navigation (and much else besides). Had there been a sound foundation on which to build, it might have coped, but, as a result of the neglect of the 1920s, there was not.

The choice of the Saro Cloud amphibian to equip the new Air Pilotage School at Andover seems a trifle bizarre and probably betrays the strong maritime tradition within the RAF's navigational community (such as it was) in the early 1930s. This one, K2898, was initially delivered to Calshot as a seaplane trainer but it eventually found its way to Manston where it flew with No 48 Sqn and the School of Air Navigation. (Chaz Bowyer)

Chapter 16

1934–36. Re-inventing the wheel – the reintroduction of observers

At much the same time as the RAF had begun to acknowledge the inadequacy of its navigational capabilities, it was also beginning to question the effectiveness of its post-1918 aircrew manning policy. To use the Air Ministry's own words in 1934, 'It has been for some time clear that the present system of providing for observer duties in the Royal Air Force by the employment of airmen as air gunners, mainly on a part-time basis, has been becoming increasingly inadequate ....' While there had been no shortage of enthusiastic volunteer gunners and the winged bullet was being worn with considerable pride, it had become apparent that there was little standardisation over the award of this badge. Notwithstanding the regulations published in 1921, the initial training of most, and the continuation training of practically all, part-time gunners was actually being conducted under squadron arrangements. Since there was no effective quality control mechanism, it was almost inevitable that the levels of proficiency displayed by individual airmen had been found to vary widely from unit to unit.

Considering that the badge was introduced in 1923 and continued to be issued for the next sixteen years, photographs of people wearing the winged bullet are surprisingly hard to come by. Since it was clearly taken in the Middle East and features a Lysander, this one probably dates from the summer of 1939. Because most inter-war gunners had originally been trained as wireless operators, the majority also sported the 'hand and thunderbolt' flash, as in this case. The significance of the latter has changed over the years. Originally introduced to distinguish wireless mechanics, it was reassigned to wireless operators in 1918 but, although subsequently worn by many aircrew, it was never a flying badge per se; *today it is worn by NCOs and airmen of ground radio engineering trades.* (RAF Museum, 5860–1)

To redress this situation, in 1934 it was decided to introduce a 'new' trade, that of the air observer.[1] It was intended that they should all be relatively experienced, having already completed some seven years' man service. They were to be drawn from a variety of trades but more than 50% were expected to be wireless mechanics or operators, the next most preferred group being armourers. Some 37% of observers were expected to be ex-apprentices, the balance being drawn from trades supported by the new boy entrant scheme.[2] Those selected were to attend a two-month course at the Air Armament School at Eastchurch.[3] The first course began on 29 October, so the first qualified observers would have begun to join the squadrons at the beginning of 1935.

Air observers were initially to be established on a basis of one per aeroplane on bomber, torpedo bomber and two-seat fighter squadrons but only one per flight in army co-operation units. Provision was made for a few to serve as sergeants, otherwise all qualified observers were to hold the rank of corporal. The long-term aim was that, with the exception of a few specific applications (notably flying boats), all part-time gunners would eventually be replaced by the new generation of observers. This was going to take an inordinately long time, however, as Eastchurch was initially tasked with running only two ten-man courses per year. Like the gunners they were supposed to replace, observers were expected to receive much of their training at squadron level. Also like gunners, they were to fly on a part-time basis only, the rest of their time being spent on duties connected with their original trades.

While the introduction of observers had been a step in roughly the right direction, it had done very little to relieve the squadrons of their training commitment. To begin with, this

[1] AMO A.196/34 of 9 August (re)introduced the trade of the air observer. The quotation in the opening paragraph of this chapter is taken from the preamble to this Order.

[2] AMO A.195/34 of 9 August introduced a new class of boy entrants who were to be employed within Trade Group II as armourers, wireless operators and photographers. The first intake, of 250, reported to the RAF Reception Depot at West Drayton on 12 October 1934.

[3] Eastchurch had been the RAF's centre for gunnery and all other aspects of basic and advanced armament training since WW I. The resident unit had had its name changed several times but it had been operating as the Air Armament School (AAS) since 1932. It moved to Manby in 1938 where (known by now as No 1 AAS – see Note 6) it focused increasingly on specialist and post-graduate armament training until, having become the Empire Air Armament School in 1944, it was merged with the Empire Flying School on 31 July 1949 to become an element of the newly formed RAF Flying College.

problem was manageable, as it soon became apparent that the RAF simply did not have enough airmen who were both suitably experienced and qualified and who also wanted to fly. The main reason for this was the heavy reliance placed on trades associated with boy entrants. Unfortunately, since the boy entrant scheme had not been implemented until 1934, it followed that it would be 1941 before any of the new intake would have accumulated the seven years' man service which was a prerequisite for selection as an observer. For the time being, therefore, it was impossible even to approach the air force's stated goal of replacing all of its gunners with observers and many more of the former had to be trained.

The minimum experience level was reduced to six years in 1935; a somewhat transparent gesture, as the first cohort of boy entrants would still have to wait until 1940 and the 1935 intake would not be eligible for aircrew training until 1941. Rather more constructively, the selection field was also widened to permit all qualified part-time gunners, who had previously been excluded from the scheme, to retrain as observers.[4] These were relatively minor changes, however, and they were quite insufficient to cope with the demand for additional manpower made necessary by the various Expansion Schemes. The arrangements for the provision of non-pilot aircrew were, therefore, reviewed again and a revised system was introduced at the beginning of 1936.[5] There were more changes to the trades from which air observers could be selected and the required experience level was further reduced from six years to four. An unfortunate side-effect of the latter concession was that it was no longer considered appropriate to guarantee automatic promotion to corporal. To avoid offending long-established peacetime conventions, the best that could be offered was elevation to corporal on completion of six years' total service.

So far as training was concerned, the commitment which had been placed on Eastchurch was specifically confined to providing formal instruction in gunnery and bombing. Any necessary role-related training in navigation, photography, signalling and 'look out' was to be provided under unit arrangements once an observer had been posted to an operational squadron. Meanwhile, in response to the early demands of the RAF's expansion, the numbers of observers passing through Eastchurch had increased significantly which had created accommodation problems. The pressure was relieved by setting up a subsidiary Air Armament School at Leuchars. This sub-unit, which was to handle the training of RAF air gunners (and armoured car crews) and naval telegraphist air gunners (see page 124), had opened on 1 April 1935. This arrangement had always been regarded as a temporary one, however, and by June plans were already being laid for the establishment of a permanent unit. These came to fruition six months later when the school at Leuchars was moved to North Coates Fittes where, now retitled the Air Observers School (AOS), it resumed operations on 1 January 1936. As its name implied, North Coates' primary function was to teach the eight-week observers course, responsibility for this having been transferred from Eastchurch, but it also trained RAF and RN air gunners.[6]

Perhaps because its withdrawal had proved to be a disincentive to prospective volunteers, the Air Council had reinstated the very substantial 'perk' of accelerated promotion to corporal before the year was out.[7] At the same time the air observer's trade was given increased substance by the introduction of a dedicated pay scale. When the introduction of observers had first been announced in 1934 it had been envisaged that they would simply continue to receive the pay applicable to their rank and seniority within their original Trade Group, supplemented by the same shilling-a-day crew pay plus sixpence per day qualification pay as was drawn by air gunners. From November 1936, however, a junior corporal observer was to be paid at an *inclusive* rate of nine shillings per day, the entitlement to additional allowances being withdrawn. The rate for a junior sergeant observer, not that there were many of them, was eleven shillings. By comparison, a junior sergeant pilot (and all airmen pilots were at least sergeants) drew twelve shillings and sixpence.

When substantial numbers of observers began to be cross-trained as pilots in 1938 it was initially assumed that they would be entitled to flying instructional pay, which was then being drawn by trainee pilots at a rate of two shillings per day. Because the flat rate for qualified observers was deemed to include an element to cover flying risks, however, it was ruled that, until they gained their 'wings' and were remustered as pilots, they would continue to be paid as observers but that they would not be entitled to any further allowances.[8]

This was clearly a cunning ruse on the part of the Treasury, as the flying element of the observer's inclusive rate was only one shilling and sixpence. The Exchequer was therefore saving itself sixpence per day per observer. No doubt this rankled, but no one appears to have been sufficiently moved by the injustice being done to corporals to make an issue of it. This anomaly would eventually be removed, but not until 1941, perhaps because by that time large numbers of potential officers were being short-changed (see page 145).

1935–38. The scarcity of observers prolongs the trade of the gunner and aggravates the training problem at squadron level

Since policy dictated that practically all gunners were eventually to be replaced by observers, in 1936 it was decided to dispense with the handful of full-time gunners still being carried on the establishment of bomber squadrons.[9] This represented only a marginal reduction in the training requirement for gunners, however, and it did nothing to compensate for the system's inability to provide the numbers of observers required.

It will be appreciated that, while an observer was expected to be able to function as both gunner and bomb-aimer, the reverse was not (supposed to be) the case. As a result, the gunner's course had been shortened to four weeks and its content confined to topics directly related to gunnery. In practice, however, like Eastchurch and Leuchars before it, North

[4]AMO A.54/35 of 14 March.
[5]AMO A.11/36 of 16 January.
[6]On 1 November 1937, although its core function did not change, the Air Observers School was redesignated to become No 2 Air Armament School, the original unit at Eastchurch becoming No 1 AAS. Since its primary task was to produce observers, however, this title was evidently deemed to be inappropriate and on 1 March 1938 the unit at North Coates reverted to being an Air Observers School (AOS), but this time identified as No 1, in anticipation of the formation of No 2 AOS, which eventually appeared at Acklington in the following November.

[7]AMO A.263/36 of 12 November.
[8]AMO A.234/38 of 30 June.
[9]AMO A.128/36 of 4 June announced that no further full-time gunners would be trained and that the trade would cease to exist once all serving gunners had reverted to their original trades or left the Service. Pending the availability of sufficient observers, part-time gunners would be used to fill the remaining established full-time posts where necessary.

Coates simply lacked the capacity to handle anything like the numbers involved. In 1936 the Air Ministry was obliged to acknowledge this in the following statement. 'In due course all air gunners for units at home and abroad will be trained at the Air Observers School in the first instance, but for the present ... airmen may be selected by COs for training in units ...'[10]

Needless to say, in-house training continued to be the normal practice in units stationed overseas. A first-hand account of what this involved has been provided by Flt Lt (then AC1) J.R. Paine.[11] Having previously qualified as a W/T operator at the Electrical and Wireless School at Cranwell,[12] and having accumulated two or three hours of airborne time in the process, Paine was posted to No 8 Sqn at Khormaksar in 1934. While stationed in Aden he picked up the rudiments of navigation, bomb-aiming, photography and the like, which made him a *de facto* observer, although he was formally recognised only as a gunner. As he recalls:

> 'The only formal instruction we ever received was on the Lewis gun, the rest we had to pick up from our fellow flying Crew.' (*Such instruction as was provided was*) 'in the time honoured Eastchurch fashion, whereby one learned the words from the Manual, and repeated it parrot fashion. It still sticks in the memory – the left stop pawl spring stop stud bears against the face of the right stop pawl spring stop stud and rotates the magazine one corrugation.'

The officer overseeing this practice (and all other RAF affairs in Aden) at the time was Gp Capt C.F.A. Portal who, in view of his own early experiences, may well have considered that Paine had little to complain about (see page 12).

Another informative description of contemporary back-seat flying has been left us by Wg Cdr C.T. Kimber, who joined the recently-formed No 83 Sqn at Turnhouse in October 1936. Then a corporal Fitter I, he was soon allocated a Hind of his own to look after and, apparently on the grounds that he had applied for pilot training, discovered that he was also expected to fly as its gunner. Like Paine, Charles Kimber was 'trained' on the squadron and, again like Paine, he found that being a gunner virtually amounted to being an observer:[13]

> 'I was flying regularly and becoming absorbed in the art of navigation by the method known as dead reckoning. Flying as navigator in a Hind involved the use of a Bigsworth board; a simple pair of hinged boards, one of which was transparent. The map was sandwiched between the boards, and a graduated straightedge, combined with a protractor, enabled the navigator to draw tracks and courses on the transparency. The navigator sat with his back to the pilot, exposed to the blast of the slipstream on the upper half of his body. He obtained his instrument readings, airspeed, height, temperature and compass, by standing erect and looking over the pilot's shoulder.'

Some idea of what Kimber meant by 'flying regularly' is conveyed by the fact that he flew on no fewer than twenty-seven occasions in February 1937, mostly bombing practice, using the *camera obscura*, rather than live weapons. During an Armament Practice Camp at Leuchars in March, he flew three times a day.

Because the shortfall in properly qualified observers meant that large numbers of these old-style, part-time gunners continued to be required, it became necessary to reconsider the arrangements for selecting and training these men. To widen the recruiting field, previous restrictions on the proportions to be drawn from each trade were considerably relaxed and airmen who were entitled to apply now became eligible for selection as gunners as early as their first year of service.

For reasons which will be explained later, responsibility for the instruction of the majority of air gunners had to remain at unit level until as late as 1939. Squadrons were well used to dealing with this aspect of training, of course, but their workload had been considerably increased since 1935 by the imposition of a substantial, post-graduate training commitment with respect to observers. Furthermore, in accordance with long-standing practice, FTSs were required to teach only basic flying skills. Pilots therefore joined their first squadrons with little awareness of applied flying within an operational context and this aspect of their instruction was carried out locally during their first post-graduate year. In effect, therefore, most squadrons in the RAF of the mid-1930s were functioning largely as advanced training units, which seriously degraded their operational capability.

The scale of the pilot training task was to be substantially increased by the need to convert to new types of aircraft, this process frequently being complicated by slow deliveries. Although it was bound to involve yet more conversion work, in order to ensure that there were at least some modern aeroplanes to fly, interim types often had to be issued.[14]

Delays and difficulties in training were not confined to pilots, because when new aircraft did arrive they often lacked vital role equipment. Early Whitleys, for example, often reached the squadrons devoid of gun turrets. Then again, while many of the new aeroplanes were wired for telephonic intercommunication, there were often insufficient helmets fitted with the necessary microphones and headsets to go round. Apart from a lack of equipment, some of that which was available was unsuitable. For instance, the standard bomb sight in use at the time had been calibrated for aeroplanes of the biplane era. When No 139 Sqn tried to use them in 1937, they found that at 10 000 feet their new Blenheims were so fast that they simply ran off the end of the airspeed scale.[15]

To cap it all, as each new squadron was formed it had to be provided with a nucleus of competent aviators. These could be provided only by robbing existing units of their more capable personnel, causing constant instability in the

[10]AMO A.11/36 of 16 January.

[11]J.R. Paine, *Getting Some In* (1990).

[12]The post-war RAF had trained its wireless operators at Flower Down until 7 August 1929 when the Electrical and Wireless School moved to Cranwell.

[13]C.T. Kimber, *Son of Halton* (1977). Kimber became a Specialist Navigation Course graduate in 1941 and a year later he navigated the Liberator in which the Prime Minister was flown to and from Moscow via the Middle East. The security surrounding this mission was so tight that Kimber rarely knew his destination until he was at the aircraft! He was, therefore, unable to prepare a flight plan and, lacking appropriate charts for much of his (unknown) route, he had to make do with a hand-drawn navigational grid on which to plot his astro, supplementing this with a Philips atlas. The expedition eventually covered some 15 000 nmls in 75 hours of flying time during which Kimber, working under unbelievable handicaps, had used 307 astro position lines to construct 102 fixes of which fifteen had been discarded.

[14]In just two years No 7 Sqn, for instance, operated Heyfords, Wellesleys, Whitleys, Ansons and Hampdens. Over a similar period No 15 Sqn progressed from Hinds through Battles to Blenheims, No 58 Sqn converted from Virginias to Whitleys via Ansons and Heyfords and No 115 Sqn flew Hendons, Harrows and Wellingtons.

[15]J.R. Paine *op. cit.* The model in use at the time would have been the Course Setting Bomb Sight Mk VII or VIII. The Mk IX was calibrated for higher speeds but it was not developed until 1937 and did not begin to enter large scale service until 1939.

A Whitley I, K7240/7·M of No 7 Sqn at Thornaby in June 1938. Like a number of early Whitleys, this one had clearly been delivered without its nose turret. (C.F. Scandrett)

constitution of crews and further diluting the experience level on the units from which they were taken.[16]

1935. A new approach to the training of pilots

In an attempt to relieve the excessive training commitment at squadron level, while simultaneously catering for the vastly increased numbers of students involved, a new approach to pilot training was announced in 1935.[17] The scheme introduced a number of innovations, the most significant of which was that, with the exception of Cranwell cadets, all prospective Service pilots were to begin their training, as civilians, at a commercially operated flying school. At the time there were already four such schools in commission and the 1935 scheme led to contracts being awarded to a further nine.[18]

The, initially eight-week, elementary course provided a grounding in basic aviation theory plus 50 hours of airborne time. Candidates for short service commissions who succeeded in completing this civilian-run phase subsequently reported to the RAF Depot at Uxbridge to be uniformed, kitted out and introduced to drill and discipline. After (notionally) two weeks, by now acting pilot officers, they were posted to a Service-run FTS. Serving airmen being trained as pilots also gained their first flying experience at a civilian school, but from there they proceeded directly to an FTS, rather than via Uxbridge.

At FTSs students were to be given their intermediate and advanced instruction on service, rather than training, types (typically variants of the Hawker Hart). The syllabus had been considerably expanded so that it now included formation, night and instrument flying plus practical experience in navigation and live armament training. The intention was to ensure that when future pilots reported to their first squadrons they would already be familiar with most of the skills that they had previously had to acquire during their first year of 'productive' service. This would lighten the burden currently being carried by Flight Commanders and permit them to integrate new pilots into operational training activities very shortly after they arrived.

Unfortunately, this aim was to be only partially realised. The same conflict between quality and quantity as had blighted RFC training in WW I cropped up again in 1935. Almost inevitably, just as in 1917, quantity had to be given the higher priority. In order to maintain the required throughput it was simply not possible to introduce the scheme entirely as planned. From the outset, therefore, the duration of the nine-month Service-run phase of the course had to be reduced to six months.

It was always the intention to introduce the full nine-month course when circumstances permitted, but circumstances never did. It was, for instance, mid-1936, a full year after the concept had been announced, before any night flying was undertaken.[19] The main stumbling block continued to be numbers but there were other complications. The greatest of these was that the schools were all equipped with single-engined biplanes with fixed undercarriages whereas the squadrons soon began to receive twin-engined monoplanes with wheels that went up and down. Even if the schools had been able to deliver the full nine-month curriculum, therefore, the squadrons would still have been faced with a major training task in that they frequently had to convert pilots onto aeroplanes with operating characteristics which were fundamentally different from those with which they were familiar.

This problem began to be addressed in the autumn of 1936 when some Ansons were made available to No 6 FTS at Netheravon but it was early 1938 before the RAF began to take delivery of substantial numbers of Oxfords, the type which had been specifically ordered for twin-engined training. Their availability permitted the consolidation of a streaming policy, which had already been introduced, whereby, depending upon their aptitude (and the, always overriding, 'exigencies of the Service'), pilots were selected for fighters or heavier types, and attended appropriately specialised courses. Further improvement stemmed from the acquisition of modern, purpose-built basic and advanced monoplane trainers, the Magister, Master and Harvard, all of which had entered service before the outbreak of war.

While these developments represented significant advances, there were still shortfalls in the applied flying content of the syllabus, although incremental improvements were introduced as time and facilities permitted. For instance, to provide students with some practical experience

[16]As a case in point, consider No 45 Sqn in 1938. The last of its three experienced flight lieutenant Flight Commanders was posted elsewhere in May. All of the remaining pilots, apart from the squadron leader CO, were first tourists. In October, in order to restore some semblance of a hierarchy, the most senior man, a flying officer, was given an acting flight lieutenancy and two of the pilot officers were made up to acting flying officer. These three then assumed the full responsibilities of Flight Commanders; they were still filling these posts when war was declared. This particular unit happened to be stationed in Egypt at the time but much the same circumstances prevailed on squadrons based in the UK. These details are drawn from the author's history of No 45 Sqn, *The Flying Camels* (1995).

[17]AMO A.135/35 of 4 June.

[18]Five commercial schools had originally been contracted in 1923–24 to provide annual continuity flying for pilots of the RAF Reserve, i.e. qualified pilots who had served on short service engagements involving a subsequent reserve commitment, plus low rate (initially a total of up to fifty per annum) *ab initio* instruction to reservists. The school operated by Beardmores at Renfrew dropped out of the scheme in 1928. The four which were still in commission in 1935 were being run by de Havillands at Hatfield, Bristols at Filton, North Sea Aerial & General Transport (a subsidiary of Blackburns) at Brough and Air Service Training at Hamble.

[19]Since this was in June, which contains the longest days of the year, one wonders whether this really was 'night' flying, in the sense of its being done in the dark, as distinct from flying after normal working hours. In point of fact, this may not actually have mattered all that much, because completion of the night flying test was not mandatory in any case. KR 811, which laid down the requirements for a pilot to gain his wings, accepted that the night flying test was 'applicable only when unit facilities permit.'

in weapons training, a month's detachment to an Armament Practice Camp (later Station) had been incorporated into the programme in 1936, and the acquisition of Link Trainers in 1938 represented a major advance in the context of instrument flying.

Nevertheless, while steady progress was made in enhancing the content of flying training, there was never enough of it. Certainly not enough to realise the RAF's stated ambition which was to produce a generation of pilots capable of coping with operational flying as soon as they reported to their first squadrons. Even so, the RAF could reasonably claim that it was training its pilots to a higher standard during the later 1930s than it had ever done before. This was just as well, of course, because the size, performance and complexity of the aeroplanes that were entering service meant that the demands that it was placing on its newly qualified pilots were also greater than ever before.

1936. The Waghorn paper

By the summer of 1936 the expansion of the RAF was well under way with most newly formed bomber squadrons being initially equipped with single-engined, biplane light bombers, usually Hawker Hinds. This was merely an interim measure, however, since current planning envisaged that the Service would soon dispense with light bombers altogether. Under Scheme F, which was expected to be complete by March 1939, the RAF's striking force was to comprise nearly 600 medium and heavy bombers with another 400 in reserve.[20] These aeroplanes, Blenheims, Whitleys, Hampdens and Wellingtons, would fly faster, higher and much further than most of those to which the RAF had long been accustomed. Those in the know were also aware that the Air Ministry had already issued specifications for the next generation of even heavier bombers, the twin-engined Warwick (B.1/35), Halifax and Manchester (B.13/36) and the four-engined Stirling (B.12/36). In informed circles, the implications of these developments were beginning to cause concern and this began to manifest itself among the trustees of the RAF's navigational expertise, the graduates of the Long N and Specialist Navigation Courses.

They knew that the increased attention being paid to navigation training since 1932 was more apparent than real. It was true that post-graduate courses had been revised and that more people were attending them but the Long N men were aware that these courses were largely theoretical and that very little time was being devoted to practical navigation training at squadron level. The key word was 'practical', reflecting the belief that a navigator probably derived more of real value in a three-hour flight than he did in three days of classroom work – and that a navigator who had done very little air work was hardly worthy of the name.

Authoritative, first-hand testimony as to the inadequacy of the training being provided at squadron level has been provided by Gp Capt F.C. Richardson. Having spent the previous three years flying around Africa in Victorias of No 216 Sqn, he reported to Manston in 1937 to attend, first an 'sn', and then a six-month Specialist Navigation Course. He found that 'the three-month preliminary air navigation course revealed that I scarcely knew anything about the theory of air navigation and also very little about its proper application! I had just been very lucky.'[21]

[20]AIR8/204.

Richardson had begun his flying training in 1933, *after* all the 'improvements' in navigation training were supposed to have been implemented. It is quite plain from his observations, however, that little of any substance had actually been achieved. It is interesting to note that, for much of his time with No 216 Sqn, 'Dickie' Richardson's Flight Commander had been Sqn Ldr Philip Mackworth. Mackworth, a graduate of the 1921 Long Navigation Course, was one of the RAF's very few real experts in air navigation. Navigation was held in such low esteem, however, that he was 'quietly and unkindly dubbed as 'a bit of an old woman' because he tried to improve the squadron's primitive navigation practices when most of his colleagues thought they were good enough.'[22]

In the summer of 1936 all of these concerns were articulated in a paper penned by Flt Lt D.J. Waghorn.[23] In this, he acknowledged that the RAF had made, and continued to make, some spectacular long distance flights. But he argued that few of these actually made much demand on true navigational skills since, for reasons of safety (and economy in recovering aeroplanes forced to land *en route*) most of these, including, for instance, the annual Egypt-to-the-Cape flight, stuck close to well-established trade routes, rivers, railways and so on. Furthermore, he claimed that in conducting these expeditions 'only once has a specialist navigation officer been employed.'[24]

Even more damagingly, Waghorn went on to review the current employment of the RAF's navigational experts. At that time the Air Force List contained a total of forty-three officers annotated with an **N**. Ten of them were squadron leaders or above and another seven were being employed on purely administrative tasks; none of these men would have had much, if any, contact with flying operations. Twenty had some academic involvement with navigation. Of these: three were specialist instructors in astronomical techniques; five were filling navigation staff appointments at a variety of headquarters and twelve were instructors at FTSs where they delivered 'a course of instruction of about ten lectures of the most elementary kind (*involving*) not one thing they learned on the long navigation course.' That left just six who were serving with bomber or flying boat squadrons and who were therefore in current practice. In short, Waghorn deplored the state of the RAF's navigational capabilities and castigated the Service for wasting the investment it had made in training

[21]F.C. Richardson, *Man Is Not Lost* (1997). Along with a few others, 'Dickie' Richardson was to become convinced that, if the RAF was to be effective, it was absolutely essential that it abandon its bad old ways and recognise the crucial importance of navigation. His contribution to this ultimately successful campaign was second to none, his most significant achievement probably being the authorship of AP1234, *The Manual of Air Navigation*, the first edition of which appeared in the summer of 1941.

[22]*Ibid.*

[23]AIR2/2860. Unreferenced paper dated 31 August 1936 on Air Ministry file S.47629. David Waghorn was one of four officers to graduate from a Specialist Navigation Course (the sixteenth) in April 1936. One had been posted to HQ 3 Gp, the other three had been sent to recently opened flying training schools, Waghorn to No 10 FTS at Ternhill.

[24]It is not clear to which particular enterprise Waghorn was referring but he was not strictly correct in his contention. For example, Flt Lts L.E.M. Gillman and P.H. Mackworth had participated in the RAF's original expedition to the Cape in 1926, Flt Lt P.E. Maitland had taken part in the extraordinary achievement of the Southampton-equipped Far East Flight in 1927–28 and Flt Lts L.E.M. Gillman (again), P.H. Mackworth (again) and N.H. D' Aeth had all been involved in the RAF's, ultimately unsuccessful, attempt to capture the World's Long Distance Record using Horsleys in 1927.

a handful of men to become specialists in this particular field.

He went on to discuss the potential of airborne radio direction finding but, while acknowledging its value for homing, dismissed it as being too reliant on the availability of vulnerable or politically unreliable transmitters and too inaccurate for long-range work in any case. Ground-based D/F stations suffered from the same inherent inaccuracy with regard to range and had the considerable disadvantage in wartime of requiring the aircraft to break radio silence. That left the sorely neglected technique of celestial navigation. Waghorn recognised the limitations of the bubble sextants which were currently available, particularly when used in turbulent conditions, but he argued that most of these could be overcome by flying at altitudes in excess of 15 000 feet where an aircraft would generally be flying above cloud and in relatively smooth air.

Finally, Waghorn observed that French airliners flying to Berlin and German airliners calling at Paris and Croydon were said to carry, as a supernumerary crew member, an air force officer masquerading as a civilian. He wondered whether this practice could not be adopted by the RAF, permitting its officers to gain experience of long distance operations by flying with Imperial Airways on routes to, say, Egypt via Malta. In conclusion, he pressed for the establishment of a course at which Specialist Navigators could teach 'real' navigation to squadron pilots and for the RAF to introduce some form of practical long-distance navigation exercise.

Since it was highly critical of the RAF's capabilities and thus, by implication, of its higher administration, Waghorn's paper was a remarkably outspoken document for a junior officer to have written in the 1930s. It might well have attracted instant retribution and/or been consigned to the wastepaper basket but, fortunately, Waghorn's Station Commander, Gp Capt C.C. Darley was sympathetic and, with his endorsement, it soon found its way to HQ 23 Gp. There the acting AOC, Air Cdre A.G.R. Garrod, added a lengthy letter of support and amplification before forwarding it to the Air Ministry.[25] It eventually landed on the desk of the very influential Deputy Director of Plans, Gp Capt A.T. Harris. The latter was sufficiently moved by the submission to write a five-page memorandum on the subject.[26] Harris agreed, at least in principle, with most of what Waghorn had to say and added his own weight by concluding that 'the general attitude in the Service towards navigation ... is deplorable and the standard is lamentable.'

Harris did have reservations over some of Waghorn's recommendations, however, particularly with regard to the Service's tendency to indulge in the theoretical when it came to teaching navigation, and he pressed for all such instruction to be made essentially *practical*. He based this recommendation on the personal experience he had acquired through his having been obliged to attend two navigation courses.[27] Harris complained that on both of these he had been subjected to 'hours of explanation of the principles of magnetism' and instructed on 'how to make a compass.' He pointed out, somewhat waspishly, that 'all I require to know about magnetism is the fact that a compass needle points in a certain direction, and I don't care a hoot why it does so.' He drove his underlying message home with the tart observation that 'the trouble with all experts is their tendency to surround their art with a mass of clap-trap, and to delight in making it unnecessarily difficult to the uninitiated, and thereby to add, by implication, to the glory of their own achievements and ability.'

Waghorn's paper had succeeded in, once again, focusing attention on the inadequacies of the RAF's approach to navigation and it had certainly served to stimulate high-level discussion of the topic. It is impossible to say whether it actually exerted any influence on policy, but it was probably no coincidence that the RAF began seriously to investigate the potential of celestial navigation in 1937. This led to the adoption of astro as a standard technique in the following year. On the other hand, while the number of people being taught something of the art of air navigation increased markedly during the remaining three years of peace, there was to be little material improvement in the quality of the instruction being provided. Waghorn's specific plea for the introduction of realistic long distance navigational exercises was never satisfied either, largely because of a lack of safety equipment which meant that most aircraft were prohibited from venturing far from land.

1937. Pilots begin to lose their exclusive authority over aircraft navigation

As previously noted, by the early 1930s the RAF had begun to accept that its navigational skills were less than adequate. Having recognised the symptoms, however, it then proceeded to diagnose their cause incorrectly and, as a result, the treatment prescribed – additional doses of navigation training for pilots – had failed to effect a cure. This was because pilots did not present a solution to the problem. In fact, they were the problem. But, having fostered the image of the omnipotent pilot ever since 1919, it had become very difficult for the air force to accept that there was anything that they could not do. It is not suggested that pilots were incapable of functioning as navigators, of course, but it is contended that few of them had much enthusiasm for this aspect of flying – which amounts to much the same thing in the end. Unfortunately, the notional increase in the attention being paid to air navigation since 1932 had failed to bring about any significant change in the attitudes of pilots and, as a result, there had been little detectable improvement in their navigational abilities over the next five years.

Since pilots had been demonstrably unable (or unwilling) to handle navigation competently in the past, there was growing concern as to how they would fare in the aeroplanes which were beginning to enter service by 1937, let alone those that were being projected for the future. The length of the intended nine-month flying training course was still

[25]It may be a coincidence, of course, but it may also not be entirely without significance that both Darley and Garrod had begun their flying careers as observers during WW I. Perhaps it had been this experience which had given them the broader and more tolerant outlook which had allowed them to endorse Waghorn's outspoken paper, thus preventing its being 'spiked' by some impatient (pilot) staff officer as it negotiated the many chicanes within the chain of command.

[26]AIR2/2860. Memorandum, concerning the state of navigation within the RAF, dated 3 November 1936 on Air Ministry file S.47629, from Harris, as Deputy Director of Plans, to the Director of Staff Duties (Air Cdre W.S. Douglas) and the Director of Training (Gp Capt R. Leckie).

[27]Sqn Ldr A.T. Harris had been a student on the only course run by the original School of Air Pilotage at Andover in 1919. With an aggregate mark of 88.8%, he had graduated top of a class of sixteen. Prior to assuming command of No 210 Sqn in April 1933, Wg Cdr Harris had also spent six months at Calshot being converted onto flying boats, this course containing a substantial element devoted to navigation.

constrained to just six months, however, so there was little realistic prospect of an early improvement in the abilities of the junior pilots in the rapidly expanding air force. As a result, most of these inexperienced young men had their hands too full simply coping with flying to be able to pay much attention to navigation. Furthermore, if navigation was to be addressed more seriously in the future, it would require more time than even the most capable of pilots could afford to devote to it.

By the end of 1936 it had been more or less accepted that it was unreasonable to expect a pilot to be able to cope simultaneously with the demands of both flying and navigating. As a means of lightening the load, some senior officers began to urge that responsibility for navigation should be transferred to observers. This suggestion was opposed by others who were most reluctant to concede any element of the pilot's authority – especially not to a corporal! In fact they counter-proposed that the observer should be done away with altogether. Their recommendation was that the air force should maintain its original aim of improving the navigational skills of all pilots and that the necessary load-sharing should be achieved by replacing the observer with a second pilot who would act as general assistant to the captain while having primary responsibility for navigation and bomb aiming.

To begin with the 'pilots only' faction had their way and in February 1937 it was decided that, wherever possible, a second pilot was to be provided in place of an observer.[28] While this approach had substantially reduced the numerical requirement for observers, it had automatically created a corresponding demand for additional (and more expensive) pilots. It would take many months for the system to recruit and train these extra pilots and, as part of the price that had to be paid for producing larger numbers, the prospect of introducing the nine-month flying training course receded even further into the future.

Furthermore, the two-pilot solution could not sensibly be applied to single-pilot Battles, Blenheims or Wellesleys. So, like it or not, to permit the pilot to be relieved of responsibility for navigation in these cases, the Service would have to rely on observers. This meant that observers, who until now had been trained only in gunnery and bomb-aiming, would in future have to be given formal instruction in navigation to the same standard as pilots. In May 1937, therefore, a navigation element 'similar to the instruction given to a pilot at a Flying Training School' was added to the syllabus at North Coates, extending the overall duration of the course to twelve weeks.[29] The announcement of this change in policy was accompanied by the caveat that observers could not 'for the present be trained up to complete operational standard at the Air Observers' School.' As a result squadrons would be expected to provide most of their new observers with further tuition for a period of six months.

Cpl Kimber was an early graduate of this extended course, having passed through North Coates in September–December 1937. He describes the course as follows:[30]

> 'Lectures, flying, analyses and remedies followed in rapid order. Each meticulously discharged. The only light relief, although full of meaning, were the *ad hoc* competitions in stripping and reassembling a Lewis gun – blindfold. No one entered the lists if his time was greater than one minute. The aircraft used in training was the Westland Wallace, reliable but not of the operational class for the immediate years ahead. Lectures were well-organised and thorough, and I learned much of the theory of bombing and navigation.'

The increased attention being paid to navigation, and official recognition of the need to provide supervised continuation training, led to the establishment of Squadron Navigation Officers on bomber squadrons being raised to one per flight. This effectively tripled the numbers required and, despite reducing the length of the 'sn' course to ten weeks, Manston was quite unable to satisfy the demand.[31] In an earlier attempt to increase the availability of Squadron Navigation Officers, it had been agreed that a broadly comparable civilian certificate would be an acceptable alternative qualification.[32] It was decided to extend this principle and two civilian schools were contracted to train additional pilots in navigation to a notionally 'sn' equivalent standard.[33]

1937. The flying 'O' is reinstated

The officers attending the February 1937 meeting, which had introduced both the two-pilot option and the concept of the observer as navigator, had spent some time considering the implications of the latter decision. Air Cdre D.C.S. Evill (SASO, Bomber Command) had emerged as the chief spokesman for observers on that occasion and he had two main points to make. The first was that the training of observers was quite inadequate for the task that they would be expected to fulfil. Evill was well aware of the intention to provide three 'sn's per squadron and he allowed that this would 'better the position, but only to a comparatively small extent.' His second point was that observers lacked the status that ought to be associated with their considerable responsibilities. The meeting eventually made the following recommendations: that corporal observers should be eligible for promotion to sergeant after a relatively brief period of squadron service; that their pay should be equal to (or only slightly less than) that of NCO pilots; that, in view of the demands that would be made on their time, on the ground as well as in the air, observers should be employed as full-time aircrew; and that they should be entitled to wear a distinguishing emblem, similar to that worn by observers during WW I.[34]

All of these things would eventually come to pass, the first positive sign being the reinstatement of the old flying 'O' badge in October 1937.[35] In order to wear it the initial requirements were that an observer had to have:

a. passed an air observers course;
b. served at least six months on a squadron;
c. flown a minimum of fifty hours as observer; and
d. been recommended by his CO.

[28]AIR2/2660. Minutes of a meeting held at the Air Ministry on 2 February 1937 to review the composition of crews. These were circulated under cover of S.40289 dated 23 February.

[29]AIR14/43. Air Ministry letter 638478/37/TW1 dated 3 May from Air Cdre W.S. Douglas to AOCinCs Coastal, Bomber and Fighter Commands.

[30]Kimber, *op. cit.* Interestingly, having begun flying less than a year before, Kimber had already logged 190 hours in the air before he began his formal observers course.

[31]Steps had been taken to increase Manston's training capacity as early as 1936 when No 48 Sqn had been moved in with, what eventually became, a very large fleet of Ansons to operate as a *de facto* navigation school in support of the newly established SAN. Since this had already been done, however, there was no room for further expansion in 1937.

[32]AMO A.1/36 of 2 January had permitted, 'as a temporary measure', pilots holding a 2nd Class Civil Air Navigators Licence to fill appointments as Squadron Navigation Officers.

[33]The Imperial School of Air Navigation at Notting Hill, London (which moved to Shoreham in 1938 to become Martin's School of Air Navigation) and a school run by Air Service Training at Hamble.

[34]AIR2/2660. (See Note 28.)

[35]AMO A.347/37 of 21 October.

It may be of interest to consider the contemporary requirements governing the award of a pilots flying badge.[36] In addition to passing written examinations in allied subjects, he had to:

a. have accumulated a minimum of eighty hours of flying, of which twenty had to be on a service type;
b. be able to fly a service type reliably and accurately by day, both in clear air and by the use of instruments, and land consistently well at low speeds;
c. be able to execute normal and aerobatic manoeuvres appropriate to the type on which he had been trained;
d. be able to recover from abnormal positions solely by use of instruments;
e. have climbed to 15 000 feet in a service type and remained there for thirty minutes; and
f. have flown a service type on two triangular cross-country flights of at least 200 miles.

It is interesting to observe that, apart from reflecting the increased capabilities of the aeroplanes of the 1930s and including competence in instrument flying, these requirements were much the same as those published as long ago as 1916 (see page 39).

The reintroduction of the flying 'O' had effectively reinstated the WW I situation in that there were, once again, two kinds of recognised, i.e. badged, aviators. Would the RAF capitalise on the lessons it had learned during 1918 and treat them with equal respect, or would it revert to the discredited practices of the RFC? With somewhat depressing predictability, it ignored past experience and reintroduced the bad old days of 1917. This is worthy of further consideration.

While the reappearance of the flying 'O' was obviously a positive step, the reintroduction of what amounted to a period of probationary service was just as obviously a step backwards. Arguably, this could have been justified by the restricted scope of the formal observers training course and the stated need for additional instruction to be provided at unit level. But, if the experience of WW I had taught nothing else, it had surely demonstrated that such a half-hearted approach to training was highly unsatisfactory. By the summer of 1918 an observer was not (supposed to be) posted to a squadron until he was qualified to wear his badge and this was not awarded until he had completed a comprehensive sequence of courses. This policy had emerged as a result of four years of bitter wartime experience and, once defined, it was regarded as being of such fundamental importance that it was implemented under wartime conditions, regardless of the complications that this had caused. The RAF was also under considerable pressure in the 1930s, as a result of the Expansion Schemes, but the demands which they made can hardly have been comparable to those of war.

For the Air Council to have placed so much reliance on squadron-based training strongly suggests that it was either ignorant of the lessons learned between 1914 and 1918 or that it had deliberately chosen to ignore them. Since its members had all been serving officers in 1918, it seems hardly conceivable that the Air Council would not have known about the training procedures in use at that time. Even if they did suffer from a corporate loss of memory, surely one of the Air Ministry's long-term civil servants would have remembered and reminded them. Furthermore, Volume V of the Official History had been published as recently as 1935 and at least one member of the Air Council must surely have leafed through it, if only to see whether his youthful exploits had been mentioned.[37] Since training was high on the current agenda, someone must also have taken the time to see what Volume V had to say about this topic. It summarised the late-war position and referred readers with a particular interest in training to FS 39.[38] Did no one take the trouble to see what this publication had said? Apparently not, since the application of a 1917-style approach was not confined to observers.

Pilots had always been allowed to wear their flying badges on completion of their training, of course, but, as FS 39 makes quite clear, by late 1918 completion of training meant a great deal more than it had a year before. It now required attendance at appropriate role-associated courses covering applied flying and tactical skills which were taught at establishments such as a Fighting School, a School of Navigation and Bomb Dropping or the School for Marine Operational Pilots. Yet the revised pilot training scheme which had been introduced in 1935 had awarded a pilot his badge on completion of only the *basic* instructional phase, at which point he would have accumulated a total of some eighty hours in the air.[39] Before he was certified as being fit for squadron service he had still to demonstrate that he possessed more advanced skills. Among those listed were: night and formation flying; aircraft operation at high all-up weights; the ability to fly a steady course, i.e. to maintain a compass heading, and flying at a constant height and speed for five minutes, as on a bombing run. As previously noted, however, there had been problems with implementing the 1935 scheme and it had proved impossible to provide all pilots with all of the training which they were supposed to receive.

In 1937, therefore, newly qualified pilots were still reaching the squadrons with very little experience of applied flying, but proudly wearing their 'wings', just as they had in 1917. Similarly, just as in 1917, observers were obliged to earn their badges by completing a period of probationary service. In effect the Air Council had succeeded in setting the clock back by twenty years; it was as if the reforms of 1918 had never happened.

[36]AMO A.99/36 of 7 May promulgated the revised qualification standards which were to be associated with the pilot training scheme announced by AMO A.135/35, although this had yet to be fully implemented, as circumstances still precluded the introduction of the full nine-month course.

[37]H.A. Jones, *The War in the Air*, Vol V (1935).

[38]FS 39, *Training Courses in the RAF for Commissioned and Non-commissioned Personnel, showing Status and Pay*. See Fig. 14 and Chapter 14, Note 15 for an indication of the content of this document, at least one copy of which (probably the one now held in the Public Record Office) would surely have been available in the Air Ministry library in the 1930s.

[39]AMO A.27/36 of 13 February stated that the flying badge would be awarded at the end of the first term of training at an FTS. Subsequent refinement of the regulations removed references to the stage of training but retained the requirement for 'not less than 80 hours' solo and dual flying'. In practice, the award of 'wings' was later postponed to the end of the course at, what became known in wartime as, a Service Flying Training School (SFTS). By the summer of 1940 a student could expect to have logged about 120 hours by this stage and this would later be raised (by the New Deal proposals of late 1941 – see Chapter 21) to something over 200. While 200 is undeniably 'not less than 80' it is still a little surprising to observe that the 80 hours minimum was still being specified in Kings Regulations (at KR 811) published as late as 1944.

Chapter 17

1921–39. The provision of commissioned observers for the Fleet Air Arm

Having followed the resurgence of the air force observer as far as the reappearance of the flying 'O' in 1937, it is timely to retrace our steps to consider what had been happening at sea. While the RAF had decided that it could safely dispense with professional back-seaters once peace had broken out, the RN had taken a very different view. Against the backdrop of a prolonged inter-Service power struggle for control of maritime aviation, which was not finally resolved until 1937, the Admiralty had unilaterally elected to sponsor its own commissioned air observers as early as 1921. In calling for volunteers, the Admiralty stressed the importance that it attached to the provision of observers since it 'considered that the development in the future of gunnery depends to a large extent on the efficiency of observation from the air.'[1] In fact, it would seem that, to compensate for the RAF's lack of interest in observers, the RN had already been supplying suitably qualified substitutes (perhaps ex-RNAS back-seaters who had elected not to transfer permanently to the RAF) for at least a year.[2]

Once formal training got under way, the Naval Observers Course proved to be very comprehensive. It involved two months of preliminary instruction at the Naval Schools of Gunnery and Signals, followed by a five-month Fleet Spotter Course conducted at the RAF Seaplane Training School at Lee-on-Solent.[3] The next six months were spent on probation, some of it at sea, and during this period additional tactical training was provided by attendance at a further course run by the RAF Training Base at Leuchars. Formal confirmation as an observer required satisfactory completion of the entire thirteen-month sequence.[3A]

To begin with, the duties of RN observers were confined to spotting, i.e. the direction of naval gunfire, reconnaissance being the responsibility of RAF personnel. Initially most of the RAF men will presumably have been ex-WW I observers, possibly supplemented by a few pilots, but it soon became necessary to start finding replacements. To meet this requirement, three RAF Fleet Observers Courses were run at Lee-on-Solent during 1922/23, producing a total of eighteen additional RAF officers qualified for naval observation duties, all but one of them actually being pilots.

[1]Admiralty Fleet Order (AFO) 289 of 2 February 1921 invited officers to volunteer to be trained as observers. At the time, the first course was expected to begin on or about 15 May, although some sources indicate that it might actually have begun as early as 11 April.

[2]AFO 1234 of 21 April 1920 had introduced rates of specialist pay for naval officers already serving as air observers and made provision for those under training. A fully accredited observer was paid six shillings per day while on duty, or four if he was not W/T-qualified; a trainee was to receive three shillings for each day that he actually flew. The promulgation of a pay scale for trainees, long before the establishment of a formal training system, suggests that the Admiralty was already resigned to having to provide its own replacements.

[3]The Seaplane Training School was renamed the School of Naval Co-operation on 19 April 1923, see AMWO 217 of that date.

[3A]AFO 2552 of 28 September 1923.

In 1923 the Balfour Committee was set up with the aim of resolving the persistent differences between the RN and the RAF and deciding how maritime aviation should be run. The outcome was that the RAF was to retain full control of its flying boats while being obliged to concede a substantial measure of its previous authority over shipborne aircraft. These arrangements became effective in April 1924 with the establishment of what was to be known as the Fleet Air Arm (FAA) of the Royal Air Force.

One of the concessions won by the Admiralty while negotiating this deal was that up to 70% of the officers employed in seagoing air units were to be provided by the RN. That is to say, 70% of the pilots, as back-seaters had been specifically excluded from the quota system. Furthermore, it had been agreed that, in future, all observation duties for the Fleet (spotting/gunnery control *and* reconnaissance) would be carried out solely by naval personnel.[4] This was almost certainly at the Admiralty's insistence but, since the RAF was rapidly running out of observers, unless it was prepared to misemploy further pilots, it would very soon have had to become policy in any case.[5]

In the meantime, to reflect the importance that the Admiralty attached to the functions of Observer Officers, it had been decided that they should have specialist status similar to that afforded to Gunnery, Navigation, Torpedo and Signals Officers.[6] Accordingly, an 'O' annotation was introduced and this began to appear in the Navy List from January 1924 onwards. This annotation was not accompanied by the reinstatement of any distinguishing emblem to be worn on the uniform. This refinement was not reintroduced until as late as 1942 (see page 183), although regulations promulgated by the Air Ministry and Admiralty had provided badges for naval pilots since 1925.[7]

Although it was no longer actually providing the back-seaters for naval aeroplanes, the RAF still had some influence

[4]AFO 1059 of 25 April 1924 provided for all FAA observers to be naval personnel. This ruling was publicised within the RAF by AMWO 551 of 25 July 1924.

[5]In practice, although the third RAF Fleet Observers Course was the last, eight more RAF officers (five of them pilots) were trained as observers between 1923 and 1925 via attendance at Naval Observers Courses. It is assumed that these additional men would have been required as gap-fillers during the transitional phase while responsibility was being transferred to the RN.

[6]AFO 3502 of 28 October 1921.

[7]AMWO 567 of 10 September 1925 stated that all RAF officers serving with units of the FAA were to wear, on the lower left sleeve, 'a small silver anchor and cable of silver embroidery surrounded by a laurel wreath of gold embroidery'. This emblem was still current during WW II, as is shown by AMO A.852/40 of 21 November which reminded those concerned that the badge was supposed to be removed when an officer's secondment ceased.

AFO 2793 of 2 October 1925 announced that a similar device was to be worn by RN and RM officers seconded to the RAF for service with the FAA, except that the laurel wreath was to be embroidered in silver (rather than gold), the whole being superimposed on a set of gold embroidered albatross' wings. This had introduced, what amounted to, a naval pilots badge, very similar to that worn today, but differing in two significant respects. First, it lacked a crown and, secondly, it was supposed to be worn only during the period of attachment to the RAF.

over seagoing observers, as it continued to train them at its School of Naval Co-operation at Lee-on-Solent (with landplanes operating from Gosport until 1934 when an aerodrome was built at Lee) for much of the inter-war period.[8] The length and content of the course, which was specified by the Admiralty, *not* the Air Ministry, was periodically adjusted to cater for changing requirements and to meet fluctuating demands. In 1928, for instance, the school advertised just one course. It was of twenty-one weeks duration and had places for ten men, only eight of whom were to be drawn from the RN, the two spare places presumably being intended for officers of the RM.

The first post-war naval three-seater, the Westland Walrus, was an adaptation of the DH 9A; this one, N9534, was photographed during a visit to Cranwell.

1923–39. The provision of air gunners for the Fleet Air Arm

While the RAF made considerable use of W/T during the 1920s, as in WW I, wireless was always of much greater significance to the RN. So much greater, in fact, that for spotting and reconnaissance duties, the FAA was to standardise on a three-man crew, one of whom was to be a wireless operator (or, to use naval terminology, a telegraphist) who would also be expected to double as an aerial gunner. The first dedicated maritime three-seater aircraft, the Westland Walrus, entered service with the RAF's No 3 Sqn at Leuchars in 1922 but, being a somewhat makeshift, interim adaptation of the wartime DH 9A, these aeroplanes spent much (all?) of their time ashore. By 1923, however, the much more capable Fairey IIID, and the purpose-built Avro Bison and Blackburn Blackburn were becoming available and all of these types could, and did, operate from aircraft carriers.

The Admiralty first appealed for volunteers from 'the W/T branch for duty as W/T Operators and as Assistants to Naval Gunnery Observer Officers carried in aeroplanes working with the Fleet' as early as 1921.[9] An initial batch was trained at Gosport the following year but it was late 1923 before the navy called for further volunteers.[10] Thereafter, seaborne aviation's having gained a substantial measure of autonomy from the RAF, the RN sought to obtain additional non-commissioned back-seaters on a regular basis.

Already qualified as telegraphists, they were introduced to airborne radio equipment and procedures at the School of Naval Co-operation at Gosport and to aerial gunnery techniques at the Air Armament School at Eastchurch (both courtesy of the RAF), a third phase, at Portsmouth, being added later to deal with other aspects of air/sea activities.[11] On completion of their training, these men were rated as telegraphist air gunners (TAG) and, as such, they received an additional two shillings per day for as long as they were assigned to flying duties (one shilling while they had been under instruction). From 1925 TAGs were identified by embroidered aeroplane badges worn on the right arm, large ones for ratings, small ones for chief petty officers, the latter also wearing small pairs of aeroplanes on the collars of their uniforms.

In the late 1920s earlier naval observation aircraft began to be supplanted by Fairey IIIFs. What had previously been regarded as quite separate activities, reconnaissance and the ranging of naval artillery, were now merged, most of the FAA's multi-seat units becoming Fleet Spotter Reconnaissance Flights. From 1933 these flights began to be grouped into squadrons as the FAA, along with the rest of the RAF, began to expand. Shortly after this, the navy allocated a third role to its multi-seat units making them Torpedo Spotter Reconnaissance Squadrons. These developments increased the demand for dual-qualified TAGs, making it necessary to widen the scope for internal recruiting. At the same time an effort was made to improve efficiency by demanding higher standards in training. From mid-1935, therefore, the selection pool was broadened to include ratings of the Seaman and Signals Branches in addition to those already being drawn from the Telegraphist Branch.

The core skills required of these men, essentially the ability to handle a Lewis gun and to send and receive Morse at twenty words per minute, were no different from what had been demanded before. On the other hand, since they were no longer being drawn exclusively from the Telegraphist

Note that each of these regulations formally acknowledged the badge authorised by the 'other' Service but that neither had referred specifically to pilots. It was implicit that the rules applied to pilots alone, however, because all of the RAF officers involved would have been pilots and only pilots of the RN and RM were actually attached to the FAA, then an RAF organisation. While RN observers may have been employed full time on flying duties, they retained their exclusively naval affiliations and were thus excluded from the provisions relating to badges.

The RN did not sponsor a pilots badge of its own until 1939 when AFO 908 of 6 April introduced the emblem which is still used today. To be worn on the left sleeve *à la* RNAS, it comprised 'wings of gold embroidery having in the centre a silver anchor and cable surrounded by a gold embroidered wreath and surmounted by a crown.' AFO 1476a of 1 June 1939 announced that a similar design, but of woven fabric, was being introduced for rating pilots.

[8]The School of Naval Co-operation eventually moved to Ford on 29 December 1937. Control was formally transferred to the Admiralty on 24 May 1939 when the RAF unit became the FAA's No 1 Observers School, which functioned as Nos 750, 751 and 752 Sqns. On the same date a No 2 Observers School was established at Lee-on-Solent where it operated as Nos 753 and 754 Sqns.

It is perhaps not widely appreciated that the RAF was also responsible for the training of all naval pilots, this task having been assigned to No 1 FTS at Netheravon as early as 1919. In 1928 this responsibility was transferred to the RAF Training Base at Leuchars which eventually became No 1 FTS when this designation was restored to use in 1935. Three years later No 1 FTS moved back to Netheravon where it continued to train exclusively naval pilots until it disbanded in 1942, although several other RAF units had been additionally assigned to this inter-Service enterprise since 1938.

[9]AFO 3303 of 7 October 1921.

[10]AFO 2555 of 28 September 1923.

[11]From 1927 onwards the Eastchurch course was probably completed before that at Gosport, with the Portsmouth element being added to the beginning of the sequence from 1931 onwards. In 1934 the Gosport phase moved to Lee-on-Solent and in 1936 responsibility for the gunnery element was transferred to the RAF's new Air Observers School at North Coates (a few courses having passed through a temporary facility at Leuchars in the interim). This arrangement ceased in the summer of 1938 (see Fig. 17), naval air gunner training being taken over by the School of Naval Co-operation, by then at Ford. Control of this unit passed to the Admiralty on 24 May 1939 and, following a reorganisation of naval aircrew training, air gunners were catered for by No 1 Air Gunners School (Nos 755 and 757 Sqns) at Worthy Down and No 2 Air Gunners School (No 758 *née* 759 Sqn) at Eastleigh for the remaining months of peace.

Naval three-seaters of the 1920s tended to be designed for comfort rather than speed, as suggested by the capacious fuselage of this Blackburn Mk II, S1048, of HMS Furious' *No 449 Flt.* (P.H.T. Green)

Branch, it was considered inappropriate to continue to call them TAGs. Regardless of their original qualifications, therefore, while they were employed on flying duties the new breed of back-seaters were to be rated simply as air gunners.[12] Existing TAGs were to be given the options of ceasing flying altogether, becoming air gunners under the new terms, remaining as TAGs for the remainder of their flying stint or undergoing additional training to qualify them for an entirely new aircrew category (see below). The new air gunner wore much the same badge as his TAG predecessor with the additional embellishment of a star above the aeroplane.

1935–39. The provision of observers mates

As previously noted, the RAF had decided to reintroduce non-commissioned observers in 1934. A year later, at the same time as it was revising its arrangements for the provision of air gunners, the RN followed suit by introducing observers mates.[13] It was their Lordships intention that the new category should be recruited from experienced gunners but, since the latter had only just been introduced, this would not be possible until 1938 at the earliest. In the meantime, therefore, they had to make do by drawing on existing TAGs.

The first batch of prospective observers mates began training in April 1935, although this rate was not formally introduced until July and the dates and details of the courses involved were not promulgated until as late as September.[14] The training sequence was to consist of three weeks of navigation at the RN Barracks in Portsmouth, followed by a month at the RN Signals School and three weeks of academic training in naval gunnery control at Whale Island (HMS *Excellent*). Having received a firm grounding in naval procedures, the observers mates then joined their commissioned colleagues at the RAF School of Naval Co-operation where they were to stay for a further twenty-two weeks. Topics addressed at Lee-on-Solent included:

Air Navigation	65 hours
Reconnaissance	25 hours
Spotting	25 hours
Armament (bombs and the Lewis gun)	25 hours
Photography	10 hours
Meteorology	20 hours

Provision was also made during the course to ensure that all students were fully up to date with the latest technical developments in W/T and R/T equipment. Observers mates were also responsible for handling the towed sleeve targets used for naval anti-aircraft gunnery practice and the course provided the necessary instruction on streaming, recovery and marking. In addition to academic and practical ground-based work, all observers mates were supposed to spend 120 hours in the air while they were at Lee, with 100 hours being specified as the minimum acceptable for qualification.

Those who completed the training sequence successfully emerged as acting observers mates and remained as such for two years when, so long as they were considered to have accumulated sufficient experience and expertise, they dropped the 'acting' prefix on the strength of a recommendation by their CO. Acting observers mates wore the TAG's aeroplane badge with a crown above, a star being added below once he was confirmed. Additional pay was drawn at three shillings and sixpence per day while acting, rising to four shillings on confirmation, plus sixpence per day 'buzzer allowance' for seaman class ratings. In 1938 both rates of pay were increased by a shilling a day, although this now included the 'buzzer allowance' which ceased to be payable after 23 February.

1936. The attitudes of the RAF and RN towards non-pilot aircrew – compare and contrast

As outlined above, the non-commissioned naval observer of 1936 was being provided with what amounted to the same training as his commissioned colleague. This comprised a total of thirty-two weeks of formal instruction, covering all of the duties that he might be called upon to undertake, and

[12]AFO 1739 of 18 July 1935.
[13]*Ibid.*
[14]AFOs 2191 and 2192 of 12 September 1935.

The flight deck of HMS Courageous *with a range of Flycatchers and Fairey IIIFs, the clutch of RN and RAF officers at left and the scatter of matelots and 'erks' among the aeroplanes illustrate the 'hybrid dark/light blue society of the inter-war FAA.'* (J.M. Bruce/G.S. Leslie collection)

included a substantial amount of airborne experience. This contrasts sharply with the limited scope of the mere eight weeks being offered to his RAF counterpart at North Coates. At that stage the RAF course covered only bombing and gunnery and provided very little flying time. It was acknowledged that RAF observers also needed to know most of the other things that naval observers were being taught but, in the Air Ministry's opinion, instruction in these topics could be safely delegated to squadrons.

This fundamental difference in approach still reflected the attitudes of WW I. In 1917 the RNAS had recognised that a well-trained observer would be an efficient observer and that an efficient observer was as valuable as a competent pilot. The RFC had never really accepted that this was true. In the 1920s the RN had insisted that it continue to be provided with comprehensively trained, specialist, commissioned observers; the RAF had done without. Ten years later, the Air Council finally began to accept that pilots could not cope alone. Perhaps because some influential senior officers had hazy memories of the 'successful' way in which squadron-based training had been carried out in 1916–17, the Service chose to reintroduce a very similar system for their successors, who were, after all, 'only' corporals, and part-timers at that. Regardless of the example set by the navy, there was no question of the air force introducing back-seat officers.

The scale of the RAF's operation in 1936 was much larger than that of the FAA's, of course, but size was not the root of the problem. The RAF had yet to be persuaded that observers were sufficiently worthwhile to warrant a substantial investment in both time and treasure. The RN *knew* that they were and, because they treated them as respected professionals, the FAA could actually do many things better than the RAF could.

1936. The capabilities of the RAF and the FAA – compare and contrast

Denied the soft option of following railway lines, carrier-borne aviators frequently flew out of sight both of land and of their (moving) operating bases and this had obliged them to take navigation very seriously. Following a practice which had been pioneered by the RNAS, the navy's peacetime observer officers also paid considerable attention to bomb-aiming, as a result of which this was another field in which the FAA could teach the rest of the RAF a few tricks.

Having attended No 22 Naval Observers Course in 1932–33, Lt (later Capt) G.A. Rotherham flew from HMSs *Glorious* and *Furious* in Fairey IIIFs of No 822 Sqn until 1936. As one who lived in the hybrid dark/light blue society of the inter-war FAA, Rotherham was well-qualified to comment on the contemporary practices of the RAF. While shore-based at Catfoss for a spell of armament training in May 1935, he noted that:[15]

> '... the RAF were not using any method to find the actual wind – they simply relied upon the Met Man's word as gospel. During the same visit we complained to a visiting Air Marshal about our bomb sight which, in our view was a lamentable device whose compass might start revolving if vibrated. With a little juggling I was able to make it do just that for his benefit. The Air Marshal told us that this was the first complaint he had ever heard on the subject. Perhaps this was because in the RAF the device was operated by "Other Ranks" whose opinions were not given much consideration.'

[15]G.A. Rotherham. *It's Really Quite Safe* (1986).

HMS Glorious *in the 1930s. On her way back from Norway on 8 June 1940 she was intercepted and sunk by* Scharnhorst *and* Gneisenau. (P.H.T. Green)

And that:

> 'I was surprised at the attitude of some of the pilots on the light bomber squadron that was there with us. I overheard one pilot, who was complaining about his bomb-aimer, suggest that the good bomb-aimers should be shared around so that the pilots would have an equal chance to get good marks. There seemed to be no recognition that bombing was a crew event that required careful co-ordination between pilot and aimer.'

From these observations it is quite clear that, by comparison with the FAA, the RAF of the mid-1930s was, in many respects, distinctly unprofessional. It is also clear that Rotherham believed that this could be directly attributed to the RAF's total reliance on pilots and its consequent lack of regard for its back-seaters. Note, incidentally, that Rotherham does not suggest that the RAF did not know *how* to find the local wind; he observes only that it was not bothering to do it – which more or less says it all.

Lest the reader should suspect otherwise, it should be made clear that Rotherham appears to have felt no overt animosity towards his RAF colleagues. Indeed, while conceding that there was some discord between 'the top brass', he notes that 'at the lower levels we got on very well together.' His comments are merely offered as those of a professional aviator, observing the practices of a sister organisation. Although, after a passage in which he explains the arcane system whereby all FAA pilots were assigned dual RN *and* RAF ranks (often involving convoluted degrees of relative seniority), a disapproving tone might be read into the following: 'We Observers, of course, carried Naval rank only since the RAF had no equivalent trade. In the RAF Pilots were God; Observers were nothing.'[16]

1939. The status of non-commissioned naval aircrew is recognised

Reflecting contemporary RAF practice throughout most of the inter-war years, all non-commissioned FAA aviators were, in effect, misemployed groundcrew. There was a significant difference, however, in that the navy recognised, much sooner than did the air force, that being an aviator could not sensibly be treated as a part-time occupation. When air gunners and observers mates were introduced in 1935, therefore, the regulations made it quite clear that they would be 'borne for air duties and will be additional to the complement authorised for Seamen, Signal and Telegraphist duties in each ship.'[17] Nevertheless, when they were not directly involved in their primary tasks, these men could be employed in their original capacities.

A flying rating was well-advised to maintain his core skills, as his career advancement was still within the structure of his original branch. As a result, their promotion prospects tended to suffer by comparison with those of their colleagues who had remained in the mainstream rather than 'wasting their time' volunteering to fly. Once it had gained full control of its air arm, however, much as the RAF was being obliged to do, the RN decided to acknowledge its aircrew by creating a Flying Branch. This branch, into which all rating pilots, air gunners and observers mates were to be remustered, was to have its own career ladder.[18]

As part of this innovation, rates of pay were rationalised. Typically, a newly qualified petty officer observer (or pilot) was now paid seven shillings and sixpence per day plus four shillings and sixpence non-substantive specialist pay. Air gunners drew the same basic rates of pay but their specialist pay was on a lower scale and factored for their assessed level of skill, 3rd, 2nd and 1st Class air gunners being paid two shillings and sixpence, two shillings and ninepence and three shillings, respectively.

The new branch was introduced, along with its associated arrangements, with effect from 1 June 1939. One of these arrangements was that observers mates were to be restyled as rating observers. By either name, however, there had never been very many of them, only about forty having qualified before training became a wholly naval responsibility.[19]

Whether they are flown by air force or naval pilots, operating aeroplanes at sea has always been an exciting business, as Fg Off E. U. G. Solbé discovered when he missed the wire landing on HMS Courageous *on 30 January 1937 in this No 820 Sqn Shark, K8466*

[16]The reason that observers were excluded from the dual ranking arrangement was because they were not actually attached to the FAA (of the RAF), rather than because the RAF did not recognise their trade. Because naval pilots were so attached, there was some potential for conflict between the terms of the Air Force Act and the Naval Discipline Act; this problem was solved by granting RN/RM officers temporary RAF commissions for the duration of their attachment. These arrangements had been introduced as early as 25 July 1924 by AFO 1982. When, some fifteen years later, the Admiralty assumed full responsibility for all aspects of aviation at sea, the dual commissioning procedure became superfluous and AFO 1288 of 18 May 1939 announced that all RAF commissions currently held by RN/RM pilots would be cancelled

[17]AFO 1739 of 18 July 1935.

[18]AFO 1221 of 11 May 1939.

[19]The schools involved in the training of observers mates are as at Note 8.

Chapter 18

1938. The demand for additional aircrew obliges the RAF to resort to the direct recruiting of observers

As early as January 1936 it had been calculated that 1264 trained observers would be needed to meet the demands of Expansion Scheme F.[1] Since the planned output from North Coates was only 200 per year, simple arithmetic showed that it would be well into 1942 before that target could be met. Unfortunately, Scheme F was supposed to be complete by the end of March 1939. The prospects of success had been considerably improved in February 1937 when it had been decided to replace the observer in most of Bomber Command's aeroplanes with a second pilot. Even so, the RAF would need to double its output of observers and at an Expansion Progress Meeting[2] in November 1937 AMP, Air Mshl W.G.S. Mitchell, presented the Air Council with two methods of achieving this aim. One involved contracting Air Service Training of Hamble to run navigation courses for an additional 200 internally recruited observers per year, their subsequent training in bombing and gunnery being undertaken by Service schools. The alternative option was far more radical. It proposed the direct recruiting of civilians to be trained as observers.[3]

So far as the first idea was concerned, AMP pointed out that it might be difficult to find an annual total of 400 airmen who wanted to fly and who were eligible for selection. Furthermore, there was a growing sense of unease over the viability of the concept of the part-time aviator. The technical demands associated with modern aeroplanes were making it both unreasonable and unrealistic to expect part-timers to be able to cope with the complexities of power-operated gun turrets while having to keep pace with corresponding advances being made within their original trades.

The aeroplanes being introduced into service in the later 1930s brought with them complicated electrical, hydraulic and pneumatic systems to operate flaps, gun turrets, retractable undercarriages and the like, metal stressed-skin construction, valved radios, variable-pitch propellers, automatic pilots and so on. All of these required new servicing techniques and a good deal more maintenance than the relatively simple airframes, systems and devices to which the Service had been accustomed since 1918. The additional demands being placed on groundcrew inevitably made it increasingly difficult to release them to go flying. It followed that, since an airman clearly could not be in two places at once, a difficult peacetime situation would become quite unworkable in the event of war. Having effectively (or perhaps ineffectively) been getting two men for the price of one for almost twenty years, the RAF was finally being forced to come to terms with the fundamental lack of realism which had underpinned its post-war aircrew policy.

J.R. Paine, who passed through North Coates in 1937 before joining No 139 Sqn as an observer, provides a succinct first-hand impression of what this all meant in practice:[4]

> 'For example, an Air Observer (Fitter) would be told to change the engine on an Aircraft. When he informed the Flight Sergeant that he was to go on a six hour flight, the answer would be, "Ho! Cpl, scrounging off flying Eh?, right, you can work all night on it when you come back!"'

A month after AMP had drawn attention to the problems involved in the provision of observers CAS, Air Chf Mshl Sir Cyril Newall, made his decision. Having accepted that it would be impractical to persist in trying to find the numbers required from within the Service, he directed that, in order to avoid creating serious undermanning problems within critical ground trades, civilian recruiting was to be introduced with the aim of completely satisfying the demand for observers by 1940.[5]

In effect the RAF had conceded that it would have to find sufficient civilians to provide 50% of the observers that it needed. Direct recruiting was a considerable departure from previous practice and it was being introduced on the understanding that it was to be a purely temporary measure. The direct entrants were being offered an engagement of only four years, simply to tide the air force over until the completion of its expansion programme(s) had provided it with sufficient manpower to allow it to resume 100% internal recruiting. It was hoped eventually to salvage most of the civilian entry by retraining them as airmen pilots in their fourth year of service.

While internal recruits would continue to be part-timers, those brought in from outside were going to be treated as full-time aircrew. This was more or less inevitable, since they were unlikely to have any other skills and there was no time to provide them with any. Nevertheless, despite their limited utility and their lack of experience, the civilian recruits, like their Service counterparts, were going to fly as corporals. This rather startling development provides an interesting commentary on the way in which the RAF was being obliged to change its attitudes, as well as its equipment, during the last year of peace.

[1]AIR8/204.

[2]From June 1935 onwards, Air Council Meetings were known as Secretary of State's Progress Meetings on RAF Expansion Measures, Expansion Progress Meetings (EPM) for short. The 200th EPM was held in July 1940 after which the original title was reinstated.

[3]AIR6/51. Note 142(37) dated 15 November 1937 submitted to the 102nd EPM.

[4]J.R. Paine, *op. cit.*

[5]This edict, which also directed that observers were to be trained in navigation to the same standard as pilots, was contained in a minute dated 13 December 1937 from CAS to AMP. The original was raised on Air Ministry file 519517/36, which appears to have been destroyed in 1954. This most significant minute is referred to in an AHB monograph (AIR41/4), a footnote stating that it is reproduced in full at Appendix 6. Unfortunately, in this instance, the appendices were contained within a separate volume and neither the AHB nor the PRO appear to have retained a copy of this document.

While the Air Council had expressed some misgivings over the introduction of 'instant' corporal observers, it goes almost without saying that they had had less difficulty with the idea of 'instant' *sergeant* pilots. As early as 1935 it had been announced that, in order to obtain the numbers required, it would be necessary to resort to the direct recruiting of airmen pilots on short (four-year) engagements.[6] The first of these had begun to enter productive service, as sergeants, in May of the following year – at more or less the same time as the RAF had been concluding that it would be quite unthinkable to permit an observer to wear even two stripes until he had been in uniform for at least six years (see page 116).

It should be noted, incidentally, that the introduction of directly recruited pilots had not met with universal approval. Since all airmen pilots had previously been drawn from within the ranks, the opportunity to obtain accelerated promotion to sergeant which this entailed had come to be seen as an integral element of the non-commissioned career structure. The fact that civilians were now perceived to be taking up some of these places was resented by regular airmen. Fortunately, the employment of direct entrant pilots had always been seen as a short-term measure and, not least because of their unpopularity, recruiting was terminated in the spring of 1937.

Meanwhile, in order to sustain the flow of volunteer observers from within the Service, yet more concessions needed to be made or, as some might have put it, the entry standard had to be lowered even further. In March 1938 the regulations governing the wearing of the flying 'O' were amended to exempt the remaining full-time gunners from having to attend a formal course at North Coates.[7] In effect, therefore, a full-time gunner could become an observer by the simple expedient of arranging for his Flight Commander to authorise him to fly as one for six months and then persuading his CO to recommend him for remustering. Unless the individual concerned was a hopeless incompetent, most COs would probably have been only too happy to oblige, as this would have filled an empty slot in his unit's establishment with a hard-to-find observer, whereas gunners, who could still be trained locally, were relatively easy to replace.

In another move to relieve the persistent shortage of observers the selection field of trades from which they could be drawn was further broadened in May 1938, the requirement for previous service being reduced at the same time to just three years.[8] Despite these initiatives, the problem was getting worse. Although the pressure had been taken off in February 1937, this relief turned out to be only temporary, as the 'no observers' policy was reversed in May 1938 (see page 132). By that time the training staffs were aiming at manpower targets set by Scheme L, which envisaged a striking force of forty-seven squadrons of heavy, and twenty-six of medium, bombers flying a total of 1352 front-line aircraft.[9] While some non-pilot aircrew would also be needed by Coastal and the various overseas Commands, the major employer was clearly still going to be Bomber Command. Including reserves, the overall bill came to 2069 observers, 3867 wireless operator/air gunners and 554 gunners without any wireless training – 6490 men in all. It was a tall order.

[6]AMO A.129/35 of 23 May announced the introduction of 'instant' sergeant pilots, AMO 89/36 of 23 April publishing their conditions of service.
[7]AMO A.90/38 of 10 March.
[8]AMOs A.166/38 and A.189/38 of 5 and 26 May revised and restated the conditions governing the internal recruiting of air observers.
[9]AIR8/240.

North Coates might be regarded as the spiritual home of the second generation of air observers, at least to begin with. This picture dates from 1931 when the station was one of three unnumbered RAF Practice Camps. (P.H.T. Green)

The direct recruiting of observers which had been approved in December 1937 actually began in the following July.[10] Four Civilian Air Navigation Schools (CANS) were contracted to provide the direct entrants with twelve week's instruction in navigation. The first courses, all early intakes being in batches of thirty, began on 18 August.[11] On completion of this phase, and still wearing their civilian clothes, trainees reported to one of the two RAF Recruit Depots for a fortnight's military induction during which they were issued with their uniforms.[12] From there they proceeded to a Service-run Air Observers School where they were given three weeks' instruction in bombing, another three in gunnery and a further six weeks of navigation training. The first direct entrants were initially expected to reach the squadrons in February 1939.

The new scheme succeeded in attracting substantial numbers of potential observers, the increased civilian intake eventually requiring the commissioning of several more commercially operated navigation schools. To cope with the instruction of larger intakes of serving airmen and the armament training of the direct entrants, the Service training system also had to be considerably expanded. A second Air Observers School opened before the end of 1938 and two more followed in the spring of 1939. All these additional Service units were created by the simple expedient of adding navigation to the tasks of existing Armament Training Stations and redesignating them.[13]

The introduction of direct entrant aircrew had made it necessary to revise the system of allowances. While under training, observer recruits were to be paid as leading aircraftmen (LAC), of Trade Group II plus flying instructional pay at one shilling and sixpence per day. On qualification they were to graduate as corporals (on probation for the first twelve months), drawing the inclusive nine-shilling daily rate that had been introduced in November 1936.

[10]AMO A.253/38 of 14 July laid down the conditions of service for direct entrant air observers.
[11]The first four civilian schools were run by Scottish Aviation at Prestwick, The Bristol Aeroplane Company at Yatesbury, Reid and Sigrist at Desford and Air Service Training at Ansty.
[12]Following a brief initial assessment and processing by the RAF Reception Depot at West Drayton, the RAF Depot at Uxbridge had provided the majority of civilians with their first exposure to the Service since the 1920s. The increased intakes associated with the Expansion Schemes had exceeded its capacity, however, so, to relieve the pressure, No 2 Recruit Depot was set up at Henlow in May 1937. The new unit moved to Cardington at the end of September, by which time Uxbridge had been restyled No 1 Recruit Depot.
[13]The first cohort of direct entrant observers requiring armament training arrived at North Coates on 21 November 1938. By this time North Coates had become No 1 AOS, No 2 having been formed at Acklington on the 15th by redesignating No 7 Armament Training Station.

Meanwhile, probably because no one cared very much about them, a number of air gunners had been rather poorly treated because of the 1926 regulation requiring them to be filling established posts in order to draw crew and duty pay. When gunners began to attend courses at North Coates, most of them did so on attachment from squadrons to which they eventually returned as observers. Since they had never been struck off the books of their original units, therefore, they continued to draw crew and duty pay until they remustered. Unfortunately, those who had been *posted* to the Air Observers School were no longer actually filling gunner posts, which cost them one shilling and sixpence a day.

This anomaly was eventually removed in November 1938 when it was ruled that any gunner previously entitled to draw crew pay and gunners pay would continue to do so while under training as an observer, regardless of whether he was or was not filling an established post.[14] This arrangement was to be short-lived, however, as the system was changed again in December. To bring them in line with direct entrants, it was decided that all Service personnel undergoing observer training should, like them, draw flying instructional pay at one shilling and sixpence per day. This one shilling and sixpence was a bonus to those airmen who were new to the flying game and compensated qualified gunners who were being retrained, all of whom now forfeited their one shilling and sixpence crew and gunners qualification pay.[15] Needless to say, flying instructional pay for pilots was still being paid at a preferential rate of two shillings per day.

1938–39. The introduction of non-pilot volunteer reserve aircrew

The RAF Volunteer Reserve (RAFVR) had been set up on 27 August 1936 with the aim of creating a large pool of part-trained personnel who would be available for mobilisation in the event of an emergency. Recruiting, began in January 1937. To begin with this was confined to airmen pilots, although provision was made for (reserve) commissions to be awarded to suitable candidates above the age of 21 years (medical and equipment officers were also required). The RAFVR resembled the Territorial Army, at least to the extent that it was organised on a regional basis, a ground training centre (the first of which opened in March 1937) being located within a town or city with flying being conducted from a nearby aerodrome.

The nucleus of these arrangements was provided by the thirteen civilian schools which had already been contracted to support the elementary stage of the 1935 pilot training scheme. Flying training for the RAFVR began in April 1937 and in July financial approval was obtained to engage a further ten civilian schools. In December all these units were given quasi-military status by centralising their administration within Training Command and numbering them as Elementary and Reserve Flying Training Schools (ERFTS).[16]

Once the RAF had decided to resort to the direct recruiting of regular observers, it followed that, like regular pilots, they too would need to be backed up by reservists. Recruiting of non-pilot RAFVR aircrew, gunners as well as observers, began in November 1938, initially at Glasgow, Coventry and Leicester. The response was generally disappointing; at the end of March 1939 only 237 observers and 124 wireless operator/air gunners had enlisted. Furthermore, little real progress had been made with training.

In fact, training was proving to be somewhat problematical. The only subjects that the few available instructors could realistically be expected to deal with were those academic aspects of navigation and wireless telegraphy which could be taught in the classroom at a town centre. There were no suitable aeroplanes available for air work and, even if there had been, the (still essentially civilian) ERFTSs could hardly have been expected to offer much in the way of practical gunnery or bombing.

Furthermore, there was a critical shortage of staff. To take just one example, only thirty-three of the 174 instructors required to teach armaments were immediately available. Steps were promptly taken to engage and train suitable instructors, the first batch of thirty embarking on a fourteen-week course at Manby in December 1938. Even so, it was expected to be March 1940 before all of the necessary instructors could be provided. There were similar problems in finding staff to deal with photography, navigation and wireless, the total requirement for instructors of all kinds amounting to some 625 men.

In the wake of the Munich crisis increased urgency was attached to the provision of *fully trained* reserves and a scheme was introduced which offered a £50 bounty (about £1750 in 1999[17]) to RAFVR personnel who were prepared to undertake six months of full time training. This was to take them as far as spending a period of quasi-operational flying with a non-mobilisable squadron.[18]

There was some uptake, 120 pilots having taken advantage of the offer by May 1939. Unfortunately, the limitations of the training facilities meant that there were no aircrew of any other categories to support them. Furthermore, there had been considerable reservations over the wisdom of extending this element of the reserve scheme to embrace observers, as it was felt that the offer of what amounted to a six-month trial with a very generous bounty would act as a disincentive to signing on as a regular.[19] Nevertheless, in the spring of 1939 the proprietors of the Civilian Air Navigation Schools were being pressed to accept VR personnel with a view to providing them with much the same training as was being given to direct entrants. A major problem with this approach was that, without an increase in overall capacity, reservists could be trained only at the expense of regulars. This was equally true in the case of pilots, of course.

On 1 May 1939 the RAFVR had 3604 pilots on its books, 89% of the (then) overall requirement of 4050. While very few of these men could be regarded as being anything like fully trained, the overall position was generally satisfactory, but this was not the case with non-pilots. The number of observers enrolled had crept up to 477 and there were now

[14]AMO A.407/38 of 3 November.

[15]AIR2/2968. Air Ministry letter S.45639/S.7 dated 12 December 1938 announced this change in policy.

[16]AMO N.55/38 of 20 January announced that the headquarters of the Superintendent of Civil Flying Schools had been renamed HQ No 26 (Training) Group with effect from 1 December 1937 and that it was responsible for Nos 1–21 ERFTSs. Although it was not specifically stated, it seems reasonable to assume that the existing schools would also have been allocated their numerical designations on the same date (although No 21 ERFTS did not actually open until 1 January 1938).

[17]See Chapter 7, Note 1.

[18]Although new squadrons had continued to form in compliance with various Expansion Schemes, by 1939 several of them had to be classed as non-mobilisable because they were manned below establishment and the lack of trained reserves meant that they could not be brought up to strength, even in an emergency. On the outbreak of war there were nine such units in Bomber Command.

[19]AIR6/55. Note EMP 174(38) dated 2 December 1938 submitted to the 146th Expansion Progress Meeting by AMP, Air Mshl W.G.S. Mitchell.

313 air gunners, but these represented only 18% of the combined target figure of 4300.[20] This sort of head count went on continually, of course, but the numbers had taken on a grimly increased significance since March, when Hitler had brushed aside the Munich Agreement to occupy what was left of Czechoslovakia; there were early indications that Poland would be next.

Some positive progress was made in April, when the civilian schools at Prestwick, Ansty and Desford each agreed (in principle) to accept a batch of twenty-four VR observers. Although this arrangement was referred to as 'full time' training, by the time that the military stage had been added, it was actually expected to take a year to complete. This was twice as long as the sequence of courses for regulars and meant that the first fully trained RAFVR observers would not become available until as late as April 1940. Even this was an optimistic forecast, however, as contractual terms had still to be agreed with the commercial navigation schools at the end of May.

By July there were 180 pilots at a variety of ERFTSs committed to voluntary six-month 'full time' courses, but the whole scheme was on too small a scale and was going to take far too long to produce results. The solution to this problem was expected to lie in the passage of the Military Training Act of May 1939 which had been hastily introduced as a reaction to the German occupation of Prague.[21] Under its provisions, the Air Ministry was able to call up reservists on initial enlistment for up to six months of *real* full time training followed by three and a half years as a 'weekend warrior' with the RAFVR. The necessary plans began to be prepared in May, the associated regulations being promulgated two months later.[22] It would take many more weeks for these arrangements to be implemented, however, because new contracts had first to be negotiated with the civilian schools. They then needed to prepare additional facilities and accommodation, and recruit and engage the necessary extra staff. Only when all of that had been done could training actually begin.

Although certain young men were required to register under the terms of the Military Training Act, they were at little risk of being called up in the short term, as there was insufficient training capacity. Nevertheless, boosted by some conscription, the RAFVR continued to attract a steady flow of voluntary applicants (by now including ground tradesmen), although, because the July regulations had made full time training for reservists mandatory, the Treasury was now able to save its £50 bounties. Regardless of rank and trade, all RAFVR trainees were to be paid one shilling and sixpence per day throughout their six-month stint, the only exceptions being aircrew who were to draw flying instructional pay at daily rates of two shillings and nine pence for pilots, two shillings for observers and one shilling and sixpence for W/T operators and/or air gunners. It is not known, incidentally, why trainee VR pilots and observers attracted, respectively, ninepence and sixpence per day more than their regular colleagues, while gunners got the same.

It was eventually agreed that the first observers, for what was sometimes informally referred to as the 'militia air force', would enter training in September. They were to spend twelve weeks at a CANS followed by eight at an Armament Training Station (which was to be set up specifically for their benefit at Jurby), the sequence being finished off by an eight-week stint with a non-mobilisable squadron. The first wireless operators were to follow in October, their training involving eight weeks of gunnery at Acklington, followed by four months of wireless training at Hamble and a fortnight with a squadron. The first courses for pilots were expected to start in November.

Sadly, it was all too late. No one knew it at the time, of course, but when serious planning for the provision of six months of full time training for reservists had begun, less than four months of peace remained. As a result, the RAF was already committed to entering the war without an effective aircrew reserve. It was true that there were substantial numbers of pilots who could be mobilised, but few of them could be regarded as being fully trained. Heavier aircraft, Harts and Audaxes, had been introduced at the ERFTSs in 1937–38 and since then pupils had been trained to something approaching the intermediate standard achieved at Service FTSs. Despite the issue of a handful of Battles in 1939, however, it had proved impossible to provide reservists with the more advanced elements of the full course and there had never been any realistic prospect of the ERFTSs providing armament training. The position with regard to non-pilots was even bleaker. The notional reserve was considerably understrength and those that had enrolled had received very little worthwhile instruction.[23]

Unfortunate as all of this was, there was another adverse factor at work which would not make itself apparent until later. Under constant pressure to increase the numbers of non-pilot reservists, the recruiting centres had tended to accept whatever applicants they could get. Needless to say, this was a very short-sighted approach, as the Service was to discover when these men began to be mobilised in September (see page 149).

1938–39. The observer is given exclusive responsibility for navigation

A year after implementing the concept of using a second pilot to handle navigation, there had been little detectable improvement in the ability of bomber crews to find their way about. This will have been due, at least in part, to the disappointing results yielded by the use of civilian schools to train Squadron Navigation Officers. These schools were not equipped to provide any flying exercises so, while the men responsible for raising standards on squadrons may have acquired some academic expertise, they were little better at dealing with the practicalities of navigation than those whom they were supposed to be teaching.

It is clear from this that, despite its having fluttered the dovecotes at the Air Ministry, one of the main thrusts of Flt Lt Waghorn's paper of 1936 had failed to find its mark. Waghorn had stressed the vital importance of practical 'hands on' experience; the RAF's response had been to provide only classroom instruction.

Since many Squadron Navigation Officers had proved to be unsatisfactory as teachers, it was eventually decided that *all* pilots would have to be individually trained to 'sn' standard by sending them on the ten-week course (ideally) immediately after graduation. It had initially been assumed that the

[20]AIR32/15.
[21]Passed by the Commons on 26 April 1939 and endorsed by the Lords on the 27th, the Reserve and Auxiliary Forces Act received royal assent on 25 May and the Military Training Act on the following day.
[22]AMO A.252/39 of 5 July.
[23]On 3 September 1939 the RAFVR's strength in observers stood at 1623 and it had 1948 wireless operators and gunners, still well below target in both cases, although the number of pilots had risen to 5646.

School of Air Navigation would handle this task but, when the sums were done, the anticipated throughput turned out to be no fewer than 1500 students during 1938–39. To provide increased capacity at Manston, some of its commitments were transferred elsewhere[24] but, even so, it still could not possibly process such numbers alone and it was necessary to sustain the use of civilian schools. The first course began at Manston in April 1938, two civilian schools accepting their first intakes in May. Four more civilian organisations, diverted from observer training, were scheduled to join the programme in the summer but by that time changing priorities had already caused them to revert to their original tasks.

By the spring of 1938 some quite influential officers were beginning to doubt the wisdom of devoting so much effort to training pilots in navigation. One of them was Philip Mackworth (see page 119), by now a wing commander, who considered that, once the anticipated war had actually started, time simply would not permit the luxury of providing all pilots with lengthy courses in both flying and navigation.[25] He argued that the observer represented an underexploited resource and that a better solution would be to make him fully responsible for navigation. In May 1938 he presented his case at a policy meeting which eventually agreed that 'the navigation of the aircraft in war should be carried out by a properly trained observer/navigator.'[26]

Making observers responsible for navigation in war had two major implications. The first was that all observers would now have to be taught the full ten-week 'sn' syllabus, previously confined to pilots. The second was that an observer would have to be added to the crews of all general reconnaissance aircraft and to those of bombers which did not already have one, thus reinstating the observers who had been deleted from the crews of large bombers as recently as February 1937. This did not, however, displace the second pilots who had been introduced at that time.

Mackworth had also argued that, since the observer would be better trained in future, it would be possible to reduce the navigation content of pilot training to basic DR. This too had been agreed but there was some uncertainty as to where and when this training ought to be provided. AVM W.S. Douglas, who chaired the meeting, was hopeful that it would be possible to shoe-horn an adequate amount of pilot navigation into the existing FTS course and he directed that this possibility was to be investigated.

Until this matter could be settled, therefore, the current pilot training sequence (including the early post-graduate ten-week 'sn' course) had to remain undisturbed, and there was some justification for this. The May 1938 decision had made observers responsible for navigation only 'in war'. Technically, therefore, pilots still retained this responsibility in peace. While this amounted to little more than sophistry, it served to block any changes within the pilot training sequence. In effect, therefore, the Service was now training three men to act as navigators in each large aeroplane and two in smaller ones.

Mackworth returned to the fray in February 1939 to point out that it was clearly an extravagance to be providing all these men with the lengthy specialist instruction necessary to reach 'sn' standard. Furthermore, it had become apparent by now that the training system was quite incapable of handling the considerable numbers involved, so the aim was not actually being achieved in any case. Mackworth suggested that, since it had already been accepted that observers would have to be responsible for navigation in wartime, they might as well do it in peacetime as well. This proposal was to be bitterly opposed.

Back in 1917–18, Lt-Col Edgar Ludlow-Hewitt had been instrumental in having many of the key functions of first-generation observers transferred to pilots (see page 53). Twenty years later, by now Air Chf Mshl Sir Edgar and AOCinC Bomber Command, he was steadfastly opposed to their successors being given formal responsibility for navigation. His uncompromising attitude was clearly revealed in related correspondence in which he used phrases such as 'the observer is the servant of the Captain of the Aircraft' and '<u>never</u> state that he is <u>responsible</u> for navigation' (L-H's underlining).[27] Ludlow-Hewitt's chief concern was that if the observer were to be made responsible for it, the captain would 'wash his hands of navigation.' Unfortunately, although no one appears to have pointed this out, that is precisely what most pilots had been doing for the previous twenty years, which is why navigation was currently proving to be such a problem.

Ludlow-Hewitt was not having it all his own way, however, as a number of other prominent and increasingly influential officers had finally begun to appreciate the adverse consequences of the RAF's peacetime crewing policy. As early as 1936, for instance, in commenting on the Waghorn Paper, Gp Capt Arthur Harris had identified the RAF's traditional practice of 'attempting to make pilots masters of all trades so that they never have time to become masters of their own' as the cause of many of the Service's operational shortcomings.[28]

Harris was not alone. There were other senior officers who would later come to share his appreciation of the situation. For example, in December 1938 Air Mshl Mitchell wrote that 'the assumption that lay behind the previous policy, that the observer need not be of the same high standard as the pilot, should be finally abandoned ... it is clear that the observer is of, at least, equal importance and it is accordingly proposed that both as regards pay and status he should be placed on an equal footing with the airman pilot.' In conclusion, Mitchell even went so far as to advocate the creation of a class of commissioned observers.[29] A year later AVM Douglas (an erstwhile back-seater himself) was to state that, in his view, the lack of faith in the early observers of WW II was because 'the prestige of pilots has been so extensively fostered in the past that there has been a tendency to belittle the importance of other members of the crew.' Douglas went on to point out that, while many pilots were opposed to the idea of observers being made responsible for navigation, 'some pilots themselves have not shown themselves very keen to become expert navigators' – which seriously undermined Ludlow-Hewitt's earlier protestations.[30]

[24]The training of pilots destined for maritime squadrons was transferred to Thorney Island where a School of General Reconnaissance was opened on 4 April 1938.

[25]Wg Cdr Mackworth was OR3 at the Air Ministry in 1938–39.

[26]AIR2/2660. Minutes of a meeting held at the Air Ministry on 16 May 1938 under the chairmanship of ACAS, AVM W.S. Douglas, to discuss the training and establishment of observers in war.

[27]AIR2/4467. Unreferenced letter of 27 February 1939 (filed on Air Ministry file S.47667) from Ludlow-Hewitt, as AOCinC Bomber Command, to ACAS, AVM Douglas.

[28]AIR2/2860. See Chapter 16, Note 26.

[29]AIR6/55. Note EMP 156(38) dated 29 October 1938 submitted to the 141st Expansion Progress Meeting by AMP, Air Mshl Mitchell.

[30]AIR2/4459. Minute dated 29 December 1939 on Air Ministry file S.75988 from AVM Douglas to AMP, Air Mshl Portal, another (possibly) sympathetic ex-observer.

Despite Bomber Command's objections, in May 1939 it was finally ruled that observers would be responsible, albeit 'under the direction of the captain,' for aircraft navigation in both peace and war.[31] This decision meant that pilots would no longer need to be trained to the same 'sn' standard as observers and permitted the navigation content of flying training courses to be reduced to little more than basic dead reckoning.[32] To sweeten the pill, it was agreed that wing commanders and squadron leaders should attend a six-week course of advanced navigation at Manston to enable them to supervise the conduct of continuation training on their units. All of this represented a significant reduction in the overall pilot training task, permitting considerable savings to be made, particularly in time. Nevertheless, it was still intended to send all pilots to one of the civilian-run schools for a six-week top-up course in basic navigation *after* they had gained their 'wings'. The stated aim was to provide them with sufficient knowledge to be able to get their aeroplanes back to base in an emergency and to permit them to monitor the observer's efforts. Little progress was made in this respect, however, as the first six-week pilots course was not scheduled to begin until as late as August 1939. In the event none had actually started before the outbreak of war put a stop to the programme.

1938. The part-time aircrew concept is finally abandoned

As noted above, the decision of May 1938, which had made them responsible for navigation in war, had also added a, still part-time, observer to the complement of every crew. This had provoked further consideration of the conditions governing the provision of non-pilot aircrew. Air Chf Mshl Ludlow-Hewitt had very strong views on this subject because, having recognised that teamwork was going to be essential for the efficient operation of large, multi-seat aeroplanes, he had inevitably been drawn to the conclusion that his bombers needed to have permanently constituted crews.[33]

While some progress was made in this context, this policy was not fully implemented until after the declaration of war, although the air force had already been drifting in this direction for some time. For instance, as early as mid-1937, the Records Office had called for periodic returns of airmen who flew regularly as wireless operators and/or gunners.[34] The object of this exercise was to limit their movements so that they could remain with their units for as long as possible. While the concept of constituted crews would clearly impose significant constraints on the staffs responsible for posting part-timers, the problems did not end there. If the idea was really going to work, all of the members of a crew would have to be available at the same time so that they could be programmed for continuation training, on the ground as well as in the air. At squadron level, this simply could not be achieved if most of the crew were part-timers subject to the whims of two masters.

By 1938 'the days of releasing the odd airman for an hour or so to loose off a few rounds from the rear cockpit of a Hind were over.' This one, K6741, clearly belonged to No 50 Sqn.

Furthermore, the performance and complexity of modern aeroplanes made increasing demands on the crew in that, apart from flights being of longer duration, flight planning, pre-flight checks and post-flight debriefs all required far more time than in the past. The days of releasing the odd airman for an hour or so to loose off a few rounds from the rear cockpit of a Hind were over. Each of the new Whitleys required an observer and two wireless operator/gunners, and probably a third gunner under training. If a squadron were required to put up, say, ten aircraft for an exercise (let alone in war) this would effectively remove as many as forty airmen from the hangar for a whole day. Such a depletion of technical personnel would plainly be unacceptable.

Having been considering this problem for some time, by the summer of 1938 Ludlow-Hewitt had devised a specific proposal for a discrete aircrew trade.[35] He envisaged that their initial training would provide an introduction to navigation, gunnery, bomb aiming, photography and wireless operation. They would all be employed as gunners initially, progressively adding formal qualifications in other skills as they gained in experience. His aim was that every member of a crew should eventually be capable of carrying out any function apart from flying the aeroplane, which was to be the exclusive preserve of pilots. On the other hand, pilots were expected to be able to carry out the duties of all other crew members, as well as their own!

If this seems a trifle ambitious, it is because it was. It will be recalled that in 1917 Ludlow-Hewitt had tended to assume that all pilots were as capable as he undoubtedly was himself.[36] Unfortunately, this simply was not the case. Given

[31]AIR2/4467. Letter S.47667/S.6 dated 22 May 1939 from Charles Evans (Principal Assistant Secretary to the Permanent Under-Secretary of State for Air) to all Commands, except Maintenance Command. This letter provided broad details of the new policy for the conduct of, and training in, air navigation.

[32]The case of the Hampden provided an exception to the rule, that observers were to act as navigators. The remarkably narrow fuselage of this aeroplane made it so difficult as to be impractical for crew members to change places. Since the Hampden required only a four-man crew, the options were to provide, in addition to a pair of gunners, a pilot and observer or two pilots, one of whom would have to act as navigator and bomb-aimer. The two-pilot solution was chosen, because a stint as a second pilot was deemed to be a pre-requisite for a captaincy. Thus Hampden pilots continued to attend a comprehensive course at the School of Air Navigation.

When Hampdens began to operate in the torpedo bomber role in 1941, Coastal Command replaced the second pilot with an observer. It is worth noting, however, that the courses routinely attended by wartime Coastal Command pilots at one of the Schools of General Reconnaissance included comprehensive instruction in navigation.

[33]AIR2/2968. It is clear from the terms in which his BC/S.21116/CinC of 14 July 1938 (see Note 35) was couched that Ludlow-Hewitt had recognised the need for constituted crews.

[34]AMO A.173/37 of 3 June.

[35]AIR2/2968. Ludlow-Hewitt provided a detailed breakdown of his proposal in a letter, BC/S.21116/CinC, which he addressed to the Air Ministry on 14 July 1938. This was not the first time that he had raised the question of an aircrew trade, however, and it had certainly been in his mind as early as March when he had suggested the idea in his annual report on the efficiency of his Command.

[36]Testimony as to Ludlow-Hewitt's early capabilities was provided by no less an authority than Maj James McCudden VC DSO* MC* MM who, as an NCO, flew as his observer before becoming a pilot himself. In his *Flying Fury* McCudden wrote that 'having flown a good deal with Major Hewitt, I intensely disliked ever going up with anyone else, for I can assure you that I knew when I was flying with a safe pilot, and I now had so much faith in him that if he said "Come to Berlin," I should have gone like a shot.'

several years of training and experience, it is possible that a few individuals might have been able to meet Ludlow-Hewitt's exacting standards, but to expect that all of the pilots serving in a largely conscripted citizen air force would all be capable of performing competently in any of the half-dozen crew stations in a large bomber was plainly unrealistic. The likelihood of this ideal ever being attained by anyone became even more remote when the constraints of the anticipated war were imposed on the concept. It had to be expected that training would be reduced to a minimum in wartime and the inevitable losses in action were likely to preclude all but a lucky few from accumulating very much experience.

Note on terminology

Up to this point in this narrative the term *aircrew* has been used to refer to aviators of all kinds, because it is both convenient and, today, familiar. This has actually been an anachronism, since an air force accustomed to thinking in terms only of pilots, all other aviators being merely misemployed ground personnel, had little use for such a label before 1938. Once the Service had begun to recruit and employ non-pilots as full-time professional flyers, however, the term did begin to enter the RAF's lexicon. At the time it was rendered as two words – *air crew* – and, although there were some deviations from this practice, it generally stayed that way until 1945–46.

At first 'air crew' was associated only with non-pilots but its meaning was gradually extended and in 1940 it was officially declared to be a generic term applicable 'to all members of the flying crews of an aircraft.'[37] These conventions will be followed from here on, to reflect contemporary practice.

1939. The ultimate pre-war scheme for the provision of non-pilot air crew

Despite Prime Minister Chamberlain's declaration of 'peace in our time' in the wake of the Munich crisis of September 1938, there were few grounds for optimism and the rearmament programme continued apace. Meanwhile, the air staff had been working on Bomber Command's idea of an air crew trade and proposals showing how it might be made to work were submitted in October.[38] Presumably believing, or perhaps hoping, that it still had time in hand, the Air Council adopted the scheme. The last major change in recruiting and training policy to be implemented in peacetime, details were announced in January 1939.[39]

The explanatory remarks contained the crucial statement that 'employment as a member of an aircraft crew will in future be regarded as full-time employment and airmen for such duties will be provided additionally to the tradesmen establishment of all units concerned.' While this was seen as a major innovation, which indeed it was, it was not really breaking new ground. Having long since seen the light, the RN had adopted this practice as early as 1935 (see page 127).

The new RAF scheme introduced a progressive concept which envisaged that all non-pilot air crew would begin their careers as, what were now to be known as, wireless operators (air crew). The underlying intention was to phase out the

Most air gunners were recruited from wireless operators who had been given a brief taste of flying at Cranwell where the Electrical and Wireless School kept a small fleet of aeroplanes, including the odd Vickers transport, for the purpose. Seen here while serving the CFS as a blind flying trainer (and being flown from deep within the bowels of the ship on instruments, hence the empty cockpit), this Victoria V, K2344, eventually found its way to Cranwell. (P.H.T. Green)

previous distinction whereby some gunners had been wireless trained but others had not. With the exception of Coastal Command, where the peculiar demands of flying boats meant that fitters and riggers would continue to be employed on flying duties, all the new generation of gunners were to be recruited from boy entrant wireless operators.[40] They would all fly as airmen for an initial period of three years. Most could then expect to continue to be employed as wireless operators (air crew) but about 25% were to be selected for further training. After a sixteen-week course of navigation and bombing these men would be remustered as air observers, at which point they were to become sergeants. It was envisaged that, following a further period of productive service, those observers who were considered suitable would ultimately become pilots.

Provision was made for observers to serve in ranks up to warrant officer with rates of pay being the same as for airmen pilots, which for a sergeant meant twelve shillings and sixpence per day. Another refinement was that the scheme made provision for a proportion of observers (and gunners) to be commissioned, although there were no indications as to when this might occur or of the numbers that might be required.

While this scheme may have been sound, it represented an essentially long-term investment which would not yield any substantial dividends for several years. This would prove to be its undoing, as time was fast running out. In fact, rather than being able to indulge in the luxury of lengthy periods of training and consolidation, the demand for manpower created by the remorseless expansion of the Service was actually making it necessary to cut back on the length of time which could be devoted to instruction. As early as June 1938 the Air Ministry had been obliged to shorten the course attended by wireless operators and to warn units to expect that new arrivals would be less competent than their predecessors.[41] Since wireless operators were the seed corn from which the Service was

[37] AMO A.94/40 of 15 February.
[38] AIR6/55. Note 156(38) dated 29 October 1938 submitted to the 141st EPM.
[39] AMO A.17/39 of 19 January.

[40] Para 3 of AMO A.17/39 addressed the continuing need to satisfy Coastal Command's unique requirements, these having been formally acknowleged by AMO A.235/36 of 8 October.
[41] AMO A.235/38 of 30 June announced that it had been necessary to shorten the time devoted to the training of W/T Operators at the Electrical and Wireless School at Cranwell and stressed the consequent need for additional consolidation training on squadrons.

expected to grow its gunners, and ultimately its observers, this did little to ease the problem of providing additional air crew, or to alleviate the training task at squadron level.

In the meantime, in accordance with provisions built in to the January 1939 scheme, and still as a 'purely temporary measure', the direct recruiting of observers was to be sustained, except that they were now to graduate as sergeants. So much for the Air Council's earlier misgivings over their sanctioning of 'instant' corporals. In the event, since the first cohort of direct entrant observers did not complete their training until the spring of 1939, none of them ever became corporals; they actually materialised as 'instant' sergeants. Furthermore, another clause within the scheme provided for all serving personnel who were already qualified as observers to be made up to sergeant as well. According to J.R. Paine, this development caused consternation at Wyton where the sergeants mess was suddenly obliged to give house room to dozens of 'jumped up corporals', the Station Warrant Officer allegedly being 'nearly in tears when he announced that the Mess was opened to us'.[42] In all probability, a very similar reaction will have occurred in every sergeants mess between Stranraer and Seletar.

If the accelerated promotion of serving airmen had been a bitter pill to swallow, there was worse to come. The first direct entrant sergeant observers began to reach the squadrons of Bomber Command in April 1939 and this time it was the AOCinC himself who reacted. Under Air Chf Mshl Ludlow-Hewitt's original proposal no one would have been given three stripes until he had qualified as an observer, which he could not possibly do in much less than four years. He was now being asked to accept as sergeants men who had been in uniform for no more than eight months and possibly even less. Protesting that 'the rank which they hold has proved extremely embarrassing', Sir Edgar complained that 'they are, of course, unable to exercise proper authority and it is ridiculous that they should be given a rank for which they are unsuited.' He fulminated on to the effect that the value of his scheme had been 'torpedoed and doomed to failure' by the introduction of these 'counterfeit NCOs.'[43] Now that conscription had been introduced, Ludlow-Hewitt wanted no more of these 'half-baked sergeant observers.'[44]

As AMP, AVM Portal responded coolly to this, not entirely unjustified, tirade (see page 139) by reminding the AOCinC that the object of the exercise had been 'to give the Observer prestige and to attract the right sort of man' and that this specific aspect of the direct entry scheme had actually been discussed with him in advance.[45] In short, it was a question of paying the rate for the job. Since all air crew had to be persuaded to volunteer, even with conscription, Portal did not believe that the air force could obtain the considerable numbers of high quality recruits that it needed without offering sergeant rank as an inducement.

Indeed, as if to underline their increased status, in August a regulation was published that made it absolutely clear that sergeant was the *minimum* rank in which an observer could serve. Any observer unfortunate enough to forfeit one or more of his stripes was to be remustered to some other trade.[46] Because there was no particular rank associated with being a wireless operator (air crew), however, most of them being mere aircraftmen, a demoted observer could continue to be employed on flying duties in that category, provided that he was suitably qualified.

Ludlow-Hewitt was obliged to manage his social and disciplinary problems as best he could, but his scheme proved to be short-lived in any case. The idea of aircraftmen flying operationally did not long survive the test of war and losses meant that it was quite impractical to wait three years for a gunner to blossom into an observer. Indeed, within a matter of months the RAF would be granting gunners, as well as observers, immediate SNCO status.

There is one other significant aspect to this spat. While AOCinC Bomber Command had been railing against the accelerated promotion of observers, he had had surprisingly little, in fact nothing, to say about 'instant' sergeant pilots. Yet all of his arguments had been specifically based on 'the old tradition that a man gets his promotion according to his experience.'[47] While this approach may well have been 'traditional', it was certainly not based on any fundamental principle. After all, non-commissioned air crew, pilots and observers, had graduated as 'instant' sergeants during WW I, the latter in relatively large numbers. More recently this practice had been revived in the context of the direct entrant regular sergeant pilots who had been trained in 1935–37 and for the reservists who had been recruited since then. While the introduction of immature sergeant observers had clearly provoked Ludlow-Hewitt's ire, should he not have been equally eloquent in condemning these young pilots?

There was clearly a double-standard at work here, but why? Was it an arrogant belief in the inherent superiority of pilots, a lack of appreciation of the demands of modern aviation or was it simply that prejudice died hard among some of the old war horses of WW I? Whichever it was, it was clear that the AOCinC Bomber Command had little time for the new breed of air observer, which was unfortunate, as most of them were destined to serve under him. Despite this unpromising start, by 1943 the true value of professional observers (by then navigators) had become plain and some of the more powerful members of the air force establishment were urging that their capabilities as airmen should be afforded a far greater measure of recognition. Ironically enough, by that time one of the most vociferous champions of the navigator would turn out to be none other than Edgar Ludlow-Hewitt (see pages 188–89).

1938–39. Air gunner training during the last year of peace

As long ago as January 1936 the Air Ministry had declared that it was intended that all gunners would eventually attend a formal course (see page 117). Two and a half years later this goal had still not been achieved. While still holding out the prospect of such a course, a revised set of regulations governing the provision of air gunners was published in the

[42]J.R. Paine, *op. cit.*
[43]AIR2/2968. Unreferenced letter dated 12 May 1939 from Ludlow-Hewitt to AMP, AVM C.F.A. Portal.
[44]Conscription, initially confined to men aged 20/21 years, had effectively been introduced in April 1939 – see Note 21. On 3 September the National Service Act made all British males between the ages of 18 and 41 liable to call-up. By the end of 1941 this legislation had been amended to extend the upper age limit to 51 and to make provision for the compulsory service of unmarried females. In the event, few men over 41 years of age were ever called up and none older than 45.
[45]AIR2/2968. Unreferenced letter dated 22 May 1939 from Portal to AOCinC Bomber Command, Ludlow-Hewitt.

[46]AMO A.329/39 of 24 August. This ruling actually represented a considerable relaxation of the previous regulations, i.e. those governing the January 1939 scheme as originally published, which had bluntly stated that any direct entrant observer reduced below the rank of sergeant was to be discharged.
[47]See Note 43.
[48]AMO A.242/38 of 7 July.

The Anson served as a trainer for non-pilot air crew from 1938 until 1958. This early Mk I, L7956, was photographed in December 1938 when it was on the strength of No 3 Civilian Air Navigation School which operated from Desford under the management of Reid & Sigrist. (CRO RAF Finningley)

summer of 1938.[48] It included the now very familiar message that 'in due course all air gunners for units at home and abroad will be trained at an air observers school but for the present all airmen at home will undergo training in Service units (*while*) airmen serving overseas will be trained locally under arrangements made by the command headquarters concerned.' The last part of this statement was a euphemism for 'on the squadrons, as at home.' Note, incidentally, that this order said that 'all' gunners would be trained on squadrons, not just some of them as in the past – the situation was actually getting worse.

While this change in policy was clearly unwelcome, there had been little alternative. Having elected to introduce large numbers of direct entrant observers, and to teach all observers to be navigators, by the summer of 1938 the non-pilot training system was running to capacity. The hard facts were that observers could not be produced without formal instruction whereas gunners could. In practice, of course, the new policy will not have created too many ripples, as gunners had long been accustomed to having to make do with squadron-level training. It is true that, in succession to Eastchurch, North Coates had been running four-week gunnery courses since 1936 but, as in the past, these had never offered sufficient places to satisfy the demands of the growing numbers of squadrons in the UK, let alone those stationed abroad.

For the time being, therefore, all gunners were to be trained at unit level with practical experience, and perhaps a few tips, being picked up during their squadron's one-month annual detachment to an Armament Training Station. Most of these units, of which there were eventually nine, had been set up in April 1938 by redesignating the substantially expanded network of Armament Training Camps. This makeshift situation could not be tolerated for long, however, as the adoption of Ludlow-Hewitt's concept of professional, full-time air crew made it imperative that all aviators should be properly trained.

Early in 1939, therefore, two more Armament Training Stations were converted into Air Observers Schools, making a total of four. By the spring, in addition to training observers, North Coates, Acklington, West Freugh and Aldergrove were all offering four-week courses, including 12 hours of practical airborne experience, to groups of up to thirty air gunners at a time.[49]

1938–39. Observer training during the last year of peace

The prolonged debate as to who was liable for what in an aeroplane was finally brought to a close in September 1939 when the decision of May 1938 was implemented and observers assumed primary responsibility for aircraft navigation. Unfortunately, it was a task for which they had been ill-prepared because the training schemes of the late 1930s, which may have been adequate in theory, had never been furnished with adequate resources. Apart from this, larger intakes and longer courses had created considerable organisational problems. Fig. 17 provides some impression of the complexity of the early course phasing arrangements which had to be employed to co-ordinate Service and civilian intakes.

When it had been decided that all observers should be trained to 'sn' standard the RAF had no school capable of running a course for them. Until more permanent arrangements could be made, therefore, the Leconfield-based, Nos 97 and 166 Sqns were pressed into service to act as a temporary navigation training unit, although their Heyfords hardly made ideal classrooms. No 23 Observers Course, the first to be trained against the new syllabus, began at Leconfield on 8 June 1938, moving on to North Coates for an eight-week armament training phase on 28 August. Nos 24 and 25 Courses were dealt with in the same way but a lack of capacity at

[49]A key difference between Air Observers Schools and Armament Training Stations was that the former were established to have a fleet of aeroplanes on which students could be flown. Armament Training Stations did not hold aircraft of their own, beyond a few drogue towers, since their function was to provide facilities for squadrons (and FTSs) carrying out one-month detachments using their own aircraft. These detachments ceased on the outbreak of war, the five remaining Armament Training Stations being either converted into additional Air Observers Schools or absorbed by the four which already existed.

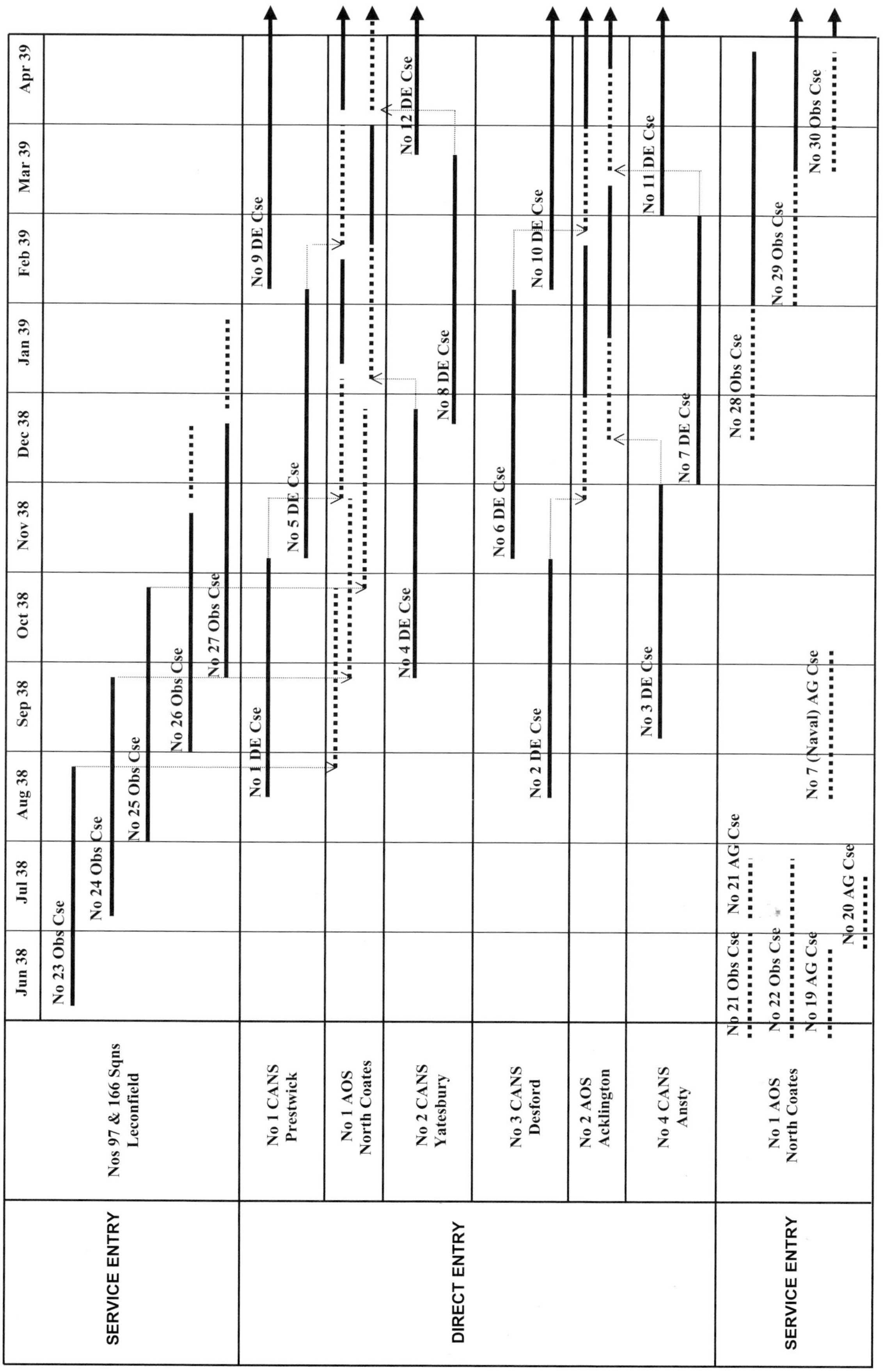

Jun 38 | Jul 38 | Aug 38 | Sep 38 | Oct 38 | Nov 38 | Dec 38 | Jan 39 | Feb 39 | Mar 39 | Apr 39

SERVICE ENTRY
Nos 97 & 166 Sqns Leconfield
No 23 Obs Cse
No 24 Obs Cse
No 25 Obs Cse
No 26 Obs Cse
No 27 Obs Cse

DIRECT ENTRY
No 1 CANS Prestwick
No 1 DE Cse
No 9 DE Cse
No 5 DE Cse
No 1 AOS North Coates
No 2 CANS Yatesbury
No 4 DE Cse
No 12 DE Cse
No 8 DE Cse
No 3 CANS Desford
No 6 DE Cse
No 2 DE Cse
No 10 DE Cse
No 2 AOS Acklington
No 4 CANS Ansty
No 3 DE Cse
No 11 DE Cse
No 7 DE Cse

SERVICE ENTRY
No 1 AOS North Coates
No 21 Obs Cse
No 21 AG Cse
No 28 Obs Cse
No 22 Obs Cse
No 29 Obs Cse
No 19 AG Cse
No 7 (Naval) AG Cse
No 30 Obs Cse
No 20 AG Cse

Fig. 17. *The complex phasing arrangements necessary to integrate the early intakes of civilian and Service observers into a joint training scheme.* Navigation; Gunnery and/or Bombing; Recruit Depot

North Coates meant that Nos 26 and 27 Courses had to remain at Leconfield and make do with just four weeks of locally organised tuition in bombing and gunnery.

Having disposed of No 22 Course, the last intake to be trained in July against the eight-weeks-of-armament-plus-four-weeks-of-navigation sequence introduced in May 1937 (see page 121), North Coates had been reorganised to provide all-through training for Service entrant observers, the first such thirty-strong course (No 28) beginning in mid-December. Prior to this, North Coates had also begun to handle the three-month, Service-based, element of training for direct entrant observers graduating from the civilian schools at Prestwick and Yatesbury. In order to provide the necessary accommodation for them, formal air gunner training had had to be suspended in the summer of 1938, hence the announcement to the effect that all air gunner training was to become a squadron responsibility (see Note 48). Even so, North Coates was unable to cope with the entire observer training commitment and in the autumn a second Air Observers School opened at Acklington to deal with the output from Nos 3 and 4 CANS at Ansty and Desford, although this school did not train Service entrants.

While the training sequence had begun to stabilise by early 1939, its effectiveness was hampered by a lack of suitable aeroplanes. When it had been decided that observers should be trained against the full ten-week navigation syllabus (twelve weeks by the time that it actually came to be implemented, at both civilian and Service schools) this was supposed to have included forty hours of airborne time. It was calculated that a total of forty-eight Ansons would be required to carry out the intended practical navigation exercises. At the time few were available, some of the civilian-run schools simply being unable to provide all the required airborne time until adequate numbers of Ansons began to materialise in the autumn.

The situation was little better at the Service-run schools where the same shortage of Ansons meant that navigation and armament training had to be carried out on an assortment of obsolete Wallaces, Gordons, Heyfords and the like.[50] So far as gunnery was concerned, these aeroplanes were armed with a single Lewis gun mounted on a WW I-vintage Scarff ring, which had little relevance to men who were expected to handle multiple Brownings mounted in a power-operated turret. These old, mostly open-cockpit, biplanes were equally inappropriate for use as navigation trainers and it was well into 1939 before the availability of Ansons permitted much real progress to be made with the practical aspects of this crucial element of the syllabus.

Inadequate aeroplanes were only part of the problem. Since the RAF had made little investment in navigation training in the past, there were very few competent and experienced uniformed air navigators available to act as instructors, and most of those who could be found were already involved in the pilot training programme. The civilian-run training organisation faced similar staffing difficulties, most of its instructors being academics or mariners, rather than aviators. They did their best to adapt but, while it was theoretically possible to read across from nautical principles to airborne practice, this approach left much to be desired.

This will undoubtedly have been one of the factors contributing to their limited success when civilian contractors had attempted to train relatively large numbers of pilots as Squadron Navigation Officers during 1937–38. Since it was axiomatic that competent instructors in air navigation would need to be experienced air navigators, little could be done to improve the situation in the short-term. This problem would not be solved until the autumn of 1940 when some of the earliest observers began to be recycled back into the system as instructors after they had accumulated some worthwhile practical experience.

With aircraft and instructors both being in short supply, the same was true of equipment. For instance, following a concentrated burst of development work to devise a (relatively) simple and practical system of sight reduction, the RAF had decided to adopt celestial navigation as a standard technique in November 1937. Although some squadron-level training had begun before the end of that year, this was initially aimed solely at pilots and each unit had to make do with just one sextant. A four-week astro course was introduced for selected pilots at Manston in April 1938 but formal instruction in astro was not provided for observers until as late as June 1939.

Similarly, while airborne radio direction finding had been technically feasible for some years, there were few ground beacons available for navigational training purposes. Furthermore, an examination of contemporary photographs of Whitleys, Wellingtons and Ansons in squadron service reveals just how few of them had actually been fitted with a directional loop aerial before the summer of 1940.[51] Obtaining bearings from ground stations was another realistic possibility but there were not many such facilities and the need to maintain radio silence meant that, except for emergencies, their use was immediately prohibited on the outbreak of war. In the absence of adequate radio aids, much reliance had still to be placed on map-reading, with lighted beacons, similar to those deployed during WW I, providing useful navigational assistance in the dark.

The combination of all of these factors meant that there can be no doubt that there were substantial deficiencies in the quality of the training being provided and in the standards being achieved. There are letters on file complaining that portions of the navigation syllabus had been too hurriedly conducted so that, despite their having carried out interception exercises, newly trained observers knew 'little about relative velocities or relative winds'. Another complaint highlighted a lack of co-ordination between theoretical instruction and practical application so that, for instance, 'methods of wind finding are taught in the class room but are not put into practice sufficiently in the air.'[52]

In May 1939 HQ No 2 Gp complained that the practical armament training of a batch of fourteen new observers recently arrived from No 2 AOS at Acklington had amounted to the dropping of an average of just thirteen bombs and the firing of 800 rounds of ammunition. This was considered to be quite insufficient, the explanation offered by the school

[50] The need for Ansons to train non-pilot air crew had been identified some time before and to this end Contract 690658/37 had been altered as early as 21 December 1937. The amendment required Avro's Chadderton factory to build an additional twenty-one aircraft (L9145–L9165) for use by North Coates. These aeroplanes did not roll off the production line until the following September, however, and by that time higher priority demands had arisen. In the event, only two of these aeroplanes were to be delivered directly to No 1 AOS.

[51] This contrasts markedly with German practice, a similar exercise showing quite clearly that D/F loops had been commonplace on the Do 23s, Ju 52s and He 70s of the *Luftwaffe*'s bomber force as early as 1936.

[52] AIR14/16. These examples are taken from BC/4140/TR, a letter to AOCinC Training Command drafted for AOCinC Bomber Command in July 1939. Whether it was ever sent is not known, but the fact that it was written at all stands as testimony to the concerns which were being felt.

Back-seaters were still gaining their first experience of live aerial gunnery on aeroplanes as antiquated and unrepresentative of operational types as the Wallace until as late as 1940. While this picture is of indifferent quality it is of interest in that it shows a Wallace I, K3675, of Manby's No 1 Air Armament School in full post-Munich warpaint; a real sheep in wolf's clothing. (P.H.T. Green)

being a lack of equipment.[53] Even worse, AOC No 6 Gp noted that of four new observers posted to his squadrons in July, one had dropped a total of twelve bombs, two had dropped eight each and one none at all, yet they had all been graded. As the AOC wrote, 'It is not understood how an airman's bombing can be assessed when he has dropped no bombs, nor how an airman who has dropped eight can possibly be considered above the average.'[54] There were similar deficiencies in wireless training which led Bomber Command to write to all Group HQs to state that 'it is considered necessary that Air Observers should be instructed in wireless and morse for thirty minutes each working day'.[55]

The professional inadequacies of the new breed were aggravated by their generally unsatisfactory nature, which had prompted Ludlow-Hewitt's outburst in May (see page 135). By July the dust at HQ Bomber Command had settled sufficiently for the direct entrants to be seen a little more clearly. They were now perceived to be well educated, intelligent, keen and willing to learn but these attributes were not enough to outweigh their shortcomings. Their 'knowledge of drill, discipline and general service' was described as being 'almost negligible'. This, especially the latter, had fostered, in some cases, an 'inferiority complex' leading to a lack of confidence and it was feared that this was bound to have an adverse effect on their overall performance. Direct entrant observers were also considered to lack much awareness of their responsibilities as SNCOs and, even within the intimate confines of a crew, there had been instances of 'embarrassing' problems involving 'men who are junior in rank yet far more experienced in their duties.'[56]

It is unlikely that its full implications were appreciated at the time but the most significant of the salient characteristics of direct entrant full-time NCO air crew, noted in July, was that they displayed 'a tendency to regard flying as their only duty in the Royal Air Force.' The RAF, having spent twenty years establishing its 'officer/pilot' ruling class, seems to have taken it for granted that its new recruits would conform easily to this pattern and automatically assume that they were to constitute a second tier of 'SNCO/air crew'. The Service was evidently both nonplussed and disappointed to find that many of the new sergeants saw things rather differently. This was hardly surprising, of course, as the RAF had not bothered to teach them about anything other than flying, and it was plain that, as yet, it was not doing even that very well.

What was just beginning to reveal itself in 1939 was a problem caused by the fact that the air force had accustomed itself to associating the exercise of authority almost exclusively with its pilots and now, by extension, with its other flying personnel. When some of these flying personnel failed to see the connection, there could be only two explanations. Either the system was based on a false assumption, which is to say that the entire concept upon which the RAF had been built was flawed, or the newcomers were at fault in that they failed to accept the responsibilities which were inherent in their status. To the 'air establishment', who were all products of the system, the first possibility was plainly unthinkable, so the blame was laid squarely on the shoulders of direct entrants. In fact, the truth lay somewhere between the two. Moreover, the problems associated with dedicated flyers were not confined to direct entrant NCO back-seaters; they would soon become just as apparent among commissioned air crew, of all categories, as these became more numerous.

We shall return to this topic later; it suffices here to acknowledge there was (and is) a fundamental contradiction between the limited obligations of people who were, in practical terms, being employed solely to fly and the elevated ranks that were bestowed upon them. This was a conundrum that would perplex and frustrate the air force's senior management for the next thirty years. Indeed, it is arguable that the problem has never really been solved.

Despite all the difficulties with which it had to contend, the air crew training machine had continued to grow. By the end of September 1939 there were ten Civilian Air Navigation Schools[57] and seven Service-run Air Observer Schools involved in the training of air observers, the latter being additionally responsible for the practical training of air gunners. The notional output of the combined system was a very respectable 4200 trained sergeant observers per year.

Strictly speaking, once war had broken out, the graduates of this system were graded as acting sergeants (acting observers). Thus, although they could wear their three stripes, until they had done six months on a squadron they could not put up their flying 'O's. Worse, since they were not yet mustered as fully qualified air crew, throughout this probationary period they were paid at the old nine-shilling daily rate that had been introduced for corporal observers back in 1936. One need hardly add that this sort of indignity was not inflicted upon wartime airmen pilots, all of whom emerged from training as fully fledged temporary sergeants drawing their full twelve shillings and sixpence from Day One.

[53]*Ibid.* Letter 2BG/38/2/Air Trg dated 11 May 1939 from AOC No 2 Gp, AVM P. H. L. Playfair, to HQ Bomber Command.
[54]*Ibid.* Letter 6G/1908/1/P.3 dated 24 July 1939 from AOC No 6 Gp, Air Cdre J. C. Quinnell, to HQ Bomber Command.
[55]*Ibid.* Letter BC/4140/TR dated 20 July 1939 from SASO Bomber Command, Air Cdre N. H. Bottomley, to HQs Nos 1–6 Gps.
[56]See Note 52.

[57]All ten CANS were collocated with an ERFTS, eight of them being run as a pair by the same contractor, e.g. No 3 CANS and No 7 ERFTS were both operated by Reid and Sigrist at Desford while No 4 CANS and No 9 ERFTS at Ansty were run by Air Service Training. There is anecdotal evidence to suggest, however, that the CANS element of some of these partnerships could have a remarkably low key presence. According to Frank Harbord's *Familiar Voices* (1998), Brooklands Aviation's joint enterprise was a case in point. Student observers who passed through Sywell in the summer of 1939 were reportedly quite unaware of the existence of No 8 CANS and understood that they were being trained by No 6 ERFTS. This impression has been confirmed in correspondence with the author.

Chapter 19

1939–40. Early changes in wartime recruiting policy

The declaration of war in September 1939 brought an immediate end to the scheme for the provision of air crew which had been introduced in the previous January, long before it had had time to mature. The wartime demand for observers meant that it was quite impractical to expect them to spend an initial three years as wireless operators (air crew) and, since it was clearly not essential for all gunners to be qualified as wireless operators, direct recruiting of 'straight' air gunners was introduced. As a result, the peacetime aim of eradicating the distinction between dual-qualified wireless operator/air gunners and 'straight' air gunners had also to be abandoned.

The initial wartime policy governing the provision of air observers (and airmen pilots) was published in September 1939.[1] It stated that observers courses for Service entrants would be suspended forthwith and that all subsequent intakes into civilian air navigation schools (and flying training schools) would be directly recruited RAFVR personnel.[2]

Ever since January 1939 it had been intended that *volunteer* reservists should be distinguished from regular servicemen, and from ex-regulars with a reserve commitment, by an appropriate badge. This emblem was not actually approved until September, however, when its introduction became a matter of some urgency as a result of the wartime policy of universal enrolment within the RAFVR. For officers the badge was to take the form of a small gilt 'VR' monogram to be worn on the uniform collar. Airmen were to wear an embroidered 'VR' immediately below the eagle at the top of each jacket sleeve.[3]

Apart from the fact that no further regular airmen (or officers) were to be engaged until further notice, the wartime arrangements also meant that airmen who were already enlisted as groundcrew were no longer eligible for consideration for flying duties as pilots or observers. The new regulations were amplified in November when it was made clear that this constraint had also applied to the provision of both wireless operators (air crew) and air gunners.[4]

It would seem that Air Chf Mshl Sir John Steel (among others) was somewhat confused by the distinction between a wireless operator (air crew) and a wireless operator (air gunner). This was a trifle unfortunate, since Sir John, who was AOCinC Reserve Command at the time, was responsible for the recruiting of all such personnel. He eventually sought enlightenment from the Air Ministry who patiently explained that there was only one trade, not two, the second term being unofficial.[5] Nevertheless, since it was clearly a better descriptive title and already in widespread use, AMP decided to adopt it. This decision was formally announced in February 1940, when it was stipulated that an airman's qualification as an air gunner was to be added (where applicable) in parentheses after his basic trade.[6] In other words, the category of wireless operator (air crew) had been superseded by that of the wireless operator (air gunner) (WOp/AG).

1939–40. The wartime RAF begins to afford observers a greater degree of recognition

Under the regulations originally published in 1937, and which were still current, an observer had to have completed six month's service on a squadron before he was entitled to wear a flying 'O'. This period was even longer than that required in WW I when so many back-seaters had been wounded or killed in action, denied even the token distinction of being able to wear a flying badge on the grounds that they were still on probation. This highly unsatisfactory situation had finally been put right in the summer of 1918 and a similar arrangement was clearly needed now that another war had broken out. A suitable regulation eventually appeared in April 1940.[7]

This permitted AOCs to authorise an airman to wear a flying 'O' so long as he had passed an appropriate course (even this was not necessary if he had previously been a qualified full-time air gunner) and had been recommended by his CO 'as the result of operational experience.' Precisely how much operational experience was not laid down but it was now clearly within a CO's gift to authorise an acting observer to put up his badge when he returned from his first sortie, although this did nothing for his bank balance, as he still remained a nine-shilling-a-day acting sergeant until he had satisfied the 'six months on a squadron' clause.

[1]AMO A.392/39 of 21 September.

[2]It is a rather esoteric point, but it is perhaps worth observing that, while this legislation had effectively reintroduced direct entrant sergeant pilots, it had not, in the strictest sense, reinstated the unpopular arrangements that had prevailed in 1935–37 (see page 129). The difference was that the men who had been recruited in peacetime had been enlisted into the RAF, whereas the new batch were to be members of the RAFVR, which had always admitted sergeant pilots. What was significant about the new intake of wartime reservists was that they were going to fly on active service alongside the pre-war regulars.

Similar provisions applied right across the Service, in all air and ground trades, in that all recruits who joined up after the outbreak of war were inducted into the RAFVR and not the RAF which accepted no further 'regulars' until 1945. Almost inevitably, there were some instances of social friction between the 'old sweats' and the 'for the duration only' brigade. This never appears to have presented a serious problem, however, probably because most regulars were rapidly promoted so that they could marshal and supervise the flood of wartime entrants and this sufficed to preserve their superior status.

Although there were technical differences between the terms and conditions of service of RAF and RAFVR personnel, these were essentially superficial considerations. Within this book, these distinctions will be referred to only where they are significant. Otherwise any references to regulations, administrative procedures and the like affecting wartime RAF personnel should be understood to embrace equally those serving in the RAFVR.

[3]AMO A.378/39 of 14 September.

[4]AMO A.469/39 of 9 November.

[5]AIR2/4456. Letter from Air Mshl Portal to AOCinC Reserve Command dated 24 November 1939.

[6]AMO A.94/40 of 15 February.

[7]AMO A.201/40 of 11 April.

While attendance at an 'appropriate course' may have been relatively easy to arrange in the UK, this was not the case in overseas commands, which still lacked permanent facilities dedicated to the training of any air crew other than pilots. A temporary navigation school was established at Abu Sueir during 1939–40 but its chief purpose was to provide a short ('sn'-style) course for pilots and it is unlikely that any airmen observers ever attended this school. On the other hand, it is worth recording that concern over the scarcity of qualified air crew eventually led to 50% of the capacity of No 4 FTS being earmarked for the training of observers and gunners (see below), the first nine-week course beginning on 26 August 1940.[8] The last of the thirty-eight observers to be trained at Habbaniyah graduated in March 1941.

Despite the 'operational experience' concession granted in April 1940, there were substantial, indeed growing, numbers of badgeless, underpaid, acting sergeants (acting observer) having to serve out their mandatory sentences of six month's on probation. In August it was decided to waive the requirement for operational experience so that all acting observers were now entitled to wear a badge as soon as they completed the final (armament) phase of their training.[8A] The same provisions applied to WOp/AGs or air gunners who had been remustered to acting observer without having to attend a formal course (see below); they too were immediately entitled to wear a flying 'O'.

While the automatic right to wear a badge will, no doubt, have been appreciated, this gesture had had little effect on the material status of an observer. It took another three months, by which time the country had been at war for more than a year, for the RAF grudgingly to accept that the observer of 1940 really did deserve much the same degree of recognition as had been afforded his predecessor of 1918. In October the requirement for a period of probationary service with acting rank was finally abolished.[9] Thenceforth, all observers emerged from training on exactly the same terms as pilots, that is to say, wearing their badges and ranked as temporary sergeants drawing twelve shillings and sixpence per day.

1939–40. Early wartime improvements in the status of gunners

Once the shooting had started there had been a marked increase in respect for gunners and, because they were now very different animals from observers, a distinctive badge had been introduced for them in December 1939. The new emblem resembled the observers badge to the extent that it had only one wing but the design of this wing differed subtly from that of the original. In place of the 'O' there was an embroidered brown laurel wreath enclosing the letters 'AG' in white.[10] The new badge was to be worn by officers on being posted to a unit as an air gunner following a course of instruction and by airmen who were mustered as air gunners and who had served, or were serving, as such since 3 September. The 'AG' badge rendered the old winged bullet obsolete, although airmen who had qualified for one, but who were no longer available for employment as gunners, were still permitted to wear it, as (for a time) were observers and airmen pilots who had previously been gunners.[11]

Introduced in December 1939, the air gunners badge provided the pattern for all subsequent flying badges presented to RAF air crew (other than pilots) for the rest of the century.

When the RAF went to war all of its airmen pilots and observers (at least those who were officially recognised as such, and there were many *de facto* observers who were not (see below) wore the three stripes of a sergeant and were paid twelve shillings and sixpence per day (or nine shillings in the case of acting observers). By comparison, depending upon his performance in training, an air gunner flying on operations might be no more than an AC2 of Trade Group V, in which case he would have earned as little as two shillings per day. He still drew his shilling-a-day crew pay, of course, and his sixpence gunners pay, although both of these were forfeit if he was unavailable for flying duties for more than fourteen consecutive days. Furthermore, if he was mustered within Trade Group V solely as a gunner, i.e. with no basic trade, he had no realistic career prospects beyond the classification of leading aircraftman (LAC). In short, apart from being socially segregated from the men with whom he was supposed to fly and fight as a member of a team, a gunner was paid less than a third of what they earned.

[8]AIR2/3077. Shortly after the introduction of full-time air crew it was decided that RAFME should be self-sufficient in this respect, as it already was in the case of pilots. In February 1939 CAS (Newall) directed that a regional school should be established to train air gunners and observers. Initially expected to be at Abu Sueir, the projected location had changed to Amman by August but little tangible progress had been made by the following July when it was decided instead to exploit some of the existing capacity of No 4 FTS at Habbaniyah.

[8A]AMO A.537/40 of 1 August.

[9]AMO A.803/40 of 31 October. Note that this regulation included provision for all personnel already serving as acting sergeants (acting observers) to be remustered immediately as temporary sergeant air observers with effect from 14 September. Seniority among those affected was to be based on the dates of their original appointments as acting sergeants.

[10]AMO A.547/39 of 21 December announced the introduction of the air gunners badge, which was to become the model for all subsequent single-winged designs. In his *Customs and Traditions of the Royal Air Force* (1961), Sqn Ldr P.G. Hering relates that the prototype air gunners badge had featured thirteen feathers. While vetting the badge, CAS (Newall) observed that thirteen had probably been an unfortunate choice. Wg Cdr E.H. Hooper (of the Directorate of Personal Services) promptly produced a pair of nail scissors and the bottom feather was deftly removed before the design was submitted for royal approval.

[11]AMO A.440/40 of 4 July removed the concession that had permitted ex-gunner pilots and observers to wear the winged bullet because of the potential for confusion which could arise from people wearing two badges. In future air crew were to wear only one badge, which was to be that of the category in which they were currently serving, although, on ceasing to be employed on flying duties, an officer or airman could elect to wear any (one) of the badges to which he was entitled.

All of this was reminiscent of some of the more unsatisfactory aspects of the RFC's man-management during WW I but, since no one appeared to remember any of this, the ground was having to be covered again.

Under the circumstances, it was hardly surprising that a detectable sense of grievance became evident within the community of gunners. While the introduction of a 'proper' badge had been appreciated, it had been no more than a cosmetic gesture. In fact, it had actually managed to focus attention on gunners, without having done anything of any substance to improve their situation. The Service authorities were well aware that an unsatisfactory state of affairs existed (after all, they had created it) and on 16 December 1939 Air Mshl Portal convened a meeting to examine the problem. It was agreed that something positive needed to be done and, as a holding measure, a statement was released to the effect that the status and pay of gunners was being reviewed and that a further announcement would be made shortly.[12]

'Shortly' turned out to have been a little optimistic. The delay in improving the lot of the gunner was due to the Treasury, who had first to be convinced that gunners really were as important as the Air Ministry claimed, and then persuaded to foot the substantial bill which would result from giving them all SNCO status. Inevitably, the eventual result was a compromise. With effect from 27 May 1940 (five months before this privilege was extended to observers) all WOp/AGs and straight air gunners were to be automatically granted the rank of temporary sergeant on completion of their training, although they were to be paid at inclusive rates of only seven shillings and ninepence and seven shillings per day, respectively.[13] In effect, therefore, while many gunners still had a basic trade to which they could revert (in their 'real' rank), so long as they remained on flying duties, they were now recognised as being fully-fledged members of the 'air crew élite'. That there had to be a pay differential between gunners and pilots/observers was unfortunate, but it was considered to be a reasonable reflection of the relative demands made by these occupations and was, in any case, the best that could be squeezed out of the Exchequer.

Sadly, the Order which elevated gunners to SNCO status was not actually promulgated until 27 June. As a result, practically all of the gunners who died flying in the Battles and Blenheims of the Advanced Air Striking Force during the fall of France did so as corporals or aircraftmen. The same was true of those who lost their lives during the early operations of Bomber and Coastal Commands.[14]

As they had done in 1939, when they had been obliged to give house room to hoards of young observers, the denizens of the RAF's sergeants messes grumbled about this second influx of 'instant' NCOs. As one of the beneficiaries of the new regulations has put it:[15]

> 'Like all changes, it took some getting used to, particularly among senior NCOs in ground trades who might well have served fifteen years before advancing to the same rank as that handed out to an eager eighteen-year-old after only six months in the service. But they soon realised that it was unfair to bear grudges; most of the new sergeants did not live long enough to justify a grudge.'

Although all recognised gunners were entitled to be temporary sergeants by mid-1940, some of those who had qualified long before 27 May were already substantive SNCOs in their own right within their original trades. Some of these men would have been out of pocket at the new inclusive rate of pay. Provision was made, therefore, for anyone who would be financially better off drawing a combination of his basic Trade Group pay plus crew pay plus gunners pay to continue to do so. Unfortunately, there was a flaw in this arrangement which was not immediately apparent.

To reflect the instability caused by wartime conditions, the two additional elements paid for flying duties had not been tied to established posts since 3 September 1939, although this was a back-dated concession which had not actually been announced until the following April.[16] So long as he was fit to fly, therefore, any wartime gunner could have his one and sixpence per day. Unfortunately, the old 'fourteen day rule' had not been rescinded, so that a wounded gunner was quite likely to lose both his crew and his qualification pay. As operations intensified this became a relatively frequent occurrence and a cause for some justifiable complaint, since gunners on the inclusive rate did not have to pay this forfeit. Since there were still significant numbers of senior gunners preferring to draw their basic pay plus one and sixpence as late as 1943, the fourteen days was extended to ninety-one with effect from 1 June of that year.[17]

As the RAF adjusted to wartime conditions, it became apparent that something needed to be done to rationalise the position of the remaining old-style airmen gunners, many of whom were still on active service. Special arrangements were introduced for the real old hands who had qualified before the introduction of the January 1939 scheme. Many of these men had accumulated a substantial amount of flying time during which (supplemented by incidental courses and the experience gained at Armament Practice Camps) they had picked up most of the skills of an observer. Indeed, some of these gunners were actually flying as observers where appropriately qualified men were still unavailable. Their position had been recognised in January 1940 and, provided that they could pass certain tests and had their CO's blessing, these men could be granted the rank of acting sergeant and remustered as acting observers.[18] This gave them a standing similar to that of a newly qualified direct entrant in that they drew the same nine shillings a day for the next six months during which, if they flew operationally, they just might be authorised to wear a flying 'O'.

If circumstances did not provide an opportunity to fly on operations, and thus the possibility of putting up an observers badge, an ex-gunner could continue to wear his old badge, at least until 7 July when this right was withdrawn (see Note 11). Fortunately, it is unlikely that many people will have been affected by this regulation because, only three weeks later, the 'operational experience' rider was waived and all acting observers became entitled to wear a flying 'O' anyway (see Note 8A).

[12] AMO A.552/39 of 28 December.

[13] AMO A.416/40 of 27 June.

[14] A glance through the casualty lists in W.R. Chorley's *Bomber Command Losses of the Second World War*, Vol 1 (1992), illustrates quite clearly that until mid-June 1940 practically all gunner casualties had been corporals or below. The exceptions were a handful of the first commissioned gunners and a few who just happened to have been sergeants in their parent trades.

[15] Richard Passmore, *Blenheim Boy* (1981). Note that 'Richard Passmore' was a pseudonym for Roger Peacock, a WOp/AG who flew in the Blenheims of Nos 90 and 40 Sqns from 1937 until he was shot down to become a POW in July 1940.

[16] AMO A.231/40 of 25 April.

[17] AMO A.985/43 of 7 October.

[18] AMO A.31/40 of 18 January.

During the summer of 1940 HQ RAFME provided facilities to consolidate the skills of the pre-war part-time aircraftmen who had been automatically upgraded to full-time sergeant air gunners and to permit some others to remuster as air crew. This is No 4 Air Gunners Course which was run at Ismailia during August. Left to right, back row: Cpl Douglas (No 216 Sqn); Sgt L.C. Murray (No 45 Sqn); Sgt C. Richardson (No 45 Sqn); LAC C. Blackshaw (No 45 Sqn); LAC Mackay (No 216 Sqn); LAC Smith (No 113 Sqn). Front row: AC Pattinson (No 211 Sqn); AC H. Marshall (No 45 Sqn); LAC R.H.C. Crook (No 45 Sqn); WO A.E. Pell (Instructor); AC Shelton (No 216 Sqn); AC Cook (No 55 Sqn) and AC Aston (No 6 Sqn). Most (probably all) of those who were not already wearing three stripes would have been made up to temporary sergeant shortly after the course.

Most of the gunners serving overseas on the outbreak of war were still in-house trained part-timers. They were invited to choose between remustering as air crew or reverting to their ground trades, mostly as wireless operators or wireless operator mechanics. Like those at home, airmen who elected to become air crew would automatically have become entitled to wear the 'AG' badge from December and most would subsequently have been made up to temporary sergeant with effect from 27 May 1940. In addition, to give these purely procedural matters a little more substance, HQ RAFME required that, where possible, gunners should attend one of a series of locally organised 'top up' courses run at Ismailia during the summer. While these courses improved the technical knowledge of those who were already qualified as gunners, the content was also deemed sufficient to permit additional wireless personnel to be remustered as WOp/AGs.

As with observers, HQ RAFME also set up a more formal means of providing additional gunners by making suitable arrangements at No 4 FTS (see Note 8). The first four-week course began at Habbaniyah on 23 October 1940, the last of a total of fifty-two (mostly officer) air gunners graduating in March 1941.

1939–40. The reinstatement of commissions for non-pilot air crew and for officers of the reconstituted specialist ground branches

With war imminent, the Air Ministry had finally recognised, what must surely have been obvious for years, that its GD officers, i.e. its pilots, would be quite incapable of administering the Service once the shooting started. An Administrative and Special Duties Branch (A&SD) was therefore instituted within the RAFVR into which members of the AAF, the RAFVR, the RAFO and other retired regular officers could be mobilised or drafted for non-flying duties in the event of an emergency.[19] War was declared five days later.

So far as air crew were concerned, an important aspect of the late-1918 position remained to be restored, the introduction of the commissions for non-pilots which had first been publicly hinted at in January 1939. The most pressing need was perceived to be for officer gunners, as it had long been clear to Bomber Command that the standard of gunnery at squadron level left much to be desired. This was hardly surprising, of course, as the vast majority of pre-war gunners had been trained somewhat informally under local arrangements. There was little in the way of doctrine and only vestigial supervisory arrangements. As a result, Ludlow-Hewitt had been pressing for the establishment of a suitable unit to devise and refine techniques and tactics, to train instructors and to produce specialist officers to fill staff appointments and to act as Gunnery Leaders. This demand was finally met on 6 November 1939 when the Central Gunnery School (CGS) opened at Warmwell, its first course commencing on the 15th.[20] While this unit would inevitably be commanded by a pilot, if it was to have any real credibility it would need to have at least some officer gunners on its staff, hence the urgency attached to the granting of commissions.

Because of the significant budgetary implications, the Treasury has a role to play in determining commissioning policy and the Air Ministry had opened negotiations over the provision of officer gunners as soon as war had been declared. Sanction for gunners to be commissioned was eventually obtained from the financiers on 19 October. Selection began immediately, with rather disappointing results. Sqn Ldr C.R. Lloyd reported that:[21]

> 'Out of some 45 RAFVR LACs interviewed up to date, only 3 had been to public schools, and although some 50% were recommended, only about 9 could be described as suitable to a peacetime standard. The remainder were definitely war standard and *NOT* officer class.'

Lloyd sought men who would exhibit 'quickness of mental reaction, dependability in an emergency and fighting spirit', all of which were characteristics which he clearly associated with the 'officer class'. But Lloyd's complaint was only superficially to do with the British bugbear of 'class'; his real problem lay within the, presumably hastily drafted, early regulations governing the selection of officers for air gunnery duties. These, it would seem, permitted a pre-war RAFVR LAC gunner to apply for a commission at the age of 18, whereas a wartime direct entrant had to be 28. The pre-war recruits were eager and forthcoming, but much too young and immature, while the age limit imposed on wartime entrants excluded much of the best material.

The first handful of gunner officers was secured under somewhat *ad hoc* arrangements[22] but these had been regularised

[19] AMO A.341/39 of 29 August.

[20] There was an equally pressing need for a similar unit to study other aspects of bomber operations but this would not materialise for another year, the Bomber Development Unit eventually being formed at Boscombe Down as late as 21 November 1940.

[21] AIR2/6146. Memo from Sqn Ldr Lloyd to DDTArm dated 25 October 1939.

[22] A common (possibly the only) method was to exploit the A&SD Branch. Examples of early officer gunners commissioned via this channel include Flt Lt A.H.S. Browne, Fg Off W.H. Carr-Birbeck and Plt Off W.S. Fielding-Johnson. The last of these, whose seniority dated from 6 November 1939, was a notable veteran of WW I. Fielding-Johnson had begun his flying career as early as 16 October 1915 when he had been attached to No 3 Sqn. Rated as a qualified observer on 15 December, he was wounded in action a month later. After recovering, he retrained as a pilot and he was eventually to claim six aerial victories while flying SE5as with No 56 Sqn. Having been decorated with the MC twice during WW I, incidentally, he was to add a DFC during Round Two.

by February 1940 when air gunners were formally introduced as a specialisation within the General Duties (GD) Branch.[23] The Air Force List for that month, the first to feature gunners, contained the names of two flight lieutenants, one flying officer and 106 pilot officers. All of them were members of the RAFVR with the seniority of individuals being antedated by up to three months. Apart from the most senior four, all were annotated as being on probation.

Meanwhile, similar negotiations had been in hand since the previous September regarding the commissioning of observers (and pilots) but little concrete progress had been made. In December ACAS, AVM W.S. Douglas, drew attention to the fact that there were still no commissioned observers, despite provision for them having been specifically included within the January 1939 air crew scheme. Indeed, commands had not, as yet, even been asked for recommendations. Douglas acknowledged that the overall performance of observers had been disappointing but he found it hard to believe that there were no suitable candidates for commissioning at all.[24]

While there was considerable concern over the competence of early wartime observers (see page 149), the delay in the granting of commissions was more to do with quantity than quality. The Treasury was not contesting the idea of officer observers, but it was disputing the numbers involved. The RAF wanted 50% of all observers, and pilots, to be commissioned. The Treasury was content with 50% of pilots but would agree to only 30% of observers. Air Mshl Portal considered this unacceptable because it undercut the principle of equal career prospects which, it was claimed, was inherent in the terms of service of NCO air crew.[25]

After some more haggling a compromise was eventually reached in January 1940.[26] Up to 50% of both pilots and observers could be commissioned but with the following constraints. No more than 33% of observers could graduate as officers on completion of training, leaving the other 17%, or roughly one-third of all commissions, to be awarded to deserving NCOs who earned this distinction on active service. The figures for pilots were to be 33% from training but only 12% in the field, the imbalance being caused by the fact that, even though the cadet entry scheme had been suspended, *all* pilots being trained at Cranwell were still graduating as officers. When allowance was made for this anomaly, the overall proportion of commissioned pilots was comparable to the 50% of observers.

The commissioning quotas for gunners were agreed in July 1941 with up to 10% of WOp/AGs graduating from training as officers and a further 10% after they had accumulated some operational experience. The proportions for straight air gunners were 5% and 15%.

Meanwhile, as with the first officer air gunners, it had been necessary to adopt a somewhat flexible approach to the provision of early officer observers. Since there was no such animal as an officer observer at the time, the first few had to be commissioned as nominal air gunners.[27] Proper commissioning arrangements for observers were finally announced in April 1940.[28] For the first time since 1926 a separate listing of observers appeared in the Air Force List for June; it contained forty-two names. As with the air gunners, they were all members of the RAFVR but in this case they were all on probation, their effective dates of seniority ranging from 10 March to 28 April.

Three weeks after the introduction of commissions for observers, an A&SD Branch was established within the RAF, i.e. the regular air force, both it and its RAFVR predecessor being organised internally to identify its members as specialists in Administration, Marine Craft, Intelligence, Photography, Physical Training or Special Duties (e.g. courier or cypher work).[29]

The same Order also created a Technical Branch for Armament, Signals and Engineering Officers. Ironically, this innovation was to see many pilots hoist on a petard which was entirely of the air force's making. In the process of creating, and then sustaining, the myth of the omnipotent pilot, the RAF had failed to provide itself with the professional technical back-up that it really needed. When the new branch was created most of the qualified engineers who were immediately available were regular officers, that is to say, pre-war pilots who had done the appropriate mid-career specialist course. Any pilots who wished to join the Technical Branch were encouraged to do so, but those who were already qualified as engineers 'shall be so employed, whether or not they apply for a transfer.'[30] There can be little doubt that Trenchard had failed to see that one coming back in 1919, and some of the pilots who found themselves pitchforked into engineering 'for the duration' may have found it hard to forgive him for denying them the chance of winning a DFC.

Nevertheless, the loop had finally been completed. It had taken more than twenty years for reality to overcome wishful thinking, but the situation which had prevailed as long ago as 1918 had at last (almost) been restored.

1941. Further improvements in conditions of service, particularly for observers

In the peacetime air force the numbers of non-commissioned personnel serving as flight sergeants or warrant officers had been fixed by the establishment of each specialisation within each Trade Group. There was also a time factor involved in that so many years had to be served before an individual was eligible for consideration for promotion. So far as the prewar direct entrant air crew introduced in 1939 were concerned, it was most unlikely that any of them would be considered eligible for promotion until the early 1950s. Indeed the initial arrangements for the provision of wartime airmen air crew (including pilots) had made no provision for any of them to serve in ranks above that of sergeant.[31]

[23]AMO A.62/40 of 1 February.

[24]AIR2/4459. Minute from ACAS (AVM Douglas) to AMP (AVM Portal) dated 29 December 1939. Apart from provision for the commissioning of observers having been enshrined within AMO A.17/39 further reference to this possibility had appeared as recently as 9 November in AMO A.476/39.

[25]AIR2/2075. Air Ministry letter 773716/38 dated 22 December 1939.

[26]*Ibid.* The agreed proportions were recorded in Air Ministry letter S.41477/S.7(e)/1 dated 9 January 1940.

[27]As an example, consider Charles Kimber (*op. cit.*), a pre-war sergeant observer who attended the first Gunnery Leader's Course at the CGS in November 1939. Returning to No 110 Sqn, he was commissioned on 17 January 1940 but as an air gunner, presumably because there was still no provision for observers to be officers. As a gunner, his name first appears in the Air Force List for May 1940. Despite his having qualified as a 'Spec N' in Canada during 1941 and navigated himself home via the transatlantic delivery flight of a Liberator, Kimber continued to be listed as an air gunner until as late as January 1942 when he was finally recognised as an observer.

[28]AMO A.188/40 of 4 April.

[29]AMO A.228/40 of 24 April.

[30]*Ibid.*

[31]AMO A.469/39 of 9 November.

The passage of time soon changed the perspective, however, and by 1941 it had been decided to 'establish an overhead proportion' of posts for senior airmen air crew. WOp/AGs and air gunners were to be considered for early promotion to flight sergeant while the ceiling for pilots and observers was set at warrant officer.[32] The only preconditions for consideration were that a candidate had to have served six months in his current rank and have his CO's recommendation. There was a small price to pay for this prospect of accelerated promotion, in that air crew with a basic trade would no longer figure on the promotion roster of their original Trade Group. They did have some preserved rights, however, which ensured that, should they be obliged to revert to their original trade, they would assume the rank and seniority which they would have attained had they not become air crew. Since, as air crew, they were only temporary sergeants, this might well involve having to forfeit their three stripes, but it did at least mean that they would not have lost any ground compared to colleagues who had chosen not to volunteer for flying duties.

These provisions, along with the reintroduction of commissions for non-pilots, represented substantial improvements in the conditions of service of air crew. The only remaining problem was that of differential rates of pay (to which reference was last made on page 130). Cadet pilots were still drawing flying instructional pay at a rate of two shillings per day while observer cadets were entitled to only one shilling and sixpence. In April 1941 attention was drawn to this unfair practice by the AOCinC Flying Training Command, Air Mshl L.A. Pattinson, who managed to explain the problem within a single (if rather lengthy) sentence:[33]

> 'It is important that during their period of training air observers should not feel themselves to be regarded as in any way of less importance than pilots and the discrimination in the rate of flying instructional pay is calculated to promote a feeling of inferiority on the part of air observers under training, particularly when it is borne in mind that a proportion have been relegated to air observer training after failing to pass through a course of flying instruction and, therefore, have experienced an actual drop of 6d a day.'

It is interesting to note Pattinson's use of a word with such negative connotations as 'relegated'. This was a trifle unfortunate, as it suggests that, despite his rational egalitarianism, and his public championing of the cause of the observer, even he may have subconsciously considered observers to be 'second best.'[34]

The AOCinC went on to point out that observers were bound to be at a financial disadvantage anyway, because they took longer to train which meant that they spent more time as (low paid) cadets than the pilots with whom they had been recruited. He acknowledged that recent changes in perspective had opened up the possibility of a few observers being promoted to flight lieutenant, or possibly even to squadron leader, but in general their career prospects were very poor when compared to the opportunities available to pilots.[35] To continue to cheat them out of sixpence a day, almost as soon as they had signed on, served only to aggravate an inherently unsatisfactory situation.

Another paragraph from Pattinson's letter is worth quoting in full:

> 'I understand that the payment of a lower rate of flying instructional pay to air observers is based on the higher flying risk borne by pilots whilst under training in that they fly themselves whereas air observers are normally flown by experienced pilots. I suggest that that argument is not one that can justify a lower rate of pay to the cadets themselves, since the majority of young men who fly would much prefer to take their own risks of being involved in a flying accident when flying as pilots than when being flown as passengers.'

Does that sound familiar? The Bailhache Committee had made much the same observation as long ago as 1916 (see page 30). The fact is that all air crew are inevitably obliged to face the same hazards as those confronted (and not infrequently actually caused) by pilots or, as one WW II WOp/AG has put it, 'you had to trust your life constantly to people who might not value it as highly as you did.'[36] The point was (and still is) that non-pilot air crew are rarely able to exert more than a marginal influence on their eventual fate. Twenty-five years after Bailhache's Report the RAF's administration was still paying its back-seaters less than its pilots, just as their illustrious predecessors in the RFC had done – and with just as little justification. Pattinson's appeal finally put an end to this discriminatory practice by restoring the situation that had prevailed in 1918. Flying instructional pay was standardised at the higher rate in July 1941.[37]

1941. The introduction of the observer (radio), *née* radio operator (air)

By the winter of 1940/41 twin-engined, multi-seat, night-fighters (initially Blenheims, to be followed later by Beaufighters and eventually Mosquitos) had begun to appear and early experience indicated a need for specialised operators to handle the early airborne interception (AI) radar sets with which they were equipped. As a 'temporary measure' a new air crew category, that of the radio operator (air) was introduced in January 1941.[38] It was envisaged that most of these men would be found among ground tradesmen and that, after appropriate training, they would be promoted to temporary sergeant. A qualified air gunner who elected to be retrained would be remustered as a radio operator (air gunner). The new category was to be paid at the WOp/AG rate of seven shillings and nine pence per day, it being possible to

[32]AMO A.326/41 of 8 May. Note that the initial promotions under these provisions were to be effective from 1 April.
[33]AIR2/2968. Letter FTC/55899/CA/DO dated 28 May 1941 from AOCinC Flying Training Command to the Air Ministry.
[34]A pilot who has been suspended from training today is no longer 'relegated to' navigator duties, as he was in the 1940s. He is now 'reselected for' them. It means the same thing in the end, of course, but the choice of words is indicative of a change from a negative to a positive approach.

[35]Pattinson's reference to flight lieutenant observers was presumably a reference to their gradual introduction as Station Navigation Officers but it would be another year before there was any realistic prospect of an observer becoming a squadron leader.
[36]Richard Passmore, *op. cit.*
[37]AMO A.579/41 of 31 July.
[38]AMO A.17/41 of 9 January. While 'Radar Operator' would seem today to have been a more appropriate title for this new category, the American 'radar' (RAdio Direction And Range) did not begin to enter the RAF lexicon until 1942 and, because of the highly classified nature of such equipment, its use continued to be restricted. The use of 'radio' in this context was, therefore, an oblique reference to what was then known as Radio Direction Finding (RDF). Within the RAF, the term 'RDF' was eventually supplanted by 'radar' on the authority of AMO A.863/43 of 2 September.

antedate remustering to radio operator (air) to as early as 5 August 1940.[39]

Apart from coaxing signals from the early, and often temperamental, radar equipment, the 'radio' operator needed to be able to visualise this data as a three-dimensional picture. Using this information, and in conjunction with any advice provided by ground-based controllers, he then had to guide his pilot to a position from which the contact could be visually identified and, if appropriate, engaged.[40] It was soon appreciated that the members of a night-fighter crew were interdependent. Just as in the Bristol Fighter of 1917, success came only with teamwork which demanded mutual trust and respect, in addition to a high degree of professional skill and airmanship.

Being a radio operator (air) was clearly not a secondary occupation and the RAF was being obliged, with its customary reluctance, to acknowledge that anyone required to fly in combat had to be regarded as professional air crew. The first intimation of this dawning appreciation came in May 1941 when a dedicated air crew badge was authorised for the new trade. Despite the reservations of the gunnery fraternity, who had successfully resisted an earlier attempt to high-jack their emblem for the benefit of flight engineers (see below), the new badge was to be modelled on that of the air gunner with the 'AG' motif supplanted by an 'RO'.[41] The wearing of this emblem was to be authorised by AOCs when a trainee, who was not already entitled to wear an observers or an air gunners badge, completed a course at an Operational Training Unit (OTU). Those already flying with night-fighter squadrons at that time acquired their badges by default on the basis of a three-week course at No 3 Radio School at Prestwick followed by what had amounted to a period of probationary operational service.

Two months later the category was redesignated as that of the observer (radio).[42] The badge remained the same but rates of pay were raised to equate to those of pilots and other observers, that is twelve shillings and sixpence per day for a sergeant (plus sixpence per day war pay).[43] At the same time, direct entrant recruiting was introduced in addition to the existing provision for the remustering of serving airmen and the transfer of officers from other branches.

1941–42. The introduction of the flight engineer

The first of Bomber Command's new generation of heavy bombers, the Stirling, began to enter service in August 1940 to be followed by the Halifax in November. Neither of these types would be committed to operations until early 1941 but their arrival would eventually lead to a major reappraisal of the way in which business was conducted on what was becoming more of a flight deck than a traditional cockpit. The most significant characteristic of the new aeroplanes was that they had four engines. It was anticipated that managing these, and the associated fuel system, would demand more time than the average squadron pilot could afford to devote to this task, not to mention a greater degree of technical expertise than was possessed by many.

Large, four-engined aeroplanes were not a new phenomenon, of course, as the RAF had been operating Sunderland flying boats since 1938 and Singapores for several years before that. Coastal Command had been able to adapt to these aircraft relatively easily, however, as many of its gunners were fitters, rather than wireless operators. Very prudently, when gunnery had become a full-time trade in 1939, Coastal Command had negotiated a concession which had permitted it to retain what had now become a unique category of dual-qualified fitter/gunners (see page 134).

While Coastal Command had made adequate provision for handling the technical complexity of four-engined aircraft, Bomber Command had not and in January 1940 serious consideration began to be given to the constitution of the crews that would be needed to operate its forthcoming aeroplanes. It was easily agreed that some form of 'engine watcher' would be required and it was generally assumed that these would be drawn from the ranks of appropriately qualified fitters and/or flight mechanics, but little progress was made in deciding exactly how they were to be trained or by whom.

Thus, when No 7 Sqn's Stirlings and No 35 Sqn's Halifaxes actually went to war in February and March 1941 neither unit had any personnel who were formally recognised as being flight engineers. But the fact that this trade did not even exist could not be allowed to interfere with operations. Expediency became the order of the day, therefore, and both squadrons were obliged to resort to employing selected ground tradesmen who had been trained in-house and locally endorsed as quasi-air crew. It is said that, in the absence of any useful advice from higher authority, some of these men were, quite unofficially, given NCO status while they were in the air and that they flew as acting sergeants.[44]

With Bomber Command's four-engined 'heavies' having embarked on their operational careers, the Air Ministry was finally galvanised into action.[45] Better late than never, a scheme covering the provision of flight engineers was introduced in March 1941.[46] Recruited from the ranks of tradesmen qualified in aero-engine technology, these men were to be given three week's training at a Bombing and Gunnery School followed by a similar period of technical familiarisation with the appropriate airframe and/or engine manufacturer. On completion of this sequence they were remustered as flight engineers and promoted to temporary sergeant. It is important

[39] By the end of June 1940 Fighter Command had received more than thirty Blenheims fitted with radar, the first successful engagement using this equipment (AI Mk IV) occurring on the night of 23 July when an aircraft of the Fighter Interception Unit destroyed a Do 17. On 12 August the unit received its first radar-equipped Beaufighter. Most of the back-seaters flying as radar operators at this stage will have been qualified air crew but, presumably from August, some technicians may have been involved, hence the need to back date the introduction of the new category.

[40] The exception to this rule (there always seems to be one) was the Defiant, which was pressed into service as an interim night-fighter in 1940, although these aircraft were not fitted with radar (AI Mk IV, later VI) until late in the following year. The pilot of a Defiant was obliged to interpret the radar himself and then position his aircraft so as to afford his gunner a firing opportunity – not an easy task, as staring into a flickering oscilloscope can have done little to enhance the pilot's night vision.

[41] AMO A.402/41 of 29 May.

[42] AMO A.503/41 of 10 July.

[43] AMO A.672/40 of 10 September had introduced war pay with effect from 31 August 1940 at the rate of sixpence per day for airmen and fourpence for airwomen, these rates being doubled in 1942 (see Note 52).

[44] D.C. Stringman, *The History of the Air Engineer* (1984).

[45] The third of the new 'heavies', the Manchester, was twin-engined and, presumably for that reason, its crew complement did not feature an engineer. Despite its size and the complexity of its 24-cylinder Rolls-Royce Vultures the Manchester was bracketed with the Wellington and Whitley and, as such, it made do with two pilots. As is well known, the Vulture proved to be a troublesome failure which led to the Manchester's being redesigned to become the Lancaster. Since the Lancaster, which entered service late in 1941, was a (proper) four-engined type, its crew included provision for a flight engineer from the outset.

[46] AMO A.190/41 of 20 March.

In 1941 the 'gunners union' succeeded in preserving the still unique design of their 'AG' badge by preventing its being adapted for the benefit of the newly introduced flight engineers, although they did have to concede that the newcomers would have to be allowed to wear it. This picture dates from this period and shows the twin .303 belt-fed Brownings in the Bristol B.I Mk IV turret of a Blenheim IV of No 45 Sqn. The occupant is F/Sgt Dave Cliffe, a WOp/AG who was credited with having probably destroyed a Bf 109 over Ghemines on 20 December 1941. (Daphne Hughes)

to appreciate, however, that they were *not* regarded as being dedicated air crew and they were designated as, for instance, fitter II(E) (flight engineer). They remained on the promotion roster for their parent trade and they continued to be paid at the rate applicable to their substantive rank and seniority, plus the old shilling-a-day crew pay and, because they were notionally qualified as gunners, sixpence qualification pay.

Following the pattern established in 1915, when the original observers badge had been introduced, it was entirely predictable that flight engineers would expect to wear an appropriate distinguishing emblem. Such a demand had first been raised in December 1940 but the official response demonstrated the same lack of energy and commitment as was then characterising the establishment of the entire trade. No badge was authorised until as late as May 1941, and when it was, it turned out to be the air gunners badge.[47]

It should be appreciated that in 1941 the air gunners badge was, like the flying 'O', a unique design. It had been suggested that it might be adapted to incorporate the letters 'FE' in place of the 'AG' but the 'gunners union' had expressed concern that its, by now much-prized, badge would be devalued if it were to be tampered with. Somewhat surprisingly, while it was clearly determined to resist any attempt to 'deface' its emblem, the gunnery lobby was content to allow flight engineers to share in the honour of wearing it. This was not entirely logical, of course, since flight engineers received relatively little formal training as gunners and gunnery was, in any case, a secondary duty so far as they were concerned. There was another slight anomaly in that air gunners received their badges on completion of their instruction in gunnery, while flight engineers had to wait until they had finished their technical courses. In several ways, therefore, the gunners badge fell well short of meeting the essential criterion of being 'appropriate'.

[47]AMO A.300/41 of 1 May.

Nevertheless, the decision had been made and there the matter rested – for the time being, at least.

1941–42. Evolutionary changes to the category of the wireless operator

By the autumn of 1941 the availability of air-to-surface vessel radar (ASV) had become sufficiently widespread within Coastal Command to have created a requirement for specialist operators. Rather than repeating the traditional exercise of making air crew out of ground crew, it was decided to try making technicians out of an appropriate category of aviator. WOp/AGs who had already completed a flying tour were, therefore, offered the opportunity of volunteering for additional training after which they would be remustered as wireless operator mechanics (air gunner) (WOM/AG), retaining their air crew status throughout.[48] In July 1943 the recruiting field was widened to include selected ground tradesmen, specifically wireless operator mechanics and wireless and electrical mechanics.[49]

Curiously, although the Order introducing the new category had stated quite clearly that it was to be identified as wireless operator mechanic (air gunner), some regulations published in mid-1942 referred to it as air gunner (wireless operator mechanic).[50] This may have been a misunderstanding, or perhaps mere carelessness, but the confusion appears to have been resolved by September and thereafter the original nomenclature is used exclusively. Here, WOM/AG will be used throughout.

In the spring of 1942 there was another significant change to the career structure of air signals personnel when a grading system was introduced.[51] All WOp/AGs were to be remustered as WOp/AGs Grade II with effect from 6 March. The rate of pay for a sergeant was now to be eight shillings per day, plus his sixpence war pay.[52] After a minimum of three month's operational service (which old hands would already have accumulated) a WOp/AG could take a trade test, which was essentially concerned with the 'WOp' aspects of his duties. Those who were successful were elevated to Grade I which attracted an increase in pay of sixpence per day. Achievement of Grade I was a prerequisite for promotion to flight sergeant, which earned a further sixpence.

It soon became apparent that, despite the introduction of the ASV-qualified WOM/AG, all Coastal Command WOp/AGs would also need 'to be conversant with the RDF organisation and procedures and to operate and maintain appropriate equipment'.[53] Furthermore, with effect from 18 May 1942, proficiency in these skills was to be rewarded by the not inconsiderable bonus of an additional shilling-a-day qualification pay. WOp/AGs who were not already qualified to carry out what were termed 'special wireless duties' were required to attend suitable courses at a Radio Direction Finding (later Signals) School and an OTU, although in-house squadron training could be substituted for the latter. To provide an additional incentive to unqualified WOp/AGs, annotation as an ASV operator was made an essential precondition for elevation to Grade I.

[48]AMO A.983/41 of 27 November.
[49]AMO A.716/43 of 22 July.
[50]Examples include AMOs A.551/42 and A.746/42.
[51]AMO A.424/42 of 30 April.
[52]With effect from 1 October 1942 rates of 'war pay' were doubled to one shilling a day for airmen and eightpence for airwomen, this change being promulgated by AMO A.1114/42 of 12 October.
[53]AMO A.551/42 of 4 June.

Chapter 20

1939. The RAF's conduct of early bomber operations – a naval view

On 18 December 1939 the RAF carried out a daylight raid against German naval units at Wilhelmshaven. This mission, in which twenty-two Wellingtons (from a force of twenty-four despatched) reached the target, resulted in the loss of twelve aircraft in action, six more being damaged in crash landings on returning to the UK, two of them so badly that they had to be written off. In terms of casualties, the cost of the operation had amounted to fifty-six lives, two wounded and five men being taken prisoner.[1] A similar operation mounted four days previously by a dozen Wellingtons had also sustained a 50% loss rate.

These early experiences served to shatter the RAF's faith in its long-held dictum that the combined defensive fire from a formation of bombers would permit it to penetrate to a target in daylight and survive. After due reflection, Bomber Command was obliged to abandon this concept in favour of night attacks by large numbers of individual aircraft. While it is understandable that the RAF's attention was sharply focused on the balance sheet, the analysis of the operation was conducted entirely by pilots. This was bound to have been the case, of course, because the RAF had no other air crew, at least none with sufficient status for their opinions to have been given serious consideration. As a result, some of the lessons which might have been learned were either overlooked or dismissed.

In fact there had been a competent non-pilot aviator over Wilhelmshaven on 18 December. He was Lt Cdr 'Hank' Rotherham, one of a pair of very experienced FAA air observers, whose attachment had been requested by the RAF because it was not entirely confident that its crews would be able to distinguish naval from merchant vessels, the latter being off limits. Rotherham later recorded his own impressions of what happened that day.[2] He has relatively little to say about the losses, which were clearly unacceptable but, from the standpoint of a professional airman, he was deeply unimpressed by many aspects of the way in which the operation had been conducted.

While recognising that it may be inadvisable to place too much reliance on the testimony of a single witness, the fact remains that Rotherham's account contains what is probably the only considered opinion rendered by a non-pilot. Furthermore, his considerable experience of practical aviation gives him an authority which cannot easily be dismissed.[3] As with most first-hand accounts, Rotherham's description of the mission tends to differ in detail from other versions. These discrepancies are not significant, however, and they do not invalidate his overall conclusions.

Having been given a familiarisation flight in one of No 149 Sqn's Wellingtons (a much bigger and faster aeroplane than any that he had ever flown in before), Rotherham tentatively mentioned to the CO, Wg Cdr R. Kellett, that, if his regular bomb-aimer were unavailable, he would be happy to take his place. He was somewhat taken aback when Kellett promptly offered him, a man who had never dropped a bomb from a Wellington, the opportunity to do it anyway!

Rotherham's surprise at this ready acceptance to disrupt a constituted crew, was compounded when he learned that the CO rarely flew with the same crew twice. He was further taken aback to be told that, while some of the squadron's observers might have dropped perhaps thirty bombs, most would have dropped less than half that number. Since Rotherham had previously dropped several hundred and was to be allowed a couple of practice sorties, his confidence was fully restored. In view of the importance of the forthcoming mission and the evident inexperience of the other bomb-aimers involved, he was a trifle surprised to find that his aircraft subsequently seemed to be the only one using the range.

On the mission itself, he flew in Kellett's aeroplane (N2960). According to Rotherham, the navigator was a young pilot with about 60 hour's flying time, and no specialist training, who drifted well to the north of their intended track.[4] He also observes that the RAF still did not appear to have adopted (or at least declined to practise) an effective method of wind-finding (see page 126). The final stage of the plan involved an approach to the target area at 14 000 feet, the signal to attack being given by the leader's descending by 1000 feet, 'a manoeuvre not calculated to improve the bomb-aimer's accuracy.' In the event, Rotherham claims that when

[1]While this engagement was clearly a major defeat for the RAF, from the German point of view it was not a victory of quite the proportions that they appear to have believed. A detailed reconstruction, of what amounted to a thirty-minute running battle, in C.F. Shores' *Fledgling Eagles* (1991) notes that the *Luftwaffe* initially claimed to have shot down thirty-eight of the twenty-two Wellingtons which reached the target area. Even after arbitration the score still stood at twenty-six or twenty-seven.

[2]G. A. Rotherham, *op cit*. The second naval observer was Lt Cdr E. H. C. Chapman who, like Rotherham, had been accredited since 1933. Chapman did fly operationally with the RAF but not on the Wilhelmshaven raid. Another FAA observer attached to the RAF later in December was Lt Cdr R. A. B. Phillimore.

[3]In May 1941 Rotherham flew in the Maryland of No 771 Sqn which discovered that the *Bismarck* had put to sea. Since he was captain of the aircraft, this exploit earned him a DSO, rather than the DSC awarded to his pilot. Later in the war, by then the youngest acting captain in the RN, but still an observer, Rotherham would command Katukurunda, possibly the largest RN air station, and ultimately the escort carrier HMS *Trouncer*. As with its aviation personnel in WW I, it is clear that the navy's more enlightened approach to back-seaters removed many of the obstacles that stood in the way of their RAF counterparts for whom such a satisfying career was simply out of the question.

[4]Although the crew included an observer, Sgt Hough, it would appear that, as was a fairly common practice at the time, responsibility for navigation had actually been vested in the second pilot, Plt Off R. A. Cruickshank. To qualify for a flying badge KR 811 specified that a pilot had to have accumulated a minimum of 80 flying hours, so Cruickshank must have logged more than the 60 reported by Rotherham. It could be that that was his total since joining the squadron, but, since he had been on its strength since July 1938, it still seems to be an improbably low figure.

he pressed the release button the bombs failed to fall off anyway, because the pilot 'had not armed the master release switch.'[5]

In Rotherham's opinion the entire operation had been a 'black comedy of errors' in which the RAF had failed with respect to tactical command, navigation and bomb-aiming. He was so incensed that, before returning to his desk at the Admiralty, he wrote a highly critical report which he handed to Kellett. Rotherham was subsequently summoned to HQ Bomber Command to be interviewed by the AOCinC. In view of his criticism of the RAF's methods, he expected the worst, but Sir Edgar Ludlow-Hewitt proved to be most cordial, merely asking that he go over the ground again for his personal benefit.

Interestingly, Kellett had considerable experience of navigation, or at least of long-distance flying, although Rotherham makes no mention of this.[6] What he does say, however, is that, as mission leader, Kellett should have closely monitored the conduct of navigation himself; something which he did not do. In his report Rotherham expressed the view that a bomber squadron 'needed to be commanded by a man who combined the talents of a good pilot, navigator and bomb-aimer. I recommended that the need for pilot efficiency be discarded first.'

What an outrageously novel idea! While the admirals may have been content to allow their pilots to take orders from back-seaters, however, the air marshals thought it no way to run an air force. Not in 1939 anyway, although some had begun to see the error of their ways by 1943.

1939–40. The capabilities of early wartime observers

It is clear that, in Rotherham's view at least, the RAF of 1939 still had a great deal to learn, or to relearn, about the conduct of air warfare. Unfortunately, as suggested by the last section of Chapter 18, its observers were unlikely to be of much help. Indeed the generally poor showing of the observers serving with squadrons at the turn of 1939–40 was causing considerable concern, particularly as this lack of success was also being reflected in training where some 30% of the intake was currently failing to complete the navigation phase of the course.[7]

In December 1939 AVM Douglas reminded Air Mshl Portal that, although all observers recruited since the outbreak of war had been civilians, the direct entrant scheme had originally been introduced as a temporary measure (see page 128). Since the civilian intake was clearly failing to come up to expectations, Douglas suggested that the Service should revert to its old ways and draw its observers from experienced wireless operators (air crew).[8] Unfortunately, in view of the timescale involved and the numbers required, such an approach could not have come even close to satisfying the RAF's needs. Nevertheless, while the majority of observers (and other air crew) would have to continue to be direct entrants, internal recruiting was reinstated in February 1940.[9]

The Director of Training, Air Cdre W.A. McLaughry, was inevitably drawn into the debate and he provided two explanations for the disappointing performance of contemporary observers.[10] First, it was now clear that the pre-war direct entry selection boards had been insufficiently rigorous. This problem had been compounded by the lack of an Initial Training Wing (ITW) phase, which had meant, on the one hand, that pre-war direct entrants had been poorly prepared for further instruction and, on the other, that the Service had lacked a convenient mechanism for the early weeding out of those who showed little potential. These early intakes, which had begun to enter productive service in the spring of 1939, had contained the observers who were now causing concern at squadron level.

This explained half of the current unsatisfactory situation, but not the alarming failure rate being experienced in training. McLaughry considered that this could also be traced to selection. When non-pilots had been introduced into the RAFVR in 1938, he believed that many local recruiting centres had perceived numbers to have been more important than standards (see page 131). As a result, a significant proportion of those enrolled had simply been lacking in ability. On being mobilised, these pre-war RAFVR observers had become the first cohorts to enter training and it was these men who were currently having such difficulty in coping with instruction.

There was another factor which was common to both facets of the problem, the inadequacy of the available training facilities. These had provided the peacetime regular intakes with a poor foundation on which to build and had done little to assist the less capable RAFVR trainees to deal with the more demanding aspects of their courses.

Having identified the probable causes of the present problems, McLaughry was able to report that several steps had already been taken to improve the situation. First, the recruiters and the selection boards had been instructed to raise the standard of those being accepted for training as observers. Secondly, the courses at all of the civilian-run navigation schools had been extended from twelve weeks to sixteen, the flying content (previously 40 hours) being increased to 60 hours. Thirdly, the competence of instructors was being improved by giving each of them a three-week course at the SAN. Finally, a batch of *ab initio* students was to be trained against a Service-run, ten-week navigation syllabus at St Athan to provide a comparison with the standard civilian-trained product.

The subsequent refinement of observer training, and that of other non-pilot air crew categories, is summarised in Chapter 22.

[5]According to No 149 Sqn's ORB, no bombs had been released because there were no legitimate targets, the only naval vessels being moored in the inner basin which was 'off limits' for fear of causing civilian casualties. If that was the case, what Rotherham had perceived to be Kellett's failure to arm the release system would have been quite intentional, although it is surprising that no one had bothered to brief the lead bomb-aimer (of all people) on this rather significant tactical limitation. In correspondence with the author in 2001, however, Capt Rotherham is still adamant that the failure to arm the system had been an oversight.

[6]In 1938 (then Sqn Ldr) Richard Kellett had led the three Wellesleys which had flown from Egypt to Australia to take the World's Long Distance Record for Great Britain. While his involvement with this considerable achievement meant that he was closely associated with navigation in RAF circles, it did not follow that he was, or even that he had needed to be, an expert practitioner of the art, as each of the record-breaking aircraft had carried a graduate of the Specialist Navigation Course. In Kellett's crew he had been Flt Lt R.T. Gething.

[7]AIR29/546. For example, based on intakes of sixty, No 6 AONS at Staverton had experienced an 18% failure rate on its first wartime course, 32% on its second and 38% on its third, which graduated in March 1940. There had been only a marginal improvement by July, the next two courses reflecting 23% and 28% failure rates.

[8]AIR2/4459. Minute from Douglas (ACAS) to Portal (AMP) dated 29 December 1939.

[9]AMO A.93/40 of 15 February.

[10]AIR2/4459. An explanation for the poor showing of observers and a summary of the corrective actions that had already been taken were provided by DofT, Air Cdre W.A. McLaughry, in a minute, dated 1 January 1940.

1939–42. The state of the art of air navigation

While the performance of the observer of late 1939 had proved to be disappointing, the Service had correctly diagnosed the reasons for this. In fact, as the last section of Chapter 18 suggests, he was, in many ways, little better off than his predecessor of 1918. This was particularly true with regard to his training, but it was not entirely the case in other respects. For instance, the introduction of enclosed crew accommodation and a supply of oxygen had provided some improvement in working conditions – although the crew of an iced-up Whitley, labouring to cross the Alps on its way to Italy in 1940, might well have been inclined to question the veracity of this statement. Significant improvements had also been made in the quality of flight instruments, as a result of which airspeed indicators, altimeters, thermometers and compasses were all now (relatively) accurate and reliable.

Needless to say, at squadron level, the hapless observers of 1939 were held responsible for the poor standards that were being achieved and there was a widespread lack of confidence in their abilities. As a result, although it directly contravened the prevailing policy, many pilots, particularly the more experienced ones, were reluctant to relinquish responsibility for navigation during the early months of the war. Thus, while the efforts of all observers tended to be monitored very closely, it was not uncommon for one of the pilots in the Wellingtons and Whitleys of Bomber Command in the winter of 1939/40 to usurp his place completely and act as navigator himself.

Unless he could persuade someone else to do it, the observer of a Whitley would have been expected to arrange his own target illumination by dropping a parachute flare down this chute. In this instance, however, he is using it to deliver bundles of leaflets. (G.R. Pitchfork)

The Hampden provided some precedent for this practice because, as previously noted, responsibility for navigation in this aircraft was formally vested in the second pilot.[11] The same trend was probably even more marked in Coastal Command where most pilots were provided with comprehensive navigation training while passing through a School of General Reconnaissance.

But it was all to no avail. The legacy of twenty years of neglect (by pilots) meant that no one was really capable of navigating an aeroplane with any confidence at night, in bad weather or out of sight of land. The air marshals were reluctant to believe this at first but the proof lay in Bomber Command's disappointing early performance. It took some time for this unpalatable truth to be accepted but painstaking analysis by D.M.B. Butt of strike photographs taken in June–July 1941 eventually provided incontrovertible proof. Performance varied, depending upon the prevailing weather conditions and the availability of moonlight, but it was convincingly demonstrated that, on average, of every five night bomber crews despatched to attack Germany, only three even claimed to have reached the target. Of these only one had actually done so, in that they had managed to drop their bombs within five miles of the aiming point. It followed that only a tiny proportion of the bombs dropped would actually have hit the target.[12]

Why was this? In short, because, with the tools and levels of skill that were available at the time, it was simply impossible for anyone (even including pilots) to navigate with the necessary degree of accuracy under wartime conditions, especially at night. Apart from map-reading, the only aids to establishing an aircraft's position were W/T bearings taken with a loop aerial and astro. Either of these would yield a single position line but it required (at least) two of these to construct a fix and, since the accuracy of neither line could be guaranteed, even a fix was of only limited value. To quantify what this meant, during 1941 Bomber Command's Operational Research Section analysed the actual conduct of navigation on 178 sorties sampled from thirty separate raids. It revealed the following:[13]

a. Astro sights were being taken on only 33% of sorties.
b. Approximately 60% of observers were using W/T bearings, the average accuracy of fixes constructed from such bearings being assessed as 20.8 miles.
c. The majority of position lines were being used in isolation, rather than as elements of fixes.
d. Quantifying the previous observation, it was found that three or more fixes had been found on only 6.5% of the sorties in the sample, the corresponding proportions for two fixes and one fix being 9% and 23.5%. On the remaining 61% of occasions the entire sortie had been flown without the benefit of a single fix.

As one would expect to find, there was a close correlation between the conduct of navigation and success in bombing. While it had already been demonstrated that only one crew in five was actually reaching the target area, it could also be shown that observers who had found it without the benefit of *en route* fixing had had to spend an average of nineteen minutes searching for the actual aiming point. Those who had

[11]See Chapter 18, Note 32. Although Bomber Command continued to employ pilots as Hampden navigators, according to pages 26 and 33 of Bruce Lewis' *Air Crew: The Story Of The Men Who Flew The Bombers* (1991), it would seem that by 1941 the training being provided was quite inadequate.
[12]From the Butt Report, reproduced in Vol IV of Webster and Frankland's *The Strategic Air Offensive Against Germany* (1961).
[13]*Operational Research in the RAF* (1963).

The operational career of this Whitley V, T4131/EY·W, of No 78 Sqn is reflected in the thirty-five bomb symbols proudly displayed on its nose. This was a worthy effort and represented a considerable investment in manpower, treasure and nervous energy. In terms of damage inflicted, however, in 1940–41 this investment probably exceeded the returns. (J.D.R. Rawlings)

obtained three or more fixes had spent only eight minutes over the target area.

It should be appreciated that poor navigation was not confined to Bomber Command; it was a universal problem. Coastal Command was experiencing similar difficulties in finding convoys, the likelihood of achieving a successful rendezvous declining with the distance off shore. In 1941 the failure rate was less than 10% for convoys within 100 miles of the coast but at 600 miles it was 60%.[14] In other words, more than half of the convoys which were most at risk from U-boats lacked any air escort at all.

The situation was actually much worse than these raw figures suggest, as only one in three crews actually flew straight to its convoy, the others having to conduct a search and the time spent doing this had to be deducted from that notionally available on station. This was not entirely the fault of the navigator in the aircraft, however, as the navigator of a ship in mid-Atlantic was unable to establish his position with much confidence either. The average along and across track errors in the notional position of a convoy were 35 miles and 15 miles, respectively.[15] Since these were average figures, it follows that the ships could often be much further away. Under the circumstances, even if the air navigator had been able to fly directly to the precise position given by the convoy, on most occasions the ships would not have been there when he arrived and he would have been obliged to start the inevitable time-wasting search pattern.

Since map-reading was not an option for maritime navigation, astro was even more important within Coastal Command than it was within Bomber Command. At the time there was little else available, but it should be understood that astro suffered from severe practical limitations. The most critical of these was the weather, because astro was simply unavailable whenever the sky was obscured by cloud. While this drawback was a significant problem for bomber observers, it was even worse for those who patrolled the North Atlantic at 2000 feet or less, as often as not under an unbroken overcast (the same overcast that prevented convoys from establishing their positions).

Astro had other limitations too, as described by 'Dickie' Richardson, reflecting on his experiences as a student on the 1938 Specialist Navigation Course:[16]

> '...we (*the RAF*) were nursing a bagful of false hopes pinned on improving astro. Unfortunately, there was simply nothing better to offer and although great strides were being taken to simplify its use, as seen from today astro was almost a non-starter. If only we had seriously considered the practical effects on a bubble sextant of a pilot weaving about, trying not to be shot down, our first years of night-bombing failures could have been anticipated and alternative electronic aids developed much more quickly.'

Richardson was one of that rare breed, a pre-war pilot who was actually interested in navigation. As such, his informed assessment of the real value of astro was perfectly valid and it would have been warmly endorsed by the majority of wartime observers. For example, FSgt Ray Silver, a veteran of Whitley and Halifax operations with No 10 Sqn in 1941–42, has left us the following personal impression:[17]

> 'Theoretically, with our Mk IX sextants we could navigate by the stars as mariners had done for centuries. In practice, few identifiable stars were visible on any night. Sighting them from an aircraft that rarely climbed above medium-level cloud was unlikely. Persuading a pilot to fly straight and level over enemy territory for star-shooting was even more improbable. And converting starlight to a precise position line under operational stress was beyond most of us.'

[14] *Ibid.*
[15] *Ibid.*

[16] F.C. Richardson, *op. cit.*
[17] L. Ray Silver, *Last of the Gladiators* (1995).

There can be little doubt that extravagant claims have been (and sometimes still are) made for the accuracy of celestial techniques. Remarkable individual feats of navigation were achieved using astro, both before and during the war, but these should not be permitted to distort the overall picture. While it could certainly give a navigator a reasonable indication of his approximate position, astro could not be relied upon to provide an accurate fix. To establish the practical accuracy of astro *under operational conditions* Bomber Command commissioned a scientific analysis of fixes obtained by the navigators of Lancasters, Halifaxes, Stirlings and Wellingtons between October 1942 and April 1943. The results showed that the probable error of a fix obtained by a Main Force navigator was 22.4 nautical miles. As was to be expected, the handpicked navigators of the Pathfinder Force were able to improve on this, their average being 15.6 nautical miles.[18] Bearing in mind that, by definition, 50% of fixes were less accurate than this, the unavoidable conclusion is that, while astro was a very useful get-you-home aid, it was never accurate enough to satisfy the essential requirement of permitting a crew to locate a blacked-out target in the dark.

While astro had its limitations, some improvement in navigational accuracy had been achieved through the progressive refinement of DR procedures to produce the air plot technique. In brief, this involved constantly monitoring the reading of the compass and the aircraft's true airspeed and logging the time of each change of heading (course) and speed. By using the time spent on each heading to calculate the distance flown and then plotting this information on his chart, it was possible for the navigator to estimate where the aeroplane would have been *in still air*. By comparing this notional position with a navigational fix, showing where the aeroplane actually was at that time, it was possible to deduce the average wind velocity over the entire period during which the plot had been carried. A fix was also essential to provide a datum from which to restart the exercise periodically, since the inaccuracies inherent in a manual air plot increase progressively with time. Apart from the difficulty in obtaining fixes, the manual air plot was well-suited to operations which involved flying long straight legs, which often tended to be the case in Coastal Command.

On the other hand, the accuracy of an air plot deteriorated very rapidly if frequent changes of heading were involved. This could occur if, for example, it was necessary to follow a complex route for tactical reasons or if the pilot was obliged to take evasive action. In either case it became practically impossible for the observer to keep track of the aircraft's progress, the more so if changes of speed and altitude were also involved. To put it another way, a manual air plot was only a really practical proposition if the observer was able to control the situation. Under those conditions he could direct changes of course, height and speed and thus (to a degree) stay 'ahead of the aircraft'. Once he lost the initiative, however, the observer would soon find himself 'chasing the aeroplane', a situation from which it was very difficult to recover.

As with astro, extravagant claims have been (and sometimes still are) made for what could be achieved by DR alone. In reality, DR actually provided no more than an informed opinion as to where an aeroplane might be and the inaccuracy of this 'guesstimate' increased inexorably with time. One of the major sources of error was that an observer was obliged to assume that his pilot would maintain precisely the briefed heading, speed and altitude. This was simply not the case, of course, especially without an autopilot, and even when 'George' was available tactical considerations meant that it was often inappropriate to use it. The errors that were inevitably introduced by the pilot were compounded by inaccuracies in instrumentation, particularly those arising from the magnetic compass which, despite years of refinement, still left much to be desired.

Another major source of inefficiency was the tiredness which steadily undermined a navigator's concentration. Fatigue could adversely affect his judgement, the accuracy of his calculations, his capacity to pay attention to detail and thus his ability to detect his own errors. All of this was bound to lead to an increased risk of accidents arising from navigational errors. In practical terms, a ten–twelve hour patrol over the North Atlantic was all that could reasonably be asked of a navigator before his performance had to be regarded as suspect. This problem was exacerbated by the introduction of very long range maritime patrol aircraft, like the Liberator and Catalina, and it eventually had to be solved by establishing two navigators per crew.

1942–43. The introduction of practical navigational aids

From the previous section, it can be seen that three technical innovations were desperately needed: a high degree of automation; an increase in overall accuracy and a means of fixing position. The first of these requirements was met by the development of the Air Mileage Unit (AMU), a device which constantly measured true airspeed[19] and then integrated this against time to calculate the air distance flown. This information was then resolved around the aircraft's heading, resulting in an indication of change of (still air) position which, by use of suitable gearing, could be presented on an Air Position Indicator (API) as latitude and longitude.[20] In other words, it would produce an automated mechanical air plot which would, within reasonable tolerances, accurately reflect the actual headings and speeds flown by the aeroplane, regardless of changes in altitude. This relieved the pilot of the tiring burden of endeavouring to fly with absolute precision for hours on end and removed most constraints on his freedom to manoeuvre the aircraft at will.

The accuracy of an API was totally dependent, of course, upon that of its inputs and much still needed to be done in this respect. The greatest single improvement had been the introduction of the Distant Reading, or Gyro-Magnetic, Compass (such a device actually being a pre-requisite for a practical API). This system used a magnetic detector continuously to correct the alignment of a directional gyroscope which then became the master instrument. Using suitable contacts, the

[18]AIR14/4129. BC/S.25858/3/ORS.1(b), Operational Research Section (Bomber Command) Report No 75, dated 16 August 1943. Note that the figures quoted are for two-star fixes including *Polaris*. If *Polaris* was not used the overall accuracies were degraded to 24.3 and 17.5 nautical miles, respectively.

[19]True airspeed is indicated airspeed corrected for the difference in air density between sea level and the height at which the aircraft is actually flying.

[20]Further development of this principle eventually permitted the output of the API to be mechanically compounded with the local wind velocity in another device, the Ground Position Indicator (GPI), which projected a lighted graticule onto a chart to indicate the actual (ground) position of the aircraft. In a different mode, the GPI could also be used to find the local wind velocity. For a variety of reasons, it was an essentially short-range aid, but it did have its uses. For instance, if the GPI was started overhead an easily identifiable position on the ground (i.e. a 'pinpoint'), it could be used to locate a poorly defined target.

Of all the electronic aids to bombing and navigation that emerged during WW II, the one with the greatest potential was ground-mapping radar. This is a wartime H_2S set installed at the navigator's station in a Lancaster. Also discernible is the 'tunnel' beneath the main instrument panel, leading to the bomb-aiming position and the flight engineer's folding seat stowed out of the way against the cockpit wall. Behind this seat, just out of shot, there is a panel of engine instruments on the starboard side of the fuselage. (Dr Alfred Price)

aircraft's heading could be picked off the gyro and relayed via an electro-mechanical transmission system to be displayed on repeater units at all necessary crew stations; it could also be fed into any mechanical devices which required such an input, including, for instance, the API and the Mk XIV bomb sight. Furthermore, it was possible to offset the output of the repeaters to compensate for local magnetic variation so that the reading displayed was of True Heading. Since it was no longer necessary to be able to see the compass itself, the magnetic sensor could be installed remotely within the airframe where it would be free of the many arbitrary unwanted influences to which direct-reading compasses were prone, e.g. a torch in the pocket of the pilot's flying suit. Needless to say, this sort of advanced technology was relatively expensive.[21]

The creation of a means of computing and then displaying an accurate still-air position was two-thirds of the battle. To complement such a device it was also necessary to provide a reliable method of obtaining accurate fixes at will. This requirement was to be met by the progressive introduction of a variety of radio and radar aids such as GEE, LORAN, ASV, H_2S and CONSOL.[22]

There was a fourth, non-technical, development during the early years of the war which also did a great deal to improve navigational standards – the introduction of drills. In place of the relatively haphazard methods used by early observers to keep track of an aeroplane's progress, latter day navigators were required to work to laid down schedules, adapted to suit specific roles and the local availability of aids. Thus a navigator might be expected to plot a fix every few minutes while flying within GEE coverage or once an hour when having to rely solely on astro. Similarly, a rate of wind-finding was specified, as were checks of vital equipment, particularly routine comparisons of all the compass read-outs within the aircraft and a periodic cross-check of these against an astro compass.

[21]AIR6/51. Note 161(37) dated 14 December 1937, submitted to the 106th EPM, stated that it would cost £176 to provide a bomber with a master unit plus three repeaters and a stand-by magnetic compass, compared to £65 for the traditional alternative of three compasses and a directional gyro.

[22]CONSOL, which employed long wave radio transmissions, was unusual in that it had originally been introduced by the Germans to provide their U-boats with an accurate means of establishing their position while on patrol in the North Atlantic. Once it had been discovered, the initial British reaction was to neutralise the transmitter sites. Fortunately, wiser counsels prevailed and it was decided instead to take advantage of the facilities, as the aircraft of Coastal Command needed a reliable long-range navigational aid just as much as did the submarines of the *Kriegsmarine*.

When it was initially set up at Cranage the CNCS operated large numbers of Ansons supplemented by a few Wellingtons. After its move to Shawbury in 1944 Wellingtons predominated, the fleet including some relatively exotic models like this Mk XIII, JA383. (G.J. Thomas)

This disciplined approach, along with the new devices which began to become available from mid-1942 onwards transformed the art of air navigation, both by day and by night, into something approaching a science. It was to be a gradual process, however, as the equipment took time to produce in quantity. When it did arrive, the early sets often proved to be temperamental and some of the new aids, notably GEE, turned out to be vulnerable to enemy interference. Furthermore, the availability of electronic aids was largely confined to the skies over Western Europe and the North Atlantic. In the more remote theatres, therefore, reliance had still to be placed on drifts, astro and map-reading for the duration of the war.

Some idea of what was achieved by the methodical application of scientific techniques and disciplined methods can be judged by the improvement in the overall performance of Bomber Command. In the spring of 1942 only 23% of aircraft despatched, in weather good enough to permit photographic analysis, were succeeding in dropping their bombs within 3 miles of the aiming point. Three years later the success rate was in excess of 95% and a substantial proportion of the bombs being dropped by that time were actually falling within one mile of the target.[23]

Similar improvements had been achieved elsewhere, notably in Coastal Command, where homing had provided the solution to the problem of finding convoys. A system had been devised whereby, once it was estimated to be within 100 miles of its convoy, the aircraft (which, in mid-Atlantic, was not at risk to air interception) transmitted a continuous signal. This was received by the ship which broadcast the bearing of the incoming signal in a brief message that was too short to be of advantage to a U-boat but permitted the aircraft to fly directly to its charges. After some initial teething troubles, this procedure proved to be so effective that by late 1943 the failure rate in finding convoys had fallen to less than 1%. This was a considerable 'force multiplier' in that it permitted the aircraft to spend the maximum amount of time on direct escort duties, since it was now very rare for it to have to conduct a search.[24]

[23]*Operational Research in the RAF* (1963).
[24]*Ibid.*

1942. The crucial importance of navigation is finally accepted and formally recognised

Despite the handicaps under which early wartime observers were obliged to operate, since navigation had been made their preserve, it followed that they would be in increasing demand both as instructors and for development work. Significant numbers of observers began to attend the 'sn' course, which was by then being conducted at No 2 SAN at Cranage, from the autumn of 1940 onwards and they gradually began to displace the pilots who had previously occupied all navigational appointments. It was a slow process but by mid-1942 navigators were becoming influential at squadron, and to a lesser extent, station level. In general, this was as far as it went, however, because staff officers handling navigational matters at group or command level tended to be squadron leaders or above and, although there were some exceptions, such senior ranks were monopolised by pilots.

Nevertheless, by 1942, with wartime pressures having forced the pace of development, considerable advances had been made in both the theory and practice of navigation. Furthermore, a number of graduates of pre-war 'Long N' and Specialist Navigation Courses had long since recognised that it was of crucial importance for the Service to have skilled navigators.[25] These men, all of them pilots, had been working steadily to improve professional standards and on 14 August 1942 they achieved a major breakthrough when No 2 SAN was reconstituted as the Central Navigation School (CNS). This was no mere change of name, however, as the

[25]Long/Specialist Navigation Course graduates who made a particularly significant contribution to the development of training schemes, the refining of navigational procedures, the fostering of an increased awareness of the vital importance of navigation or who commanded the SAN or one of the other influential training units included: Flt Lt J.K. Summers; Flt Lt N.H. D'Aeth; Flt Lt F.J. Fressanges; Flt Lt W.E. Oulton; Flt Lt G.I.L. Saye; Flt Lt P.D. Robertson; Flt Lt D.J. Waghorn; Flt Lt F.C. Richardson; Flt Lt L.K. Barnes; Flt Lt N.C. Ogilvie-Forbes; Flt Lt R.T. Gething; Fg Off E.C. Chilton; Fg Off. R.J. Cooper; Fg Off J.H. Dand and Fg Off P.H. Mackworth (ranks given here are those held while attending the course, not those subsequently achieved, most of these men eventually becoming at least group captains, and many of them air officers).

new title implied that Cranage was now a centre of excellence with a status similar to that of the CFS.[26]

By this time the academic content of the increasingly intensive Short Navigation Course was actually approaching that of the Specialist Navigation Course, which had not been significantly updated since pre-war days. Reform was clearly overdue and a review of advanced navigation training was undertaken during the latter part of 1942. The first Specialist Navigation Course to be run against the new syllabus began on 20 November, although it had been publicly announced that the course was to be overhauled as early as August.[27] Prior to this it had taken only fifteen weeks to acquire an **N** annotation. It now required nine months and about 150 hours of flying time, which cast some doubt on the validity of existing **N**s. Since the people actually wielding the new navigational broom were prominent 'old **N**s', there could be no question of removing their labels. Nevertheless, a three-week refresher course was offered to bring earlier graduates up to date. Four such courses were run during 1943, permitting forty students to revalidate their qualification.

Sgts Straddle and Winde had been potential members of the crew of cartoonist Bill Hooper's inspirational creation, Plt Off Prune, since 1941. The revision of air crew categories in 1942 led to more characters being added to the family, including this navigator, Fg Off Fixe. (Tee Emm, April 1943)

While the Specialist Navigation Course was being revamped, the content of the short course was similarly revised, its academic level being raised to the equivalent of that demanded by the old specialist course. To mark this change it was renamed to become the Staff Navigator Course, permitting it still to be known as the 'SN', although now usually rendered in upper, rather than lower, case. Graduates of the course, which was also run by the CNS, were classified as Staff Navigators.[28] Individual 'Staff Nav' courses were dedicated to Coastal, Bomber and Flying Training Commands, the content being adjusted accordingly, length varying between ten and fourteen weeks. Flying Training Command actually had three options, one for recent graduates, one for veterans and one for pilots. The latter reflected the fact that one of the aims of the course was to improve both the awareness and the standard of navigation throughout the air force so, while some of Cranage's *alumni* became instructors or staff officers, others simply rejoined the ranks of working navigators – and/or pilots.

In view of all this, it could be said that 1942 was the year in which the RAF finally came to accept that navigation really was as important as pure flying. It followed that navigators were as important as pilots, although this rather novel idea took some time to gain a measure of acceptance. As part of the campaign to 'sell' navigation, the CNS offered an occasional course aimed specifically at Bomber Command pilots who were invited to find out how the other half lived by playing at being a navigator for three weeks. This generally proved to be a salutary experience. Their respect for navigators considerably increased, most of these students returned to their squadrons eager to spread the word.

Another sign of the RAF's decision to promote the concept of navigators as people was that the one associated with the hapless Plt Off Prune had acquired an identity by early 1943. He was Fg Off Fixe and, while the attractions of alliteration are obvious, it may not be without significance that Freddie Fixe actually outranked his pilot.[29]

[26]A summary of the units which have subsequently carried the navigational torch within the RAF is as follows. On 11 February 1944 the CNS moved to Shawbury where it became the Empire Air Navigation School on 28 October. On 31 July 1949 it reverted to its earlier title, only to become the Central Navigation and Control School on 10 February 1950 when it absorbed the School of Air Traffic Control. In May 1952 the Specialist Navigation Course moved to the RAF Flying College at Manby. On 1 July 1962 this unit became the RAF College of Air Warfare, later taking over the Staff Navigation Course which led to the unit at Shawbury being restyled as the Central Air Traffic Control School on 11 February 1963. The Specialist Navigation Course was superseded by the General Duties Aerosystems Course in 1968. In 1974 the College of Air Warfare closed down, its navigation (and other) courses moving to Cranwell where they continued to be run under the auspices of the newly established Department of Air Warfare of the RAF College.

[27]AMO A.817/42 of 6 August.

[28]AMO A.1220/42 of 12 November.

[29]Fixe first appears in the March 1943 edition of *Tee Emm*. He was not alone among Bill Hooper's non-pilots in being named, however, the first being Sgt Straddle, who had been around since the summer of 1941, although it is interesting to note that, while he was drawn wearing an 'O' badge, he was referred to as a navigator or navigator/bomb aimer, rarely, if ever, as an observer. Another early non-pilot was an air gunner, Sgt Winde. Following the demise of the observer and the arrival of Fixe, Sgt Straddle was remustered to become an air bomber and the crew was completed by the addition of Sgt Backtune, a wireless operator.

Chapter 21

1941. The 'New Deal'

Throughout the first two years of the war, the training system had been hard-pressed to keep up with the demand for air crew. As a result, the RAF had been obliged to tolerate minimal standards in order to achieve maximum output. The inevitable consequences were high accident rates[1] and inefficient operational forces. By the autumn of 1941, however, the situation was being transformed by the arrival of a rapidly increasing flow of trained air crew from overseas. Some of these men had gained their 'wings' in the USA but most had qualified at schools which had been set up in the Dominions under, what the British were pleased to call, the Empire Air Training Scheme (EATS).[2] (See pages 170–171 for a brief account of the background to the EATS.)

With the pressure caused by the previous shortage of air crew beginning to ease, it became possible to consider increasing the amount of training they were being given. In December 1941, the Air Member for Training (AMT), Air Mshl Sir Guy Garrod, submitted a paper to the Air Council proposing that the time spent in the air by trainee pilots and observers should be virtually doubled.[3] Although not specifically stated in the paper, in the latter case this was to involve an increase to a notional 130 hours of which at least 25 were to be flown at night. In view of the success of the various overseas training schemes, it was also recommended that responsibility for practically all basic pilot and observer training should now be transferred to the Dominions. Although a number of reservations were raised for subsequent resolution, the broad thrust of AMT's proposals was promptly endorsed.[4]

While such positive steps were to be welcomed in isolation, they coincided with a dawning realisation that the air force needed to adopt a radically new attitude towards all air crew. The prevailing mindset within the Service still tended to reflect the outlook of the inter-war RAF when crews had operated on a 'pilot plus' basis. Plus who? Plus anyone really; it hardly mattered – only the pilot was of any real consequence. Two years of war had demonstrated just how ill-conceived this approach had been. Change, long overdue, was now becoming a matter of urgency because the increasingly sophisticated detection, navigation and bombing aids which were beginning to reach the squadrons was causing the centre-of-gravity within a crew to shift away from the pilot and towards the observer.

Garrod, among others, wanted the air force to abandon its entrenched 'pilot plus' philosophy and replace it with one which recognised that crews were teams of specialists whose individual expertise and professionalism were just as crucial to the success of a mission as those of the pilot. These ideas were adopted, in principle, in March 1942 but it would be September before most of the necessary changes were in place and another year before the echoes died away.

The substantial improvements in training sponsored by Garrod came to be known as the 'New Deal'. With hindsight, however, one can see that other ideas which were crystallising at much the same time were just as significant and, in the context of this book, these too will be treated as consequences of New Deal thinking.

1942. Flight engineers are formally recognised as being air crew

Symptomatic of the New Deal ethos was the adoption of a more realistic attitude towards flight engineers. Based on a year's experience, revised regulations governing their provision and terms of service were published in March 1942.[5] The main change was that '*while employed in the air* they will be

More reminiscent of the bowels of a ship than the inside of an aeroplane, this is the front face of the main spar of a Stirling; the substantial hand wheels provided the flight engineer with a means of jettisoning fuel. His normal station was a little forward of this where he had a panel mounted on the starboard wall of the fuselage. This provided him with quadruple banks of dials and switches permitting him to monitor oil pressures and cylinder head temperatures, control the fuel system, adjust engine rpm, feather propellers, operate fire extinguishers and so on. (G.R. Pitchfork)

[1] AIR6/61. When Air Mshl Garrod submitted his arguments to the Air Council in his memorandum AC 70(41) of 6 December, he stated that in late 1941 the average monthly losses of operational aircraft from accidental causes were running at sixty-seven in Bomber Command, seventy-eight in Fighter Command and twenty-five in Coastal Command. The regular loss of 170 aeroplanes, the equivalent of more than ten squadrons, was accounting for some 20% of the production output of operational aircraft.

[2] AP3233, Vol 1. The output of the EATS in the twelve months to 2 September 1941 had amounted to 1822 observers and 3041 WOp/AGs and air gunners (plus 7265 pilots), to which totals, over the same period, the schools in the UK had contributed a further 2158 observers and 8320 WOp/AGs and air gunners (plus 6792 pilots). These raw figures are misleading, however, as the UK schools were operating close to capacity whereas the overseas system was just beginning to hit its stride and its output would increase dramatically in 1942.

[3] AIR6/61. See Note 1.

[4] AIR6/72. Minutes of Air Council Meeting AC 23(41) held on 9 December.

[5] AMO A.262/42 of 19 March.

regarded as members of the aircrews for all purposes other than promotion' (author's italics). This had not gone quite far enough, however, as flight engineers remained on their Trade Group rosters and, if promoted beyond the rank of sergeant, they were to cease flying and resume their duties on the ground. As a result, although flight engineers effectively answered to their Flight Commanders on a daily basis, the various Engineering Officers on their squadrons retained a substantial element of responsibility for what were still regarded as being essentially ground crew personnel. Flight engineers, it would seem, were neither fish nor fowl – or perhaps they were both!

By this time flight engineers had become a familiar feature of the air crew community but, unfortunately, not familiar enough. By August only a third of the 6000 airmen required had volunteered themselves for flying duties and a substantial proportion of them had failed to make the grade in training. The unavoidable conclusion was that ground personnel simply did not want to fly, at least, not in anything like the numbers required. This turned out to be less critical than had initially been feared, because the Service was beginning to suspect that it had been demanding an unnecessarily high level of technical competence of its flight engineers; indeed, it was even beginning to doubt that it was essential for them to be experienced ground tradesmen. As early as December 1941, SASO Bomber Command, AVM R.H.M.S. Saundby, had expressed the view that mental agility, alertness, intelligence and keenness were the most important qualities that a flight engineer needed to possess. While his responsibilities obviously required him to understand the systems that he was operating, since he was not expected to carry out any maintenance procedures more complicated than Daily Inspections, Saundby argued that he did not need to be a highly skilled fitter.

Since experienced engine fitters were not volunteering in sufficient numbers and because their skills had, in any case, turned out to be less critical than had been anticipated, the recruiting field was widened in the summer of 1942 to include airframe (as distinct from engine) fitters and mechanics.[6] At the same time the potential for divided loyalties was removed by declaring that 'flight engineers now form a separate air crew category', the notional severing of their remaining ties to the Technical Branch being underlined by the introduction of commissions within the GD Branch. The new status of the flight engineer was marked by the replacement of their previous entitlements to air gunner and crew pay by an inclusive air crew daily rate of (for a sergeant) eleven shillings.

While this clearly indicated a major change in policy, it took a surprisingly long time, in some quarters at least, for the system to cater for its implications. Witness J. Norman Ashton's recollections of his arrival on No 103 Sqn as late as May 1943:[7]

> 'On joining a new unit, it was customary for members of a crew to report to their respective leaders and to meet the other boys in the section. At that time, however, this did not apply to flight engineers. They had neither leader nor section and the only person to take the slightest technical interest in them was the Squadron Engineering Officer. Usually, he was too busy with the maintenance of the aircraft to devote much time to flight engineers and they were left very much to their own devices.'

Things did change slowly, however, and when Ashton joined No 156 Sqn in October 1944 he notes that it had a Flight Engineers Section, complete with a flight lieutenant Leader.

In the meantime, large, mostly four-engined, aircraft were being operated in ever-increasing numbers and in a widening variety of roles, practically all of these aeroplanes requiring a flight engineer. Apart from the demands of Bomber Command's 'heavies', Coastal Command needed flight engineers for its Sunderlands, Fortresses, Catalinas, Halifaxes and Liberators to which Transport Command would soon add Stirlings, Yorks and more Halifaxes. Unfortunately, despite broadening the spectrum of trades from which flight engineers could be drawn, adding air crew rates of pay to the prospect of wearing three stripes and a badge had still been insufficient of an incentive to persuade serving airmen to volunteer for flying duties in anything like the numbers required. In July 1943, therefore, the RAF had been obliged to turn to direct recruiting.[8] At much the same time, the commissioning quota, previously only 6%, was increased to match that of WOp/AGs, i.e. up to 10% on graduation and a further 10% on active service. While the new rules did not preclude suitably qualified fitters from continuing to volunteer to fly, the proportion of civilian entrants was to rise steadily over the next two years until they far outnumbered those being drawn from the ranks.

1942. The composition of heavy bomber crews is revised

It will be recalled that in 1937, in an attempt to improve standards, it had been decided to make navigation the responsibility of a second pilot who was (where this was practical) to be added to the crews of bomber aircraft. The following year this responsibility had been transferred to the observer, but the additional pilot had been retained. By 1942, with the flight engineer having taken on the task of engine management, there was little work of any substance left to occupy this second pilot. Bomber Command's requirement for pilots was much greater than that of any other Service organisation, partly because of its size, partly because of the need to replace heavy losses but mostly simply because it employed two pilots in most of its aeroplanes. Since one of them was no longer earning his keep, a reappraisal of the responsibilities of pilots was clearly overdue.

In March 1942 the Air Ministry convened a policy meeting to review the overall constitution of bomber crews, not just their pilots. It was at this meeting that it was decided to dispense with co-pilots altogether.[9] Since this would permit either the demand on the training machine to be reduced by something like 1000 pilots per year, or a substantial extension of the time spent under instruction, it was difficult to argue with this decision. Nevertheless, AOCinC Bomber Command, Air Mshl A.T. Harris, did express some misgivings, as he considered it necessary for captains to have someone to relieve or assist them at the controls on long flights and/or in an emergency. It was agreed to allay his concerns by the provision of autopilots and by an undertaking to train another crew member in basic aircraft handling. It was initially decided that a suitably trained non-pilot would be referred to as a 'pilots mate' but this term was rapidly superseded by 'pilots assistant'.

[6]AMO A.978/42 of 15 August.
[7]J. Norman Ashton, *Only Birds and Fools* (2000).

[8]AMO A.538/43 of 3 June. Interestingly, in view of the need to attract additional volunteers, this Order actually reduced the pay of a sergeant flight engineer from twelve shillings to ten (allowing for war pay in both cases), although those already drawing the 1942 rate had preserved rights.
[9]AIR2/2662. Note of a Meeting held in the Air Council Room on Sunday, 29 March 1942, under the chairmanship of CAS, Air Chf Mshl Sir Charles Portal, to discuss the composition and training of air crews in medium and heavy bombers.

Typical of the power-operated four-gun turrets of WW II, a Boulton Paul Type E fitted to a Liberator II. (Boulton Paul via Jonathan Falconer)

Along with the decision to do without a second pilot came a reduction in the requirement for dual-qualified WOp/AGs. Since there was only one wireless station in a bomber, it was agreed that the current establishment of two WOp/AGs per crew should be reduced by half. It was also agreed that the dorsal and tail turrets should be manned by straight air gunners, which rather begged the question of which guns the remaining WOp/AG was supposed to man, once the Wellingtons and the early Halifaxes had been withdrawn along with their free-mounted beam guns. This question was not raised at the time, but it would be eventually (see pages 184–185). It is worth noting that this change in manning policy applied only to Bomber Command. As was often the case, Coastal Command went its own way, continuing to require the majority of its wireless operators to be fully qualified as gunners.

Having dealt with pilots and gunners, the meeting turned its attention to relieving the ever-increasing workload which was being carried by observers, the only members of a bomber crew who worked ceaselessly and under constant and considerable pressure from take off until a few minutes before touch down. To quote Bruce Lewis, a veteran of thirty-six Lancaster sorties flown with No 101 Sqn:[10]

> 'When I flew as a wireless operator I was able to observe at close quarters the unimaginable stress under which the navigator worked for long periods of time. He had to maintain almost superhuman detachment, even when the enemy was doing his best to destroy the aircraft in which he was working, and when his pilot was twisting and turning and diving and climbing in a corkscrew effort to escape that destruction.'

While there may have been less tension in other roles, the pattern of working under constant pressure was not confined to Bomber Command. Edward Nichols, a WOp/AG who flew in Whitleys, Wellingtons and Halifaxes of Coastal Command for much of the war, notes that the two or three crew members of his trade were able to relieve each other by rotating every hour or so between stints in the tail and/or mid-upper turret, at the wireless position or as radar operator. Similarly, the two pilots (which Coastal Command retained) were able to take turns at the controls. Only the observer/navigator was required to work continuously, and largely unaided, for the entire duration of a flight.[11] Much the same heavy burden was carried by observers in Ferry (later Transport) Command and even in Fighter Command, although, in the latter case, the fact that night fighter and intruder missions were of relatively short duration probably made the strain less apparent.

The demands being placed on bomber observers by 1942 had been considerably increased by a change in tactics. For the first two years of the night bombing campaign the concept of operations had involved each crew finding its own way to and from its target. In practice, although many of them did

[10]Bruce Lewis, *op. cit.*

[11]Edward Nichols, *We Held the Key* (1996).

not realise it at the time, it would have been more accurate to say that they failed to find their way to and from their targets. Nevertheless, despite its disappointing results, the bomber offensive had provoked the Germans into creating an increasingly dense and efficient network of defences. As a result, the RAF's losses had risen.

The British counter to the strengthened German defences was the bomber stream which involved all crews following a predetermined track within strict time limits, the aim being to pass as many aircraft as possible over the target in the shortest possible time. The object of this exercise was to create a local concentration of force which would focus the effect of the raid while reducing losses by overwhelming the target's defences. Success in this endeavour depended upon each aircraft's staying on time so that it maintained its place in 'the queue' which would also help to minimise the risk of collision. It was equally important that each aircraft should also stay on track, because those which strayed from the herd were more easily singled out by searchlights permitting them to be picked off by anti-aircraft guns and/or *Luftwaffe* night fighters.[12]

The increasing availability of GEE made it possible to navigate with the necessary accuracy – so long as the set kept working and the nominated target was not too far east of the Ruhr. The equipment could not do it by itself, however, and it required the almost constant attention of the observer to achieve the desired results. At the March meeting Harris explained that it was no longer practical for the observer to leave the navigator's station 50 to 100 miles from the target in order to become a bomb-aimer. After some debate, it was eventually decided to make bomb-aiming a discrete trade which was to be conducted by a dedicated crew member.

There was some initial uncertainty as to the label to be applied to this new air crew category. Bombardier gained some early currency in staff circles, but in April the Air Council ruled this out in favour of air bomber.[13] Relieved of the task of bomb-aiming, the observer would now be able to devote his whole attention to navigation so, to reflect this change in his duties, it was intended that the observers who flew in heavy and medium bombers (later extended to include those who flew in night and long-range fighters) should be redesignated as navigators. As an aside, it should perhaps be recorded that by the summer of 1941 it was already commonplace for observers to be referred to as 'navigators', even in some official documents.[14]

[12]While the stream provided the core of Bomber Command's later, and ultimately spectacularly successful, methods from 1942 onwards, this brief description conveys little impression of the real complexity of the conduct of a night bomber raid. Many other techniques were developed to increase the effectiveness of the campaign and to minimise losses. Space precludes these being explored in detail here. Suffice to say that by 1944/45 a typical raid would involve deceptive routeing and be supported by diversionary attacks, both of which served to distract and divide the defences. Apart from defining and, if necessary, refining the aiming point, the Pathfinder Force would often place markers along the route to the target. Selected crews would determine the 'Zephyr wind' *en route* and this was broadcast for the benefit of the Main Force, the use of a common wind velocity assisting in maintaining the coherence of the stream. Further support was provided by No 100 Gp which employed a variety of electronic and other methods to jam, mislead and confuse the enemy's defences and, ultimately, a force of night-fighters which accompanied the bomber stream as a direct counter to the *Luftwaffe*.
[13]AIR6/73. Minutes of Air Council Meeting 7(42) held on 24 April 1942.
[14]*Tee Emm*, for instance, was referring to navigators and/or navigator/bomb aimers from as early as May 1941. Since the learned staff of that august organ made a virtue of having their editorial ears close to the ground, this use of a strictly incorrect term is far more likely to have been a well-informed reflection of current *patois*, than a mistake.
[15]AIR2/2662. HQ Bomber Command letter BC/S.20173 dated 24 June 1942.

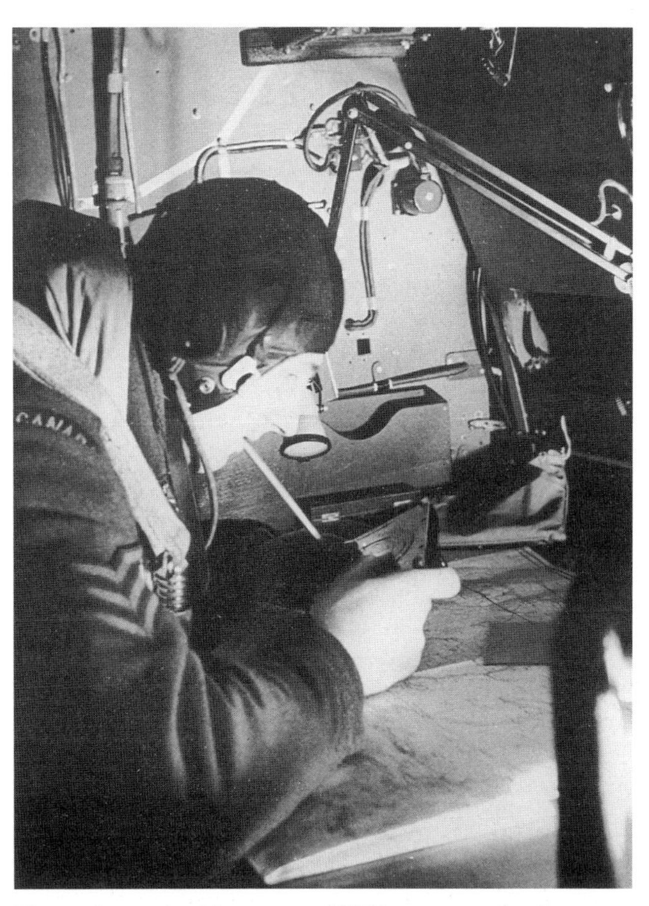

The navigator, in this case an RCAF sergeant, of a Lancaster. (Jonathan Falconer)

It remained to be decided who best to employ as pilots assistants, a question that took some time to answer. The navigator, wireless operator and gunners were soon ruled out on the grounds that they could all be expected to be fully occupied in a combat situation. That left either the flight engineer or the new air bomber. In June 1942 Bomber Command eventually stated its preference to be for air bombers.[15] The air bomber therefore became the designated pilots assistant in Stirlings and Halifaxes, but not in Lancasters, because the layout of the flight deck of these aircraft made it far more appropriate to use the flight engineer.

By early May, most of the implications of these decisions had been digested and advice was being disseminated within Bomber Command as to how the new policy was to be implemented.[16] The deletion of second pilots was to begin immediately, although it was anticipated that there would be some delay before qualified pilots assistants, i.e. air bombers, became available in significant numbers.[17] It was also considered necessary to make a start on relieving the observer of his bomb-aiming tasks as soon as possible. Pending the availability of air bombers, therefore, some of the WOp/AGs who had recently become surplus to requirements were to be trained in bomb-aiming as a stopgap

[16]*Ibid*. HQ Bomber Command letter BC/S.20173/Trg dated 4 May 1942 from SASO, AVM Saundby, to all subordinate Group HQs.
[17]Because of the necessary post-graduate training that he would be required to undergo, an observer cadet who had been remustered to the new category of air bomber as he approached the end of his navigation training course in Canada at the end of May 1942, would not have reached a squadron in the UK much before January 1943. A summary of what post-graduate training involved and of how long it could take is provided at Chapter 22.

measure, although it was not intended to remuster them to the new category. To supplement in-house training on the squadrons, an Air Bomber Training Flight was set up within each of the four heavy bomber groups. Formed in June 1942 these units were closed down in the following March by which time formally trained air bombers were beginning to reach the squadrons in substantial numbers.

1942. The Ottawa Air Training Conference – the introduction of the air bomber and the replacement of the observer by the navigator

While the Air Ministry and Bomber Command had been pressing ahead with revised arrangements for the manning of bombers, it is questionable whether they could, in practice, have actually implemented this policy unilaterally. This was 1942, not 1939, and by this time many of the air crew flying with RAF squadrons were RAAF, RCAF and RNZAF personnel. While their various governments were content that these men should serve under British command, they deserved to be consulted over such a major change in manning policy. Furthermore, a large, and rapidly increasing, proportion of British (and other) air crew were receiving their basic training overseas. The changes in Bomber Command's requirements, not least the introduction of an entirely new air crew category, were bound to have a considerable impact on the joint training machine. At the very least it would be necessary to adjust the content of existing courses and the numbers of each trade required. Consultation was clearly advisable, if not essential.

An appropriate forum at which to discuss this and many other matters was provided by the Air Training Conference held in Ottawa in May–June 1942.[18] The conference was a major international affair, involving the British, the Dominions, the free allied governments and the Americans, who were now directly engaged in the war. Convened to review all aspects of training, the conference had several aims. Perhaps the most important was to renew the mandate under which training was being conducted in Canada, since this was due to expire in March 1943. It was agreed to underwrite this joint enterprise for another two years, the scheme being known as the British Commonwealth Air Training Plan (BCATP) with effect from 6 June 1942 (but see page 171). An attempt was also made to co-ordinate the BCATP with the rapidly expanding American training programme, although little of substance was ever achieved in this respect.

Much of what was discussed at Ottawa need not concern us here but it was one of its sub-committees, chaired by AVM R. Leckie, which endorsed, on behalf of the other concerned governments, the latest British policy for the composition of RAF bomber crews.[19] With the decision already having been made, however, planning for the provision of air bombers was well in hand and the trade was formally introduced while the conference was still in session.[20]

While his primary tasks were to be the aiming and dropping of bombs, an air bomber was also to be trained in navigation so that, by providing him with pin-points and other visual cues, he could act as the 'eyes' of the designated navigator within a crew. Furthermore, apart from being able to assist the pilot when required, the air bomber was also to be qualified in gunnery so that he could man the nose turret. Such multi-skilled crewmen would plainly have to be very capable individuals and their entry standard, rate of pay and commissioning quota were to be similar to those previously applied only to pilots and observers and, like them, once qualified, they were to hold the minimum rank of sergeant.

Associated with the advent of the air bomber had been the introduction of the navigator, although it had initially been planned to retain some categories of observer. This was causing some confusion in Ottawa and the British High Commission eventually sought clarification from London. This was provided by a signal of 27 May which confirmed that, while navigators were to be introduced for most roles, observers were to be retained for general reconnaissance aircraft and certain light bombers, and announced that a new sub-category, the observer (W/T), was to be introduced for Mosquito bombers. The need to respond to this question having concentrated minds, however, it was soon appreciated that this was unnecessarily complicated and on 2 June the Air Council decided to do away with the observer altogether in favour of a variety of sub-categories of navigator.[21]

The Canadians were formally notified of the final version of the new titles of all air crew categories on 10 July with a request that they concur. The Canadians having agreed, the authorities in Australia, New Zealand and Rhodesia were informed on the 14th and they too agreed to adopt the new nomenclature.[22]

1942. The Ottawa Air Training Conference – air crew and commissioning policy

It will be recalled that a few months after the outbreak of war it had been agreed to commission up to 50% of pilots and observers, the proportion of gunners being fixed at 20% in 1941. To ensure parity with the RAF, the Dominions had been requested to use the same proportions within their own air forces.[23] All had agreed to do so.

Since then, however, the RAAF, RCAF and RNZAF had all been considerably expanded and they had all matured as fighting services. As a result, the Australian, Canadian and New Zealand governments had begun to develop their own perspectives on the status of air crew. In view of the considerable contribution that these Dominions were now making to the prosecution of the war, they expected their views to be taken into account.[24] While the British had been more or less

[18] AIR20/4101. Ottawa Air Training Conference, Minutes and Proceedings, 19 May–5 June 1942.

[19] Despite the significant implications of Bomber Command's new manning policy, the Minutes of the Conference indicate that Leckie's sub-committee had had little hesitation in approving its introduction. Many other major decisions appear to have been taken with a similar lack of argument. This was because most of the business transacted at Ottawa (as at most major conferences) will actually have been conducted during pre-conference meetings of specialist staffs and informal discussions between the principals. This was certainly the case with the manning of bombers, details of which had been circulated in advance, the British delegation being obliged to seek clarification from the Air Ministry on a number of specific issues prior to the 'main event'.

[20] AMO A.505/42 of 21 May.

[21] AIR6/73. Minutes of an Air Council Meeting 10(42) held on 2 June 1942.

[22] AIR2/8369. The Canadians were informed of the new titles by signal X817732 of 10 July 1942.

[23] AIR2/8179. The South African government was requested to adopt the UK's commissioning quota by Air Ministry letter A.82118/40/S.7(e)3 dated 1 November 1940. This letter stated that Canada had already accepted the British proposal and that early agreement was anticipated from Australia and New Zealand.

[24] The provision and training of air crew for the RAF was not confined to Australia, Canada and New Zealand, but only these three Dominions participated jointly with the UK in the integrated BCATP. Under separate

able to dictate employment policy in the early days, a much greater degree of compromise was called for by 1942 and this became very apparent at the Ottawa Conference where commissioning policy proved to be a contentious issue.

The sub-committee dealing with this topic was chaired by Sir Guy Garrod, who was presented with a wide range of opinions. In essence, the New Zealanders advocated an ultra-conservative approach, withholding all commissions until an individual had demonstrated his ability in service. At the other extreme, the egalitarian Canadians wanted to commission *all* air crew. The workmanlike Australians held the middle ground, recommending the abolition of the quota system and commissioning anyone who deserved it.

For the record, the US Army Air Force delegation reported that they were currently commissioning 80% of pilots, 100% of navigators and 50% of bombardiers, although it was intended to reduce the proportions of both pilots and navigators employed as officers.[25] The Americans did not commission any of their air gunners, radio operators or flight engineers.

For the British, it was the Canadian view which presented the greatest difficulty, since, it was argued, if all air crew were to become officers it would seriously undermine the entire concept of the commission. The Canadians countered that the question was somewhat academic, as leadership was hardly a factor in an aeroplane where the efficiency of a crew depended on the skills of its individual members and teamwork, not the issuing of commands. Furthermore, the existing arrangements frequently resulted in the ridiculous situation of an officer gunner's being subordinate to an NCO pilot in the air, their precedence being reversed when they were on the ground. Finally, the Canadians pointed out that, since they all faced the same hazards, it was invidious for some members of a crew to be treated differently from others, especially as NCOs were paid less for taking the same risk.

There was little prospect of reconciling the extreme points of view that were presented and the end result had to be a compromise. The British insisted on retaining the quota system, at least in principle, but conceded that it need not be imposed rigidly. The constraints on the proportions of pilots, navigators and air bombers who could emerge from training as officers, i.e. up to 33%, were to remain in force but there was to be no limit on the numbers who could subsequently be commissioned while on active service.[26] The ultimate arbiters on the standards required were to be the various national authorities. While it was not publicly acknowledged to be the case, the end result probably resembled most closely the Australian idea of commissioning anyone who deserved it. Suitable provision was made for the resolution of any disputes which might occur. For example, if the British authorities were to reject the commissioning recommendation of, say, an Australian airman serving in an RAF squadron, it would be possible for him to be transferred to an RAAF unit.

1942. The rationalisation of air crew categories

The air crew trade structure, as it existed in the spring of 1942, had been cobbled together in a series of reactions to changing circumstances. Most of these changes had been, and still were being, brought about by increasing specialisation and this needed to be reflected within the range of available air crew categories. So far as observers were concerned, for instance, while a core of common practice remained, the new mechanical and electronic aids which had begun to reach the squadrons meant that the specific activities of individuals could differ quite markedly, depending on the type of aircraft and role to which they were assigned. Thus, there were few similarities between the airborne duties of observers flying in Halifax and Lancaster bombers, and those who flew in maritime strike Beaufighters, Mosquito night-fighters or Catalina flying boats. The requirements of different roles and the demands imposed by various types of aircraft had also complicated the categorisation of gunners and it was apparent that they too needed to be sub-divided.

These topics had been discussed at Ottawa and there had been broad agreement that it was time for reform and a revised matrix of air crew categories was eventually introduced in July 1942.[27] The salient characteristics of the new arrangements are summarised at Fig. 18.

Introducing the new categories was a complicated business which made waves within the training system and had some impact on the employment patterns of individuals already on active service, many of whom had to be reclassified to match one of the new categories.[28] Furthermore, while the range of sub-categories of navigator had been intended to cover all operational roles, there were inevitably cases which did not fit comfortably into one of the recognised slots and these anomalies took time to sort out.[29]

bilateral agreements with the UK, broadly similar programmes were undertaken in Rhodesia and South Africa, but even here there was sufficient flexibility to permit the use of African facilities to train, for instance, some RAAF personnel.

[25]See Note 18. It would seem that Col R.E. Nugent, representing the US War Department's Personnel Staff, who volunteered this information, may not have had his ear quite as close to the ground as he might have, as USAAF manning policy was about to be changed in quite the opposite sense. On 8 July 1942, only a few weeks after the Ottawa Conference, it was decided that virtually *all* air crew flying in key crew positions, i.e. pilots, navigators and bombardiers, should be officers. The minimum rank of a pilot thereafter was that of the newly created flight officer (equivalent to warrant officer, junior grade). Few of these flew in combat, however, most of those who did being employed on co-operation duties with the Field Artillery and even here they had become a rarity by mid-1944. Practically all navigators and bombardiers were commissioned, most other air crew continuing to fly as enlisted men.

At this stage (early 1942) the majority of navigators in the US Navy were dual-qualified pilots. Most were commissioned but where a crew included three pilot/navs, as in long-range patrol aircraft, one could be an enlisted man. All naval gunners, radio operators and engineers had non-commissioned status.

[26]The British had been content to agree to this concession as, in their experience, while the agreed (up to) 33% of pilots and observers had emerged from training as officers in the past, there had never been enough postgraduate commissions to fill the remainder of the permitted 50% quotas, although this situation was to change later on. Within Bomber Command, for instance, by 1944 an NCO pilot, navigator or air bomber lucky enough to survive a full tour of operations had a reasonable expectancy of completing it as an officer.

[27]AMO A.746/42 of 23 July.

[28]A full six months after the new scheme had been introduced the reclassification process was still incomplete, leading to the issue of AMO A.52/43 of 21 January which urged COs to ensure that all air crew were appropriately categorised.

[29]A case in point was the two-seat light bomber which was supposed to be crewed by a Nav(W). This was appropriate enough for the Mosquito, but not for the Vengeance. The Vengeance was unique in being the only dive-bomber ever to be used by the RAF and unusual in that it was employed operationally only over Burma. Probably for these very reasons, it appears largely to have escaped the attention of the training and personnel staffs in London. While it undoubtedly was a 'two-seat light bomber', there was clearly a case for the back-seater in a Vengeance to be a WOp/AG and it required a prolonged exchange of correspondence between Air HQ India and the Air Ministry before a final solution was agreed – see AIR27/864. In the event the establishment of a Vengeance squadron was eventually set at fourteen WOp/AGs and seven Nav(W)s, with Nav(B)s being an acceptable substitute for the latter.

Category	Duties	Badge
Navigator	Navigation plus gunnery in an emergency.	N
Navigator (B)	Navigation, bombing and gunnery.	N
Navigator (BW)	Navigation, bombing, gunnery and wireless operation.	N
Navigator (W)	Navigation and wireless operation plus gunnery in an emergency.	N
Navigator (Radio)	Radio operation. Navigation.	N
Air Bomber	Bombing, map-reading plus gunnery in an emergency. Also to act as pilots assistant where no flight engineer was established to do so, i.e. able to fly straight and level and steer a course.	B
Wireless Operator (Air Gunner)	Wireless (and possibly ASV radar) operation and gunnery.	AG
Air Gunner	Gunnery.	AG
Wireless Operator Mechanic (Air Gunner) Air Gunner (Flight Mechanic [Airframes]) Air Gunner (Flight Mechanic [Engines])	For heavy aircraft of Coastal Command only. To carry out the duties of their trade plus gunnery. Wireless Operator Mechanics were to be additionally qualified to handle ASV.	None, but AG if rated.
Flight Engineer	Monitoring of engine instruments and the operation of certain controls and able to act as pilots assistant, i.e. fly straight and level and steer a course, plus gunnery in an emergency.	E

Fig. 18. *Matrix of non-pilot air crew trades introduced in July 1942 and the associated badges which were introduced in the following September (although, apart from the 'AG', these did not become widely available until 1943).*

(N.B. In this context the term 'wireless' refers specifically to W/T, while 'radio' is a euphemism for AI radar.)

Associated with the revision of air crew categories was the RAF's adoption of the 'PNB' concept, an idea which was already in use in America. Endorsed in May 1942, the policy was not actually applied until August but thereafter, only potential flight engineers and air gunners continued to be earmarked at the initial selection stage; the rest, unless there was some specific medical problem, were simply categorised as PNB, i.e. as potential pilots, navigators or air bombers.[29A]

It took more than a year for most of the ripples caused by these changes to die away, not least because wartime conditions created a dynamic situation and changes continued to occur. For example, by early 1943 questions were being raised over the necessity for a flight engineer to be trained as a gunner. While it might be useful for him to be able to handle a turret or a beam-gun, it was argued that, in a combat or emergency situation, he would more than likely be fully occupied helping the pilot. The logic of this argument prevailed and, before the year was out, the formal gunnery course had been deleted from the flight engineer training sequence.

1942. New air crew categories – new badges

Two months after the revision of air crew categories had been announced the changes involved were highlighted by the authorisation of new air crew badges[30] (see Fig. 18). All of these were variations on the theme of the air gunners badge of 1939, the only difference being the monogram contained within the laurel wreath.

Under the new regulations the 'RO' badge and the flying 'O', both of which had been superseded by the 'N' wing, became redundant. Although it was now obsolete, the rules authorised the continued wearing of the flying 'O' (and the 'RO' badge) by personnel who had qualified for it 'but who were no longer available by reason of age, medical standard, or otherwise for posting for the duties of one of the new categories of air crew.' This provision permitted men who had flown as observers in WW I to retain their badges while serving with the RAF (see pages 193–195) in other capacities during WW II, this having been legislated for as early as September 1939 when large numbers of veterans had signed on again.[31]

While it was plainly intended that anyone who was currently engaged on flying duties should be wearing a current badge, this rule proved to be almost impossible to enforce. By 1942 many observers had logged a considerable amount of operational flying time and some of them felt a deep attachment to their battle-stained badges. As a result, substantial numbers of, what were now, navigators defied authority by declining to replace their flying 'O's with the new-fangled 'N'. The waters were muddied further by the fact that 'B' badges had not yet been introduced, when the category of air bomber had been instituted. In anticipation of the graduation of the first home-grown batch of air bombers from Millom on 3 August, advice was sought as to what kind of badge they should be presented with. The only option at the time was the flying 'O' and this was notified to all concerned, including the Canadian training schools, on 29 July.[32] Few, if any, air bombers will have flown on operations before the 'B' badge became available but, even so, many of them proved to be reluctant to trade in the badges that they had been awarded on their graduation parades.

Something similar had already occurred in the context of observers being trained in the USA under a commercial arrangement with Pan American Airways (see pages 172–173). Because this course covered only navigation, its graduates left Miami still as aircraftmen and without badges, pending further training in bombing and gunnery. In view of the anticipated introduction of the category of the pure navigator, however, it was arguable that these men could now be regarded as being fully qualified against the more sharply focused requirements of the new trade. On 10 June the RAF Delegation in Washington signalled the Air Ministry to ask whether future graduates from Miami would be classified as navigators.[33] The Air Ministry sent a holding reply to the effect that they were not really sure but, in the meantime, authorising the award of a flying 'O'. Since the Miami men were to be awarded their badges, it followed that they should also be given their three stripes and Washington sought confirmation of this on the 13th.

[29A] AIR29/603. All Aviation Candidate Selection Boards were instructed to adopt the new procedure with immediate effect on the authority of Air Ministry letter A.372400/42/P.7 of 9 August 1942.
[30] AMO A.1019/42 of 17 September.
[31] AMO A.402/39 of 28 September.

[32] AIR 2/8369. This question was raised by DDTArm in a memo of 25 July 1942, the answer being contained in Air Ministry signal PX6112 of 29 July.
[33] *Ibid.* The correspondence on this topic, six signals released between 10 and 18 June 1942, is contained on this file.

It would seem that the author of the first response had exceeded his authority. On the grounds that these American-trained personnel still could not be regarded as being fully qualified, even against the revised RAF requirements, London's second signal vetoed the award of sergeant rank and withdrew the right to wear a badge. The denial of sergeant rank was not a problem but, having already passed on the good news about badges to Miami, the reversal of the first decision was extremely embarrassing to the staffs in Washington who pleaded for the original ruling to be reinstated.

The Air Ministry acceded to this request on the clear understanding that the badge would be withdrawn if the wearer were to fail any of the subsequent courses that he was required to attend. Thus, for a time, the RAF was obliged to live with the anomaly of part-trained LACs already sporting flying 'O's while attending their post-USA courses in the UK. These men would eventually graduate as navigators (or possibly air bombers) but, since they had once worn an 'O', it is quite likely that some of them continued to do so.

In the event, the problem of inappropriate badges was to drag on for many months, because, although the Order which had introduced the 'N' and 'B' (and the 'E') had been published in September, stocks of these emblems were not actually available. As a result, it is known that newly qualified navigators were still being presented with obsolete flying 'O's well into 1943. These men should all have swapped their badges once the new patterns became available but, like the early air bombers, many of them were determined to hang on to the badge they had been presented with on graduation.

Nevertheless, by 1944 ample supplies of all of the correct badges were readily available and there was no real excuse for anyone to be wearing the wrong pattern. In October of that year, therefore, the rules governing the wearing of badges, both current and obsolete, as enshrined within King's Regulations, were restated.[34] While everyone was aware of 'KRs', of course, they were hardly bedtime reading, which is why significant changes were always reflected in an Air Ministry Order, which everyone was supposed to see. In this case the Order had been published in the previous June; it read:[35]

> 'Members of aircrews, irrespective of their having qualified at some time for more than one of the air crew badges, are not in any circumstances to wear an air crew badge other then that appropriate to the particular air crew duty in which they are categorised or mustered. An officer, on ceasing to be employed on air crew duties, and an airman, on being remustered out of air crew category, may elect to wear any one of the badges for which he may have qualified.'

This could hardly have been clearer. Moreover, this was not a new rule; it merely reinforced the regulations which had been in place since 1940 (see Chapter 19, Note 11). There could now be no doubt whatsoever that, since the category of observer no longer existed, no one being employed on flying duties was entitled to wear a flying 'O'. It was all to no avail. People who had been awarded a flying 'O' since the outbreak of war (or earlier[36] – and perhaps even some of those who had not) were determined to show that they were old hands. This venerable badge continued to be worn, quite illegally throughout the war and well into the 1960s.[37]

As previously noted (see page 147), the initial attempt to introduce a distinguishing 'FE' emblem for flight engineers had been frustrated and they had been obliged to masquerade as air gunners. This decision had been contested, however, and a campaign for a dedicated flight engineers badge had rumbled on into 1942, being given added impetus by the precedent set by the introduction of the 'RO' badge. Exactly what happened next is a little obscure, but when a general revision of their conditions of service was published in March 1942 this contained a reference to 'the flight engineer's badge.'[38] Was this the 'AG', which *was* the badge authorised for flight engineers at the time, or was it an oblique reference to the possibility of a dedicated badge being introduced?

It has been suggested that the staffs at Coastal and Bomber Commands had submitted a case for a new badge; that the submission had been approved, but that this approval had subsequently been withdrawn.[39] In any event, as early as July – two months before a dedicated badge was officially introduced – individual flight engineers were reportedly being locally authorised to unpick the 'AG' lettering on their gunners badges and re-embroider them with an 'FE'.[40] Another possible source of 'FE' badges could have been the RCAF, which *may* have introduced a single-winged 'FE' for the benefit of Canadian flight engineers being trained in the UK. If this did happen, however, these badges were certainly unofficial.[41] Before long some of the more enterprising haberdashers and military tailors had begun to manufacture and lay-in stocks of (approximately) RAF-pattern 'FE' badges. All of these emblems were illegal, of course, until the new range of air crew badges was finally introduced in September. Unfortunately, when that did happen, the officially sanctioned monogram for flight engineers turned out to be a simple 'E', rather than the anticipated 'FE'!

To begin with, Service channels were unable to provide the appropriate emblem so, eager to replace their inappropriate gunners badges, many flight engineers elected to obtain their own. Since commercially manufactured 'E's (and 'FE's?) were relatively easy to find, a variety of non-standard styles became commonplace until 1943 when the supply system finally caught up. By this time, of course, as with the obsolete flying 'O', the illegal 'FE' had earned its battle honours and those who had survived a tour of operations wearing one were reluctant to give them up. Examples of illicit engineer's emblems were still being worn, very proudly, in the late 1950s.

[34]KR 198 as amended in October 1944.
[35]AMO A.512/44 of 8 June.
[36]At the time of writing, QR 206(3) of the latest (fifth) edition of Queens Regulations, still provides specific authority for any veterans who qualified for a flying 'O' before September 1939 to continue to wear it.

[37]Wartime photographs of individuals wearing observers badges long after they had been superseded are commonplace. For instance, opposite page 152 of A. Maitland's *Through the Bombsight*, there is a photograph of eight (seven RAF and one RAAF) visual bomb aimers of No 7 (Pathfinder) Sqn taken in April 1945. All of the RAF men, including Maitland, are wearing flying 'O's. By his own account, Maitland was not awarded his air crew badge until October 1942, a month after the flying 'O' had been officially declared redundant. It is quite possible that, purely as an interim measure, he may actually have been presented with an 'O' on graduation, but this should have been replaced as soon as stocks of 'B's became available. Whether the other personalities in the photograph had ever been entitled to their 'O's has not been established. Even if they had, however, there can be no doubt that none of them should have been wearing a flying 'O' while serving on a squadron in 1945. But these miscreants were not alone.
[38]AMO A.262/42 of 19 March.
[39]For a more detailed account of the confusion surrounding the introduction of an appropriate badge for flight engineers; see Stringman, *op. cit.*
[40]Stringman, *op. cit.*
[41]For a brief summary of the evolution of non-pilot badges in the RCAF (and other Commonwealth air forces), see Chapter 23, Note 52.

1942. Controversy over the design of air crew badges

While the new styles of badge had caused some minor practical problems, these paled into insignificance when compared to the controversy which had preceded their introduction. When the revised composition of bomber crews had been under discussion in March 1942, it had been proposed, by CAS himself, that all air crew 'should wear a double wing similar to that worn by pilots' with an appropriate distinguishing mark to indicate the function of the wearer.[42]

Ostensibly, Sir Charles Portal made this proposal because there was some concern that the public did not fully appreciate the significance of single-winged badges. This, it was thought, might be having an adverse effect, both on recruiting and on the morale of those who were obliged to wear them. It is tempting to speculate, however, that Sir Charles might also still have been smarting from a sense of injustice at having been obliged to begin his own flying career by being shot at while wearing only 'half a badge'. Whatever the reason, it was agreed that his idea warranted deeper consideration. This task fell to AMP, Air Mshl P. Babington, who wrote to the AOCinCs of the five UK-based flying commands, seeking their reactions to the idea of twin-wings for all and advising them of the likely introduction of the extended and revised range of air crew categories, which were then still in the planning stage.

Only Bomber Command felt able to give any measure of support to the proposal, suggesting a twin-winged design, smaller then the pilots badge, and of a different colour, and featuring appropriate emblems, such as crossed spanners for flight engineers. Otherwise the response was overwhelmingly negative, and occasionally quite outspoken. At Fighter Command, Sholto Douglas was 'strongly opposed to ... any change in the present design of badge.' Douglas had canvassed the opinion of his Group Commanders and they too were opposed, AOC 10 Gp, AVM A.H. Orlebar, considering it 'a great pity to change the flying badge', while AOC 11 Gp, AVM T.L. Leigh-Mallory, thought that 'it would be resented by pilots' and AOC 12 Gp, AVM R.E. Saul, believed that 'the pilots badge should stand out above all others.'

Sir William Welsh at Flying Training Command provided a lengthy and considered response, although he too rejected the idea of a double wing. He went further and suggested that, apart from possibly changing the present 'O' to an 'N' there was little justification for any further meddling. In fact, he questioned the need for some crew members to have a badge at all, likening the flight engineer to the many drogue operators at his Air Gunners Schools, each of whom was flying up to 60 hours per month without having to be given a badge of any kind.[43] Coastal Command's Sir Philip Joubert de la Ferté was deeply affronted by the proposal, declaring that he had the 'strongest objection to non-pilots being given a two-winged badge' and ending his letter, 'Yours, at a very high temperature'.

AMP reported his findings to the Air Council who discussed the matter on 28 April. Undeterred by the generally negative reaction and mindful that, since Bomber Command was the major employer of non-pilots, its response probably counted for more than the others, CAS directed that the AOCinCs should be asked to reconsider.[44] After some revision, to reflect Bomber Command's specific suggestions, Babington circulated the proposal again. This time some of the AOCinCs seem to have been distinctly put out, presumably at having had their opinions ignored. Whatever the reason, Babington's second trawl certainly provoked some intemperate language. Air Mshl Sir Arthur Barratt at Army Co-operation Command deplored the fact that the pilots badge was to be 'prostituted' but, if it was, he thought that any symbols devised to identify trades would be too small and that it would be better to use a simple letter. Joubert de la Ferté excelled himself, restating his 'strongest objection' to anybody but pilots wearing double-wings and protesting his resentment that 'Bomber Command should be forcing (*the idea*) upon us because it happens to suit their book'. As to what sort of symbol should be incorporated in the design, Sir Philip suggested 'a penguin.'[45]

This second wave of rejections settled the matter and by 19 May the Air Council had virtually agreed to drop the twin-wing idea, this decision being confirmed at a meeting held on 2 June.[46]

1942. The new air crew categories – were they 'new' and were they necessary?

Since the New Deal and its aftermath had ultimately led to the demise of the observer, it is worth considering just how 'new' all of this had really been and reflecting on the necessity for its introduction. There can be little doubt that all Garrod's reforms, particularly the extension of training time, had been needed. It is unlikely, however, that many (any?) of the RAF's senior officers will have appreciated that what the subsequent redefinition of air crew categories had done, in effect, was to implement a scheme that had been devised by Sefton Brancker as long ago as 1918 (see page 100).

So, if Brancker had already solved the problem, why did it have to be solved again in 1942? The answer clearly lies in Trenchard's decision to dispense with professional non-pilot air crew in 1919. With hindsight there can be little doubt that this had been a serious error. One of its more unfortunate consequences was that it had obliged the RAF to go over so much ground again. During WW I it had taken three years (1915–18) for the activities of non-pilot air crew to diversify to the extent that they needed to be recognised as separate trades. Surprisingly, since it had not had to cope simultaneously with having to develop *every* aspect of military aviation from scratch, as its predecessors in the RFC and RNAS had had to do, it took the RAF *another* three years (1939–42) to do more or less the same thing in WW II. This had clearly been lost or, more precisely, wasted time.

[42]AIR2/2662. See Note 9.
[43]AIR2/5837. Air Mshl Babington's letter of 30 March 1942 and the various responses it attracted are all on this file.
[44]AIR6/73. Minutes of Air Council Meeting 8(42) held on 28 April 1942.
[45]AIR2/5837. Air Mshl Babington's letter of 28 April 1942 and the various responses it attracted are all on this file.
[46]AIR6/73. Minutes of an Air Council Meeting 10(42) held on 2 June 1942.

Chapter 22

The wartime evolution of non-pilot air crew training

The RAF had gone to war with just three non-pilot air crew trades, observers, wireless operators (air crew) and air gunners. None of them were commissioned; many were mere aircraftmen. Three years later there were eleven recognised categories and sub-categories (thirteen by 1945) and by then all qualified flying personnel were at least sergeants and very large numbers of them were officers. This remarkable transformation had been supported by a vastly expanded and far more capable training organisation. Some references to specific developments have already been made and others crop up in later chapters but to attempt to describe all the changes which occurred within the wartime air crew training system in any detail would require a book to itself. Nevertheless, while it can hardly be described as comprehensive, the following outline of its evolution may be helpful.

Fig. 19 provides an impression of the main organisational changes that were involved but this too needs to be treated with circumspection, as it features only the mainstream training units, and only those which operated in the UK. Furthermore, while the diagram does provide a reasonable indication of when changes occurred, they were not always implemented instantly. A spate of redesignations, the conversion of B&GSs into AGSs and AOSs for instance, could take a year or more to complete. It will be appreciated, therefore, that the dates shown are notional and do not relate to individual units of which some 300 are represented within the diagram.[1]

The award of an air crew badge, of any description, was normally conditional upon the recipient's having completed a prescribed series of courses, the associated ceremony at the end of the sequence representing a kind of 'right of passage'. Nevertheless, it should be appreciated that, under certain circumstances, it was possible to acquire the right to wear a badge by other means. By the end of 1941, for instance, there had been several instances of officers and airmen, untrained in flying duties, having to be pressed into service to meet urgent operational requirements, one example being the photographic tradesmen who flew as camera operators on reconnaissance missions over Burma and elsewhere. If this situation prevailed for long it was only reasonable for the air force to accept that these men had effectively become air crew by default.

This sort of thing had occurred during WW I, when deserving cases had been granted the right to wear an observers badge on the authority of the GOC (see, for example, page 88). A similar arrangement was clearly required during WW II. From the beginning of 1942, therefore, AOCs were officially authorised to award an appropriate air crew badge to anyone whose CO was prepared to certify that he had passed an OTU course (or could pass the associated tests) and had logged a minimum of thirty hours of operational flying time accumulated in the course of at least ten sorties.[2]

This regulation, which remained in force for the rest of the war, was also invoked to permit Army officers who flew with the RAF as air gunners to wear an 'AG' badge.[3] This was a temporary concession, however, and the badge had (was supposed) to be removed when the attachment ceased.

Selection and initial training

The point should perhaps be made that in RAF parlance the term 'initial' implied (and it still does) the introductory phase of training, i.e. the period during which a civilian is transformed into something that bears a passing resemblance to a military man. Some professional instruction, possibly including an introduction to the handling of small arms, may be included but the essential content of initial training involves: the issue of a uniform; a sensible haircut; a 'survival kit' of Service procedures and Air Force Law, sufficient to give a tyro a better then even chance of keeping out of trouble; 'jabs' to immunise the subject against most of the diseases known to the medical profession; instruction on the perils of consorting with the opposite sex, including horrifyingly graphic illustrations of the effects of VD; some basic instruction in first aid and personal hygiene; and plenty of drill, physical training and route marches, mostly accompanied by a great deal of shouting. Depending upon circumstances, the duration of this phase has varied over time from a couple of weeks to several months.

Most civilians who had enlisted in the air force during the immediate pre-war period had received their military indoctrination courtesy of one of the RAF's, by then three, Recruit Depots. Following general mobilisation, in order to cope with the sudden and massive influx of volunteers and conscripts, not to mention the thousands of reservists who were called to the colours, many more recruit training units had to be opened.[4] While these 'boot camp' facilities were adequate for the majority of ground tradesmen, it was considered necessary to provide something a little more sophisticated for potential air crew. At

[1]Readers wishing to study the intricacies of the wartime training system in greater depth are referred to *Royal Air Force Flying Training and Support Units* (1997), co-authored by R. Sturtivant, J. Hamlin and J. Halley. This book is not concerned with training policy, philosophy or techniques but it does provide key details of the date and place of formation, subsequent movements and ultimate disbandment of practically every training unit ever sponsored by the RFC/RAF.

[2]AMO A.89/42 of 29 January.

[3]A specific instance of this is cited by Mike Henry in his book, *Air Gunner* (1964). He was a Capt J.W. Casserley (Henry calls him Cassidy) of the Royal Berkshire Regt who flew as a gunner in Bostons of No 137 Wg, to which he was attached as an ALO (Army Liaison Officer) between 31 March 1944 and 8 March 1945.

[4]To supplement the Recruit Depots at Uxbridge and Cardington, a third had been opened at Padgate in April 1939. Another was set up at Bridgnorth in October, by which time all four had been redesignated as Receiving Centres. In January 1940 they became Recruit Centres and this title remained in use for the expanding network of such units throughout the remainder of the war.

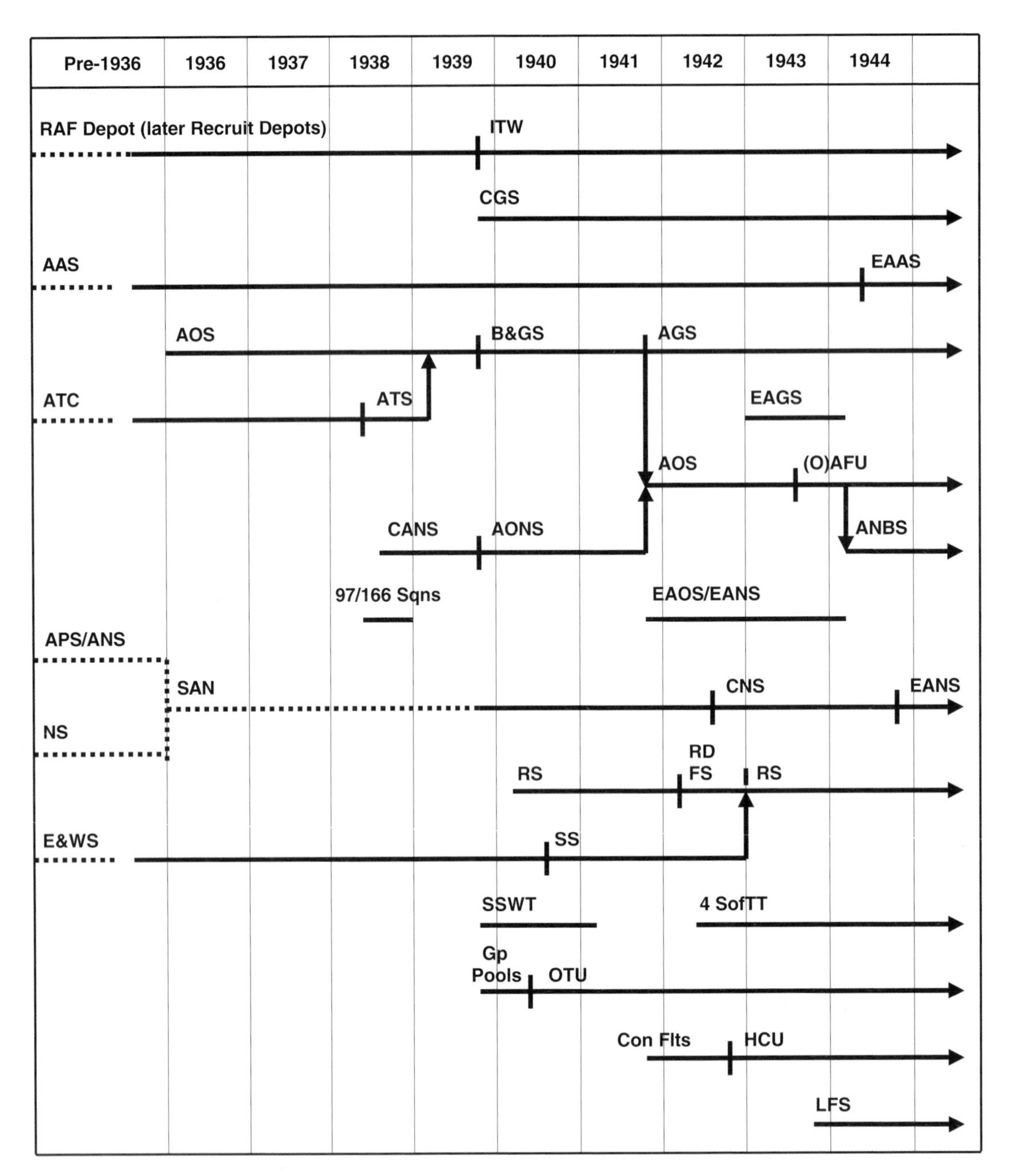

AAS – Air Armament Schools; **AGS** – Air Gunners Schools; **ANBS** – Air Navigation and Bombing School; **ANS** – Air Navigation School; **AONS** – Air Observers Navigation Schools; **AOS** – Air Observers Schools; **APS** – Air Pilotage School; **ATC** – Armament Training Camps; **ATS** – Armament Training Stations; **B&GS** – Bombing and Gunnery Schools; **CANS** – Civilian Air Navigation Schools; **CGS** – Central Gunnery School; **CNS** – Central Navigation School; **Con Flts** – (Heavy Bomber) Conversion Flights; **E&WS** – Electrical and Wireless Schools; **EAAS** – Empire Air Armament School; **EAGS** – Elementary Air Gunners School; **EANS** – Empire Air Navigation School; **EAOS/EANS** – Elementary Air Observers (later Navigation) School; **HCU** – Heavy Conversion Units; **ITW** – Initial Training Wings; **LFS** – Lancaster Finishing Schools; **NS** – Navigation School; **(O)AFU** – (Observers) Advanced Flying Units; **OTU** – Operational Training Units; **RDFS** – Radio Direction Finding Schools; **RS** – Radio Schools; **SofTT** – School of Technical Training; **SAN** – School of Air Navigation; **SS** – Signals Schools; **SSWT** – Supplementary Schools of Wireless Telegraphy.

Fig. 19. Schematic of the evolution of UK-based, mainstream training units dealing with non-pilot air crew during WW II.

the suggestion of Brig-Gen Critchley (see Chapter 8, Note 27) some consideration was given to recreating, at Hastings, what amounted to the RFC/RAF Cadet Brigade which had operated there in 1917–18.[4A] This is more or less what eventually happened, except that it was decided to set up a network of regional units, rather than putting all of the RAF's eggs in one basket.

[4A]On the outbreak of war Critchley was commissioned into the RAFVR as a flying officer. Promptly promoted to acting air commodore, he was appointed AOC No 54 Gp and as such he designed and created the wartime initial training system which he continued to supervise until 1943.

The first dedicated unit, No 1 Initial Training School, opened at Cambridge on 7 September 1939, only to be restyled No 1 Initial Training Wing (ITW) on the 15th. Three more ITWs had opened before the end of the year but they were unable to handle all the volunteers who were flooding to the recruiting offices and it soon became necessary to introduce 'deferred service'. That is to say that, once they had been accepted by an Aviation Candidates Selection Board (ACSB), recruits would be sent home to await call-up. Depending upon the capacity of the system and the demand for manpower, a volunteer would often have to wait six months and later in the war it could be a year or more. The first eight ACSBs had been set up at Uxbridge (four), Cardington (two) and Padgate (two) on the declaration of war. Thereafter they proliferated steadily so that by the summer of 1941 there were thirty of them, operating in clusters centred on Oxford, Birmingham, Edinburgh, Blackpool, Penarth, Weston-super-Mare (later Doncaster), Cardington and London (Euston).

To smooth out fluctuations in the intake a Receiving Wing was opened at Babbacombe in July 1940, a second being established at Stratford-on-Avon in November. These two units acted as pools from which the various ITWs were fed. Until mid-1941 they were the first port of call for prospective air crew on joining the Service and it was there that they were medically examined (again, having already been given a cursory once over at the ACSB), inoculated, kitted out and introduced to drill and PT.

On 14 July 1941 the two Receiving Wings were converted into additional ITWs, their original functions having been taken over by the Air Crew Reception Centre (ACRC) which had been set up in London in the previous month.[5] Occupying a substantial number of requisitioned properties in St Johns Wood in the vicinity of Regents Park (where meals were taken in the cafeteria of the London Zoo), and including Lords Cricket Ground, the notional capacity of the ACRC was 5100 men, the intake rate being 1700 per week. These figures suggest that a cadet could expect to spend three weeks at the ACRC before being allocated to an ITW. In practice, however, some people were held there for as long as three months.

For a time, cadets who had failed at some stage of training returned to the ACRC to be reselected for some other category. By the autumn of 1941, however, the entire capacity of the ACRC was occupied by new recruits so it became necessary to make other arrangements for reselection. This requirement was satisfied on 6 October by the establishment of a dedicated unit. Set up in Brighton, it was initially assigned the rather depressing title of the Air Crew Disposal Wing.

To begin with all pilots, observers and air gunners were expected to attend an ITW course, although there was insufficient capacity to cater for the latter until April 1940 when the first batch reported to No 4 ITW at Bexhill. As described below, there was no provision for WOps (or flight engineers) to pass through an ITW until as late as 1943. By that time there had been a major change in the structure of the system due to the introduction of the PNB scheme in 1942. Prior to this a cadet had been earmarked for a particular air crew category at the Receiving Wing/ACRC stage, and there had been a tendency for individual ITWs to specialise. Under the new scheme the initial selection was carried out by the ACSBs, but only on the coarse basis of PNB, flight engineer or air gunner, the streaming of PNB candidates into specific categories being postponed to the end of a common ITW phase.

On passing their ITW courses, cadets moved on to begin their professional flying training. Until the middle of 1940 this would have been done in the UK but from then on pilots and observers (later navigators and air bombers) were increasingly likely to be sent abroad. Most of them went via No 1 Personnel Distribution Centre (PDC), initially at Uxbridge and later at West Kirby, until August 1941 when the Air Crew Despatch Centre (ACDC) was set up at Heaton Park (Manchester) specifically to handle this outbound traffic. By early 1942 overseas training had become the norm, cadets routinely proceeding from their ITWs to the ACDC where they were assembled into drafts and assigned to convoys bound for Canada or South Africa. Between September 1941 and October 1945 Heaton Park's intake would total 134 490 cadets[5A] but it could accommodate only 2000 or so at a time. It often had many more than that on its books and when the ACDC was operating to capacity, cadets awaiting a passage overseas could find themselves detached elsewhere to act as unskilled labour, MT drivers, or, at harvest time, even being put to work in the fields.

The problem of surplus cadets had first manifested itself at the ACRC in 1942. To handle the overspill until places could be found for them at ITWs, an Air Crew Camp was established at Ludlow. Opened in May, Ludlow was able to handle as many as 12 000 cadets at a time, providing organised activities in a healthy outdoor environment – a euphemism, some would have said, for hard labour, as the cadets were employed to dig the necessary drainage ditches and lay the foundations for such temporary buildings as were erected. Most of the accommodation was under canvas, however, leading to the camp's closure in October, although it reopened to provide similar facilities between May and October of 1943. By that time the bulge in the flow of cadets, which had been between the ACRC and the ITWs in 1942, had passed through the system so that it was now making itself felt between the ITWs and Heaton Park. As a result, many of those who were stuck at the ACDC awaiting passage abroad were sent to Ludlow. Ironically, many of these cadets turned out to be the same ones who had cooled their heels there a year before.

So far as navigators were concerned, an attempt was made to provide an alternative form of constructive occupation while Ludlow was unavailable during the winter of 1942/43. In September a Navigator Bomber Pool was set up in Hastings as a detachment of No 3 Personnel Reception Centre (PRC) at Bournemouth.[6] The idea was to take some of the cadets backed up at Heaton Park and provide them with some basic continuation training while waiting for their outbound passages. Unfortunately a six-aircraft hit-and-run raid by the *Luftwaffe* on 24 September killed three cadets and injured forty others so the unit (940 cadets and seventy-three staff) was promptly evacuated to Harrogate. On 11 November it returned to the south coast, taking up residence at Brighton where it remained until the re-opening of the Air Crew Camp permitted it to be disbanded on 31 May 1943, although training had ceased in mid-April.[7]

[5]Because the majority of wartime air crew entered the RAF via London, the unit concerned tends to be thought of as *the* ACRC. This actually was the case for a time but six others were to be established from 1943 onwards, leading to the allocation of numerical designations, the original unit in St Johns Wood becoming No 3 ACRC. Three of the additional ACRCs were set up in the UK, the others being in Algeria, Egypt and Palestine.

[5A]AIR29/477. Operations Record Book for the ACDC.

[6]If Heaton Park was the 'way out' for cadets leaving the UK, No 3 PRC at Bournemouth became the 'way back in' when they returned wearing their air crew badges. By mid-1941 the throughput was running at some 500 officers and 1500 NCOs (of all trades) per month and it stayed that way until October 1942 when the unit began to handle only Dominion personnel. This refinement was taken a stage further in May 1943 when it was redesignated as No 3 (RCAF) PRC after which it dealt exclusively with Canadians. At the same time similar independent provision was made for Australians and New Zealanders by the establishment of No 11 (RAAF) Personnel Disposal and Reception Centre (PDRC) and No 12 (RNZAF) PDRC; both were set up in Brighton, moving to Padgate in May 1944. For the remainder of the war, the majority of returning RAF air crew passed through Harrogate where No 7 PRC had been operating since 23 March 1942.

[7]In point of fact the unit had been divorced from No 3 PRC with effect from 3 November 1942 when it had been established in its own right at Harrogate as No 2 Navigator Bomber Pool. It retained this designation until it disbanded, suggesting that there may also have been a No 1 Pool, although, if there was, this writer has been unable to trace it.

By the time the unit closed the rolling programme provided a cadet, who was in residence for a month, with the following (hours): parades (36); drill (18); navigation (18); signals (18); law/admin (4); armament (4); swimming (9); arms drill (12); cinema (9); aircraft recognition (4); organised games (12); current affairs (4); geography (4); PT (12); first aid (4). Throughput between 3 November 1942 and 12 April 1943 had amounted to 3185 cadets.

For the first two years of the war the RAF had been able to recruit its personnel from the upper, i.e. the better educated, echelons of society. This was a finite resource, however, and by 1941 the Service was being obliged to lower its sights. This is not to say that the men coming forward in 1941 were lacking in enthusiasm, in aptitude or in intellect but it was clear that the national education system had failed to prepare them adequately. As a result an increasing proportion of cadets was experiencing difficulty with the more demanding academic aspects of flying training.

With the aim of reducing the wastage rate, an education test was introduced at the ACRC stage in June 1941. Those deemed to be in need of extra tuition were sent to Brighton where an Air Crew Training Wing (ACTW) was established to operate alongside the Disposal Wing and the Officers School (see below). In September 1942 these three units were reorganised to become component parts of the Air Crew Reselection and Training Centre.

The function of the Officers School, which had opened for business in May, was to provide an appropriate entry point into the Service for PNB candidates arriving from universities. The three pre-war University Air Squadrons (UAS) had been closed down in September 1939 but the Air Ministry later discovered that the War Office had continued to offer inducements to students undergoing higher education. In order to ensure that the RAF obtained its fair share of graduates, the UAS scheme was restarted in October 1940. In fact the system was considerably expanded so that by mid-1941 twenty universities had air squadrons, in addition to the pre-war units at Oxford, Cambridge and London, all of which had been re-established. Some of the standard academic university courses had been abbreviated, compared to peacetime practice, and the RAF sponsored its own 'University Short Course'.

The RAF's university courses were a combination of academic study and what amounted to ITW training, the latter being provided by the UAS of which all students were required to be a member. Little practical flying was involved, however, the immediate aim being to turn high grade material into potential officers, rather than to train aviators. While the ground instruction and exposure to Service procedures was deemed to be sufficient to permit a UAS graduate to by-pass the formal ITW phase, he still needed to be given some form of introduction to the 'real' air force, hence the need to spend three weeks at Brighton.

Six UASs were closed during 1943 and by the autumn of the following year the end of the war could be predicted with sufficient confidence for the RAF to conclude that anyone entering university from then on was unlikely to see active service. Furthermore, although the Air Ministry wished to offer graduates a full peacetime career, it was impossible to forecast how many might be needed. For these reasons the university intake was considerably reduced from October 1944 onwards. Nevertheless, more than 4500 prospective wartime aircrew joined the wartime RAFVR via the University Short Course scheme, the majority of these eventually being commissioned.

Meanwhile, during 1942 the numbers of ordinary entrants assessed as needing remedial training had increased to such an extent that the ACTW could no longer cope. To provide the necessary additional capacity the Air Ministry co-opted the assistance of a country-wide network of polytechnics and technical schools, institutes and colleges. This arrangement, the Preliminary Air Crew Training (PACT) scheme, came into being when the first four PACT Centres opened in March 1943, offering six-month courses.

By this time candidates were sitting their education tests at the ACSBs. Those who were considered satisfactory were sent home on deferred service to await call up, whereupon they reported to the ACRC for their three weeks of formal induction. Those assessed as being in need of further tuition were sent to the PACT Wing, which had been set up within the ACRC at Regents Park on 18 February 1943. This unit, which could handle up to 600 cadets at a time, served as a pool from which the PACT Centres could be fed.

For a while the Air Crew Reselection and Training Centre (which left Brighton for Eastchurch in May 1943 when it was restyled the Combined Reselection Centre) maintained its involvement in remedial training. By the summer, however, the civilian-based system was sufficiently well-established to permit the ACTW to be closed down on 8 August. By September there were twenty-one PACT Centres in operation, providing pre-ITW training for more than 3000 cadets.

By early 1943 the ITW system had hit its stride with each unit now handling a specific group or individual category of air crew broken down as PNB, WOp/AG, flight engineer and/or air gunner. Depending upon trade, courses lasted between six and twelve weeks (fourteen for Poles passing through their own school).[8] The syllabus content also varied, but in each case, while it still involved ample quantities of drill and PT, it always contained a good deal of very relevant basic instruction in airmanship, mathematics, meteorology, navigation, aero-engines and the theory of flight. This approach reflected Air Cdre Critchley's belief that, once they were engaged in practical flying training, cadets could become so preoccupied that they could think of little else. The aim of Critchley-style initial training, therefore, was to strengthen the body and hone its reflexes while filling the mind with academic knowledge to be exploited at a later stage. This philosophy had worked well during WW I and it proved to be equally effective in WW II.

By the end of 1943 there were twenty-three ITWs distributed between fifteen locations, this organisation being able to accommodate no fewer than 17 500 cadets at a time.[9] Having achieved such mammoth proportions, the training system had actually outgrown itself and, in line with a cutback in the BCATP programme (see below), there was a major rationalisation of initial training early in 1944, the number of wings being halved. Even this swingeing reduc-

[8]Prospective air crew, recruited from refugees or ground personnel already serving with the free Polish Air Force (which operated under the aegis of the RAF), were initially dealt with under quasi-national procedures at No 1 (Polish) FTS at Hucknall. To bring these arrangements in line with British practice, a dedicated Polish Squadron was formed within No 12 ITW at St Andrews on 9 August 1941. On 23 July 1942 this unit was hived off to be re-established at Brighton as an autonomous Polish ITW. It moved to Croughton on 31 May 1944, remaining there until it disbanded on 1 November 1945.

[9]To provide the necessary bed spaces, most ITWs were at seaside resorts to take advantage of the ready-made accommodation that could be obtained by requisitioning hotels. For the same reason, many of the Recruit Centres which provided induction and initial training facilities for non-aircrew airmen were also located in seaside towns, e.g. Morecombe, Weston-super-Mare, Whitley Bay, Blackpool, Skegness, Redcar, Great Yarmouth and so on.

tion was insufficient, however, and the system continued to contract so that by July only five wings remained in commission. Since responsibility for selection had been reassumed by the ACRC, each of the remaining ITWs was now dedicated to a separate air crew category.[10] The reduction in intake also relieved the pressure on the PACT scheme which until then had had to be restricted to direct entrant PNB candidates. From April 1944 it became possible to extend these facilities to prospective air crew of all categories.

Despite its marked reduction from the spring of 1944 onwards, the residual intake still turned out to exceed the requirement for air crew and there was a further major cutback in the autumn. By the end of the year it had become possible to process practically all cadets, of all categories, through a single ITW, No 50, at Bridgnorth, although Usworth's No 60 ITW did not close until mid-1945 and the Polish and French ITWs, both of which had escaped the previous cull, continued to function in isolation, at Croughton and Filey (later Stormy Down) respectively. The reduction in numbers also meant that selection standards could be raised, rendering the PACT scheme superfluous. The PACT Centres began to shut down in August, the last two closing in February 1945.

There is one other aspect of the selection and initial training system which should be mentioned – grading. In 1941 it was decided to send candidates, earmarked by the ACSBs as pilots, to an Elementary Flying Training School for initial handling tests to confirm that they had the anticipated potential. Since it permitted weak prospects to be weeded out at an early stage, this approach saved a great deal of wasted time and effort, reduced the failure rate in formal training and enabled the Service to redirect cadets into a more appropriate category. When the PNB concept was introduced in 1942, grading became an integral part of the selection process, all PNB candidates being given the opportunity to demonstrate their potential as pilots at the end of a common ITW course.[11]

Grading (which generally involved about twelve hours of flying, during which a prospective pilot could normally expect to go solo) continued to be employed for the remainder of the war, although it subsequently had to be rescheduled so that it took place earlier within the selection and training sequence. This was because, as noted above, from mid-1944 onwards each ITW offered a course tailored to the needs of only one category of air crew. As a result, it became necessary to identify the specific allocation of a PNB cadet immediately after the ACRC stage so that he could be posted to the appropriate ITW.

UK-based observer training to 1942

The state of observer training immediately prior to the outbreak of war was reviewed on pages 136–138. Internal recruiting of observers ceased abruptly in September 1939 and by the end of the following month the last of the peacetime Service intakes had passed through the system. Thereafter the role of the Service-run Air Observer Schools was confined to providing armament training for direct entrant air gunners and for direct entrant observers who had previously been trained in navigation by the civilian-run schools. To reflect this change in function, during November and December, seven AOSs were redesignated as Bombing and Gunnery Schools (B&GS).

At much the same time, and as part of the same rationalisation process, the ten Civilian Air Navigation Schools were restyled as Air Observers Navigation Schools (AONS), an eleventh being opened on 20 November. Despite their new titles, these units continued to be commercially operated, although reports of civilian instructors experiencing disciplinary problems with uniformed students led to most of the instructional staff being mobilised and commissioned into the RAFVR on 1 January 1940.[12]

During the first year of the war there was constant dissatisfaction with the capabilities of observers and, on more than one occasion, Bomber Command directly challenged the wisdom of a policy which had given them responsibility for navigation. The criticism of observers was undoubtedly justified, but the Air Ministry took the view that it was not the policy that was at fault so much as its application. The process whereby observers were selected was considered to be insufficiently rigorous and their subsequent training was ill-designed, too short and inadequately carried out. The efficiency of the civilian schools was also being viewed with some scepticism, as it was suspected that there might well be a conflict of interest between commercial considerations and the Service's needs. There were, for instance, misgivings over Scottish Aviation's use of three large Fokker airliners at its school at Prestwick. These 'flying classrooms' permitted pupils to be flown in batches of up to thirty at a time, which was plainly a very cost-effective way of providing each individual with his contracted allocation of flying hours. On the other hand, it is doubtful whether many of them gained very much from the experience.

As an experiment, a course, combining navigation and armament training, was tried at the Service-run No 2 B&GS at Millom early in 1941. This was considered to have been a success in that it had produced a better product in less time, while avoiding the more unsatisfactory aspects of using a civilian organisation. Navigation was progressively introduced at other selected B&GSs during the summer, resulting in their being redesignated (again) as a new generation of Air Observers Schools (AOS). With the transfer of navigation training to Service-run schools, the commercial enterprises gradually closed down, the last of them (No 6 AONS at Staverton) on 17 January 1942.

Although civilian organisations no longer handled instruction, it is worth noting that, for a time, several of the new AOSs continued to rely heavily on commercial concerns, No 1 AOS

[10]The five ITWs which remained in use for most of 1944 were:

Unit	Location	Category	Capacity	Length
No 40 ITW	Newquay	Pilot	1150	8 weeks
No 50 ITW	Bridgnorth	Nav/Air Bomber	825/425	8 weeks
No 70 ITW	Bridlington	WOp (Air)	1800	6 weeks
No 80 ITW	Bridgnorth	Air Gunner	1200	6 weeks
No 90 ITW	Cranage	Flight Engineer	1100	6 weeks

[11]While the intention was clearly to ensure that square pegs were slotted into square holes, the 'exigencies of the Service' always took precedence. Thus, despite the fact that a cadet might have demonstrated an adequate level of natural piloting ability, he could still find himself earmarked as, say, an air bomber if there was a priority demand for air bombers at the time.

[12]This innovation led to the creation of a discrete Navigation Instructors element within the GD branch, this having its own section within the Air Force List. A chronic shortage of instructors meant that these men had to be screened from operational service until the manpower situation eased but AMO A.658/43, of 8 July, eventually offered any appropriately qualified/experienced instructors who were able to satisfy the age and fitness requirements the opportunity to fly as navigators or navigators (B).

at Wigtown, for example, being supported by Airwork. Unfortunately, experience soon showed that there were many points at which friction could occur. Disputes most commonly arose in the areas of discipline, working hours, restrictive practices and pay, in all of which the conditions of servicemen compared unfavourably to those of civilians.

It was eventually concluded that a training unit could be either civilian- or Service-manned but that joint-manning was impractical. Since the RAF continued to harbour reservations over the quality of civilian instruction, there was little option but to terminate civilian involvement. This seems to have been a popular decision. When Marshalls gave up its catering and maintenance contracts at Bobbington on 31 June 1942, for instance, No 3 AOS recorded that 'the changeover to Service personnel has caused great satisfaction among the personnel on the station.'[13]

By mid-1941 a substantial flow of overseas-trained observers had begun to arrive in the UK. This relieved the previous shortage and the improved manning situation made it possible to consider lengthening the time devoted to training. As early as May 1941 Gp Capt L.K. Barnes had proposed the insertion of a preparatory phase of academic training for observers between completion of their ITW course and reporting to an AOS. This was finally achieved in October when No 1 Elementary Air Observers (later Navigation) School opened at Eastbourne.[14] This unit, which moved to Bridgnorth a year later, provided six weeks of ground-based instruction in subjects related to flying in general and navigation in particular and it continued to do so until early 1944.

The creation of the Empire Air Training Scheme

The history of the EATS, has been sufficiently well documented elsewhere in the past to permit a brief summary to suffice here.[15] The possibility of carrying out flying training in Canada (and elsewhere) had been proposed as early as 1936 in a memorandum submitted to the Director of Training, Air Cdre A. Tedder, by a member of his staff, Gp Capt R. Leckie. Little tangible progress had been made before war was declared but in October 1939 a British delegation, led by Lord Riverdale, set off for Ottawa. There it was to meet Canadian, Australian and New Zealand representatives with a view to setting up a joint system to train British and Dominion air crew.

The training scheme which had operated in Canada during WW I had been a British-run affair and, since London suspected that the tiny RCAF lacked both the expertise and the organisational capacity to handle the task, it was envisaged that any similar scheme would also have to be supervised by the RAF. Despite Britain's wish to control affairs, however, it was hoped that the other governments could be persuaded to underwrite a substantial proportion of the cost. Such an attitude failed to take sufficient account of 'colonial' sensitivities, however, the point being that Dominions were *not* colonies.

Since Canada (unlike Australia) had not formed an air force of its own during WW I, all Canadian airmen (and New Zealanders and many Australians) had served in British uniform. As a result, Canada felt that her substantial contribution to the first war in the air had been largely overlooked and that her sovereignty had in some way been impugned. This still smarted and in 1939 Prime Minister Mackenzie King was determined to ensure that this should not happen again. Australia and New Zealand were in full sympathy with Canada over the question of national recognition. Furthermore, while the RAAF and RNZAF were content to take advantage of the potential offered by the proposed joint scheme, they fully intended to sustain and expand their own independent training organisations at the same time.

After lengthy negotiations, the Riverdale Agreement was eventually signed on 17 December, bringing into being, what was initially referred to (at least by the British) as, the Dominion Air Training Scheme.[16] The British had been obliged to suppress their reservations over the perceived limitations of the Canadians and had agreed to the control of (almost) all training activities in Canada being exercised by the RCAF. For its part, Canada's residual mistrust of British ambitions was overcome by the admirable expedient of seconding Air Cdre Leckie, a Canadian serving with the RAF, to Ottawa where he was given a seat on the Canadian Air Council from where he was able to direct operations.[17]

The negotiations had also revealed significant practical difficulties in ensuring that the efforts being made by the various national authorities would be adequately recognised. This aspect was addressed by Article 15 of the Riverdale Agreement but the sensitivities involved were such that it took until January 1941 to decide exactly how its provisions were to be implemented. In brief, in addition to expanding, manning and operating their own national air forces, the Dominions undertook to raise entire squadrons to serve under RAF command.[18] They also agreed to furnish additional trained air crew to fly with British units but, rather than being subsumed into an 'imperial' air force, Australians, Canadians and New Zealanders who served with the RAF would do so as RAAF, RCAF and RNZAF personnel.[19]

It is interesting to note that in January 1940 the Secretary of State for Air, Sir Kingsley Wood, appointed a Standing Committee of the Air Council, which he was to chair himself, to be known as the Empire Air Training Scheme Committee. Its terms of reference began as follows: 'To keep in touch with developments of the Dominion Air Training Scheme….'[20]

[13]AIR29/544. Operations Record Book for No 3 AOS.

[14]Although this unit was designated as No 1 Elementary Air Navigation School, there never was a No 2. The syllabus covered basic navigation theory, plotting practice (i.e. 'dry swims'), signals, meteorology, armament and aircraft recognition. The student population stood at more than 1000 cadets for most of 1942, but it had dwindled to 325 by the end of the following year. This sort of pre-training was eventually transferred to the collocated No 50 ITW and the elementary navigation school ceased trading on 28 January 1944.

[15]For additional detail, and atmospheric anecdote, see, for instance, *Aircrew Unlimited* by John Golley and *By the Seat of Your Pants* by Hugh Morgan; for a particularly Canadian perspective, try *Wings for Victory* by Spencer Dunmore, *The Plan* by James Williams and *Aerodrome of Democracy* by F. J. Hatch.

[16]AIR8/3160 contains a copy of the Report (to the UK Government) on the Riverdale Mission to Canada, dated December 1939, which uses the term Dominion Air Training Scheme, plus a copy of the Agreement itself, which does not. In fact, while the Agreement outlines in some detail the obligations accepted by each of the four participating governments, it is interesting to note that it diplomatically avoids assigning any form of title to these arrangements. Lord Riverdale of Sheffield was, incidentally, the erstwhile Sir Arthur Balfour.

[17]After flying with the RNAS/RAF during WW I, Robert Leckie had returned to Canada but, like several of his compatriots, he had subsequently rejoined the RAF. He was commanding the RAF in Malta when he was posted to Canada in 1940 to become, in effect, the director of the EATS. In 1942, by then an air vice-marshal, Leckie was transferred to the RCAF.

[18]There would eventually be more than seventy of these so-called Article XV squadrons.

[19]This provision applied only to Australians, Canadians and New Zealanders enrolled in their 'own' air forces. It did not apply to those who had elected to enlist directly in the RAF.

[20]AIR2/1360. Office Memorandum 15/40 dated 23 January 1940 announced the setting up of the EATS Committee.

Despite the evident uncertainty as to the precise terminology to be used, this committee ensured that the EATS label soon became firmly affixed within RAF circles. This was not so elsewhere, however, and it is a little surprising to find that such a large-scale, international enterprise seems to have operated until 1942 without the benefit of a universally recognised title.

While the RAF was content with its 'EATS', correspondence raised by the RCAF and by diplomatic offices on both sides of the Atlantic, throughout 1940–41, used a variety of terms to refer to the activities in Canada. These included such variations on a theme as: the Joint Air Training Plan; the Air Training Scheme Agreement; the Dominion Air Training Scheme; the Commonwealth Air Training Plan; the British Commonwealth Air Training Agreement; the British Commonwealth Joint Air Training Plan and so on.[21] Reading between the lines it seems that most agencies were so conscious of the unfortunate connotations of the imperial tag and were at such pains to avoid using it that they could not even acknowledge that they were doing so; as a result it appears to have been too embarrassing even to raise the question of a formal title.

It should be understood that (at least to begin with) what the RAF meant by the EATS embraced only the training of RAF, RAAF, RCAF and RNZAF personnel under Canadian-run arrangements in Canada plus the training under domestic arrangements of additional RAAF and RNZAF air crew for service with the RAF. The co-operative system was actually far more complicated than this. For example, it had been agreed that, apart from the schools being run by (or on behalf of[22]) the RCAF, the RAF would also be permitted to establish and operate its own training organisation on Canadian soil. Although some of the schools involved in this arrangement would actually be formed in Canada, the basis of the organisation was created by moving a number of units, the so-called 'transferred schools', from the UK. While this British-run affair was obviously heavily reliant upon Canadian goodwill and administration, strictly speaking it did not operate under the auspices of the EATS.

Although the Canadian enterprise was the largest, the British developed other joint overseas training facilities, notably under bilateral arrangements with Southern Rhodesia and South Africa. In addition, while they were chiefly concerned with IAF personnel, some of the capacity of training schools set up in India was also used to train RAF air crew.

The concept of the Rhodesian Air Training Group (RATG) was broadly similar to that of the Canadian undertaking, which it actually pre-dated, in that it provided both for the training of British air crew and for the supply of Rhodesian personnel to fly with the RAF. The South African arrangement was somewhat different because Pretoria was not prepared to participate actively in the war until the Union itself was directly threatened.[23] In anticipation of that event, however, the South Africans recognised that they would need to build up their own armed forces and while so doing they were content to assist with the training of British personnel. As with the Canadian case, the negotiations were protracted but the 'Van-Brookham' Agreement was eventually signed on 1 June 1940.[24] As originally drafted this involved RAF training units operating independently of SAAF schools but a year later this arrangement was revised, the systems being merged into what became known as the Joint Air Training Plan (JATP).

At the Ottawa Training Conference in 1942, the British agreed to relinquish control of RAF-run training units in Canada to the RCAF. This organisational change was significant enough to warrant changing the name of the whole Canadian enterprise or, to be more accurate, seemingly agreeing to give it a mutually acceptable name for the first time. Thereafter it was officially known as the British Commonwealth Air Training Plan, the Dominions clearly being far more comfortable using the co-operative-sounding 'commonwealth' rather than a title with imperial overtones. Strictly speaking, therefore, it was now appropriate to refer to the arrangements with the various Dominions as the BCATP, the JATP and the RATG.[25]

Because they alone were involved in all three of these activities, however, from their strictly Anglo-centric perspective, the British needed an umbrella term to embrace all of these arrangements and by 1942 it was generally understood that the 'EATS' meant virtually all training being conducted 'overseas' on behalf of the RAF. It was such a convenient and familiar tag that, rightly or wrongly, the British persisted in using it to describe training in Canada and elsewhere, for the remainder of the war. It is interesting to note, incidentally, that most Canadian writers tend to describe all wartime training activities in Canada as having been conducted under the BCATP from the outset[25A] while their British counterparts still tend to use the EATS label somewhat indiscriminately (as this one will from here on).

Observer, navigator and air bomber training under Commonwealth arrangements

The first Canadian-run training units became operational, on schedule, at the end of April 1940, with the first RATG school opening a month later. These units were concerned with pilots, although those dealing with other air crew categories were running only a few weeks behind; the first Canadian observers to be trained under the EATS graduated on 24 October and the first air gunners four days later.

While the Dominions had been establishing their own schools, substantial material assistance was being provided by the British. Apart from large numbers of aeroplanes, this had included the men and equipment necessary to set up a number of complete RAF units. In the specific context of

[21]AIR46/7. This file contains the correspondence dealing with the implementation of Article XV. It includes numerous variations on the theme of the title of the project covered by the Riverdale Agreement, all of which studiously avoid using the words 'empire' or 'imperial'.

[22]The operation and staffing of many wartime Canadian training schools was carried out by civilians under contract to the RCAF.

[23]This circumstance was not considered to have arisen until the start of the East African campaign in June 1940, and even then the SAAF was confined to operations on the African continent until mid-1943 when it was eventually permitted to cross the Mediterranean to fight in Italy. Despite these constraints, a number of SAAF personnel on secondment to the RAF did fly on operations elsewhere, in theatres as remote (to South Africa) as North West Europe and Burma.

[24]This agreement was named after the chief negotiators for each side, General Sir Pierre Van Ryneveld for the Union of South Africa and Air Chf Mshl Sir Robert Brooke-Popham for the UK.

[25]To be pedantic, Southern Rhodesia actually had the constitutional status of a self-governing colony. This gave it such a degree of autonomy, however, that in practical terms it tended to be regarded, and treated, as 'the fifth white Dominion'.

[25A]F. J. Hatch's officially sponsored history of the Canadian enterprise, *Aerodrome of Democracy*, for example, does not even include 'EATS' in its glossary.

non-pilots, during 1940/41 sufficient resources were sent abroad to establish a total of nine schools.[26] This contribution was dwarfed by the efforts of the host nations in every case and by the end of 1942 the Canadians alone had commissioned: ten Air Observers Schools; two Air Navigation Schools; a General Reconnaissance School; four Wireless Schools; nine Bombing and Gunnery Schools and their own Central Navigation School.

Because the system was constantly evolving, it can only be a snapshot, but it may be of some interest to consider the training sequences being followed by RAF navigators and air bombers in the summer of 1942. After selection and induction, they attended an eight-week ITW course and in some cases this was followed by six weeks at the Elementary Air Navigation School. The majority of cadets then sailed for Canada to undergo their professional training. The various courses are outlined below.

a. *Navigators*. Navigation training only, involving twenty weeks at an Air Observers School or an Air Navigation School, including four weeks of astro.
b. *Navigators (B)*. A six-week course at a Bombing and Gunnery School followed by twenty-two weeks of navigation at an Air Observers School, including four weeks of astro.
c. *Navigators (W)*. The category of Navigator (W) was unique to the RAF so these men spent the first twenty-four weeks of their professional training at a Radio School in the UK before sailing for Canada where they underwent the standard twenty-week navigation course at an Air Navigation School.
d. *Air Bombers*. A six-week course at a Bombing and Gunnery School followed by six weeks of basic navigation at an Air Observers School or an Air Navigation School.

Until 1944, the training of radio operators (air), observers (radio) and navigators (radio) represented something of a diversion from the mainstream. These special cases are discussed on pages 185–186.

Observer training in the USA

Having already inaugurated a variety of training schemes within the Commonwealth, and with plans to establish a network of flying schools in the vicinity of Vendôme (in France) rapidly becoming unravelled, in May 1940 the UK began to explore the possibility of training additional air crew in the USA. The initial approach came to nought for a variety of reasons. One was that, despite his sympathy for Britain's plight, President Roosevelt needed to avoid exacerbating isolationist sentiment; another was a lack of capacity, because the Americans were embarking on a major expansion programme of their own. Part of this scheme involved the innovative (to the USAAC) use of civilian flying schools, much as the RAF had been doing since 1935. Under one of these arrangements, the US Army announced on 10 August 1940 that it had contracted Pan American Airways to train a total of 850 flight navigators by the end of 1941.

By this time (partly due to the publicity attracted by what would later become known as the Battle of Britain) some American politicians were beginning to regard Britain as the USA's first line of defence, making it possible to view the RAF's requirements in a more favourable light. By October the Americans felt able to enter into formal negotiations with a view to training RAF air crew.[27] The offer included the training of observers using the Pan Am school which operated under the aegis of the University of Miami.[28]

To circumvent its Neutrality Laws, Washington required that all students should be civilians so that they could be represented as being trained for a civil air transport company. The State Department also preferred that students should be provided from the Americas and specifically requested that the first batch, at least, should be Canadians. Since they were already operating a comprehensive training organisation of their own, the Canadians were disinclined to become involved south of the border. Another proposal, involving the provision of cadets recruited in the West Indies, foundered on the rock of American racial prejudice. This problem delayed matters for several months until it was finally agreed that British cadets could be accepted, so long as they had been notionally discharged from the RAF before leaving the UK and subsequently entered the USA via Canada, wearing civilian clothes. The first ten-man course eventually began on 22 March 1941.[29]

The Pan Am school was located at Coral Gables, just outside Miami. Students were accommodated in the San Sebastian Hotel, alongside the US Army navigators who were attending similar courses. Practical exercises were flown from the flying boat base at Dinner Key. Unfortunately, the airline insisted on retaining responsibility for the syllabus. Since political sensitivities made it impossible to involve RAF instructors, the British were initially unable to exert much influence over the content of the fifteen-week course. As a result, the training provided turned out to be something of a curate's egg.

The curriculum, which concentrated heavily on oceanic navigation, placed great emphasis on the use of astro. As a result the theory of celestial navigation was well-taught but such practical work as was done involved the use of a US-pattern octant, rather than a British Mk IX sextant. Unfortunately, practically no instruction was provided in such crucial, to the RAF, skills as map-reading, log keeping and the air plot technique. Furthermore, being a peacetime commercial organisation, Pan Am had little awareness of applied navigation in a military context and provided no instruction whatsoever in tactical matters. Thus, the course offered little or nothing relating to reconnaissance techniques, search procedures, signalling, photography and so on. The

[26]During 1940 sufficient resources were despatched to South Africa to establish two Combined Air Observers Navigation and Gunnery Schools plus a General Reconnaissance School while No 1 (originally 'the') School of Air Navigation was transferred from St Athan to Port Albert (Ontario) where it became No 31 Air Navigation School. In 1941 a Combined Air Observers Navigation and Gunnery School was set up in Rhodesia, Canada receiving the makings of two more Air Navigation Schools, a Bombing and Gunnery School and a General Reconnaissance School.

[27]Long before they had entered the war themselves, the US Government would sanction the presence of six British Flying Training Schools (BFTS) on US soil. Apart from participating actively in the establishment of these schools, the Americans absorbed a large proportion of the cost of the project under Lend-Lease. In addition, they undertook to train British air crew at US military and naval flying schools. The US Navy-sponsored Towers Scheme was named for Vice-Admiral J.H. Towers (Chief of the Bureau of Aeronautics), the US Army's corresponding Arnold Scheme for General H.H. Arnold (Deputy Chief of Staff, US Army and Commanding General, US Army Air Corps).

[28]AIR2/8065. The first formal offer to train RAF observers was notified to London by signal X.1593 transmitted from Washington by the British Air Attaché on 17 October 1940.

[29]These ten prospective observers were actually the first RAF cadets to be trained in the USA, the first batch of pilots (of whom we inevitably hear so much more) starting their courses, somewhat later than planned, in June (under the BFTS and Arnold Schemes) and July (under the Towers Scheme).

practical aspects of the course also left much to be desired as only four aeroplanes (Consolidated Commodores) were available for airborne work. Flying in batches of up to ten at a time, each cadet accumulated about fifty hours in the air during his course but of this only four hours was as 'navigator in charge'.[30]

Despite its limitations, however, the RAF was more than content to take advantage of the Pan Am school and from July 1941 onwards intakes were increased to 150 per course. At the same time, it became possible to increase the number of RAF Liaison Officers and these were able to provide tuition in some of the subjects which were missing from the original Pan Am syllabus.[31] Nevertheless, Miami graduates had much to learn before they could be regarded as being fully trained to RAF standards. The most obvious need was for additional instruction in bombing and gunnery, topics which it had been hoped would be covered by the RCAF. In the event, while the Canadians were able to handle the output of the first two (ten-man) courses, at No 2 B&GS at Mossbank, they could not cope with the later ones which, even allowing for a 20% wastage rate, were expected to amount to 120 cadets every eight weeks from the autumn of 1941 onwards.

Some thought was given to solving this problem by transferring an RAF B&GS to Canada but it was eventually decided to return all Miami graduates to the UK and to provide them with their additional training there. Forward planning at the end of 1942 anticipated that forty of each batch of 120 would go straight to No 3 Radio School at Prestwick to become observers (radio). Forty-eight would go to Nos 1, 2, 9 or 10 AOSs before moving on to No 3 School of General Reconnaissance at Squires Gate and thence to a Coastal Command OTU. The remaining thirty-two, who were destined for Bomber Command OTUs, were to do a similar AOS course, preceded by a month's armament training at Manby.[32]

The last British course to use the facilities at Miami graduated on 17 October 1942, by which time Pan American Airways had trained a total of 1177 observers for the RAF. These were not the only observers to be contributed by the USA, however, as a further 538 had been trained by the US Navy at Pensacola (Florida) under the Towers Scheme. The first thirty-strong course had commenced at the end of July 1941, the last one graduating a year later.

Changes in the role of UK-based observer training units

While the EATS had been working up to speed, the UK-based system had initially continued to run in parallel. Over time, however, an increasing proportion of basic training was carried out in the Dominions and, under the New Deal, it had been agreed to transfer practically all of this activity overseas. By the end of 1941 large numbers of fully trained men were already beginning to return to the UK and it soon became apparent that, to aviators who tended to be accustomed to flat terrain, relatively clear weather and empty skies, the frequent (and sometimes rock-filled) cloud cover, the black-out, the balloon barrage and the generally crowded airspace of wartime Britain represented something of a culture shock.

It was clearly necessary to provide acclimatisation training and, as the basic training commitment at the home-based AOSs declined, their facilities were progressively adapted to meet the needs of newly trained airmen returning from abroad. Specific courses, generally of four to eight week's duration, were developed to meet the requirements of air bombers and the various categories of navigator (and, in some cases, the needs of UK-trained WOp/AGs). To signify its new role, as each AOS switched to familiarisation training it became an (Observers) Advanced Flying Unit [(O)AFU], the first in February 1942, the last of them two years later. With the demise of the air observer half way through this process, yet another wave of redesignations might have been in order, but, curiously enough, this never happened.

The transitional period while the New Deal was being introduced must have been rather confusing for the UK-based units. Some impression of the flow of traffic passing through the system during the early months of 1942 can be gauged from the records of No 1 AOS/(O)AFU.[33] No 6 Course consisted of forty Miami-trained LACs who arrived at Wigtown on 7 February via an armament course at Manby's No 1 AAS; they moved on to their OTUs (presumably, by then as sergeants) a month later. No 7 Course, forty sergeants who had been trained by the US Navy, followed them out on 16 May. In the meantime, on 17 January thirty-two pilot officers and forty-eight sergeants, all of them EATS-trained, had arrived from No 3 PRC for acclimatisation training. They were split into two batches and labelled as Nos 1 and 2 AFU Courses. No 2 AFU Course was posted out on 14 March but No 1 seems to have been put on hold for some reason and did not start training until 3 May; they left on the 30th.

At much the same time, No 3 (O)AFU had received a batch of thirty WOp/AGs on 11 May along with its first consignment of seventy air bombers.[34] Forty of the latter reached Bobbington via Bournemouth. Having recently passed through EATS schools, they will have required only a relatively brief acclimatisation course. The other thirty came direct from grading at an EFTS and, as *ab initio* students, they will have needed comprehensive instruction in both bomb aiming and navigation. It is interesting to observe, however, that the unit's records state that this was the first official notice it had received of the establishment of the new aircrew category of the air bomber, so one wonders just how well prepared it was to train these men.

By late 1943 the situation had more or less stabilised. Most AOSs had become (O)AFUs and were now offering three separate four-week courses tailored to meet the specific requirements of navigators, air bombers and wireless operators. It goes, almost without saying, that there was an exception to the rule. In this case it involved No 5 AOS at Jurby which, instead of becoming an (O)AFU, was renamed the Air

[30]AIR2/4459. This file contains a number of reports on the competence of early graduates of the PAA School, a particularly informative example being that raised by No 23 OTU on 6 January 1942 and appended to HQ Bomber Command letter BC/S.24606/Trg dated 19 January.

[31]AIR2/8065. On 7 July 1941 the Air Ministry agreed to amend Establishment WAR/MISC/107 to reflect the provision of a flight lieutenant and three flying officers at Miami, in addition to a wing commander and a flight lieutenant who were already there. All of these officers were to be **N** or SN annotated.

[32]Although four AOSs were initially nominated to participate in the instruction of US-trained students, most soon appear to have been channelled through No 1 AOS at Wigtown. This commitment was later assumed by No 3 O(AFU) at Bobbington where an eight-week course, specifically tailored to the requirements of American trainees, was on offer by September 1942.

[33]AIR29/544. Operations Record Book (ORB) for No 1 AOS which became No 1 (O)AFU with effect from 1 February 1942.

[34]*Ibid.* Operations Record Book for No 3 AOS which became No 3(O)AFU with effect from 11 April 1942.

	EATS (RATG/JATP/BCATP)								
Category	**Southern Rhodesia**	**South Africa**	**Canada**	**Total**	**Canada (by the RAF)**	**USA**	**ME & India**	**UK**	**Grand Total**
Obs/Navs	717	10 170	13 882	24 769	1 896	1 715	59	9 869	38 308
Air Bombers	–	2 404	7 581	9 985	–	–	–	1 728	11 713
Totals	717	12 574	21 463	**34 754**	1 896	1 715	59	10 597	**49 021**

Fig. 20. *Global output of RAF observers, navigators and air bombers trained to 'wings' standard between 3 September 1939 and 2 September 1945.*

Air Force	**Obs/Navs**	**Air Bombers**	**Total**
RCAF	12 855	6 659	19 514
RAAF	7 633	958	8 591
RNZAF	1 748	634	2 382
SAAF	2 072	56	2 128
RIAF	97	1	98
Total	24 405	8 308	32 713
RAF (*cf* Fig. 20)	38 308	11 713	49 021
Grand Total	62 713	19 021	**81 734**

Fig. 21. *Total numbers of observers, navigators and air bombers who qualified to fly with the British Commonwealth air forces during WW II.*

Navigation and Bombing School (ANBS). By the spring of 1944 it was the only UK-based unit still carrying out basic training in navigation and bomb-aiming, part of its function being to provide a yardstick against which to measure the product of the overseas schools.

The balance sheet

As shown by Fig. 20, some 49 000 observers, navigators and air bombers gained their RAF air crew badges during WW II.[35] While these numbers ostensibly represent British personnel, they do include a few who were not. The totals include, for instance, French, Dutch, Polish, Greek, Yugoslavian, Belgian, Czechoslovakian and other refugees who were trained to fly with the RAF and/or allied air forces.[36] The figures also embrace a handful of SAAF personnel who were trained by the RATG, specifically for service with the RAF. These 'British' figures also include foreign nationals who elected to serve in the RAF as volunteers. Thus, for instance, a New Zealander who enlisted in, and was trained by, the RAF will be reflected in the totals at Fig. 20, despite the fact that he may subsequently have transferred to the RNZAF.

As can be seen, the output of the various Commonwealth schools, was more than three times that of the UK-based system. At first sight, this marked difference in performance might suggest a lack of national efficiency or capacity, but it was actually a consequence of the New Deal. Until the end of 1941 the numbers of observers emerging from British schools had more or less matched those gaining their air crew badges overseas but thereafter, with all basic training being progressively transferred abroad, the numbers qualifying overseas continued to increase while the domestic product entered a relative decline. The numbers trained in the UK peaked at 3232 in the twelve months to September 1943. By that time, however, only two AOSs were still functioning and by February 1944 the only navigator/air bomber training facility remaining in the UK was the ANBS at Jurby. Total output of the much-reduced UK system during the last two years of the war amounted to only 1198 navigators and 130 air bombers, a mere 2.7% of the global wartime RAF total.

Since, apart from the above caveats, Fig. 20 represents *only* RAF personnel, Fig. 21 has been provided to put these numbers in perspective. Fig. 21 records the overall numbers of observers, navigators and air bombers trained by and/or for the various Commonwealth air forces.[37] These raw figures present a slightly misleading picture, however, as many of these men were trained elsewhere. Of the RNZAF total, for instance, only 165 qualified for their air crew badges at home, the vast majority of New Zealanders being trained in Canada under the EATS/BCATP. Then again, while the time and distances involved had made it impractical for the British to ship cadets to and from Australia, this did not preclude the RAAF's training Australians specifically for service with the RAF. This contribution amounted to some 6271 observers, navigators and air bombers (73% of the RAAF total). Some of these men were fully trained in Australia; others were part-trained there before being transferred to Southern Rhodesia or Canada to complete their qualification. As with this Australian contingent, large numbers of personnel from the other Dominions actually flew with the RAF while wearing the uniforms of their 'own' air forces, many others serving under RAF command in one of the squadrons raised under Article XV of the Riverdale Agreement.

Wireless operator and air gunner training

The basis of wireless operator (air crew) training when war was declared was a six-month course at No 1 (originally *the*) Electrical and Wireless School at Cranwell followed by a month's gunnery at an Air Observers School. Although a second wireless school had opened at Yatesbury in 1938, capacity was still insufficient to cope with wartime demand and by November 1939 Air Service Training and Scottish Aviation had been commissioned to run Nos 1 and 2 Supplementary Schools of Wireless Telegraphy at Hamble and

[35]The figures presented at Figs 20 and 21, and those which crop up elsewhere within the narrative of this chapter, have been derived from statistics compiled by AHB and published in AP3233, Vol 1 and AIR41/70.

[36]In all, some 8750 foreign nationals were trained under such arrangements, mostly as pilots, only 200 or so becoming observers, navigators or air bombers.

[37]It may be of interest to note the corresponding figures for pilots who gained their wings with one of the Commonwealth air forces during WW II. There were 117 669 of them, 62 909 of whom wore RAF uniform. As with backseaters, however, responsibility for training having been transferred overseas, the output from UK-based schools during the last two years of the war amounted to just 1000 pilots or 1.6% of the national total.

Principal wartime trainer for air signals personnel was the Dominie. This pair, X7398 (209) and X7390 (205), belonged to No 2 Radio School at Yatesbury. (MAP)

Prestwick respectively. The bulk of the instructional staff at these civilian-run schools consisted of hastily recruited ex-GPO telephone engineers and telegraphists.[38]

By mid-1940 the training sequence for, what were now, WOp/AGs generally involved four weeks of 'square bashing' at a Recruit Centre, followed by sixteen weeks of ground instruction at Hamble or Prestwick, another eight weeks, including a brief introduction to airborne work, at Cranwell or Yatesbury and six weeks at a B&GS. Once qualified as an operator, incidentally, before completing his air crew training, it was not unusual for a prospective WOp/AG to be posted to a station to gain practical experience working in its Signals Section.

In August 1940 the training units at Cranwell and Yatesbury became Nos 1 and 2 Signals Schools, a third (No 4) being opened at Madley in August 1941.[39] At much the same time, in succession to the Bombing and Gunnery Schools, a total of (eventually) ten dedicated Air Gunners Schools began to be formed, the first of them appearing in June 1941. In the meantime, Coastal Command's gradual acquisition of ASV radar from 1940 onwards had introduced a requirement for specialist courses which were provided by No 3 Radio School at Prestwick. In the summer of 1942 this unit was redesignated as No 3 Radio Direction Finding School and joined by No 4 in the autumn.

The last major change in the organisation of signals training occurred in 1943 when the Signals Schools and the Radio Direction Finding Schools were all retitled to become Radio Schools. There would eventually be fifteen such units in the UK, all of which were involved in one or more aspects of the training of radio and/or radar mechanics and/or operators for ground as well as air duties. Each unit tended to deal with a particular aspect of signals work, only Nos 1, 2, 4, 10, 11, 12 and 14 Radio Schools being established as flying units. Of these, Nos 2 and 4, at Yatesbury and Madley respectively, handled the bulk of the basic wartime air crew training commitment. Nos 10, 11, 12 and 14 were also involved to the extent that they provided, largely post-graduate, courses tailored to the peculiar requirements of Coastal Command, notably the operation of ASV.

Meanwhile, as previously noted, when ITWs had first been established no provision had been made for them to cater for WOps. As a result, compared to other air crew categories, newly trained WOps had tended to be somewhat lacking in their awareness of general airmanship. Steps had eventually been taken to redress this situation in November 1941 when Air Crew Wings were established at both Yatesbury and Madley. These provided ground personnel, already qualified as telegraphists, with what amounted to a quasi-ITW course. The syllabus included an academic content resembling that taught at a 'proper' ITW with the added bonus of a notional ten hours of airborne time.

This innovation was symptomatic of an overall improvement in the manning situation which permitted more time to be devoted to preparing WOps for service as air crew. The training philosophy that was introduced at this time involved a prospective WOp/AG's being a fully qualified *and experienced* ground telegraphist before becoming air crew.[40] This required

[38]It had originally been intended to open two more supplementary schools but, as with observers, there was some dissatisfaction with the commercially trained product and civilian participation was eventually abandoned early in 1941 in favour of an all Service-run system.

[39]There were eventually seven Signals Schools altogether but only Nos 1, 2 and 4 were directly involved with air crew training.

[40]AMO A.804/41 of 2 October announced details of the new approach to the training of WOp/AGs and gave some indication of the standards expected. So far as Morse was concerned, an AC2 was expected to achieve eighteen words per minute, an AC1 twenty and an LAC twenty-two.

a four-phase sequence which began with ten (later fifteen) weeks of initial training at No 10 (Signals) Recruit Centre at Blackpool during which, in addition to enduring the usual 'boot camp' regime, the ability to cope with Morse at ten words per minute had to be demonstrated. The second phase comprised twelve (later fourteen) weeks of technical training at a Signals School followed by at least three (but sometimes as long as nine) months of active service as a ground operator at a station. The third phase involved eight weeks at an Air Crew Wing, the stamp of approval finally being applied on completion of another eight weeks at an Air Gunners School.

Although this approach had the advantage of ensuring that the Service was well provided with ground operators, it was a very long-winded way to go about the provision of air crew and the sequence was revised during 1943. At much the same time, dedicated ITWs were established to provide initial training facilities for air signals personnel, Nos 18 and 19 at Bridgnorth and No 20 at Bridlington.[41] Thereafter the standard training sequence involved: three weeks at an ACRC, eight weeks at an ITW, five or six months (depending upon previous qualifications) at a Radio School (either Yatesbury or Madley) and eight or twelve weeks at an Air Gunners School.

While the training organisation had been evolving, as described elsewhere, there had been a number of changes in the nature of air crew specifically employed in the fields of communications. By late 1944 the functions of the wireless operator (air crew) of 1939, the WOp/AG of 1940 and the WOM/AG of 1942 were being discharged by the WOM(air) and the WOp(air). The introduction of the last two of these categories is discussed in Chapter 23, but it is convenient to note here the training sequences that they followed:

a. *WOMs(air).* Like WOM/AGs, WOMs(air) were internally recruited from a variety of qualified signals tradesmen. The general pattern of training began with preliminary processing at an ACRC followed by an ITW course. Appropriate instruction was provided at a Radio School to ensure that all of these personnel were skilled to a common Trade Group I standard. This phase was followed by airborne training and experience with the Air Crew Wing of the same, or possibly another, Radio School. In all, this process took between six and nine months, depending upon the candidate's previous qualifications. On graduation from Radio School they became 'S'-badged (see page 184) sergeants and, although it was not essential for them to do so, the majority of WOMs(air) will subsequently have spent between six and twelve weeks at an Air Gunners School.

b. *WOps(air).* The training of WOps(air) was broadly similar to that of WOMs(air), but, since many of these men were directly recruited as civilians, there was less variation between individuals. Following an eight-week ITW at Bridgnorth, a typical WOp(air) received his professional training at Yatesbury and/or Madley where he attended a twelve-week Technical Signals (Ground) course followed by a twelve-week Technical Signals (Air) course, the latter including about 20 hours of airborne time in Proctors, Dominies and/or Ansons. Having gained his 'S' badge, a WOp(air) could then expect to spend a month or so at an O(AFU) consolidating his skills alongside navigators and air bombers who had been trained abroad.

[41]No 20 ITW moved to Usworth in the autumn of 1943. In the following spring Nos 18 and 19 ITWs moved to Bridlington where they were merged to create a new No 70 ITW.

Compared to the other air crew categories, the training of straight air gunners was relatively brief. In the popular consciousness air gunners tend to be associated with Bomber Command but they were extensively employed elsewhere, not least in Coastal Command. This is the Bristol B. IV turret which was fitted to the Beaufort torpedo bomber. (G.R. Pitchfork)

Being far less complicated than that of their dual-qualified colleagues, the training of 'straight' air gunners had always been relatively brief. In 1940 the ACRC/ITW sequence for a gunner occupied some six weeks and he qualified for his badge after another six weeks at a B&GS. By 1943 air gunner training typically involved six weeks with Nos 14 or 15 ITWs at Bridlington followed by six weeks of preliminary ground instruction at No 1 Elementary Air Gunners School at Bridgnorth and another six weeks of practical work at an Air Gunners School.[42] Following the closure of the elementary school in 1944, the course at an Air Gunners School was extended to twelve weeks.

In contrast to pilot and observer/navigator training, the RAF never made any serious attempt to relocate signals or gunnery training abroad and the bulk of its wartime requirement in these categories was satisfied by the home-based system which produced 27 190 air crew wireless operators of all kinds plus 28 243 straight air gunners. Nevertheless, both Canada and the USA (under the Towers Scheme) offered training facilities for RAF WOp/AGs while South Africa and Southern Rhodesia could train straight air gunners. This overseas activity was on a relatively small scale, however, the Canadians contributing a total of 2147 qualified personnel, South Africa 445, Southern Rhodesia 1591 and the Americans 662 (the last USN-trained WOp/AGs graduating in September 1942).

Needless to say, in every case these overseas figures represented only a tiny proportion of the overall output. For instance, while the Canadian schools may have trained relatively few wireless operators and/or gunners specifically for the RAF, their overall contribution in these categories was prodigious, amounting to 704 for the FAA, 2565 for the RNZAF, 3119 for the RAAF and no fewer than 25 661 for the RCAF. As with observers and navigators, of course, many of the men trained for these Dominion air forces actually

[42]Similar in concept to the preliminary school for observers/navigators (see Note 14) No 1 Elementary Air Gunners School (EAGS) was set up at Bridlington in April 1943, although it had moved to Bridgnorth to operate alongside its predecessor before the end of May. The reorganisation of initial training arrangements in the spring of 1944 involved the closure of the existing air gunner units at Bridlington, their facilities being reprovided at Bridgnorth by the newly established Nos 80, 81 and 82 ITWs which absorbed the collocated EAGS on 21 April 1944.

served with the RAF. For example, in addition to satisfying its domestic requirements, the home-based Australian training system produced 4174 RAAF WOp/AGs and 2295 RAAF air gunners specifically for service with the RAF.

Flight engineer training

Despite a need for them having been identified well in advance, the RAF did very little to provide itself with flight engineers before the spring of 1941 when the requirement suddenly became urgent. As a result, the first few were obtained on a somewhat *ad hoc* basis, in effect, by misemploying qualified engine fitters. The flight engineer's function soon gained a degree of official recognition, however, and they began to be acknowledged as quasi-air crew on completion of a three-week stint at a B&GS and a short manufacturer's course.

A year later the training sequence had been more formally defined, a qualified fitter selected for flying duties spending five weeks at an ITW before embarking on the same brief manufacturer's and gunnery courses as his predecessors. This sequence was more protracted for a flight mechanic (engines) who had volunteered to fly, since he had first to be given the necessary additional technical training to permit him to be remustered as a Fitter II(E) and he was also required to pass the Junior NCO Course.

In the summer of 1942 the flight engineer was finally recognised as being a fully-fledged air crew category and, in an attempt to obtain the numbers required, it was decided to broaden the intake to include airframe fitters. This involved their having to be given appropriate instruction on aero-engines at No 4 School of Technical Training (SofTT) at St Athan. This unit soon began to assume responsibility for the necessary special-to-type instruction as well and attachments to industry had ceased before the end of the year.

Since the numbers required were still not forthcoming, in mid-1943 the RAF introduced direct recruiting and from then on the bulk of flight engineers were civilian entrants. After six weeks at No 21 ITW at Usworth (later Bridlington and later still at No 90 ITW at Cranage), these men went to St Athan where they were given seventeen weeks of basic and seven weeks of applied technical training. Direct recruiting did not preclude serving airmen (fitters) from continuing to volunteer for flying duties and those who did followed much the same sequence as civilian intakes, except that they by-passed the seventeen-week technical course on the strength of their previous qualifications. The sequence was rounded off by a three-week gunnery course after which an airman was awarded his air crew badge and promoted to temporary sergeant.

It is worth pointing out, however, that flight engineer training was largely synthetic, involving rigs (some of which utilised redundant or salvaged airframes) and, until it was dropped altogether in 1943, even their gunnery training was generally conducted on ground-based facilities. As a result, flight engineers were unique among wartime air crew categories in that it was quite normal for them to qualify for their badges without their ever having flown in an aeroplane.

To satisfy the requirements of their own air forces, some flight engineers were trained in Canada, Australia and South Africa but not until 1944 and on a relatively small scale even then, the combined total amounting to just over 2000 men. By contrast all 17 885 RAF flight engineers had been home grown at No 4 SofTT.[43] At its peak St Athan's student population exceeded 5000 men, output sometimes running as high as 500 per week.

Rank and status while under training prior to the award of an air crew badge

Among the spate of regulations devised to convert the Service onto a war footing in 1939 was one dealing with the status of trainee air crew.[44] It stated that internal recruiting had been suspended with effect from 3 September and that, irrespective of their eventual category, all civilian entrants were to be enlisted into the RAFVR as aircrafthands of Trade Group V and classified as AC2s. As such, they were to be paid two shillings per day.

On completion of their initial training, prospective observers (and pilots) were to be remustered into Trade Group II and reclassified as LACs, retaining this status throughout the remainder of their professional training. As LACs, their basic pay rose to five shillings per day plus two shillings instructional pay for pilots, but only one and sixpence for observers until 1941 (see page 145). On completing their courses pilots were immediately awarded their 'wings' and graduated as temporary sergeants. As we have seen, until late 1940, observers were treated far less generously, as they emerged initially as acting sergeants (acting observers) and, as such, they were paid three and sixpence per day less than their colleagues. Only after the completion of six month's service did observers become temporary sergeants entitled to wear a flying 'O' and to draw the full daily rate of twelve and sixpence.

Wireless operators (air crew) and air gunners were even less fortunate, remaining as AC2s of Group V throughout their training. As a result, their rate of pay stayed at two shillings per day and, moreover, they received no instructional pay. On completing their courses wireless operators (air crew) were remustered to Trade Group II, air gunners remaining in Group V. Both were entitled to wear a winged bullet but they remained as aircraftmen, their classification as LACs, AC1s or AC2s depending on the marks achieved on passing out.

As described previously, these early arrangements did not survive for long, as it soon proved necessary to make radical improvements to the status of all non-pilot air crew and to introduce additional categories. The first change in the rules had to be made as early as February 1940 when the system, which had been intended to deal solely with direct entrants, was complicated by the reinstatement of internal recruiting (see page 149).

The problem was that, while internal recruits retained their real ranks (and rates of pay), as students, they needed to be treated in exactly the same way as direct entrants. The answer lay in reinstating, what amounted to, the procedures in force within the RFC/RAF in 1918 when all prospective air crew had been regarded as cadets, while undergoing initial training, and as flight cadets during their professional training. From May 1940 onwards, therefore, regardless of their actual rank, from the beginning of the ITW phase until they gained their 'wings' all trainees were referred to as cadets, or as air cadets in the case of those earmarked for commissioning.[45] All prospective air crew could be distinguished, incidentally,

[43] In point of fact, St Athan had become so oversubscribed by early 1944 that it became necessary to farm out the first ten weeks of the seventeen-week basic course to No 5 SofTT at Locking, this arrangement probably being sustained until the end of the year.

[44] AMO A.469/39 of 9 November.

[45] AMO A.273/40 of 9 May.

[46] AMO A.102/40 of 15 February.

Grade (of AC2)	Rate of Pay	PNB	WOM/AG	Flight Engineer	WOp/AG	Air Gunner
A	3/-	At ITW	–	At ITW and during the first part of the technical course	At ITW and during the first part of the technical (signals) course	At ITW & EAGS
B	5/-	–	On posting to a course involving airborne instruction	Throughout all subsequent training until the award of an air crew badge	Throughout all subsequent training until the award of an air crew badge	On posting to an AGS
C	7/3d	Throughout post-ITW training until the award of an air crew badge	–	–	–	–

Fig. 22. Grades and rates of pay for air crew under training introduced in June 1943.

by a white peak to their field service caps, this innovation having been introduced in February 1940.[46]

Subsequent changes within, and additions to, the air crew structure tended to provoke a series of debates as to who should be paid how much and when, the first of these being prompted by the Canadians. When the EATS had originally been set up it had been run in accordance with British regulations but the RCAF soon took issue with the discriminatory practice of reclassifying only pilots and observers as LACs. The Canadians argued that all air crew should be treated equally and, with the concurrence of the Australians and New Zealanders, they unilaterally decided to 'promote' all WOps being trained for air crew duties to LAC.

Fortunately for the Air Ministry, who would not agree to this procedure at the time, no RAF WOps or gunners were being trained in Canada during 1940 so the discrepancy will have escaped the notice of most British airmen. Nevertheless, in March 1941 the RAF conceded that, on posting to a B&GS, all student WOps and air gunners should be reclassified as LACs and that they would also be entitled to draw flying instructional pay at a rate of one shilling per day.[47] In November similar provisions were made to cover the various specialist ground tradesmen who flew as air gunners in Coastal Command.[48]

Apart from the obvious financial consideration, the Air Ministry's objection to making everyone an LAC had been one of principle. While the term 'LAC' is often referred to as a *rank*, it was actually one of three relative *classifications* of aircraftman (2nd class, 1st class and leading). Ideally, reclassification should be conditional upon passing a trade test. In the case of direct entrant air crew, however, they had no basic trade in which they could be tested. On the other hand, it could reasonably be argued that successful completion of an ITW course represented a sufficiently rigorous test to justify reclassification from AC2 to LAC at that stage. Yet, as the Canadians had pointed out, while this was done for pilots and observers, it was not for other categories. What the air force had been doing, in effect, was to misuse the classification system in order to create a pay differential in favour of the more demanding air crew categories.

Following a lengthy review of the system, the rates of pay and conditions of service for trainee air crew were restated in June 1943.[49] In essence, the new regulations avoided the inappropriate use of the classification scheme by making the system even more complicated. All trainee air crew were now to remain as AC2s throughout their training, the desired pay differentials being maintained by introducing three grades, the highest of which would be reserved exclusively for PNB categories. As before, of course, where it was to his advantage, although his true rank was effectively suppressed by his cadet status, an internally recruited airman who already had a basic trade retained his original rate of pay. The revised arrangements, at the time of their introduction, are summarised at Fig. 22. Needless to say, these regulations were subsequently amended as required to deal with further changes in the categorisation of air crew, but, in principle, these rules prevailed for the remainder of the war.

Operational and conversion training

The underlying aim of the pilot training scheme that had been introduced in 1935 had been to deliver newly qualified pilots to their first squadrons in a fit state for their Flight Commanders to begin training them in operational procedures. Unfortunately, the necessary level of initial competence had never been achieved because the scale of the RAF's expansion and the urgency with which it had been carried out had conspired to prevent the intended nine-month course from ever being introduced. The Service was well aware that it was failing to achieve its aim and as early as 1938 AOCinC Bomber Command had suggested the creation of an interim, post-FTS, stage during which pilots (and, presumably other air crew, although at this stage these still tended to attract little attention) could consolidate their newly acquired skills before proceeding to their squadrons.

This proposal had been accepted and it was planned to establish a 'Pool' within each group of both Bomber and Fighter Commands. Unfortunately, this plan was to be frustrated by a lack of resources, although some bomber squadrons were issued with a few Ansons to provide some additional training facilities. In the event, only No 11 Group's Pool had opened before war was declared, presumably because the training requirements of pilots destined to fly short-range, single-seat day fighters were relatively modest compared to those of the crews of long-range, multi-seat, multi-engined night bombers.

If it had proved impossible to realise the ideal of a thirty-nine week intermediate/advanced pilot training sequence in peacetime, it certainly could not be done once war had broken out and the pre-war twenty-six week curriculum soon had

[47]AMO A.189/41 of 20 March.
[48]AMO A.984/41 of 27 November.
[49]AMO A.635/43 of 24 June.

to be reduced to just sixteen. It was still supposed to yield the same amount of flying time, however, so that even less time could be devoted to allied subjects. This made it even more important that a post-graduate phase be provided.

This was achieved in September 1939 when No 6 Gp was made responsible for the co-ordination of pre-squadron training, the necessary resources being found by transferring to its control a number of non-mobilisable bomber squadrons (see Chapter 18, Note 18). These were stationed in Battle-, Blenheim-, Wellington-, Whitley- and Hampden-equipped pairs to create units (which were being referred to as Group Pools by November) at which individuals could be formed into new crews and given a few flying hours before moving on to join the squadrons of Nos 1–5 Gps respectively where they would complete their work-up.

Over the next few months it became clear that the original 1935 concept had never really been a satisfactory one, since it was totally inappropriate to expect an operational unit to carry out *any* significant training tasks during wartime – yet another lesson of 1914–18 which had been forgotten. What was really required was for all crews to be fully competent on reporting to their squadrons so that they could take their place in the front line more or less as soon as they arrived.

The Group Pool concept was not this sophisticated, so the system had to be revised yet again. In April 1940 the two notional squadrons embedded within each of Nos 1–5 Group Pools were formally disbanded. Their resources were reallocated to create five Operational Training Units, several others being formed within No 6 Group at the same time. Thereafter, although there were to be many more refinements, the OTU stage became an integral part of the training sequence for the remainder of the war. Bomber Command subsequently formed many more such units, others being set up within Coastal, Army Co-operation, Transport and Fighter Commands and yet more being established overseas. Each unit tended to specialise so that in Coastal Command, for instance, there were separate OTUs to deal with crews earmarked for flying boats, long-range Liberators, maritime strike Beaufighters, photo-reconnaissance Mosquitos and so on.

Since each command sponsored its own units their operational training systems differed but, because it was the largest and most complex, the subsequent development of the organisation dealing with heavy bomber crews provides the best example. Bomber Command's OTUs generally flew a mixture of Whitleys and Wellingtons, eventually standardising on the latter, and these provided adequate pre-squadron experience until the arrival of the more demanding, second-generation 'heavies'. Towards the end of 1941, therefore, a series of semi-autonomous conversion flights began to form to introduce crews emerging from the OTUs to the specific characteristics of Manchesters, Stirlings, Halifaxes and Lancasters. These units were collocated with, and served, a particular operational squadron. With one or two exceptions, they also took the number of the squadron with which they were associated so that, for instance, No 83 Conversion Flight was affiliated to No 83 Sqn. This arrangement lasted until the autumn of 1942 when the conversion flights were divorced from their parent squadrons and absorbed into a new series of quite independent units. No 1660 Heavy Conversion Unit (HCU), for instance, was formed from Nos 61, 97, 106 and 207 Conversion Flights.

By 1944 the training sequence for a typical crew earmarked to fly heavy bombers involved the pilot, navigator, air bomber, WOp(air) and tail gunner (and occasionally the mid-upper gunner) first coming together at an OTU where they were introduced to operational techniques and began to fly as a team. Since the Wellington lacked both an engineer's station and a dorsal turret, however, the flight engineer always, and the second gunner usually, crewed-up at the next, HCU, stage.

For a time, most bomber HCUs operated only Stirlings and Halifaxes, so crews destined for Lancasters had to complete a further type-conversion at a Lancaster Finishing School (LFS). Ideally, at some stage during this sequence a crew would also attend a course at an Air Crew School. There, apart from being briefed on the latest tactical and technical developments, they might undergo a modicum of physical training along with practical and theoretical instruction in such topics as survival and escape and evasion techniques.

What all of this meant in time could vary considerably. One major determining factor was the rate at which crews were being lost. Another was the different policies adopted by different commands. It is impossible, therefore, to be precise but a heavy bomber crew passing through the system in late 1944 could generally expect to spend ten weeks at an OTU, during which they would fly about 80 hours, and six weeks at an HCU where they might accumulate another 40 hours. If it was required, an LFS course might last a fortnight and yield another 10–15 hours in the air, a course at an Air Crew School requiring another two weeks. On reaching their squadron, a crew would usually be given three or four shake-down flights during their first few days at which point they would be considered fit to fly their first operational mission. At this stage of the war a bomber navigator could reasonably expect to have a total of not far short of 300 flying hours in his log book before he flew in combat, two or three times as many as his predecessors of 1940.

This section has provided no more than a summary of post-graduate training during WW II, and that largely confined to Bomber Command. It should be appreciated, however, that the system was far more complex than this and that many air crew personnel attended additional courses at specialist training units. Most Coastal Command navigators, for instance, routinely passing through a School of General Reconnaissance.

Other, more specialised, units tended to be set up when a newly developed device was being introduced into service. Once the equipment had been produced in quantity and become a standard fit, instruction on its use was provided by one or more of the major training units or else the original unit became a mainstream school itself. An early example of this process is provided by the establishment of the AI/ASV School at Prestwick in October 1940 to provide instruction in the use of early airborne radar sets. Two months later this unit was to become No 3 Radio School. This pattern was sustained throughout the war, a much later example being provided by No 1323 Flt which was formed at the end of 1944 to teach the intricacies of the radar-aimed Automatic Gun Laying Turret which was about to reach the squadrons. Had the war gone on, there is little doubt that, once it had become a standard fit, gunners would have been taught how to handle this equipment as part of their HCU course.[50]

[50]There were many more such specialist schools, other examples include, for instance, the LORAN Training Unit which operated at Mullaghmore and Limavady in 1944–45, latterly as the Coastal Command Anti U-Boat Devices School, and the Pathfinder Force Navigation Training Unit which flew from Gransden Lodge and Warboys in 1943–45.

The length of air crew training and the run-down of the BCATP

At the beginning of the war it was taking about twenty-five weeks to produce an unbadged, acting sergeant, acting observer, nominally qualified in bombing and gunnery as well as in navigation. Including the ITW phase, by 1943 it was taking a basic navigator a notional thirty-six weeks to graduate as a badged sergeant or pilot officer. He would have been qualified solely in navigation, however, those requiring additional skills obviously taking longer to train, the most highly qualified, the navigator (BW), taking no less than sixty-four weeks. By comparison, a contemporary pilot took forty-four weeks to earn his flying badge; an air bomber took thirty and a straight air gunner, eighteen.

It should be appreciated that, despite its significance to the individual, gaining his air crew badge represented only a half-way stage in his training because he still had to attend a succession of post-graduate acclimatisation, operational training and type conversion courses, not to mention lengthy voyages to and from Canada or South Africa, all of which more than doubled the time required. In broad terms, therefore, it took a bomber navigator who entered training in 1942 a minimum of sixteen months to reach his first squadron. Even this represented a best case situation, as the time involved could be considerably increased by lengthy delays between courses.

This was not as alarming as might at first appear, however, as the EATS/BCATP had been so successful in training PNB categories that a substantial surplus had been created by the end of 1943 and a further 3000 were being added to the total every month. The UK-based system had also excelled itself so that Yatesbury, for instance, was holding more than 1000 fully trained WOps(air).

All of this tends to suggest that wartime training was so badly co-ordinated as to be almost chaotic. It is an unfortunate fact, however, that it was (and still is) very difficult to arrange a precise match between training output and current demand and the more unstable the situation, the greater the margin for error. The root of the problem is the length of training which automatically defines the notice required of any change in future manning levels. Since the wartime recruiting and training sequence occupied well over a year, it followed that the system would have to be given at least that much lead time in order to adjust its intake. Needless to say, the uncertainties of the wartime situation, certainly until 1943, had meant that this sort of notice simply could not be provided. The only sensible thing to do under such circumstances was to cater for the worst case and this, in effect, was what had been done.

In the event, losses, while severe, had not been as heavy as some had predicted and the inevitable result had been an overprovision of flying personnel. While this had been expensive, in purely financial terms, it had actually saved lives because the only way to have dealt with a shortage of air crew would have been to truncate their training. This would simply have recreated the conditions of 1917 (and of 1940–41) with all that had implied in terms of accident rates and operational ineffectiveness.[51]

While much of the air crew surplus of 1944 had been due to overprovision by the training machine, some of it had been caused by changes in policy. For instance, a surplus of gunners was inadvertently created by a decision which had made a ventral gun position a standard fit in all heavy bombers.[52] This proposal raised Bomber Command's requirement for air gunners from two to three per aircraft and arrangements were made to provide the additional men. By the end of 1943, however, it had been decided to make H_2S a standard fit in all Main Force aircraft, newly built Lancasters being delivered with it already installed from March 1944 onwards. The belly-mounted radar scanner was incompatible with a ventral gun position, so the original plan had to be abandoned, but by that time hundreds of additional gunners were already being trained against the earlier requirement.

The most significant consequence of the surplus of trained air crew was that it caused frustrating delays between courses. Since there was no urgent requirement for them to qualify, it was often decided to shunt batches of part-trained men into a siding rather than add to the numbers who were already backed-up in holding units.[53] One suspects that cost would have been an even more persuasive argument, it being much cheaper to postpone the completion of training, because cadets were paid as mere aircraftmen, rather than as the sergeants or officers that they would become once they had gained their 'wings'.

At Ottawa in 1942 the participants in the programme had agreed to continue to underwrite the BCATP until 31 March 1945. This did not mean, of course, that they were all committed to sustaining its output at what was to become an extravagantly high rate. Following a further review of the Plan in February 1944, it was agreed to start an immediate, gradual run-down. The initial target was set at a 40% reduction in output over the next twelve months but even this still provided a considerable excess of trained air crew.

From all of the above, it is plain to see why so many air crew, especially pilots and navigators, who enlisted in the RAF in 1943 or later never managed to become operational before the war ended.

[51]This problem is fundamental. It had first been encountered in WW I when the response to a serious shortage of trained men in the spring of 1917 had resulted in a surplus by the autumn of 1918. There are many aspects to this problem but its severity is clearly proportional to the length of training, since that determines the necessary notice of any change in demand. Thus, since it took eighteen months or more to recruit and train a pilot in the early 1950s, it took that long to respond fully to the crisis caused by the Korean War. Conversely, the unexpected withdrawal of the Valiant in 1965 resulted in a surplus, because the next generation of Valiant crews was already in the training pipeline.

[52]Some Lancaster Mk Is (and a few Mk IIIs) had been delivered with a Fraser-Nash FN 64 ventral turret from very early in the production run and it was a standard fit on Mk IIs. It began to be withdrawn from January 1944 and the only FN 64-fitted Lancasters still operating at the end of the year were those aircraft of No 3 Gp which had been equipped to carry an 8000 lb bomb, this modification precluding the installation of H_2S.

Following a lengthy series of trials, Halifax Mk IIIs began to be provided with a single 0.50 inch Browning in a Preston-Green mounting aft of the bomb bay from February 1944 onwards. Although a few were still in service in the autumn, this ventral gun position never became a standard installation because, as with the Lancaster, it was soon displaced by an H_2S scanner.

[53]As early as March 1942 there were already more than 4000 newly qualified, EATS-trained pilots in the UK awaiting operational assignments. To the staffs concerned with manning and planning they were known as the 'Bournemouth Boys' because they were held on the books of No 3 PRC at Bournemouth. It was this considerable surplus and the decision to delete the second pilot from bomber crews, thereby substantially reducing demand, which permitted the SFTS course to be extended from seventeen to twenty-four weeks – a crucial element of the New Deal. Even so, it was estimated at the time that during the transition phase the surplus might peak at as many as 8000, and that was only pilots.

Part III

The Post-Observer Era 1942–2000

Chapter 23

Loose ends

As originally conceived, this book was primarily intended to chronicle the evolution of the air observer within the RFC, the RNAS and the RAF. The replacement of observers by navigators and air bombers in 1942 brings this history to an end. While the RAF may have dispensed with observers *per se*, however, it continued to employ large numbers of other non-pilot air crew. To end here too abruptly would, therefore, leave many loose ends. So, to tie these off, four further chapters have been added, one to provide a brief summary of significant changes in the employment of non-pilot air crew during the remaining three years of WW II and the others to sketch in the next half-century or so.

Naval observers and TAGs

Although the FAA was free of direct RAF influence by 1942, it is appropriate to make one last reference to naval back-seaters. Almost as if to underline its independence, the navy elected not to follow the air force's lead and it continued to employ air observers, rather than navigators, as it still does today.[1] On the other hand, it can have been no coincidence that on very same day that the Air Ministry authorised its new range of air crew badges for the RAF, the Admiralty made a long overdue announcement of the introduction of a badge for commissioned naval observers.[2] At the same time another badge was authorised for rating observers and air gunners.[3] It is interesting to note that, as with the original RNAS observers badge, both of the new naval emblems had *two* wings.

Two weeks later it was announced that naval air gunners were to have their old title of TAG, which had been withdrawn in 1935, restored (see page 125). This change in terminology was antedated to 1 July 1942.[4]

Although no further references will be made to naval air crew, it is perhaps worth commenting on one last aspect of nautical nomenclature. Between 1924 and 1939 the operation of aeroplanes at sea had been conducted under the aegis of the Fleet Air Arm *of the Royal Air Force*. When the Admiralty assumed responsibility for this activity, it established dedicated Air and Flying Branches for its commissioned and non-commissioned aviation personnel but it failed to provide a new name for the overall organisation.[5] While the navy had initially endorsed the FAA 'label', it appears that, perhaps because of its air force origins, this may have been frowned upon in some quarters. In 1941 an attempt was made to minimise the use of the FAA tag, although this stopped well short of actually legislating it out of existence.[6] Such a half-hearted measure failed to have much impact so, in 1946, the Admiralty ruled that the correct term was Naval Aviation and that Fleet Air Arm was no longer to be used, other than in an historical context.[7] The bureaucracy dutifully adopted the new terminology but it made less impression in the ward room and below decks. On 24 May 1953, in a written answer to a Question in the House of Commons, the First Lord of the Admiralty, the Rt Hon J.P.L. Thomas MP, announced that the title of Fleet Air Arm had been restored to use.

The introduction of meteorological air observers

Coastal Command established its first dedicated meteorological reconnaissance units, then of flight status, in 1941. It was envisaged from the outset that it would be preferable to employ a qualified meteorologist to make informed observations and to take any necessary readings. It took a surprisingly long time to formalise these arrangements, but a Meteorological Air Observer Section was eventually set up within the GD Branch in September 1942.[8] The numbers required were never large, the original estimate being for ten officers and fifty NCOs.

Qualified meteorologists, selected for flying duties, were given a fairly cursory introduction into the world of practical aviation. To begin with, their training was to consist of: a brief stint at an ACRC; three weeks of gunnery at Manby (which was deemed to be sufficient to entitle them to wear an 'AG' badge); three weeks of navigation at Millom; and role familiarisation at Aldergrove.

The first of these men began to fly operationally in the late spring of 1943. After the first five courses had passed through the system, the requirement for formal gunnery training was dropped, leaving later, and what soon became the majority of, flying 'Met men' without an 'AG' badge. Needless to say, this caused some discontent and permission was sought for them to wear some other appropriate emblem, one early suggestion being the, now defunct, flying 'O'.[9] The Director of the Meteorological Office, Sir Nelson Johnson, raised this

[1]It is doubtful whether the FAA would ever have evinced much interest in adopting the new RAF-style terminology but, whether it had wanted to or not, the option would presumably have been denied because the title of 'navigator' was already spoken for within the RN where it was a long-established specialisation among seafaring officers.
[2]AFO 4490 of 17 September 1942.
[3]AFO 4491 of 17 September 1942.
[4]AFO 4705 of 1 October 1942.
[5]AFO 1358 of 22 May 1939 was a lengthy (seven-page) document laying down in some detail the basic arrangements for the administration of the new naval organisation which was referred to throughout as the Fleet Air Arm.
[6]AFO 2112 of 22 May 1941 encouraged personnel to replace 'Fleet Air Arm' with 'naval', as in, for instance, 'naval aircraft' and 'naval air training', and reminded all concerned that it was an improper practice to use FAA as post-nominal letters to identify individuals. The Admiralty evidently pressed the Air Ministry to support this campaign as RAF personnel were encouraged to observe the same conventions by AMO A.959/41 of 13 November, this Order repeating much of the navy's exhortation verbatim.
[7]AFO 5631 of 6 September 1946.
[8]AMO A.973/42 of 10 September.
[9]There was a precedent for this, in that, following a hasty navigation course, the very first 'flying Met man', Flt Lt E. Kraus, had been authorised to wear an observers wing in 1941. It is believed, however, that this remained a unique case.

Sub-category	Skills
WOp(air)	Wireless operator only
WOp(air)(E)	Wireless operator and emergency gunner
WOp(air)(G)	Wireless operator and air gunner
WOp(air)(ASV)	Wireless and ASV operator (but not a gunner)
WOp(air)(ASVG)	Wireless and ASV operator and air gunner

Fig. 23. *Annotations to distinguish skills possessed by individual WOps(air).*

matter several times but the war in Europe was almost over before his request was granted.

Those in favour of awarding a badge, notably the AOCinC Coastal Command, Air Chf Mshl Douglas, contended that *flying* meteorologists were self-evidently air crew. Others, most critically AMP, Air Mshl Sir Bertine Sutton, whose department had ultimate responsibility for the administration of such matters, considered that they were essentially ground personnel who needed to fly on occasion. Sutton's argument had some substance because the bulk of meteorologists, the NCOs, were paid at Trade Group II rates plus a shilling-a-day crew pay, rather than receiving a consolidated air crew rate. There was something of an anomaly here, however, in that, because they were commissioned into the GD Branch, the handful of officers involved did have air crew status, albeit badgeless. Sutton had a second reason for withholding his approval in that the award of any air crew badge was conditional upon completion of a suitably demanding course of flying training and, in his opinion, the relatively brief indoctrination provided for meteorologists did not measure up to this yardstick. Furthermore, since they could not be regarded as being qualified in any of the other recognised air crew trades, it was not appropriate to invoke AMO A.89/42 (see Note 2 to Chapter 22).[10]

The flying badge dispute dragged on until the autumn of 1944 when Sutton neatly side-stepped the issue by referring the whole question of air crew badges to the recently established Committee on the Composition of Air Crew (see page 189). Since this committee was chaired by Douglas, the outcome was fairly predictable. In April 1945 the air crew category of the meteorological air observer was formally recognised, qualified personnel being authorised to wear an 'AG' pattern badge featuring the letter 'M' within the laurel wreath.[11]

Recruiting of meteorological air observers ceased in June 1945. Since their introduction, thirty-four officers and 190 airmen had been trained for airborne meteorological duties. Nineteen of these, mostly unbadged, aviators had been killed on active service. 'Mostly' unbadged, because, as with flight engineers, once it was known that a dedicated badge was likely to be introduced, some 'Met men' reportedly took matters into their own hands and made appropriate modifications to a navigator's 'N' badge.[12]

[10]AIR2/5837. These arguments were set forth in a letter from AMP to AOCinC Coastal Command dated 4 November 1944.

[11]AMO A.409/45 of 26 April.

[12]The practice of wearing 'home made' 'M' badges has been attested to by at least two ex-meteorological air observers, P. Rackliff, in conversation with the author, and J. Tindale, in a letter published in the spring 1999 edition of *Intercom*.

Changes within the fraternity of wireless operators and air gunners

In the air force of the inter-war years, the terms wireless operator and air gunner had become almost synonymous. The introduction of increasingly sophisticated equipment during WW II had demanded a much higher degree of technical expertise and this had led to a polarisation within what had once been a joint trade. By 1942 six categories and sub-categories had been defined: AG; WOM/AG; WOp/AG Grades I and II; AG/FM(A) and AG/FM(E). This evolutionary process was not yet complete. In Bomber Command, for instance, turrets were being increasingly manned by straight air gunners who had little need for expertise in handling a wireless set. Conversely, the growth of Transport Command meant that the RAF was operating large numbers of aeroplanes which carried long-range communications equipment but lacked any armament at all. It was becoming clear that the traditional WOp/AGs were over-qualified so that, wherever they were employed, half of their skills tended to be superfluous. In December 1943 the long-standing dual-qualified trade was abolished.[13]

All existing WOp/AGs were to be remustered to the new trade of wireless operator (air) [WOp(air)] with effect from 9 November, accompanied by the grading system which had been imposed upon their predecessors. Thereafter their primary responsibilities were to be confined to wireless and visual signalling. Depending upon their specific assignments, however, provision was made for them still to act as gunners if and when required. Similarly, while all new recruits to the trade would initially be trained only in communications techniques, they remained liable for additional training in gunnery if this was a requirement of their subsequent employment. In essence, the majority of WOps(air) employed by Bomber and Transport Commands were expected to handle only communications, while those posted to Coastal Command were still likely to be additionally involved in gunnery and/or with ASV radar.

From the above it will have become clear that there was a good deal of sub-specialisation within the overall trade of the WOp(air). This eventually led to the application of a series of suffixes (see Fig. 23) which, while obviously intended to show the degree of expertise possessed by an individual, were aids to the personnel staffs as much as professional distinctions.

Prior to this, all wireless operators had undergone a formal gunnery course which had entitled them to wear the 'AG' badge and those who were already qualified continued to do so. On the other hand, a WOp(air) graduating under the new arrangements would not automatically be awarded a gunners badge, which left him without any kind of air crew emblem. There was clearly a need for yet another air crew badge to distinguish the new category. Introduced in January 1944, it comprised a standard pattern single-wing with the letter 'S' within the laurel wreath.[14] The 'S' stood for signals, although it was to be more than a year before this was to be reflected in the official title of the wearer.

[13]AMO A.1242/43 dated 2 December, the details of which were amplified by AMO A.244/44 dated 23 March.

[14]AMO A.3/44 of 6 January. Apart from introducing the 'S' badge, this Order noted that the 'O', 'RO', 'AG', 'N', 'B' and 'E' badges were all still current (although the first two of these were no longer being awarded). A month later this Order was amended to state, yet again, that, regardless of which badges an individual may have, at some time, been entitled to wear, air crew currently employed as such were to wear *only* the badge of the category in which they were presently mustered or listed.

The peculiar requirements of Coastal Command were to lead to yet another recategorisation of signals personnel. Ever since air crew categories had been redefined in 1942 it had been accepted that airmen of certain technical trades who were qualified as gunners would be entitled to wear the 'AG' badge (see Fig. 18). One of these was the WOM/AG but, as with WOp/AGs, experience had shown that, contrary to expectations, WOM/AGs were rarely called upon to fire guns in anger.

Furthermore, it was anticipated that the introduction of more complex electronic devices would make increasing demands on the technical skills of the WOM/AG who was expected to be the only man capable of carrying out running repairs on such equipment. The situation was rationalised with effect from 13 March 1944 when the category of WOM/AG was replaced by that of the wireless operator mechanic (air) [WOM(air)], although this change was effected in arrears, as it was not publicised until the following September.[15]

In essence these men needed to be as handy with a Morse key as they were with a soldering iron.[16] Like their WOp(air) colleagues, WOMs(air) were to wear the recently introduced 'S' badge in place of the old 'AG' which was now awarded only to (and to be worn only by) 'straight' air gunners. In practice, however, WOMs(air) continued to be employed almost exclusively by Coastal Command (and its overseas equivalents) whose larger aircraft tended to have more gun positions than professional gunners. To man, for instance, the waist gun positions of Liberators and Catalinas therefore, it continued to be necessary to train other crew members to act as emergency gunners when necessary. As a result, although gunnery skills were not listed among the essential attributes of a WOM(air) most, if not all, of them continued to be formally trained as gunners.

These changes had effectively resulted in communicators being completely divorced from gunners, the *decree absolute* having been marked by the introduction of the 'S' badge. Nevertheless, subsequent cohabitation was commonplace, especially within Coastal Command where, since 'signallers' were still required to function as gunners on occasion, it could be argued that the 'AG' was as appropriate an emblem as the 'S'. As with the flying 'O' and the illicit 'FE', therefore, many of the WOps and WOMs who had long since qualified for their gunners badges, declined to adopt the new pattern and some of the older hands continued to sport their 'AG' badges for the remainder of the war.[17]

[15]AMO A.916/44 of 21 September.

[16]It is some indication of the core skills required of the WOM(air) that these men were to be drawn from volunteers from the following trades: wireless operators, wireless operators (air), wireless and electrical mechanics, wireless mechanics and wireless operator mechanics. This list also conveys some impression of the confusing complexity which had developed within the overall groundcrew trade structure by 1944. There had been two main reasons for this. First, the increasing complexity of equipment, which demanded increasing specialisation, and secondly, the need for economy. The latter consideration was more to do with time than money. It was not sensible to invest two or three years in producing multi-skilled, apprentice-quality tradesmen in wartime, especially as most of them were in uniform only 'for the duration'. It was far more practical to provide only sufficient training to enable an airman to function productively, as quickly as possible, in a relatively narrow field and then to remuster him to progressively higher qualified trades as his expertise increased through experience and post-graduate instruction. The inevitable result of this pragmatic approach had been a proliferation of trades; the fifty which had sufficed at the beginning of the war had become 235 by VJ Day.

[17]Note that, since they declined to follow the RAF's lead over the introduction of WOps(air) and WOMs(air), the RAAF, RCAF and RNZAF did not adopt the 'S' badge during WW II, all of these air forces continuing to employ WOp/AGs.

The flight engineer replaces the air bomber in the role of pilots assistant

With the passage of time it became apparent that the 1942 decision, to use air bombers as pilots assistants, had been ill-judged. This was, in part, because some air bombers had turned out to be rather less capable than had been expected, but it was also felt that the air bomber had probably been given too many strings to his bow and that the amount of time he was obliged to devote to studying airmanship and practising in the Link Trainer would have been better spent on navigation and bomb-aiming. But the most telling argument was that there had been 'hardly any authenticated cases of an Air Bomber being able to bring an aircraft back after the Pilot has been incapacitated.' All of these points were raised in a formal Bomber Command submission of May 1944, recommending a change of policy.[18]

Having previously canvassed the opinions of its subordinate groups, Bomber Command had concluded that, although it appeared most unlikely that he would ever have to take the controls 'in anger', it was still considered highly desirable, for morale purposes, to have a second crew member capable of flying the aeroplane in an emergency. The consensus of opinion was that flight engineers were the most suitable choice. Since experience with the Lancaster (where the flight engineer had always acted as pilots assistant) had demonstrated that they could certainly do the job, Bomber Command recommended that all pilots assistants should be flight engineers, rather than air bombers. The Air Ministry agreed to this change in June.[19]

In the light of this development, it is perhaps worth recording that the flight engineer of 1944 was held in much higher esteem than his predecessor of 1941 had been. As previously noted, the Service had been very slow to introduce them in the first place and, even when it had, it had been just as slow to accept that flight engineers really were air crew and that they needed to be recognised as such (see page 157). It had taken all of three years for flight engineers to gain the degree of respect to which they should always have been entitled but their true value had finally been accepted by mid-1944. This was particularly true within No 8 Gp where, as one veteran, J. Norman Ashton, recalls, his potential was being very fully exploited:[20]

> 'The flight engineer was certainly regarded by the PFF as a very versatile member of the crew: he was expected to be a first-class engineer; have the ability to pilot the aircraft in an emergency; be capable of manning any of the gun turrets; act as bomb-aimer in certain crews; be able to identify stars and constellations; learn to use the sextant and be able to take reliable "shots" with that instrument!'

The refinement of certain sub-categories of navigator

By late 1943 the employment pattern of the various sub-categories of navigator was broadly as summarised at Fig. 24. When the system had been devised in 1942 it had been envisaged that the navigator (BW) would fly in overseas-based bomber Mosquitos. In the event Mosquitos were not deployed abroad in the bomber (as distinct from fighter-bomber) role, most navigators (BW) eventually

[18]AIR2/2662. Bomber Command letter BC/S20173/Trg dated 21 May 1944.

[19]*Ibid*. Air Ministry letter S.91149/TO1 dated 23 June 1944.

[20]J. Norman Ashton, *op. cit.*

Category	Role	Types
Navigator	Bomber	Halifax Lancaster Stirling Wellington
	Transport	Dakota York
	Special Duties	Halifax
Navigator (B)	Bomber	Liberator Baltimore Blenheim/Bisley Boston Mitchell Ventura Mosquito
	Maritime (long and medium range convoy escort, anti-submarine patrol and recce, coastal recce, Met recce and torpedo bomber)	Liberator Fortress Catalina Sunderland Halifax Warwick Wellington Baltimore Hudson Blenheim/Bisley Ventura Beaufort Hampden
	Airborne Forces	Halifax Whitley Albemarle
	Special Duties	Halifax Wellington Hudson
	Air/Sea Rescue	Warwick
Navigator (W)	Bomber Intruder Torpedo Fighter Fighter-Bomber Photo-Recce	Vengeance Mosquito Beaufighter Mosquito Mosquito
Navigator (BW)	Met Recce	Mosquito
Navigator (Radio)	Night Fighter	Beaufighter Mosquito

Fig. 24. *Distribution of navigator sub-categories, 1943.*

serving with Coastal Command where they flew Mosquitos on meteorological and photo reconnaissance duties. This requirement was too small to justify a dedicated category, however, and the navigator (BW) was declared obsolescent in January 1944.[21]

In the meantime, attention had been focused on the navigator (radio). In early 1941 a cadet earmarked as an AI operator had gone straight from ITW to No 3 Radio School for a three-week radar course at Prestwick and from there direct to a night-fighter squadron, still as an AC2. After what amounted to a month's probation, he was promoted to sergeant and authorised to wear his 'RO' badge. Apart from brief familiarisation courses on later marks of AI, few of the early radio operators (air) and/or observers (radio) received any further professional training. Nevertheless, despite the fact that many of them had never attended a navigation course, they had all been automatically recategorised as navigators (radio) in 1942.[22]

In September 1941, two months after the introduction of the observer (radio), No 6 AONS (later AOS) at Staverton had begun to run navigation courses for them. Over the next twelve months the duration of this course fluctuated between six and twelve weeks, involving anything between 20 and 75 hours of airborne time. In September 1942, by which time the students were prospective navigators (radio), the course was standardised at eight weeks, but this was barely sufficient to justify the title of 'navigator'.

The rather ill-defined approach to the training of 'Nav(R)s' persisted until the end of 1943 when it was decided, in effect, to treat radar operation as a secondary skill. In future, therefore, all Nav(R)s were to be drawn from personnel who were already fully qualified as 'proper' navigators, only then would they be selected to attend the necessary technical and specialist course(s) to be taught how to handle AI equipment.[23] By this time (in fact since the summer of 1942) primary responsibility for the provision of AI training had been transferred from Prestwick to No 62 OTU at Usworth, later Ouston.

Improved promotion prospects for airmen air crew

When airmen air crew had begun to appear in relatively large numbers shortly before the war it had been envisaged that very few of them would attain a rank higher than sergeant. Wartime conditions had made this an unrealistic constraint, however, and since 1941 there had been provision for substantial numbers of airmen to be overborne as flight sergeants and, in the case of pilots and observers, warrant officers (see page 145). By 1943 it had become necessary to review the situation again and it was agreed to remove the differential between what had become PNB and non-PNB categories. Thenceforth, all airmen air crew were eligible to become warrant officers.[24] The downside to this improvement in conditions of service was that the time-served requirement was doubled from six months in the previous rank to a year.

Needless to say, a degree of flexibility was permitted and, in deserving cases, the year could be reduced to nine months. Furthermore, any airman (in practice, always a pilot, but see below) appointed to captain a heavy aircraft could be immediately elevated to acting flight sergeant on the authority of his AOC and made up to acting warrant officer when certified as being efficient. After three months of satisfactory service he could be promoted to temporary warrant officer. Then again, special rules were introduced for the Pathfinder Force where, establishment vacancies permitting, an airman could be made up to acting flight sergeant on completing fifteen operational sorties and to acting warrant officer after another five.

Other minor concessions were being made in the specific cases of navigators (BW) and (W) whose training took so much longer than that of a straight 'Nav' as result of the additional bomb-aiming and/or signals content. It was agreed that all Nav(W)s should be given an antedate of seniority of twelve weeks on qualification and all Nav(BW)s eighteen weeks. Neither of these grants carried any entitlement to back pay but they did accelerate promotion. The same antedates were given to serving airmen already qualified in these categories and, where appropriate, they became entitled to immediate promotion.[25]

[21] AMO A.42/44 of 20 January.
[22] For a firsthand account of the training undergone by an early observer (radio), see Sqn Ldr Lewis Brandon's *Night Flyer* (1961).

[23] AMO A.1241/43 of 2 December.
[24] AMO A.426/43 of 13 May.
[25] AMO A.497/43 of 27 May.

The abolition of the 'VR' badge

While air crew were not the only people to wear the 'VR' badge, since its introduction was noted (on page 140), it is appropriate to record its demise. When it had been conceived in 1938–39 the 'VR' emblem had been intended to differentiate between pre-war *volunteers* and the ex-regulars who were *obliged* to complete a reserve commitment. As such it had been intended to be a mark of distinction. Once the war had begun, however, all recruits were enlisted into the RAFVR, irrespective of whether they had volunteered or been conscripted. Thus, the original significance of the badge had been somewhat degraded. In fact, in the eyes of some, rather than being a badge of distinction, it was seen to mark out the wartime 'amateur' from the pre-war professional.

Pointing out that this divisive influence was hardly conducive to a 'feeling of unity within the Service', AMP, Air Mshl Sutton, had concluded that 'the VR badge has actually been harmful and may become so to an increasing degree.'[26] In June 1943, therefore, all RAFVR officers were instructed to cease wearing the badge, leaving them with neat holes in the collars of their tunics.[27]

It was not considered necessary formally to prohibit the wearing of 'VR' emblems by airmen, however, because many of them did not do so anyway. Wartime scarcity of fabric had long since made it impossible to ensure that all airmen were issued with their badges and, although it was possible to buy them, they were difficult to find. As a result, the wearing of the cloth 'VR' patch had effectively become optional for non-commissioned personnel. Rather than withdrawing permission for it to be worn, therefore, it sufficed for the badge to be declared obsolescent and it was simply allowed to fade away.

Interestingly, the significance of the very similar 'A' badge, which was worn only by pre-war members of the Auxiliary Air Force, had not been diluted by wartime arrangements. The wearing of an 'A' still served to identify a particular group within the air force and its exclusivity gave it a certain cachet. While this contained an unfortunate hint of élitism, AMP considered that, on balance, the 'A' badge still exerted a positive influence on the *esprit de corps* of those entitled to wear one. No steps were therefore taken to abolish it.

Non-pilots in relation to captaincy and other executive functions

From 1920 onwards the majority of pilots had been officers and those who were not were at least sergeants. Since no one else who flew was likely to be ranked higher than corporal, the pilot had always automatically assumed the role of aircraft captain. Perhaps because the recent introduction of sergeant observers had raised the possibility of their eventually challenging this assumption, in January 1939 a regulation was introduced which made it quite clear that captaincies were the preserve of pilots alone.[28] Nevertheless, there were some who doubted the logic underpinning this exclusivity. The first person of any consequence to question the current arrangements was probably Air Cdre H.G. Crowe in June 1941.[29] His main contention was that, under certain circumstances, it might well be preferable for the observer to be in command of an aircraft. In seeking the views of commands, he went on to point out that, if the principle of observer captains were to be accepted, it could reasonably be argued that they should also be able to command a flight or squadron. It may be no coincidence, incidentally, that Crowe was an ex-back-seater, having flown as an observer with No 20 Sqn in 1917–18. It goes almost without saying that there was absolutely no support for his suggestion, although Coastal Command did admit that four of its Polish Air Force observers had been nominated for captaincies.

The question did not go away, however, and it was raised again in the autumn by AOC No 5 Gp, AVM J.C. Slessor.[30] Since it was primarily the efforts of the observer which enabled a bomber to find and hit a target, Slessor argued that he was clearly the key member of a crew. It followed that 'the status of the observer should now be raised to one of equality with the pilot, that observers should not be debarred from being captains of aircraft, and that they should be put on an exactly equal footing with pilots for promotion and command.' He went on to point out that it was quite normal for observers to act as captains of aircraft in the FAA and that naval observers frequently commanded squadrons and even shore stations. This was in marked contrast to RAF practice where the most senior observer one was likely to come across was a solitary flight lieutenant Station Navigation Officer on each airfield, plus, perhaps, one flying officer per flight on each squadron. This, it was pointed out, hardly reflected the vital importance of navigation and bomb-aiming.

Slessor's plea for observers to be recognised as captains appears to have been well-received and before the end of November the Air Ministry had decided to seek the opinions of senior commanders again.[31] The reaction was as unfavourable as it had been in June, a typical reply (from Air Chf Mshl Sir Philip Joubert at Coastal Command) being that 'Observers who shew particular qualities of leadership during their first tour of duty should, on completion of same, be given a pilots training course.'[32] Or, to put it another way, if an observer were good enough to captain an aeroplane then he jolly well ought to become a pilot. Similar responses were received from other veterans who presumably regarded 1917 as having been a golden age, when an observer still knew (or could be kept in) his place.

Nevertheless, despite the generally negative reaction, some senior officers were beginning to accept that, because it was so rational, it was difficult to dismiss the case for observers (and perhaps other non-pilots) to be entitled to fly as captains. But, if the rate of progress towards this end is anything to go by, it would seem that few of them were very enthusiastic about actually seeing this happen. The topic was formally aired again during April 1942 when it was noted that a few observer captains were already being employed by one of the groups of Bomber Command and it was again pointed out, this time by VCAS, Air Chf Mshl Sir Wilfrid Freeman, that this practice was commonplace within the FAA.[33]

Regulations which would have permitted observers to fly as captains were being circulated in draft form before the end

[26]AIR2/4021. Unreferenced letter dated 11 May 1943 from AMP to all AOCinCs at home and abroad and all AOCs at home, explaining the reasons behind the abolition of the 'VR' badge.
[27]AMO A.572/43 of 10 June.
[28]AMO A.6/39 of 12 January.
[29]AIR2/8270. Air Ministry letter A.255910/41/Air Tactics dated 13 June 1941 from the Director of Air Tactics, Air Cdre Crowe, to AOCinCs Bomber, Coastal, Army Co-operation and Flying Training Commands.

[30]AIR14/1941. HQ 5 Gp letter 5G/504/1/Org/DO dated 1 November 1941 from AVM Slessor to AOCinC Bomber Command, Air Mshl Sir Richard Peirse.
[31]AIR2/8270. Air Ministry letter A.255910/41/S.7A dated 25 November 1941.
[32]*Ibid.* Coastal Command letter CC/S.7407/Trg dated 2 December 1941.
[33]AIR6/73. Conclusions of Air Council Meeting 8(42) held on 28 April 1942.

of the month but it was July before anything was published.[34] The new rules grudgingly allowed the possibility of non-pilot captains but only on the personal authority of an AOCinC, which was in itself a strong disincentive to anyone's name being put forward. At much the same time the views of the operators were canvassed for a third time. Bomber and Coastal Commands continued to oppose the concept of observer captains. Army Co-operation and Fighter Commands offered some lukewarm support, which both could afford to do, because neither of them were major operators of multi-seat aircraft.

Undeterred by the general lack of enthusiasm, the Air Ministry encouraged commands to employ non-pilot captains on a trial basis and report back in due course.[35] Nothing having been heard by the autumn, commands were formally requested to submit their comments. There was little progress to report, beyond the fact that Army Co-operation Command had authorised four navigators on the staff of No 42 OTU to fly as captains.[36] Bomber Command was later to adopt a similar practice, albeit on a limited scale, but as yet no one had any operational experience on which to report.[37] On the other hand, in a rather startling development, Bomber Command had appointed an air gunner, Wg Cdr A.E. Lowe, to command a squadron.[38] While this was not a unique occurrence during WW II, the appointment of non-pilots to executive flying posts was extremely unusual.[39]

By 1943 there was growing concern over the whole question of captaincy within the RAF and the Inspector General made it the subject of one of his investigations.[40] In broad terms, Sir Edgar Ludlow-Hewitt reported that there was considerable scope for improvement. He found: that policy differed between commands and between groups within commands; that training in leadership was poor; that individual attitudes towards captaincy were extremely confused, to the extent that many air crew questioned the need for captaincy at all; and that the whole situation was complicated by the frequent need to disregard the traditional rank structure, there being many instances of airmen pilots 'commanding' crews containing officers. Sir Edgar was particularly concerned that the long-term effects of the latter practice might be so corrosive as to permanently devalue the concept of the commission.

The appointment of non-pilots to executive positions was an extremely rare occurrence during WW II but it did happen. This is Wg Cdr W.D. Watkins DSO DFC DFM who commanded No 15 Sqn from 15 April 1944 until he was shot down on 16 November; the only member of his crew to survive, he spent the rest of the war as a PoW. (The Mildenhall Register)

In the context of this book, it is necessary to consider only those aspects of Sir Edgar's findings which relate specifically to non-pilots. He claimed to have begun his investigation 'prejudiced in favour of the idea of navigator captains', which was a considerable about-face, considering his disdain for the observers of 1939 (see page 135). He reported that he had come across many commissioned navigators 'who would make or have made first class captains and compare favourably with any pilot in their qualifications for flight, squadron or higher command.' In the light of this finding, he was very critical of a policy which routinely continued to confer captaincies on freshmen pilots, even when their crews contained an experienced second-tour navigator. Although Sir Edgar stated that there were no non-pilot captains in Coastal Command in early-1943, and only a few in Bomber Command, he had found that 'the pilot's prejudice seems largely to have disappeared in units where the non-pilot captain has proved to be successful in practice.'

Despite their apparent suitability, however, Sir Edgar eventually accepted 'the weight of evidence of navigators themselves (*which*) convinced me that, when acting as such, the

[34]AMO A.756/42 of 23 July.

[35]AIR2/8270. Air Ministry letter A.255910/41/S.7(a) dated 1 July 1942.

[36]*Ibid.* Army Co-operation Command letter AC/3528/P2 dated 10 November 1942.

[37]While never numerous, the employment of navigator captains at Bomber Command OTUs continued for the remainder of the war. For example, three who flew with No 30 OTU in 1943 (with the date of their certificates of competence) were Plt Off A.J.L. Hickox (18 July), Fg Off G.F. Brantingham (18 July) and Flt Lt R. Rook (14 August).

In addition to the above there is anecdotal evidence to suggest that by late 1943 there were occasional instances of navigators flying as captain at squadron level. One example was Sqn Ldr J. Vivian, Navigation Leader on No 57 Sqn, who is said to have acted as captain whenever he flew with a crew on an operational sortie (although the squadron's F.540 contains no specific indication that this was the case).

[38]Appointed to command No 77 Sqn with effect from 10 December 1942, just as the squadron was completing its conversion from Whitleys to Halifaxes, Wg Cdr Lowe remained in post until 12 October 1943.

[39]Another air gunner who exercised executive authority was Sqn Ldr C.A. Maton who commanded a flight of No 502 Sqn from September 1943 to May 1944 when he was promoted to wing commander and took over as CO, remaining in post until October when his aircraft was forced to land in Sweden.

Examples of navigators filling executive appointments included Wg Cdr W.D.G. Watkins, OC No 15 Sqn in 1944, and Wg Cdr A.C. Dowden, OC No 10 Sqn in 1945. Wg Cdr R.C. Alabaster, Sqn Ldr J.E. Oram and Sqn Ldr N.L. Shove were Flight Commanders with No 97 Sqn in 1943, No 40 Sqn in 1944 and No 76 Sqn in 1945, respectively. Note that, as in WW I, ranks were often held on a temporary or acting basis and that people tended to be ranked one notch up in the Pathfinder Force, hence Alabaster's being a wing commander. He later qualified as a pilot, incidentally, and in that capacity he was to command No 608 Sqn in 1945.

[40]AIR14/1012. Inspector General's Report No 277, IG/974 dated 6 March 1943.

navigator is too busy to give the time and attention that he must be able to devote to the remainder of the crew if he is to fulfil his proper function as their captain and leader.' He did not rule them out, however, and his report concluded that non-pilot captains were perfectly viable. He recommended that the associated regulations should be extensively rewritten to make this quite clear and to specify in much greater detail exactly what captaincy involved.[41] In March 1944, after nearly two years of procrastination, the rules were finally amended to read that 'in multi-seater aircraft one member of the crew will be appointed to act as captain of the aircraft. He may be of any air crew category.' Furthermore, authority for such appointments was now vested in COs, rather than AOCinCs.[42]

Just two days after publication of the amended regulations, Coastal Command nominated Flt Lt R.A. Irving to be its first operational navigator captain.[43] Even so, while there was no longer any constraint on their appointment, non-pilot captains remained a rarity for the remainder of WW II, although they did become more numerous in later years within Coastal Command.

Before leaving the topic of captaincy, it should be recorded that the semi-autonomous Polish and French Air Forces, operating as integral elements of the wartime RAF, had little sympathy with the overdeveloped sensitivities of British pilots.[44] In the case of the Poles, for instance, the captaincy of multi-seat aircraft had always been handled by the navigator/observer in the inter-war Polish *Lotnictwo Wojskowe* (Military Aviation) but when Polish squadrons were formed to operate with the RAF they complied with British regulations. In 1940–41, therefore, many senior observers were obliged to fly under the notional captaincy of junior pilots, although, once in the air, the formers' authority was tacitly acknowledged. Full advantage was taken of the loophole presented by the revised regulations of 1942, the option of navigators flying as captains being widely exercised in Polish bomber, maritime and special duties squadrons for the remainder of the war.[45]

Much the same was true of the French. In both of the French-manned Halifax squadrons which operated with No 4 Gp, for instance, it was standard practice for the senior member of the crew to act as captain, regardless of his air crew category. Of the 128 constituted crews which flew with Nos 346 and 347 Sqns between June 1944 and the end of the war in Europe, fifty-six were captained by pilots, sixty-eight by navigators and four by air bombers. Of the thirty-four crews lost, to all causes, sixteen were commanded by pilots and eighteen by navigators. Since these figures reflect almost exactly the proportions of pilot and navigator captains, it strongly suggests that the category of the man in charge had had very little bearing on the outcome of a variety of catastrophic situations.[46]

Planning for the last lap

The revision of air crew categories in 1942 had been tailored to suit the operational needs of the time, the changes that were made having been driven mainly by the need to rationalise the functions of the seven-man crew of a four-engined heavy bomber. While this had more or less established the pattern for the remainder of the war, the size and shape of the air force did not remain the same, nor did the classic seven-man crew suit all aeroplanes. For instance, the late-mark Liberators of 1944 were significantly more expensive in terms of manpower than their British equivalents. Furthermore, the crew complement varied depending upon the role in which they were employed. For example a Liberator Mk VI, operating over the Atlantic on long-range maritime duties, required a crew of ten (two pilots, two navigator (B)s, two air gunners, a flight engineer, two WOps(air) and a WOM(air), the last three all being additionally qualified as both gunners and ASV operators). By contrast, a similar airframe, being flown as a heavy bomber in Italy or India, needed a crew of eleven (two pilots, a navigator, an air bomber, a WOp(air), a WOp/AG, a flight engineer and four air gunners).

To investigate the possibility of resolving some of these inconsistencies, while making a start on considering the RAF's post-war requirements, in September 1944 Air Chf Mshl Sir Sholto Douglas was appointed to chair a Committee on the Composition of Air Crew. It was initially charged with answering two basic questions:[47]

a. What changes needed to be made to the current composition of air crews, and to their relative grading and rates of pay?
b. Which air crew categories would be required after the war and what should be their relative gradings?

Having consulted widely across the RAF, the Douglas Committee's report produced a number of recommendations in response to the first of these questions. The more important of these may be summarised as follows:

a. The categories of navigator (B) and air bomber were now so similar that they could safely be amalgamated. Current air bombers would continue to serve but no more should be trained and the trade should be allowed to waste away.

[41] *Ibid.* Sir Edgar was very concerned that the failure to recognise the need for captaincy, which was widespread throughout the Service, obscured the potential value of the function of the captain and resulted in the majority of them having little idea of their responsibilities and thus exerting little authority. With the aim of raising the status of captains he convened a meeting of very senior officers, including a number of operational AOCinCs, on 25 August 1943. Although it took almost a year to materialise, one of the more obvious consequences of this meeting was the introduction of a brassard to be worn by captains of aircraft in Bomber and Coastal Commands. Authorised by Air Ministry letter S.100641/P.1 of 30 June 1944, the armlet was to be of 'Blue-Grey Serge, with a centre section of Light Blue Cloth bearing the letter C in Red surmounted by an Eagle and Crown of gilded metal.' The brassard proved to be unpopular with air crews, many of whom declined to wear it, and by November both operational commands were already requesting that it be withdrawn. This was not formally approved until as late as 5 November 1945 (by Air Ministry letter S.94096/E.13D) by which time the armlet had already virtually disappeared.

[42] KR 806, which dealt with aircraft captaincy, was extensively amended by the publication of AMO A.252/44 of 23 March.

[43] Flt Lt Irving had previously been decorated with a DFC and Bar while flying Beaufighters of No 236 Sqn in the maritime strike role. Having subsequently spent some time on the staff of HQ 16 Gp, he was posted to No 111 OTU at Nassau (Bahamas) for a Liberator conversion course which began on 25 March 1944. Returning to the UK in July, he and his crew completed a maritime patrol course with No 1674 HCU at Aldergrove before joining No 59 Sqn at Ballykelly on 15 August.

[44] The precise status of the various free allied air forces serving with and within the RAF was complicated. For an appreciation, see Alan Brown's *Airmen in Exile* (2000).

[45] The author is indebted to the Official Historian of the Polish Air Force Association, J.B. Cynk, for this brief appreciation of Polish practice.

[46] Free French practice was brought to this writer's attention by Paul F. Jacquemier, who flew with No 346 Sqn as a WOp(air). The figures have been extracted from Louis Bourgain's *Nuits de Feu sur l'Allemagne* (1991).

[47] AIR2/8638. The establishment of the Douglas Committee and the nature of its enquiries was publicised by Air Ministry letter S.103928/S.10(d) dated 27 October 1944.

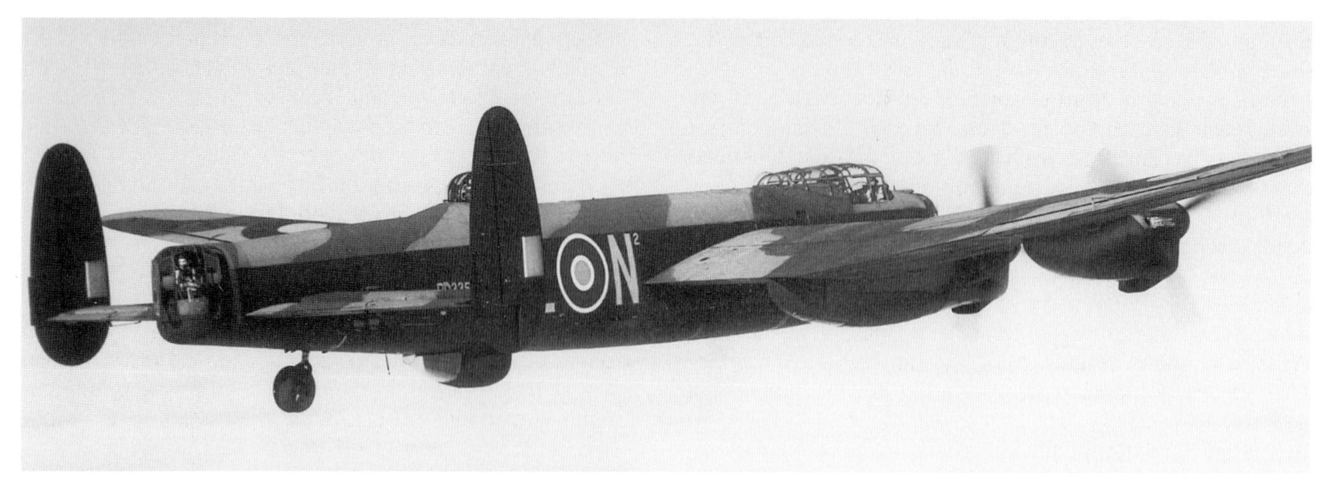

American aeroplanes tended to make much heavier demands on manpower resources than their British counterparts. A Lancaster, like this one (above), PD235/UL.W2 of No 576 Sqn, normally flew with a crew of seven. (D.M. Hannah) *By comparison a Liberator bomber, like this Mk VI, EW157, of No 356 Sqn, needed as many as eleven.* (via G.J. Thomas)

b. Since they were really left-overs from the pre-flight engineer era, Coastal Command's dual-qualified air gunners (flight mechanic) had become something of an anachronism. They too should be allowed to fade away, those who were suitably qualified being remustered as flight engineers.
c. Experience had shown that requiring the WOM(air) to have the high-grade skills of a Group I tradesmen had been unnecessary. In practical terms, he could do little more in the air than replace suspect electronic boxes, a task that was well within the capabilities of (and was often carried out by) the WOp(air). The separate category of the WOM(air) should, therefore, also be permitted to wither away.
d. The grading of WOps(air) should be abandoned because it was a very cumbersome and unsatisfactory procedure which had given rise to a number of unfortunate anomalies.

Apart from the committee's own ideas, its trawl of the various commands had stimulated a number of additional proposals. For instance, Transport Command had recommended that the RAF should introduce an air crew category of 'despatcher' to supervise the RASC personnel, i.e. soldiers, who actually did the work involved in the air-dropping of supplies. It was further requested that a category of 'air quartermaster' be introduced to oversee passengers and the loading and unloading of freight on long-haul routes. While the committee recognised the need for RAF personnel to act as air quartermasters and/or despatchers, it was not persuaded that they needed to have air crew status. After all, Douglas was trying to reduce the number of air crew categories, not create new ones. It was considered that the demand could be adequately satisfied by continuing to rely on army air despatchers and by using airmen from an existing trade for the other tasks.[48] This fell a long way short of what Transport Command had had in mind, but it had to suffice until the 1960s.

On the other hand, the Douglas Committee accepted that the status of meteorological air observers was long overdue for formal recognition and recommended the authorisation of their air crew badge (see page 184). While it may be no more than a coincidence, of course, it may not be without significance that, whereas he had dismissed Transport Command's suggestion, Sir Sholto Douglas had approved a not dissimilar bid from Coastal Command – of which he just happened to be the AOCinC at the time.

The committee ruled favourably on another of Coastal Command's submissions, recommending the introduction of the entirely new air crew category of the radar operator (air). He was to be of PNB quality and take over the responsibility for ASV currently discharged by the WOp(air), many of whom were expected to be remustered to the new specialisation. If a specialist category were to be introduced to handle ASV, however, it was considered that it would no longer be appropriate to pay the shilling-a-day allowance that had previously been paid to suitably qualified WOps(air) (see page 147). This rationale was based on the precedent established by Bomber Command which had initially assigned

[48]AIR2/8636. In November 1945 letter PWM/TSC/S.10(m) noted the subsequent recommendations of the Trades Sub-Committee of the Post-War Manning Committee, which had been set up on 13 October 1944 to review all RAF and WAAF trades. They were: that air quartermasters should be drawn from equipment assistants of Trade Group IV; that they should be of at least corporal rank, and preferably sergeants; and that they should be entitled to draw crew pay. But they were not to be categorised as air crew.

responsibility for the operation of GEE to the WOp/AG who, like his ASV-qualified counterpart in Coastal Command, had been paid an extra shilling-a-day for his pains. This arrangement had not lasted for very long, however, as responsibility for this equipment was soon transferred to the navigator. Apart from being more practical, this was also a much cheaper option because, it was argued, GEE was a basic tool of the navigator's trade so it was neither necessary nor appropriate to pay him anything extra for looking after it.

Bomber Command submitted two proposals for consideration. The committee agreed to recommend the introduction of a new sub-category of air gunner (radar), to handle the anticipated early introduction of Automatic Gun Laying Turrets, but rejected a similar request for formal recognition of the special duty operator, i.e. German linguists and others who handled certain airborne jamming and deception devices.

The only other significant suggestion was sponsored jointly by Transport and Coastal Commands, both of whom wanted flight engineers to be selected from PNB quality candidates. While the abilities of current flight engineers were adequate for Bomber Command's purposes, it was contended that many had experienced difficulty handling the additional maintenance requirements demanded by aircraft which routinely operated away from base. The committee acknowledged that a problem existed but considered that it could be solved by better management of the existing resources, i.e. by ensuring that flight engineers posted to Transport and Coastal Commands already had a substantial amount of experience and/or were basically qualified as Fitter Is or IIs, rather than being first tourist direct entrants. The proposal was rejected.

Finally, the committee noted that air crew pay scales had become so complicated that by 1944 there were nine different rates applicable to sergeants alone. It recommended that all NCO air crew should be classified as belonging to one of only three grades, each of which would have an appropriate pay scale. No proposals were made with respect to the pay of officers.

Moving on to the second question – the long-term future requirement – the committee concluded that the (currently) thirteen categories and sub-categories[49] of wartime air crew would be overspecialised for peacetime purposes. It therefore recommended that these should be reduced to just five, tentatively identified as pilot, navigator/bomb aimer, flight engineer, radio operator (air) and air gunner/armourer. It was recognised, however, that it would be unwise to attempt to implement such a sweeping change until the fighting was actually over.

As to relative grading, the committee recommended that all five categories 'should be of equal status as regards conditions of service and rates of pay.' This degree of equality was justified on the grounds of the significantly increased level of technical skill that it was proposed to demand of the lineal descendants of the 'non-PNB' trades.

While acknowledging that it was exceeding its brief, having spent some time reflecting on the provision of post-war air crew, the Douglas Committee considered it appropriate to offer some further thoughts on their status. It recommended that the granting of commissions should be restricted to the numbers required to do specific jobs, i.e. to fill leader posts on squadrons and associated appointments at station level, and on the specialist staffs at headquarters. That would mean that the vast majority of air crew would be airmen and the committee considered that they should revert to 'the normal Service custom of working up through the ranks.'[50] This was not enlarged upon, but it plainly implied removing the wartime, fast-track, 'instant NCO' option and reinstating something like the aircraftmen gunners of the 1920s, except that this time, even pilots were to be consigned to oblivion.

After it had begun work the Douglas Committee had been asked to consider two further topics, captaincy and air crew badges. The question of badges is dealt with separately below but, so far as captaincy was concerned, somewhat predictably, the committee recommended that 'normally the captain of *(an)* aircraft should be the first pilot.' It did go on to concede that, 'exceptionally, other members of air crew of proven merit and experience should be eligible for selection', the unavoidable implication clearly being that pilots did not need to display any particular degree of merit or to have accumulated any worthwhile degree of experience. This did little more than endorse the *status quo* but the committee did go on to stress two points which had originally been raised in the Inspector General's Report of 1943. First, that, in heavy aircraft, the captain should always be an officer and, secondly, that this should also be the case where crews of mixed status were concerned, although it was not considered practical to insist that he must also be the senior man on board.

Rather like Sefton Brancker's proposals of late 1918, all of this turned out to be too late. Within days of the Douglas Committee's recommendations being published, the war in Europe ended. The formal recognition of the flying 'Met men' had already been authorised but most of the other changes which had been recommended were overtaken by events. Had the war continued into 1946, as had seemed likely when the committee had been set up, several of its other proposals would probably have been implemented but the sudden ending of hostilities in August 1945 rendered any interim changes redundant. Attention now needed to be focused on the post-war situation.

The desirability of twin-winged air crew badges is reconsidered

Having last been subjected to serious scrutiny in 1942 (see page 164), the contentious issue of air crew badges had lain dormant for a year. There had been a brief flurry of interest in March 1943 when a proposal, which would have reorganised the various air crew trades into thirteen categories and redesignated some of their badges, was under consideration. In commenting on this idea, Air Cdre H. Gordon-Dean suggested that the whole business of badges was out of control. Pointing out that no attempt was made to distinguish between different types of pilot, he failed to see why it was necessary to do so for non-pilots. He considered, therefore, that 'all air crew other than pilots should be satisfied with one common brevet' which, he suggested, might be an 'AC'.[51]

Nothing came of this and the subject of air crew badges was sidelined again. That is not to say, however, that it was

[49]The thirteen were: pilot; navigator; nav(B); nav(R); nav(W); air bomber; flight engineer; WOM(air); WOp(air) Grade I; WOp(air) Grade II; air gunner; air gunner/FM(A) and air gunner/FM(E); a fourteenth, the meteorological air observer, was about to be introduced.

[50]AIR2/2662. From the Report of the Committee on the Composition of Air Crew, published as S.103609 dated May 1945. This document is also the source of most of the observations summarised in this section.

[51]AIR2/8482. Memo BJ186/DTT dated 6 March 1943 from Gordon-Dean (DTT) to Air Cdre D.V. Carnegie (DTF).

no longer a sensitive issue. Although most senior officers (*all* of whom were pilots) preferred to brush the question aside, there can be no doubt that some of the 'half-a-badge' fraternity harboured some feelings of resentment. Apart from the perceived indignity of having to wear a badge with only one wing, there was dissatisfaction with the fact that the badge worn by pilots featured an 'RAF' monogram. Some questioned the logic of this. Were not all British flyers members of the RAF? However many wings pilots decided to award themselves, would it not be more appropriate for them to be identified by a 'P'?

Then again, some people were irked by the fact that a pilots badge featured a crown while no else's did. Why, asked the malcontents, were non-pilots denied this token of royal approval? This particular complaint may have been stimulated by the fact that a new range of single-winged badges introduced by the RCAF in the spring of 1943 did feature a crown.[52] From this evidence, it could be argued that, apart from being afforded a lower status than all pilots, RAF non-pilots were even outclassed by 'colonials'. The presence in the UK of rapidly increasing numbers of USAAF personnel from the summer of 1942 onwards had inevitably added fuel to the fire, because all the badges worn by American air crew had two wings. To cap it all, and as previously noted, the RN had recently introduced twin-winged badges for its non-pilots.

[52]While Canadian pilots wore badges featuring an 'RCAF' monogram, all other Canadian aircrew originally had to make do with RAF emblems, locally produced versions of these tending to be rather larger than the official British pattern. Resentment at having to wear British badges grew to such an extent that the Canadian Air Council was obliged to spend much of 1942 pondering the problem, this process including serious consideration of the possibility of introducing twin-winged national badges for all categories. It was eventually decided to stick with single wings but to add a crown and to incorporate the letters RCAF within the lower arc of the laurel wreath. Inexplicably, since they were never approved, some twin-winged non-pilot badges were manufactured and some were actually worn in early 1943, although the authorities had managed to stamp them out before the end of April.

The definitive single-winged Canadian badges were introduced by an Air Regulation of 26 March 1943, the details of which were promulgated via AMO A.1291/43 of 16 December for the benefit of RCAF personnel serving under the aegis of the RAF. There were five patterns: 'N' for all categories of navigator, 'B' for air bombers, 'E' for flight engineers, 'AG' for air gunners and wireless mechanics (air gunner), and 'WAG' for WOp/AGs.

The latter represented something of a victory for popular opinion, as an 'RAF-style', i.e. crownless, 'WAG' badge had been introduced in Canada, quite unofficially, in 1942. The RCAF had rapidly outlawed these, but the point had obviously been made. It is not impossible, incidentally, that some RAF WOp/AGs may also have gained access to examples of the illicit Canadian 'WAG' badge. Even after the definitive selection of 'crowned' RCAF badges had been introduced non-standard versions continued to appear, 'NW's and 'NB's for Navs(W) and Navs(B), for instance, neither of which are believed to have been formally authorised, although both appear to have been tolerated.

For the record it should be noted that, for the benefit of BCATP trainees, the Canadians offered similar ranges of crowned badges incorporating RAF, RAAF and RNZAF monograms within the lower arc of the wreath (the latter being woven in blue for Australians). These were little used, however, and most of those that may have been issued on graduation were soon replaced by the appropriate national emblems. That is to say that British, New Zealand and Southern Rhodesian air crew wore standard RAF pattern badges, while Australians wore RAF-style emblems with the wreath woven in blue (and, uniquely, with the observer's 'O' set within the wreath). The only non-pilot badge sponsored by the SAAF appears to have been for observers/navigators and consisted of a single wing attached to the Arms of South Africa, set within a laurel wreath and surmounted by a crown. South Africans serving in other non-pilot categories are presumed to have worn RAF-style badges.

As a footnote, the reader should be aware that the authentic-looking, RAF-style 'WAG' badges which may be purchased today (2000) are replicas produced for the 'collectors market'; no British 'WAG' badge was ever approved by the Air Council.

Question	% Yes
Do civilians know what each of the current badges stands for?	37%
Do civilians consider the twin-winged pilots badge to be 'superior' to single-winged badges?	89%
The original observers badge was 'earned in action'; does this honourable association read across to current non-pilot badges?	27%
Are the current single-winged badges satisfactory?	38%*
If 'No' to Q.4, is it desirable to change to twin-wings, even if it confuses the public?	84%*
Should non-pilots have twin-winged badges?	72%

* *Excluding pilots.*

Fig. 25. *Results of a poll conducted among 180 untrained prospective air crew in May 1944.*

This problem should not be overstated; there was no incipient mutiny, or anything like it. But, on the other hand, neither should it be dismissed. While discontent was far from being felt universally, it should be acknowledged that there was a low key sense of injustice over the design of air crew badges.[53] Nevertheless, the air force was largely successful in ignoring the problem until May 1944 when AMT, Air Mshl Sir Peter Drummond, revived the question of twin-wings. Wearily pointing out that this matter had been settled only two years previously, Air Mshl Sir Bertine Sutton nevertheless undertook to test the water again.[54]

Seeking the opinions of crusty old air marshals could be expected to elicit much the same sort of impatient response as the previous review, so Sutton decided to try a different approach. This time, the aim was to establish the relatively unbiased view of inexperienced personnel who had yet to have their opinions distorted by loyalty, bigotry and partisanship. Only Flying Training Command was therefore consulted. Having overseen the 1942 exercise as Sutton's predecessor, the AOCinC, Sir Philip Babington, was an old hand at the air crew badge game and he quickly arranged for a poll to be taken among cadets who had yet to embark on formal flying training.

Thirty each of prospective pilots, navigators, air bombers, flight engineers, air gunners and WOps(air) were asked six questions. The responses are summarised at Fig. 25.[55] The results of this survey appear to be quite conclusive with a three-to-one majority in favour of twin-winged badges for non-pilots. When they were presented to the Air Council, however, considerable emphasis was placed on the fact that, in responding to Q.6, the thirty prospective pilots had been split 50:50. By giving such undue weight to the relatively uninformed opinions of this small sub-group of cadets, simply because they were pilots – or might be one day – the overall picture was grossly distorted. As a result, surprising as it may seem (or perhaps not), it was concluded that the poll had failed to establish a clear cut case one way or the other and AMP recommended that the question should be referred to the Douglas Committee.

[53]For example, on page 50 of his *One Wing High* (1995), Harry Lomas describes the disappointed reaction of some of his colleagues on being awarded their 'N' badges at the end of 1943.

[54]Yet another of the very senior RAF officers of WW II who had begun his flying career as an observer in WW I, Air Mshl Sutton had qualified for his flying 'O' with No 5 Sqn as early as 14 December 1915.

[55]AIR2/8369. Air Mshl Babington informed AMT of the results of the poll in his letter FTC/AOCC/42 dated 27 May 1944.

Initially, Douglas' team thought that it might well be a good idea to dispense with the single-winged pattern and to replace it with pilot-style 'wings' carrying appropriate monograms to distinguish each trade. It was felt that this might be good for morale in general and, more specifically, that it might make it easier for trainees who, for whatever reason, failed to make the grade as pilots to come to terms with their reassignment to a less glamorous occupation. In the end, however, the double-wing once again failed to find favour. As the committee explained:[56]

> 'For traditional and sentimental reasons, and in view of the fact that a cross section of opinion recently taken in Flying Training Command revealed no strong desire for abandonment of single-wing badges, a result which we consider would certainly be confirmed if a free vote in the operational commands were taken, we do not recommend that there should be any change in the design of air crew badges.'

As has already been pointed out, this was a most curious interpretation of the results of the recent poll which had actually shown that 62% of non-pilots were dissatisfied with the single wing, that 84% of them would have preferred a double wing and that, even allowing for the views of prospective pilots, 72% of those polled thought that twin-wings ought to be introduced. On the other hand, it might have been unwise to place too much reliance on the opinions of such an inexperienced group and it was almost certainly true that by 1945 some single-winged veterans would have been most reluctant to part with their old badges. In any event, on 8 June 1945, when AMP held a meeting to consider the Douglas Committee's recommendations, the retention of single-wings was endorsed. But this was far from being the end of the matter.

The wearing of RAF badges by personnel of other Services

Meanwhile, while the question of twin-wings had been raised and dismissed twice, another problem to do with air crew badges had been simmering ever since the beginning of the war. By 1945 it had become such a contentious issue that it eventually provoked a Parliamentary Question.

It will be recalled that in 1918, following the establishment of the RAF, the Army had decided that it wanted little more to do with air matters and that it would be inappropriate for ex-RFC officers, electing to return to the fold, to continue to wear their flying badges (see page 89). This policy proved to be short-lived, however, because a steady trickle of army officers was seconded to the RAF for flying duties during the inter-war years. Since the Army no longer had a pilots badge of its own, it was agreed that these soldiers should wear RAF 'wings' while actually serving with the RAF and for the next four years, during which they were liable to recall in an emergency. In 1938 the position was reviewed and it was agreed that these men could wear their pilots badges permanently, even after the RAF had ceased to have any claim on them.

Some of the soldiers who re-enlisted in the army, following the outbreak of war in 1939 were veterans who had flown as pilots during WW I. After some deliberation the Air Council conceded that these volunteers were covered by the 1938 decision. From June 1940, therefore, any army personnel whose documents showed that they had qualified for RFC, RNAS or RAF pilots badges were granted the privilege of wearing current pattern RAF 'wings' on their army tunics.[57]

No one ever seems to have raised the issue at the time but, in view of the way in which old rules were subsequently invoked to justify the wearing (or not) of old badges, it is worth reiterating that, in theory at least, a WW I pilot's grasp on his RFC 'wings' was not totally secure. The Army Order which had introduced the RFC pilots badge in February 1913 had specifically required that the wearer remain 'efficient' as a pilot. This rule was relaxed in 1916 to the extent that it permitted the badge to be worn permanently, even if the wearer ceased to be employed on flying duties, so long as he continued to serve with the RFC. For a pilot who had ceased to be employed by the RFC to retain his badge, however, required the permission of the Army Council. This permission was granted only if the individual had left the RFC as a result of wounds or some disability directly attributable to flying.[58] Hence the previously noted War Office ruling that had required any ex-RFC men exercising their right to return to the Army, following their automatic transfer to the RAF in April 1918, to forfeit their flying badges.

Leaving aside such arcane considerations, it was inevitable that, once all ex-pilots had been given the right to wear their 'wings', ex-observers would expect to be granted a similar dispensation. One would have thought this a reasonable enough claim but the Air Council decided that, while a WW I observers badge could be worn on RAF uniform, it was inappropriate for it to be worn on khaki. The rationale for this decision was that, unlike army pilots of the inter-war years, ex-observers had never had any obligation to fly with the RAF. While this was a defensible argument, its logic was stretched beyond its breaking point by the concession which had permitted soldiers upon whom the RAF no longer had any claim, or, even worse, upon whom it had *never* had a claim, to continue to wear their pilots badges.

The Air Council's policy was seriously compromised by this inconsistency and the repeated rejection of soldiers' requests to wear observers badges rankled.[59] By 1942, in an effort to shore up its case, the Air Ministry had resorted to exploiting some of the more esoteric aspects of military dress regulations. It was contended that the RAF's pilots badge was not 'a decoration', but an integral element of the unique RAF uniform and that inter-Service cross-dressing was quite inappropriate.[60] To support this argument, it was pointed out that the RN did not permit the wearing of any RAF-sponsored badges on its uniforms and, likewise, that the Army did not permit air force or naval badges to disfigure its immaculate khaki.

Since the RAF flying badge represented a glaring exception to the latter rule, this argument was so transparent as to be totally unconvincing, especially to ex-observers. Furthermore, while the Admiralty may not have permitted RAF badges to be worn on RN uniform, it did recognise their status and a pilot, observer/navigator, gunner or WOp(air) who had qualified as such in the RAF, but who subsequently served

[56]See Note 50.

[57]ACI 660 of 29 June 1940. These regulations were subsequently refined and restated, the final iteration being in ACI 1263 of 20 September 1944.

[58]AIR1/818/204/4/1308. This file contains correspondence relating to the refinement of the regulation governing the wearing of 'wings'.

[59]Although the prohibition on the wearing of the flying 'O' by soldiers was publicised from time to time throughout the war, this did not prevent the more determined ex-observers from sporting their badges.

[60]In October 1944, the Air Ministry buttressed its arguments by enshrining them within Kings Regulations (Amendment List 135), thus providing them with the legal basis which they had previously lacked.

Most of the RAF Regiment's senior members were seconded army officers. While they wore RAF Regiment shoulder flashes, however, they retained their army ranks and when this unidentified colonel was photographed in Belgium in October 1944 he should certainly not have been wearing the flying 'O' that he had presumably acquired during WW I. On the other hand, it would probably have taken a general to tell a colonel that he was improperly dressed and that presupposed that the general knew the rules (and cared). (via B.L. Davis)

in the RN, was permitted to wear the equivalent FAA badge. This option was not available to the Army, of course, since it no longer sponsored any appropriate forms of air crew badge.[61] On the other hand, the War Office had endorsed the wearing of the 'AG' badge by properly qualified army officers while flying with the RAF (see below). Furthermore, the Admiralty had permitted its naval gunlayers badge to be worn by appropriately qualified soldiers serving with the Maritime Royal Artillery as Acting Gunlayers (Defensively Equipped Merchant Ships).[62] Going back to WW I, of course, one could also cite the fact that the RN had been content that Army officers seconded to fly with the navy as observers should wear the RNAS eagle (see Chapter 4, Note 7).

So much for the Air Ministry's contention that there was no precedent for cross-dressing within the military, but its willingness to misrepresent the facts did not end there. Determined to deny the back-seaters of WW I the right to wear their badges, the Air Ministry had claimed that the flying 'O' was an exclusively RAF emblem. This was patently not the case, of course, as it had initially been sponsored by the Army and as such had narrowly missed being manufactured in khaki (see Chapter 3, Note 4C). Indeed many of the soldiers who were asking to be allowed to wear their old badges had actually earned the right to do so *as* soldiers.

Applications to wear flying 'O's were not confined to soldiers serving with the British Army, incidentally. The Air Ministry was obliged to fight a running battle with Pretoria in 1940–43, which succeeded in denying South African veterans the right to wear their badges. The whole question eventually became a matter of public interest when Maj Oliver Stewart made the issue the subject of a press campaign,[63] but the Air Ministry was unmoved.

In January 1945 official intransigence over this matter was eventually raised in the House of Commons by Mr Edgar Granville (Eye) who stressed that, in contrast to a pilots 'wings', the RFC's observers badge was not awarded 'because one had done so many hours in the air (*but because one had flown*) so many operations against the enemy.' Col T.G. Greenwell (The Hartlepools) and Maj F.W. Cundiff (Rusholme)[64] expounded along much the same lines.[65]

The MPs' case hinged on the fact that, since most observers badges had been won in battle, they amounted to *de facto* decorations and were almost regarded as such by some who had worn them. For the Air Ministry to insist that they had been no more than a piece of uniform, it was argued, showed a lack of appreciation of the reality of the situation. It was, said Granville, 'a very niggardly thing to take away a treasured distinction from men who had worthily earned it'. Furthermore, even if the badge was no more than a piece of uniform, until 1918 it had been a piece of *army* uniform, so, it was argued, there were no grounds to prevent its being worn on khaki.

It fell to the recently appointed Parliamentary Under-Secretary of State for Air, Cdr R.A. Brabner, to present the case for the defence. Although he rehearsed the old arguments, he had nothing new to say and it was clear that over the previous five years the Air Ministry had 'painted itself into a corner' over this issue. Its only options were to concede or to continue to hide behind its rather moth-eaten veil of inconsistent dogma and illogical regulations. Brabner did his best with the material available to him but it was plain that he failed to persuade the House of the justice of his Ministry's position.

This was of little consequence, however, as it was not a matter of debate. No vote was to be taken. Brabner's task had simply been to respond to a question that had been asked. It did not matter that he had been obliged to present an unconvincing answer. He had been required only to make it plain that the answer was final.

Following post-war demobilisation, the incidence of requests declined rapidly, the last one of which this writer is aware being submitted in 1950. The Air Ministry stuck resolutely to its guns, however, and none of the dwindling band of old soldiers ever regained the right to wear his hard won observers badge.

Further problems with the wearing of badges

In the context of badges, the Air Ministry's preferential treatment of erstwhile pilots proved to have opened a Pandora's

[61] To be strictly accurate, ACI 768 of 11 April 1942 had introduced an Army Flying Badge, but this was to be worn only by AOP and glider pilots. The detail changed from time to time but, broadly speaking, pilots were entitled to wear this badge on completion of elementary flying training, i.e. an EFTS course, followed by conversion onto Austers at No 43 OTU or onto gliders via a course at the Glider Training School and/or a similarly specialised unit. While this level of instruction was clearly sufficient for the purpose, the overall demands of these courses were far less stringent than those which had to be passed prior to the award of an RAF (or FAA) flying badge. Since the two badges did not reflect the same level of skill or breadth of achievement it was presumably considered inappropriate to substitute the army-sponsored emblem for RAF 'wings'.

For the record, it should be noted that ACI 1128 of 9 August 1944 introduced a Second Glider Pilots Badge which was to be worn by the co-pilots of dual-controlled heavy assault gliders. These men were trained at the same units as 'proper' glider pilots but they attended less comprehensive courses.

[62] ACI 1380 of 18 September 1943.

[63] *Evening Standard*, 25 November 1943.

[64] Cundiff had flown as an observer with No 2 Sqn in 1917.

[65] *Hansard*, 18 January 1945.

box. If soldiers, including the Home Guard, could wear RAF 'wings' what of such paramilitary forces as the Royal Observer Corps? Then again, could a policeman wear a flying badge? Along with other similar organisations, both of these were ruled out of court. But in 1944 this policy was inadvertently subverted by King George VI who, in effect, personally authorised the Commissioner of the Metropolitan Police, Sir Philip Game, a retired air vice-marshal, to wear his flying badge on his police uniform. Sir Philip promptly passed on the good news to half-a-dozen lesser members of the constabulary who had similarly been pilots at one time. This called for a degree of delicate diplomacy which eventually succeeded in righting the regally upset applecart. Sir Philip and his men dutifully toed the party line and took their badges off again.[66]

Meanwhile, the Air Ministry's restrictive attitude towards the wearing of flying badges by erstwhile non-pilot air crew had disadvantaged certain ex-gunners, as well as ex-observers. Some of these men were soldiers. In February 1941 an officer of Anti-Aircraft Command had accompanied an RAF crew on a bombing mission; his observations had been so useful (to Fighter and Bomber Commands, as well as to the Army) that further similar flights were arranged. In October a batch of twenty army officers was formally trained by the RAF as air gunners and in January 1942 they became the staff of the newly established AA Observation Section. Proudly wearing RAF 'AG' badges, they were authorised to fly operationally with Bomber Command to observe German *Flak*. The section was disbanded in May 1942, by which time it had lost seven of its members in action in the course of flying a total of 168 sorties. Although the section no longer existed, a few army officers continued to fly with the RAF until the end of the war (see, for instance, Chapter 22, Note 3).

In June 1943 the GOCinC Anti-Aircraft Command, Gen Sir Frederick Pile, pointed out that RAF air gunners were allowed to continue to wear their 'AG' badges after they had ceased flying and he asked the War Office to permit his officers to do the same.[67] His request was strongly supported by HQ Fighter Command, whose AOCinC urged the Air Ministry to press the War Office to allow its soldiers to wear their RAF badges.[68] Unbeknown to Air Mshl Leigh-Mallory, however, it was not the War Office that was dragging its feet; the problem lay much closer to home. But it was all to no avail in any case.

With hindsight, one might consider that, rather than simply pleading for equality with RAF gunners, the general would have done better to base his argument on the clear precedent set by the fact that any soldier, recognised by the RAF as having once been accredited as a pilot, was permitted to wear his 'wings'. As previously discussed, however, by 1943 the position of the Air Ministry's mandarins had become so deeply entrenched that they had denied themselves any room to manoeuvre. As a result, they were quite incapable of acknowledging the justice of the Army's submission and the Air Council declined to extend its flying badge concession to embrace ex-air gunners.[69]

The same dismissive attitude was displayed in the cases of a handful of pre-war RAF ex-gunners who were still serving. This was because any airman wearing a winged bullet and mustered as air crew on or after 3 September 1939 had been required to exchange it for the new 'AG' badge when this had been introduced in the following December. Anyone, airman or officer, who had completed an appropriate flying training course since then would automatically have qualified for an 'AG' badge (see page 141). These regulations took care of all wartime gunners, of course, but they did not cater for people who had once been air gunners but who had ceased to be employed as such before the war. Those who had remained as airmen were still permitted to wear their obsolete winged bullets but these had never been worn by officers, so any airmen gunners who had since been commissioned had been obliged to forfeit the distinguishing emblem that showed that they had once been recognised as aviators.

Most were content to do without but the publicity surrounding the introduction of the range of new air crew badges in September 1942 (see page 162) prompted a few pre-war ex-gunners to request permission to wear one of these. Perhaps the most deserving case was that submitted by Sqn Ldr R. Wright.[70] As an aircraftman, he had qualified for a winged bullet at Eastchurch in 1926 (No 22 Course). He subsequently served with No 39 Sqn in the UK and India until 1933, initially as a wireless operator mechanic (air gunner) but from 1931 as a full-time air gunner (wireless operator mechanic) (see page 110). During this period he won the squadron's annual bombing trophy once and its gunnery trophy twice, earned an AOC's commendation and was decorated with a Distinguished Flying Medal for his service during the Chitral Relief of 1932.

In view of his experience, and the fact that he had been a *full-time* air gunner, he would have been eligible for automatic remustering as an observer in 1938 (see page 129). In fact, however, he had ceased flying by then and on being commissioned he had lost the right to wear his old arm badge. Wright considered that he was amply qualified to wear all or any of the 'O', 'AG', 'N' and/or 'B' badges. His question, therefore, was not actually whether he could wear one of these badges, but which one he ought to ask for.

His case was supported by Air Cdre J.R. Cassidy at HQ 27 Gp who forwarded it to the Air Ministry. They promptly ruled that Wright was not entitled to wear a flying badge of any kind. Thus, while a part-time Home Guard private soldier who had logged perhaps fifty hours, permitting him to qualify as a pilot just before the war ended in 1918, could wear a flying badge, a regular RAF officer with over 1000 hours of airborne time under his belt (well over 300 of these having been flown on operations) and the ribbon of the DFM on his chest could not. If ever there had been a case for the Ministry to exercise some discretion, this had surely been it. The mandarins were adamant, however; there were to be no concessions where non-pilots were concerned. Sqn Ldr Wright's case was firmly rejected and No 27 Gp was advised not to bother lodging an appeal.

[66]AIR2/4062. The correspondence relating to this affair, in which the key players were AMP (Sir Bertine Sutton), the Secretary of State for Air (Sir Archibald Sinclair) and the King's Private Secretary (Sir Alan Lascelles) is on this file.

[67]AIR2/6336. Letter AAC/30147/A, of 4 June 1943, from Gen Pile, GOCinC Anti-Aircraft Command, to the War Office.

[68]*Ibid.* HQ Fighter Command letter FC/S.27927/Ops3(b) dated 22 June 1943 from Air Mshl T. Leigh-Mallory to the Under-Secretary of State at the Air Ministry, Sir Hugh Seely.

[69]*Ibid.* Air Ministry letter A.15766/39/S.7.(a).1 of August 1943.

[70]AIR2/8369. The correspondence relating to Wright's submission is on this file.

Chapter 24

Planning for peace

While the Committee on the Composition of Air Crew had concentrated on what changes might usefully be made to air crew categories for the remainder of the war, it had also given some consideration to longer-term arrangements. The Douglas Committee had not been set up in isolation, however, and several other bodies had been working on a number of other, closely related, topics at much the same time. Among these were: the Post-War Manning Committee and the Personnel Reserves Committee, both of which were chaired by DGM, AVM J.W. Cordingley; Air Mshl Sir Roderic Hill's Committee to determine the Future of the Technical Branch and a Committee, chaired by Air Mshl Sir Philip Babington, to decide the RAF's Future Administrative Requirements.

All of this activity was prompted by the realisation that in 1946, just as it had had to do in 1919, the RAF would have to deal with massive demobilisation and reorganise itself on a peacetime basis. One bitter lesson that had been learned from WW I was that the national economy, which would be in the throes of switching from a wartime to a peacetime footing, with all that that implied in terms of cancelled military contracts, would be unable to absorb several million men all at once. To avoid creating mass unemployment, demobilisation was to done in phases with release dates being broadly decided on a 'first in, first out' basis with priority being given to older personnel.

While the government's imposition of this formula had settled the demobilisation issue, the RAF had to find its own solutions to the problems of internal reorganisation. While the questions that had to be answered in 1946 were much the same as those of 1919, the circumstances in which they were being asked were very different. The Armistice of November 1918 had come as something of a surprise and, with no previous experience of how to run a peacetime air force, and no guarantee that there would even be one, it is perhaps understandable if some mistakes were made. None of these uncertainties applied to the end of WW II. With the Allies firmly re-established on the continent by the autumn of 1944, victory was only a matter of time. It came rather sooner than had been anticipated, but, as the establishment of the various 'Post-War' Committees shows, the end had been predictable enough for planning for it to have been put in hand in good time. Furthermore, a permanent air force was a matter of fact, not conjecture, and there was ample experience upon which to draw. The RAF should, therefore, have been able to make a much better job of its second transition from war to peace. So far as its air crew were concerned, it failed to do so.

The nature of the problem

It will be recalled that the days of the omnipotent commissioned pilot, assisted, when unavoidable, by a part-time airman gunner or a corporal observer, were over by the time that war had broken out. Somewhat reluctantly, the RAF had accepted that its part-time air crew would have to become full-timers and that some of them, the observers, would have to be sergeants. The introduction of these 'instant' SNCOs in 1939 had caused some protest which AMP, AVM Portal, had dismissed at the time, although it would seem that these objections had been registered. By early 1940 it had been agreed that all gunners would also have to be sergeants. This development was bound to lead to a further proliferation of very junior 'senior' NCOs which, in turn, provoked another wave of concern for the social and disciplinary well-being of the Service. AMP was, therefore, obliged to reconsider the problem.

Portal, by now an air marshal, eventually suggested a scheme under which all airmen air crew, including pilots, would become a discrete corporate entity.[1] They were to have no executive authority outside their own community and were to live and mess together, segregated from 'proper' NCOs. It was proposed that they should all wear three chevrons but in a different colour from those of real sergeants. Among themselves, air crew would be graded as Class I, II or III, the first two being distinguished by an appropriate numeral in the vee of their stripes, with selected Class I airmen possibly being authorised to wear a flight sergeant's crown.

Reading between the lines of this proposal, one can see that after only six months of wartime experience the RAF was already finding it difficult to work within the constraints imposed by the traditional military rank structure. The root of the problem was that, broadly speaking, seniority in rank was supposed to come with age and experience, and it implied an increased level of responsibility. None of these criteria applied to the majority of air crew who were, typically, very young, very inexperienced and responsible only for their own actions within a crew. Yet, if they were going to be able to handle complicated equipment, under fire in an airborne environment, air crew needed to be very capable people. It followed that they needed to be accorded an appropriate level of pay and respect and, within a military society, this could only be done by granting them an appropriate rank. Portal's ideas were an attempt to break out of this straightjacket but, at the time, they were not adopted.

This problem was not confined to NCOs, of course, and, in some respects, it was even worse where officers were concerned. Reference has previously been made to changing attitudes towards commissions, notably in the context of the Ottawa Conference of 1942. Although the RAF had continued to accept that up to 50% of its air crew might have to be officers (which was, after all, its own invention) this had never been more than a rather hastily devised wartime expedient. Unfortunately, the educational and behavioural standards, the degrees of enterprise, mental alertness and courage, and the sense of responsibility which were expected of an officer were much the same as those demanded of many air crew. The

[1] AIR2/4456. Unreferenced letter dated 5 February 1940 from AMP, Air Mshl Portal, to all AOCinCs.

inescapable conclusion was that most air crew deserved their commissions. If this approach were to be sustained in the peacetime RAF, however, it would make the Service permanently 'top heavy' with what would be, in effect, quasi-officers who had little, if any, executive function.

The end of the war was seen to present an ideal opportunity for restoring a more traditional balance between commissioned and non-commissioned personnel and, perhaps, for finding a means of avoiding the over-ranking of air crew. The Post-War Manning Committee suggested that the problem might be solved by treating air crew in the peacetime air force as a new form of, what was loosely termed, 'sub-officer' who would fall somewhere between warrant and commissioned officers. This rather *outré* proposal was circulated to all commands, both at home and abroad, and a wide cross section of opinion was sought at other relatively senior levels within the command structure, a total of sixty-eight addressees in all.

The response could fairly be described as inconclusive. Consider, for example, the replies to a question regarding the need for separate messes for sub-officers. Of those who had been asked, 43% had been in favour and 9% had been against. Unfortunately, since the remaining 48% had declined to offer any opinion at all, this had left the question substantially unanswered. Similarly indeterminate views were expressed over the desirability of reintroducing short service commissions. Twenty-one responses were in favour; nineteen were not, leaving twenty-eight who either knew or cared not. Nevertheless, when reduced to a crude 'for' or 'against' assessment, 63% of the responses could be considered to be in favour of the 'sub-officer' idea. Most of those who dissented counter-proposed a reversion to a form of 'tradesmen air crew', some going so far as specifically to recommend the reinstatement of pre-war practice.[2]

Devising the solution to the problem

With the ending of the European war the urgency attached to the deliberations of the various committees increased and it fell to the recently appointed AMP, Air Mshl Sir John Slessor, to consider their recommendations and to adopt or adapt them as necessary to create a coherent policy. He concluded that, whatever proposal emerged, it would have to possess three fundamental characteristics. First, it would have to preserve the coherence of the RAF, that is to say, avoid its polarisation into air and ground factions. Secondly, it would be necessary to reduce the wartime overprovision of officers to the numbers actually required to 'manage' the Service. Thirdly, something would need to be done about warrant and non-commissioned ranks which, so far as air crew were concerned, had lost their true significance and become little more than pay grades.

AMP proposed to solve the first problem by accepting the five permanent air crew categories proposed by the Douglas Committee, drawing the engineers, signallers and gunners from ground tradesmen who, after a period of flying duties, would revert to their original occupations. Since these men would be required to maintain currency in their original trades, this was expected to provide sufficient air/ground cross-fertilisation to ensure the desired degree of cohesion. On the other hand, the demands placed on pilots and navigators made it impractical to expect them to be dual-qualified as technicians. It was accepted, therefore, that most of them would have to be directly recruited as professionals and that any serving airmen who were selected for pilot or navigator training would have to be permanently remustered as air crew.

There was no dispute over the second problem, since there was widespread agreement that it would be necessary to reduce significantly the overprovision of air crew officers. It followed that the majority of air crew would not be commissioned in the future, which led directly to the third problem, that of the status which they were to be accorded. In view of the Service's ambivalent reaction to the 'sub-officer' idea, this was rejected. Nevertheless, AMP recognised that air crew were 'different' and that this difference needed to be acknowledged in some way. He also considered that a similar distinction should be granted to certain highly skilled technicians, mostly those of Trade Group I, especially as it was anticipated that three of the five post-war air crew categories would be drawn from this pool. He proposed therefore to treat these tradesmen as a new class of 'artificers' and to muster them on the same semi-privileged basis as that envisaged for air crew, perhaps also hoping by this means further to cement the cohesion between ground and air personnel.

So far as air crew were concerned, AMP's concept involved new rank titles which would have a status equivalent to warrant and NCO ranks within the other traditional groups. While senior members of the new air crew structure were to have notional executive authority over all airmen, however, it was expected that this would normally be exercised only within the group, Sir John anticipating that 'in the ordinary way, I do not think that the question of executive command over airmen of other groups will arise.' To this end, it was envisaged that air crew (and artificers) would be mustered separately on parades and, to reflect their superior status, that they were unlikely to become involved in fire picquets, orderly sergeant and other such mundane barrack duties. His thoughts also embraced the need for segregated messes, dedicated rank badges and even the possibility of a different style of uniform for the air crew, the old RFC 'maternity jacket' being suggested for walking-out dress.

While some of its details would be discarded, within AMP's overall mid-1945 concept can be seen most of the key features of the scheme that was to be implemented a year later.[3] On the other hand, it also bore more than a passing resemblance to Sir Charles Portal's ideas of 1940 which, considering that he was CAS when the post-war plans were being laid, is perhaps not too surprising.

Note on terminology

Introduced informally in 1938, the term 'air crew' had had a specific meaning since 1940 (see page 134) but, although it was still supposed to be rendered as two words, by the end of the war it was becoming increasingly common for them to be run together. In anticipation of the introduction of revised arrangements for the provision of post-war flying

[2]AIR2/8638. These examples are taken from PWMC/S.10/P/49, dated 17 March 1945, which had summarised the responses to some of the key questions previously posed by the Post-War Manning Committee in preparation for its forthcoming (fifty-seventh) meeting.

[3]AIR2/8494, AIR6/65 and AIR6/75. AMP laid out his conclusions in a ten-page draft paper, A.766116/45 of 25 June 1945. His proposals were refined at a meeting, attended by most of the Air Ministry's Departmental Director Generals and concerned Heads of Finance Departments, on 4 July. As paper AC 31(45), the final version (which differed only marginally from the original) was submitted to the Air Council on 20 July and received its general approval on 27 August.

personnel, the single word 'aircrew' was adopted from early 1946.[4] Despite widespread use of this style of nomenclature, however, it was March 1947 before officialdom spelled out exactly how it was to be applied.[5] The new rules specified that pilots, navigators, signallers, gunners and engineers were to be described generically as 'flying personnel'. Only flying personnel below commissioned rank were to be referred to as 'aircrew' or, in the singular, as an 'airman (aircrew)'. The correct term to describe those who were commissioned was 'officers (flying)'. To reflect contemporary practice, 'aircrew' will be rendered as a single word from here on.

This very precise legislation had been dictated by the concept underpinning the post-war scheme which envisaged that the vast majority of flying personnel would not be commissioned (see below). For them, a new range of aircrew ranks was to be introduced, these being signified by, what were to be known as, aircrew badges. The term aircrew (or air crew) badge already had a specific meaning, however, having been in use since 1942 to describe the range of qualification badges worn by the various categories.[6] To remove the potential for confusion, therefore, in 1947 it was announced that the pre-existing term 'aircrew badge' was to be replaced by 'flying badge'.[7]

Unfortunately, this, in turn, compromised the established use of 'flying badge' which had long been associated solely with the 'wings' worn by pilots. Thereafter, to conform to the new pattern of navigators, signallers, gunners and engineers badges, these 'wings' were to be described as 'pilots badges'. This is still the correct term today, although the colloquial 'wings' remains in widespread use.

As an incidental aside, this is as convenient a place as any to note that it is, and always has been, incorrect to describe any form of flying badge as a 'brevet'. Despite its always having been a misnomer, however, this term gained considerable currency during WW II and it continues to be (mis)used today.

The 1946 Aircrew Scheme

The permanent arrangements for the provision of aircrew in the peacetime air force were announced in June 1946.[8] As expected, the only aircrew categories to be retained were those of the pilot, navigator, signaller, engineer and gunner. In September, therefore, the following wartime categories were declared to be obsolete: the overspecialised navigator and navigators (radio), (B) and (W); the WOp(air); the WOM(air); the air bomber and the flight engineer.[9] Personnel previously serving in any of these redundant categories who remained in uniform as aircrew were to be given any necessary additional training and remustered as appropriate.

Needless to say, it was not quite as straightforward as that. Under the new scheme individual signallers, engineers and gunners were to be graded A or B, as in 'signaller (B)', those graded A being more technically competent than the Bs.[10] The stated requirement was for 100% grade As in all categories. This could only be an ideal, of course, because many of the ex-wartime personnel had been direct entrants whose technical expertise lacked depth when compared to that of aircrew who had previously served in a related ground trade. Many of these veterans would therefore have to pass through an interim B stage until their academic and trade skills had been brought up to the required standard.

There were some curious inconsistencies within the new arrangements. For instance, while the flight engineer had apparently been done away with, he had in fact survived the cull with the loss of little more than his 'flight' prefix. Conversely, the air gunner, who had *not* been declared redundant, had also lost his prefix. Then again, the meteorological air observer had not been among the categories which had been abolished, but it had not been listed for retention either. In fact, rather than dispensing with them immediately, the RAF had decided to allow this small sub-branch to wither away and to use navigators to replace the remaining flying meteorologists as and when they reached the end of their engagements, this course of action being among the many recommendations which had been made by the Douglas Committee.

While the rationalisation of aircrew categories had been relatively straightforward, the RAF's long-term plans were far less so and they proved to be very unpopular. The root of the problem was status, in that only pilots (and relatively few of those) were to be trained as officers, the RAF College at Cranwell being re-established for this purpose.[11] All other aircrew, which included the majority of pilots, were to be non-commissioned but with entirely new titles and badges of rank.[12] In effect, the post-war air force was to have a novel, three-tier structure, comprising traditionally ranked officers, traditionally ranked airmen *and* 'aircrew'.

Once the necessary domestic facilities could be provided, it was intended that aircrew, who were to be regarded as a quite separate 'third' entity, would live in segregated messes. This idea harked back to the separate messes which were to have been provided for the sergeants involved in the NCO pilot trials of 1918 (see page 78). While little had come of this idea during WW I, rather more progress was made in the late 1940s, although separate aircrew messes had still not been provided everywhere before the scheme was abandoned.

The scheme provoked some resentment, a major cause of discontent being that it had significantly degraded the status

[4]AMO A.158/46 of 21 February.
[5]AMO A.191/47 of 13 March.
[6]The changes in the categorisation of aircrew introduced during 1942 had caused the Air Ministry to specify the nomenclature to be used in association with their badges. AMO A.1019/42 of 17 September stated that a pilots 'wings' were to be referred to as a 'flying badge', non-pilot emblems being identified as a 'badge, navigator', 'badge, air bomber' and so on. Endorsing what had already become common practice, AMO A.3/44 of 6 January formally sanctioned use of the generic term 'air crew badge'. It went on to state that the pilots emblem would continue to be called a 'flying badge' but changed the style associated with non-pilot emblems to 'navigator badge', 'flight engineer badge', 'wireless operator (air) badge', etc.
[7]AMO A.337/47 of 1 May.
[8]AMO A.492/46 of 6 June.
[9]AMO A.768/46 of 5 September.

[10]These suffixes were directly related to sub-divisions within the early post-war ground crew trade structure which was divided into A, B, C and D groupings for pay purposes, the most highly qualified/paid 'fitter' trades being within the A group, 'mechanics' within the B and so on; see AMO A.683/46 of 8 August. While most non-PNB aircrew would be recruited from A or B groups, some were later drawn from D trades, resulting in that suffix also occasionally being applied, most commonly to gunners.
[11]Although flying training had continued at Cranwell throughout the war years, the formal cadet scheme had been suspended in September 1939. Nevertheless, a certain *cachet* still attached to a Cranwell-trained officer, even a wartime one, and the commissioning quota allowed for up to 100% of the output from what was known as the RAF College SFTS (until March 1944 when it was numbered as No 17 SFTS, this unit later being superseded by No 19 SFTS) to emerge as officers, as against 33% from other SFTSs. The cadet scheme was reintroduced in October 1946, the senior course in residence being identified as No 45 entry; see AMO A.58/47 of 23 January.
[12]AMO A.498/47 of 12 June introduced the rank badges to be used by aircrew.

A trainee navigator in an Anson Mk I in 1948. His rank badge is that of an Aircrew Cadet. Aircrew IV, III and II sported one, two and three stars, respectively, within the laurel wreath. An Aircrew I added a crown on top. The Master Aircrew badge, which was worn on the forearm, had the eagle moved down, to fill the space within the wreath previously occupied by stars, and the crown replaced by the Royal Arms, i.e. warrant officers insignia. The wreath and eagle were embroidered in pale blue on a background of blue-grey cloth as were the stars for aircrew rated (A); for those rated (B) to (D) the stars were in white. The rank of Master Aircrew was the only feature of the 1946 Scheme to survive its abandonment, the badge being slightly modified in that a brass eagle was substituted for the original woven version. (CRO, RAF Finningley)

of the majority of aircrew, even including pilots. In fact, what had started out as a 'sub-officer' proposal had become so debased that most aircrew actually turned out to be more like '*sub*-NCOs', the majority having a rank that equated broadly to that of corporal.[13]

[13]AMO A.492/46 stated categorically that aircrew were *not* to be referred to as NCOs. Nevertheless, for matters such as marriage allowance, pension rates and the like, it was necessary to define some sort of equivalence with traditional ranks. This was as follows:

Master Aircrew	Warrant Officer
Aircrew I	Flight Sergeant
Aircrew II	Sergeant
Aircrew III	Corporal
Aircrew IV	Corporal

In the case of individuals, the words Pilot, Navigator, Signaller, Engineer or Gunner were used in place of the generic 'Aircrew' in all of the above examples. Aircrew ranks were initially abbreviated as, e.g. PI, NII, SIII, EIV. AMO N.438/48 of 3 June directed that Arabic numerals were to be adopted in place of Roman ones. This order had actually been specifically concerned with the mark numbers of aeroplanes and aero-engines, and the designation of a variety of stores, but, following its publication, Arabic numerals were soon adopted universally.

Basic training was undertaken as a Cadet and operational training as an Aircrew 4. Flying personnel could normally expect to be promoted to Aircrew 2 in their fifth year of service. That is to say that they would complete the whole of their first (and in most cases only) operational tour as an Aircrew 3.

Furthermore, the new scheme offered poor career prospects because it generally involved short-term contracts. Although it had been envisaged that pilots and navigators would be directly recruited as such, in practice, rather than implementing this principle from the outset, the Service elected to live off its fat. Under an extended service scheme, which had been introduced at the end of 1945, qualified wartime NCO pilots and navigators, cadets under training and enlisted airmen still waiting to start their courses had all been offered three-year engagements.[14] In the case of trainees, this period was to begin from the date on which they gained their flying badges.

While this approach sufficed for a time, the interim arrangements were suspended in April 1947 when they were superseded by the recruiting of direct entrant civilians on short service terms.[15] These offered five-year engagements, followed by four years on the reserve, although there was some prospect of re-engagement for up to twenty-two years, leading to a pension and the possibility of attaining a rank approximating that of warrant officer.

Under the 1946 Scheme all signallers, engineers and gunners were expected to be internally recruited from airmen serving on twelve-year engagements. But, because they were to fly for only five years, aircrew in these three categories were not expected to attain a rank higher than Aircrew II and this only shortly before they were to resume their duties on the ground. This meant that, in practice, they would spend most of their stint on flying duties in a rank roughly equivalent to that of the man who looked after the Bedding Store. While a start was made on internal recruiting, much of the short-term requirement for signallers, engineers and gunners (often abbreviated to SEG when referred to as a group) was met by retaining wartime personnel under the same three-year extended service terms as were (initially) being exploited to provide 100% of pilots and navigators.

The 1946 Scheme included the statement that 'all aircrew in the post-war air force will be eligible for consideration for commissions.' This may have provided some grounds for optimism, but, in reality, the numbers involved were bound to be relatively small, because the Service's immediate needs were largely satisfied by the retention of ex-wartime officers in all categories. Furthermore, the commissions available to most officers promoted 'from the ranks' offered terms which compared very unfavourably with those of the permanent commissions on which Cranwell graduates served.

It should be stressed that this summary represents merely an overview of what was a very complicated plan. Furthermore, it reflects only the regulations as they were originally announced plus a few of the more significant amendments; many other refinements had to be introduced as weaknesses, omissions and defects in the arrangements made themselves apparent.

The 1946 Scheme in perspective

With the benefit of hindsight, we can see that much of the content of the 1946 Scheme seems almost deliberately to have flown in the face of more than thirty years' experience of military aviation, including two World Wars. If nothing else,

[14]AMO A.1153/45 of 5 December, the amended provisions of which were subsequently reiterated in AMO A.963/46 of 14 November.

[15]A.312/47 of 17 April made 30 April the last date for applications under the extended service scheme, which meant that the last pilots and navigators to be engaged under these terms would still be serving in 1950.

these wars had surely demonstrated that many aircrew, and particularly pilots and navigators, needed to be officer grade material. The RFC of 1914 had felt this intuitively and, in the case of pilots at least, the NCO trial of 1918 had suggested that it had been right to trust its instincts (see pages 77–79). The RAF of the 1920s had more or less obliterated any remaining distinction between officers and pilots by making most of them one and the same. By 1940 it had once again been found necessary to commission large numbers of non-pilots, particularly observers, and by 1942 the Canadians were advocating the commissioning of *all* aircrew. Yet in 1946 the Air Ministry had simply dismissed all of this.

Despite its reluctance to learn from the past, the post-war RAF did come to terms with one aspect of reality in that it decided to retain a variety of specialist branches to handle non-flying matters.[16] In practice, however, a large proportion of the officers in these branches tended to be pilots who had transferred to ground duties. Furthermore, as they climbed the ladder of success, it became standard practice for career officers to alternate their flying tours with periods on the ground, during which they tended to monopolise the more prominent and influential administrative posts at station level. As a result, the RAF of the late 1940s (and 1950s) still looked remarkably like that of the 1930s and the casual observer could have been forgiven for thinking that it was still essential to possess a pilots badge in order to succeed in almost any field.

While the RAF had not, strictly speaking, re-established its officer-pilot dominated *ancien regime*, even if it did rather look as if it had, its treatment of all other aircrew had certainly represented a step backwards. Although non-commissioned pilots and navigators were to be employed as professionals, albeit many of them on short-term engagements, the other three categories would all be ground tradesmen, all of whom were to fly for only a limited period. This was not quite a reversion to the part-time crewmen of the 1920s, but it was not much of an advance either, and the Air Council's decision to impose such low ranks on practically all aviators seems almost perverse. What the peacetime Service had needed was a scheme which would fulfil its own requirements whilst satisfying the aspirations of its people. What it had produced matched the first of these criteria admirably, but entirely at the expense of the second. In effect, the 1946 Scheme reintroduced the outmoded, pre-war concept of a small and carefully groomed corps of officer pilots who would exercise authority over 'the troops'.

Such an approach does work in an army or a navy, but an air force is neither of these. The fundamental nature of warfare on land or at sea means that, in a combat situation, large numbers of soldiers, or the entire crew of a ship, will be directly involved. Each soldier or seaman represents a small cog in a large machine which is operated by a handful of officers. In an air force it is *only* the handful of officers who do the fighting – or, to be pedantic, a handful of men, many of whom need to have much the same qualities as are traditionally associated with officers.

The officer/aircrew relationship is clearly a problem which is peculiar to air forces. The 1946 scheme was an attempt to solve it by imposing an army/navy style solution. It was simply the wrong answer. If the RAF was to have high quality aircrew it needed to recruit them from the same pool as its officers, and, if it was to be successful in doing that, it needed to pay them something like the rate for the job. That could only be done, in practice, by giving them commissioned, or at the very least SNCO, rank.

But in 1946 it is unlikely that such considerations would have been seen to present a significant problem. At the time the RAF still had thousands of surplus aircrew, adequate numbers of whom were content to remain in uniform, especially as these veterans had some precariously preserved rights, provided that they could find their way through the chicanes of sub-sub-clauses built into the new regulations. Furthermore, conscription was still providing a virtually unlimited supply of fresh manpower from which to select additional aircrew, this source being guaranteed in 1947 by the institution of peacetime National Service.[17]

The flaws within the 1946 Scheme

The fact that the 1946 Scheme worked, for a while, does not mean that it was a success. Far from it. Despite its obvious appeal to the Treasury, it proved to be deeply unpopular, not least because of its divisive nature. The post-war UK may not have been a workers' paradise, but it was certainly a socialist democracy. The RAF's blatantly class-based system was far too much at odds with the tenor of the times to be tolerated for long. Inevitably, the result of all this was that recruiting proved to be a problem.

If the RAF had really expected to be able to retain a substantial proportion of its National Servicemen, it will have been disappointed. Some did opt to become regulars but, on balance, National Service proved to be of little value to the RAF, beyond the fact that it provided a substantial reserve of manpower in the event of general mobilisation. The root of the problem was that the RAF was a highly technical service. This meant that, for ground tradesmen and aircrew alike, it required practically all of a conscript's engagement to provide him with all of the skills that he needed to fulfil a useful function. Before he had really had time to become proficient, he was 'de-mobbed'.

As a result, the RAF was to discover that, while it was obliged to spend a great deal of effort on training personnel, it gained very little return on its investment. In national terms, of course, the Service was making a major contribution to post-war recovery by training the workforce for 'UK Ltd'. Skilled manpower was becoming a scarce resource in a period of near full employment and it was particularly galling for the RAF to discover that, having provided men with their skills, it was unable to persuade them to stay in uniform. After the trauma of the Great Depression, followed by the instability of six years of global warfare, people wanted security above all. The *Zeitgeist* clearly called for a 'job for life

[16]In addition to the GD Branch, and the equally long-standing 'professionals' of the Medical, Dental, Chaplains and Legal Branches, there were by 1947: Technical, Equipment, Secretarial, Education, Catering, Flying Control, Provost and Physical Fitness Branches plus the RAF Regiment. All of these were to become permanent features of the RAF. Although of shorter duration there was still an Administrative and Special Duties Branch plus Balloon, Meteorological, and Medical and Dental Quartermasters Branches.

[17]The National Service Act of 18 July 1947 superseded the existing arrangements for wartime conscription (which had never been terminated) with effect from 1 January 1949. Affecting men aged 18 to 26, the obligation was originally expected to involve one year's full-time service plus three in the reserve but the National Service (Amendment) Act of 16 December 1948 added six months to the period of active service. As a result of the Korean War, on 1 October 1950 the period of active service was further extended to two years. Aircrew trained as National Servicemen were expected to meet their reserve commitment via membership of the RAFVR or the RAuxAF.

[18]The age of an officer's retirement depended upon his rank and differed from branch to branch. In the specific case of GD officers serving on *permanent* engagements, a flight lieutenant could expect to be compulsorily retired at 41 years of age, a squadron leader at 43, a wing commander at 47 and a group captain at 50; see AMO A.278/47 of 24 April.

with a pension'. The RAF was still offering short-term engagements, even to most of its officers.[18]

So far as the SEG aircrew categories were concerned, there had been insufficient takers from among ground tradesmen. It seems that, to airmen who wished to pursue a technical career, a five-year stint of flying was perceived to be a detour during which colleagues, who had kept their feet firmly on the ground, would forge ahead. It had been intended to prevent this happening by requiring groundcrew to maintain currency in their parent trade while engaged on flying duties. This had proved to be more easily said than done. For instance, an engineer flying three, four, even five sorties a day on the Berlin Airlift had quite enough to do without having to practise tin-bashing or keep his hand in on a lathe. Similarly, a Sunderland signaller flying lengthy patrols during the Malayan Emergency had little 'free' time to spend in the Signals Section or the Radio Bay.

Nevertheless, while such factors seem to have deterred many serving airmen from volunteering, there were still some who were keen to fly. Unfortunately, many of them wanted to fly permanently; but this was not an option under the 1946 Scheme. In short, the whole concept had proved to be deeply flawed and in many respects quite unrealistic.

Since internal recruiting was failing to produce the numbers of aircrew required, the termination of the extended service scheme early in 1947 served only to exacerbate the problem. In the autumn of 1948, therefore, the Service was obliged to reintroduce direct entrants into the SEG categories. Furthermore, it was now offering them eight-year engagements with the possibility of further service to complete twenty-two years.[19] In effect, this struck the 1946 Scheme a mortal blow, although it took almost two more years to die.

The regulations introduced in 1948 had offered similar eight-year contracts to newly recruited pilots and navigators, and to those currently serving on five-year engagements. Curiously enough, however, while the revised terms of service had honoured any existing twenty-two year contracts, this option was specifically denied to new pilots and navigators. It is not known whether this had been intentional, or merely a bureaucratic oversight, but their eligibility was restored less than a year later.[20]

The demise of the 1946 Scheme

The initial post-war scheme for the provision of aircrew was abandoned in 1950. It was replaced by one which removed 'certain disadvantages which practical experience of the present policy has revealed,' which was probably as close as the Air Council could be expected to come to publicly admitting that it had got it badly wrong.[21] The most obvious outward indication that things were changing was the withdrawal of the unpopular alphanumeric soup of N1s, P2s, S3s, G4s, etc. Overnight the minimum rank of all qualified non-commissioned aircrew was restored to that of sergeant. Another obvious sign of the restored status of aircrew was that they were to wear a gilt eagle in the vee of their chevrons.

Equally as significant was an early increase in basic pay, along with the introduction of flying pay at four shillings and sixpence per day for pilots and navigators and a shilling less for all other categories.[22] For a junior sergeant, the basic daily rates of pay were eighteen shillings for pilots, navigators and air signallers (A), air engineers (A) and air gunners (A). Although the (B) and (D) suffixes had been dropped in 1948,[23] it was still considered appropriate to maintain a pay differential between SEG aircrew who possessed superior levels of technical skill and those who did not. Thus, on initially gaining their flying badges, and until they upgraded their qualifications, direct entrants were paid one shilling and sixpence per day less than (A) graded ex-tradesman.

By this time air gunners were becoming surplus to requirements, as the remaining turret-equipped bombers were about to be replaced by unarmed Canberras. As a result the option of long-term service as a gunner had been withdrawn in late 1949, although five-year engagements continued to be available for a while.[24] In practice, by 1951 practically all new gunners were short-term National Servicemen and even these ceased to be recruited in 1953, the last of them being earmarked by the Aircrew Selection Centre at Hornchurch in August of that year. The air gunner was effectively declared redundant in the autumn of 1954 when those who remained were offered the options of transferring to a ground trade or of retraining as air signallers.[25] The RAF continued to operate cannon-armed Shackletons until the 1970s but the Service was content to rely on its air signallers to handle these, especially as a significant proportion of them had once been gunners.

Although it was not specifically highlighted at the time, the revised regulations had involved another, somewhat cosmetic, innovation. From 1950 onwards gunners had regained the 'air' prefix which they had lost in 1946 and the same 'air' was now added to signallers, engineers and meteorological observers.

As important as all of the other changes associated with the terms of service introduced in 1950 was a realistic prospect of a full career. As ever, there were a variety of constraints and preconditions. The option of a five-year flying stint was still available to serving airmen but, depending upon their trades, some were now able to remuster permanently to aircrew duties. Direct entrant air signallers and air engineers retained the 1948 offer of an initial eight years of active service with the prospect of re-engagement for a total of twenty-two years as aircrew, but, if mutually agreeable, there was now the possibility of further service, usually in a ground trade, terminating in a pension at age 55. Similar re-engagement provisions applied to serving NCO pilots and navigators but by this time recruiting in these categories was confined to officers (see below).

As a footnote to these developments, it is worth observing that the employment of groundcrew was also being completely reorganised. Depending upon his aptitude, an airmen's career could now follow one of two paths. If deemed suitable, he could pursue a 'command' career, which required him to develop his management, as well as his technical, skills. This option was associated with traditional ranks, i.e. corporal, sergeant, flight sergeant and warrant officer. For those who were temperamentally less well suited to management functions, or who preferred to concentrate on being pure tradesmen, the alternative of a technical career was available. Men who elected to pursue this option were distinguished by the new ranks of corporal technician, senior technician and chief technician, all of whom wore their chevrons inverted.

[19]AMO A.733/48 of 9 September.
[20]AMO A.335/49 of 12 May.
[21]AMO A.545/50 of 31 August.
[22]AMO A.780/50 of 14 December.
[23]AMO A.733/48 of 9 September.
[24]AMO A.701/49 of 6 October.
[25]AMO A.285/54 of 25 November.

Interestingly, this innovation contained more than a hint of history repeating itself. It will be recalled that, when Air Mshl Portal had been AMP in 1940, his ideas on how the air force ought to handle its non-commissioned aircrew had not been adopted (see page 196). Yet the post-war aircrew scheme, which was devised five years later, towards the end of Sir Charles' long term as CAS, incorporated many of his earlier thoughts. It would seem that Sir John Slessor may also have been able to realise one of his earlier goals in arrears. As AMP, his proposals for an 'artificer' class had not been taken up in 1945 (see page 197) but, five years later, as CAS, he was able to oversee the introduction of the technician scheme, which reflected much of the ethos of his original concept.

Note on terminology

One of the divisive features of the 1946 Scheme was that the term 'aircrew' had been confined to flying personnel holding non-commissioned rank, which had tended to emphasise a distinction rooted in social class. In 1950 this practice ceased, and since then all flying personnel have been referred to generically as 'aircrew', their individual status being distinguished, when appropriate, as 'officers (aircrew)' or 'airmen (aircrew)'.[26] This change effectively deleted 'flying personnel' from the official lexicon but, although it no longer had a specifically defined meaning, it has remained in use as a handy and self-explanatory label.

The evolution of early post-war commissioning policy for aircrew

In 1945–46 it had been anticipated that, once the transition from war to peace had been completed, the bulk of the air force's flying personnel would be provided by the new breed of 'sub-NCOs'. By relying so heavily on airmen aircrew in the future, it followed that there might be no need to reintroduce short service commissions. This, in turn, raised the tantalising prospect of an 'ideal' peacetime air force, that is to say, one which could be managed by a relative handful of officers, all of whom would serve on permanent commissions. (The reinstatement of permanent commissions and some of the implications of this development are discussed on pages 221 *et seq.*)

Nevertheless, the pros and cons of short service commissions were given due consideration, although there were mixed feelings over reintroducing a pre-war practice which had sometimes been a rather contentious issue.[27] To tide the air force over while these matters were being debated, extended service commissions had been introduced in 1945.[28] There was the usual plethora of terms and conditions (and later amendments) but, in essence, the scheme offered wartime officers terms broadly similar to those which would shortly be made available to wartime NCOs (see page 199), although there were two significant differences. First, extended service for officers was not confined to flying personnel. Secondly, two periods were on offer, four years plus four on the reserve for non-regular officers, i.e. those commissioned from the wartime ranks on qualification or later, and seven years for ex-regular, i.e. pre-war, airmen who had been temporarily commissioned during the war.

It has been suggested above that the beginning of the end of the 1946 Scheme could be discerned in 1948 when the shortage of tradesmen volunteers had obliged the Air Council to forego its ideal of having an exclusively internally recruited SEG workforce. In the context of pilots and navigators, the first symptoms of decay had actually appeared long before that. Unsurprisingly, many potential pilots and navigators seem to have failed to appreciate the attractions of flying as pseudo-corporals. So, to provide an added enticement, less than a year after the new concept had been implemented it had been decided to reintroduce the prospect of short service commissions. These arrangements, which were announced in February 1947, effectively replaced the transitional system of extended service commissions.[29]

Short service commissions were available in practically all branches, but, so far as flying personnel were concerned, only to pilots and navigators. Furthermore, while the direct recruiting of officers was envisaged for some ground branches, this was not to be the case for GD officers, most of whom were expected to be obtained by commissioning selected direct entrant airmen candidates on completion of their flying training. Apart from them, short service commissions were also on offer: to officers holding extended service commissions; to recently released officers who wished to re-engage; and to airmen currently serving under the terms of the 1946 Scheme. Those who accepted such commissions were to serve for a total of six years, including any previous service as an airman, plus the usual four years on the reserve. There was a sting in the tail so far as navigators were concerned, because, at the time, there were no vacancies for them.

The initial response to the new arrangements was disappointing and in the spring of 1948 AMP, Air Mshl Sir Hugh Saunders, took the problem to the Air Council. There were three causes for concern. First, the current standard engagement was too short to permit pilots and navigators to develop their skills fully. Secondly, because engagements were short, the turnover was high, which drove up training costs. Finally, and most importantly, the terms presently on offer were simply failing to attract the numbers required. The solutions to these problems were self-evident – longer engagements and a juicier carrot.[30]

From September onwards any civilian who applied for pilot or navigator training was offered 'a guarantee of a short service commission,' so long as he could persuade the Selec-

[26]AMO A.721/50 of 23 November.

[27]The short service commission of the 1920s had been a purely RAF initiative and one which had been rather frowned upon by the other two Services, particularly the Army, who believed that all officers should be dedicated military men committed to serve on long-term, pensionable engagements. There was also a degree of opposition from other influential sectors, including educationalists and some politicians, who contended that it was not in the national interest for the air force to take advantage of the formative years of a young man's career and then return him to society, ill-prepared for life, other than in the precarious occupation of an aviator. It could, of course, be countered that, having been expensively trained as a pilot, he was well placed to pursue a career in the growth industry of commercial aviation and that, although he lacked a pension, his terminal gratuity was sufficiently generous to cushion his transition to civilian life.

It is evident that certain senior RAF officers were also unconvinced of the merits of the innovative short-service commission which led Trenchard to ask his Director of Personnel, Air Cdre O. Swann, to prepare a letter from CAS to AOCs explaining the party line. It is not known whether the final version was ever distributed but AIR8/19 contains a copy of the draft of 25 January 1922.

[28]AMO A.775/45 of 31 July.

[29]AMO A.127/47 of 13 February announced that short service commissions were to be reintroduced to replace the interim extended service commission, 31 March being the last date for applications under the earlier scheme. Full details of the short service scheme were published in AMO A.592/47 of 17 July.

[30]AIR6/84. Conclusions of Air Council Meetings 27(48) held on 26 April 1948 and 40(48) held on 26 June.

tion Board that he was officer grade material.[31] Confirmation of the commission, which would now involve eight years of active service, was conditional upon satisfactory performance during, and completion of, training. This development did not preclude the direct recruiting of Ps and Ns, which continued as before. The new arrangements also made provision for pilots and navigators who had been selected as officers, but who had subsequently failed to make the grade as such, to transfer to non-commissioned terms on an, initially, eight-year engagement.

Within the community of serving non-commissioned aircrew, the prospect of becoming an officer was still confined almost exclusively to pilots and navigators. The regulations did permit signallers, engineers and gunners to apply for commissions but, if granted, this usually involved a transfer to a ground branch, because the RAF already had sufficient wartime officers still serving on emergency commissions[32] and/or extended service terms to meet its limited requirements in these categories. Some of these officers were committed until as late as 1954 but a substantial proportion was due to leave the Service in 1949–50 so, to avoid a sudden exodus, they were offered the opportunity of extending their engagements to a total of eight years. This usually involved a formal transfer to short service terms but, whatever the arrangements, the retention of these veterans served to restrict commissioning opportunities for SEG aircrew who wished to continue flying as officers.

This constant tinkering with commissioning policy during the later 1940s was symptomatic of the difficulties that the air force experienced in redefining itself during a period in which erstwhile allies, the USSR and China, became the potential opposition, leading to an increasingly polarised international political situation. By 1950 early post-war uncertainties had crystallised into the Cold War. This relative stability made it possible to take a longer-term view and thus to adopt a more radical approach to the provision of aircrew, including officers.

In November of that year, a few months after the restitution of traditional NCO ranks, it was declared that it was 'the aim of the Air Council that all pilots and navigators shall be commissioned officers.'[33] This did not mean that any applicant with the necessary flying aptitude would automatically be commissioned but that the air force would train only those applicants who were assessed as being suitable to hold a commission – which is not quite the same thing. This was a startling departure from the policy prevailing only three years before when the Service had been expecting to manage with mere P3s and N3s. The problem was that it had proved to be extremely difficult to obtain enough of either, as had been shown by the RAF's consistent inability to find the navigators that it was supposed to have been providing for meteorological observation duties (see below).

The air force was finally being forced to grasp a nettle which it had been carefully avoiding for years. However unwelcome, it was being obliged to accept the fact that the essential characteristics required of a pilot or navigator were much the same as those which were demanded of an officer. There were probably some who would still have disputed the truth of this, but even if there were, these dissenters could hardly have denied that people with the educational qualifications, speed of reaction, resourcefulness and other qualities necessary to be pilots or navigators were a valuable commodity. If the RAF wanted its share of this commodity it would have to pay the market price. Within a rigidly hierarchical military structure, however, there is an inextricable link between pay and rank. While some minor perturbations in pay scales may be tolerated, it is very difficult for such a system to accept an arrangement which might involve a twenty-year old sergeant aviator being paid more than (say) a forty-year old flight lieutenant in a ground trade.

The idea of making aircrew a separate third entity had been, in some respects, an attempt to avoid, rather than to solve, this problem. Since this concept had proved to be so unattractive, the RAF had had little alternative but to offer commissions to virtually all pilots and navigators, and even then it became necessary to top up their income with specialist 'flying pay'.[34]

What all of this amounted to was, to quote John James, that the RAF had effectively adopted the slogan, 'if a man's good enough to be a pilot (*or a navigator – CGJ*), he's good enough to be an officer,' which was almost exactly the reverse of what Trenchard had been saying in the 1920s – that, 'if a man were good enough to be an officer, he must also become a pilot.'[35]

While it was now official policy to recruit only officers as pilots and navigators, large numbers of NCOs were still serving in these categories. Over the next several years, many of these men would be commissioned, on a variety of terms, but others would not, in some cases because they were considered unsuitable but often because they chose not to change their lifestyle. To a limited degree, the NCO community was replenished by trainees who, having failed to make the grade as officers, elected to continue flying as sergeants. Inevitably, however, the numbers of non-commissioned pilots and navigators gradually declined, although they continued to fly until well into the 1960s, by which time most were ranked as warrant officers, i.e. as master aircrew.

Difficulties with the provision of flying personnel for meteorological duties

Because it was so small, the meteorological section of the GD Branch tends to be overlooked, but the fact that it was small did not mean that it could not suffer from a manning crisis. Once the early peacetime situation had stabilised, the RAF found itself committed to sustaining regular long-range meteorological reconnaissance sorties from Aldergrove and Gibraltar. Forecasting that the majority of its wartime flying personnel would have been demobilised by the end of 1947, the senior executives of the Meteorological Department held a meeting in May of that year to consider the way ahead. Noting that it was the RAF's stated intention to provide navigators for observation duties,[36] it was calculated that the overall requirement would be for forty-five men, of whom seven would need to be officers. It was thought that they would

[31] AMO A.733/48 of 9 September.
[32] AMO A.476/39 of 9 November made early provision for relatively large numbers of ground tradesmen to be commissioned for wartime service. These regulations were progressively refined until they were restated in AMO A.366/40 of 13 June in which the phrase 'for the duration of hostilities' was amended (by AMO A.834/41 of 9 October) to read 'for the duration of the emergency'. Hence the term 'emergency commission', which referred to the specific arrangements whereby ex-regular, i.e. pre-war, airmen could be commissioned into the RAF while wartime recruits would be commissioned into the RAFVR. The granting of emergency commissions was terminated by AMO A. 169/48 of 19 February.
[33] AMO A.750/50 of 30 November.
[34] AMO A.780/50 of 14 December.
[35] John James, *The Paladins* (1990), page 147.
[36] This provision had been included in para 3(b) of AMO A.492/46.
[37] AIR2/4692. Minutes of a meeting chaired by the Director of the Meteorological Office on 7 May 1947.

require some ten–twelve weeks of training, including eight flying exercises.[37] This proposal was submitted to the air staff.

Unfortunately, there was a shortage of navigators at the time. Since the Service was unable to meet its obligation, the air staff counter-proposed that the employment of professional meteorologists be reinstated. This idea had to be rejected by the Meteorological Office which was suffering from its own shortage of manpower. Eventually, a compromise solution was reached. Having first pruned the numbers down to twenty-nine, it was decided to use surplus pilots. Nine of those selected turned out to be fully qualified men who were stuck in interminable queues for refresher flying courses. The remainder were trainees who had reached 'wings' standard but who, for a variety of reasons, were unlikely to be absorbed into operational training.[38] These unfortunates were offered the alternatives of discharge, transfer to a ground trade or of completing their engagements on meteorological duties. Even though it could, in some cases, have meant losing their pilots badges, the necessary volunteers were forthcoming and by the end of 1948 all the places had been filled.[39]

This was only an interim solution, however, and, either because they had been recalled to flying duties or because they had left the air force on completion of their engagements, the temporary pilots soon began to melt away. The resultant gaps were plugged by using surplus gunners so that by November 1949 there were ten pilots and thirteen gunners being misemployed as flying 'Met men'. A shortage of gunners was already being forecast, however, and there was still no sign of the promised navigators.

The experience of 1948–49 had served only to confirm, what all concerned had really known all along, that the RAF would be much better off employing flying scientists than misemploying spare (and probably, in some cases, disgruntled) aviators as meteorologists. Furthermore, it was intended soon to replace the tired old Halifaxes which were then being used for 'Met Recce' with the Hastings and this prospect led to a more determined attempt to solve the problem.

In 1950 the Meteorological Office agreed to try using appropriately qualified volunteers who were slated to carry out their National Service commitment as civilian scientific assistants. Those who were successful would be given the rank of sergeant and be entitled to wear the old flying 'M'.[40] This experiment was not entirely successful as the National Servicemen proved to be too inexperienced. The following year the proposal was adapted to attract scientific assistants who had already completed at least two years' service as meteorologists. The scheme offered a single two-and-a-half-year flying tour as a sergeant (complete with flying 'M') after which successful applicants would return to ground duties. Six months later they would be eligible to apply for a second stint of flying if they so desired.[41] In the meantime the numbers needed had been considerably reduced in line with a cut back in the flying task. At the beginning of 1951 the requirement had stood at sixteen observers for sixteen aircraft committed to flying fourteen sorties per week. By the end of that year it was down to twelve observers (now two per sortie) for only five aircraft making just five flights per week. This reduced establishment sufficed until 1964 when the availability of alternative methods of keeping track of the weather, e.g. weather ships and satellites, permitted the RAF to give up its met recce commitment.

The refinement of commissioning policy for pilots and navigators

Apart from Cranwell cadets (and a fortunate few who were selected for similar long-term engagements), the terms being offered to the bulk of pilots and navigators in 1950 were those of an eight-year short service commission. It soon became apparent that a more flexible system was required and one which specifically included the option of much longer periods of service. While it was hoped that a more attractive package might improve recruiting, this was not the only argument in favour of long-term engagements.

In response to the increase in international tension caused by the outbreak of the Korean War in 1950, the RAF had raised its planned annual intake of pilots from 300 to 3000. It had also arranged for the re-enlistment of up to 500 ex-navigators; the recall of 1000 aircrew reservists; and the activation of the fighter squadrons of the Royal Auxiliary Air Force (RAuxAF) for a period of three months' continuous training in 1951. All of this created a huge demand for basic and refresher training facilities, leading to the recall of reserve flying instructors who were required to serve for up to eighteen months.

There was also a considerable increase in the number of National Servicemen being selected for pilot and navigator training, which now automatically involved their being commissioned. In practice, of course, by the time that a conscript had been trained as an officer, taught how to fly and converted onto an operational type, he was virtually at the end of his engagement and few yielded more than six months of pro-

Throughout the later 1940s the RAF encountered recurrent difficulties in finding sufficient meterologists to man its 'met recce' aeroplanes. These were eventually overcome in the 1950s, more through a reduction in demand than by solving the recruiting problem. This Hastings Met 1 of No 202 Sqn, TG623, was photographed during a visit to Turnhouse in 1961. (N.D. Welch)

[38]*Ibid.* Memorandum from DNav, Air Cdre N.H. D'Aeth, to DCAS, Air Mshl Sir Hugh Walmsley, on Air Ministry file C.28040, summarising the situation as at 1 November 1948.

[39]Although a pilot was awarded his flying badge on completion of his advanced flying training course, in order to retain it, all subsequent role-related and/or type conversion courses had to be passed and a period of productive service completed. Similar conditions applied to the permanent retention of the badges worn by all other aircrew categories. Those pilots who were being seconded to meteorological duties who had never reached a squadron, would (should), therefore, eventually have been obliged to forfeit their 'wings'. On the other hand, it would seem that at least some of the pilots involved were allowed to log time actually flown as 'Met men', as second-pilot hours. This created the impression that they were still in the flying game, a subterfuge in which a system with in-built sympathies towards pilots was perhaps content to collude; see a letter from one such, B. Alborough, published in the autumn 1988 edition of *Intercom*.

[40]AMO A.152/50 of 2 March.

[41]AMO A.202/51 of 12 April.

ductive service. A proportion of these men did convert to a regular engagement, but the majority preferred to resume (or start) their civilian careers, some of them putting their newly acquired skills to good use by finding jobs in commercial aviation.

Those who left the Service were required to maintain a degree of currency during their reserve commitment. Some pilots did this by enlisting in the RAuxAF. Most of the others kept their hands in by spending time with one of twenty-three civilian-managed Reserve Flying Schools (RFS), most of which had been set up in 1947–48.[42] These schools operated a variety of aeroplanes ranging from Tiger Moths through Chipmunks and Prentices to Harvards and Oxfords. In addition, some offered opportunities for navigators and air signallers to fly in Ansons. The RFSs lacked appropriate facilities for air engineers and air gunners, however, so limited provision was made for them, and indeed for all aircrew categories, to fulfil their reserve training obligations through short attachments to regular units.

One of the lessons learned from the Korean crisis was that it was no longer realistic to place too much reliance on reserve forces. It was becoming increasingly difficult and expensive to provide aircrew reservists with even a notional degree of currency and this problem was bound to get worse with each successive generation of aircraft. Reservists could be recalled to the colours in an emergency, of course, and they could be given the necessary refresher training, but it would all take time, probably too much time. It would, for example, take several months to get an ex-Lincoln pilot, who (apart from having logged a few hours in a Tiger Moth during his fifteen-days of annual reserve training) had been out of touch with flying for as long as four years, sufficiently 'back up to speed' for the RAF to entrust him with a Canberra. By the mid-1950s, it was becoming clear that this would all take far too long, since WW III was not expected to last more than three or four days.

Doubts also began to be expressed over the viability of the RFSs in wartime, as the original plan to use them to provide elementary training for *ab initio* students, would be similarly confounded by the short timescale of a nuclear war. As a result, all but seven of the schools were shut down in 1953 and the Parliamentary Under-Secretary of State for Air, Mr George Ward MP, announced to the House that the aircrew strength of the RAFVR was being reduced from 7600 to 3200.[43] This was the beginning of the end, because, even allowing for the contribution being made by attaching reservists to regular RAF units, the remaining RFSs simply lacked the capacity to cope realistically with the residual task.[44]

Meanwhile, to alleviate the shortage of trained manpower caused by the expansion of the Service during the early 1950s, many personnel were being kept in uniform beyond their anticipated release dates. In effect, they were being required to serve on longer term engagements and, ultimately, this was seen to be the only realistic way to meet the requirements of the future. To fight a nuclear war at little or no notice, or, better still, to provide a deterrent credible enough to prevent this happening, the RAF would need to have its expanded front line permanently manned with fully-trained personnel.

This alone argued for the retention of aircrew for as long as possible, but there were other reasons too. A new generation of high performance combat aircraft (Canberras, Sabres, Hunters, Javelins, Swifts, Valiants, Vulcans and Victors) was planned to enter service during the 1950s. These aeroplanes would be more capable than their predecessors and, while some would be far more complicated, all would be much more expensive. The cost of training people to fly these more advanced aircraft could be expected to increase remorselessly. One way to minimise this expense would be to reduce the numbers passing through the system, which could be achieved if each of them were to stay in uniform longer. Furthermore, lengthening the duration of active service would also allow training costs to be amortised over a longer period. This 'longevity principle' was persuaded to yield even greater dividends in 1955 when it was decided to double the length of many flying tours, thus effectively halving the cost of the OCU system.[45]

While such an approach made good sense in purely financial terms, reducing throughput would also have the considerable advantage of easing the pressure on recruiting, because it was expected to be much easier to find one man who was prepared to serve for, say, twenty years than four men who were willing to serve for five years each. This was a particularly persuasive argument in 1955, when the recruiting situation was so depressing. Only eight navigators had been selected during the first three months of that year, and there were reservations as to the real officer potential of some of those.

This example was cited by AVM A. Earle in a paper written to support a major change in policy which was then being advocated. It was being argued that, if the RAF was to succeed in attracting adequate numbers of men of suitable calibre, substantial improvements would have to be made in the fields of status, pay, gratuities, pensions, resettlement facilities and the provision and standard of accommodation, particularly married quarters. In order to realise a worthwhile return on the considerable expenditure which this would involve, it followed that aircrew officers would need to serve on much longer engagements.[46]

For all of these reasons, the RAF had already decided to abandon short service commissions. Stating, once again, that its aim was 'that all pilots and navigators shall be officers', the Air Council introduced a much more flexible and comprehensive package in 1955.[47] The revised scheme offered a

[42]The post-war RFSs reinstated the provision for reservists to fly that had originally been introduced as early as 1923 (see Chapter 16, Note 18) and which had subsequently evolved into the network of ERFTSs of the later 1930s. Apart from their facilities permitting fully qualified pilots to 'keep their hands in' while fulfilling their reserve obligations, the RFSs also provided volunteer reservists with elementary *ab initio* flying training. To recognise the achievements and commitment of these individuals AMO A.631/49 of 8 September introduced a preliminary flying badge for each of the five aircrew categories which were to be awarded to RAFVR personnel on satisfactory completion of the basic stage of training. As they could be awarded to WRAFVR personnel, incidentally, these were the first Air Ministry-sponsored flying badges that could be worn by women. Supplies of the pilots preliminary flying badge were immediately available and it was certainly awarded; it is still in use today at UASs. Supplies of the badges for non-pilot aircrew were not immediately available, however, and, because of the limited training facilities, it seems unlikely that many (any?) will actually have been issued.

[43]*Hansard*, 17 June 1953.

[44]AIR6/100. Appendix F to paper AC 53(55) of 17 November 1953, submitted to the Air Council by Mr Ward, noted that 332 pilots, 80 navigators, 65 air signallers, 141 air engineers and 164 air gunners of the RAFVR had been attached to regular units during the first ten months of 1953. This represented only about 15% of the total annual reserve training commitment at that time.

[45]AIR6/118. At its meeting SC 15(55), held on 4 July 1955, the Air Council Standing Committee agreed virtually to double the duration of a standard flying tour on (initially) V-bombers and Javelins to four-and-a-half years. In practice, this might involve stints with two different squadrons but, and this was the point, the second one would not need to be preceded by a full OCU course.

[46]AIR8/1882. Brief for CAS prepared by ACAS(Pol) dated 20 April 1955.

[47]AMO A.110/55 of 31 March.

variety of contracts, ranging from a twelve-year engagement (with the option of leaving after eight) to a permanent commission involving service to the age of 55.[48] Within certain constraints, practically all pilots and navigators still serving as regular airmen were entitled to apply for one or more of these types of commission.

At the same time the terms of service available to air signallers, air engineers and the remaining air gunners and air meteorological observers were restated to reflect detailed changes that had been incorporated over the previous five years.[49] One point that is worthy of note is that, while National Servicemen could still apply for training as pilots (with the associated bonus of an automatic commission), this option had not been available to navigators since 1953. The only other aircrew category open to a conscript was as an NCO air signaller but only at the cost of signing on for eight years, and thus becoming a regular.

By this time, however, conscription was becoming increasingly difficult to sustain politically and, while opinion within the military was divided, there were growing doubts as to its effectiveness. These reservations were felt particularly strongly within the 'hi tech' sectors, which included much of the RAF. Rather than providing its conscripts with technical skills, therefore, the air force had for some time been tending to employ its National Servicemen on low-grade, menial tasks to insulate its élite regular tradesmen from such mundane matters.

One of a series of major shifts in defence policy announced in 1957 was an early end to conscription along with a corresponding reduction in the strength of reserve forces. In fact the flying units of the RAuxAF had actually been disbanded several weeks before the publication of the White Paper. Since the last seven RFSs had been closed down in 1954, the loss of the RAuxAF squadrons meant that there was no longer any practical means of providing worthwhile continuation training for ex-conscript aircrew. In effect, therefore, the disbandment of these units had meant the end of pilot and navigator training for National Servicemen.[50]

Meanwhile, something had begun to be done about pay and there had been some upward movement in 1954. Curiously, since poor recruiting was a major factor, those who benefited most from these increases were the squadron leaders and above, who were already in harness, rather than the flight lieutenants and below that the Service needed to attract. The effect was a marked increase in differentials so that, whereas a pilot officer had earned 45% of a wing commander's pay in the 1920s, by 1954 he received only 28%.

Apart from an increase in rates of basic pay, flying pay was now recognised as being an essential supplement to income. The rates payable in 1954 had not changed since their initial introduction in 1950. They were: seven shillings for a pilot officer, eight for a flying officer, and nine for flight lieutenants and squadron leaders. Since they could expect to fly less, wing commanders and group captains drew only five shillings per day, falling to three shillings in the latter case after six years in rank.

In the general context of rates of pay, it is worth pausing to observe how little these had actually changed over the previous thirty years or so. Some examples of comparative rates of pay are at Fig. 26 and it is a little surprising to see that in 1947 a junior officer was actually being paid *less* than he would have been in 1922.[51] Indeed pilot officers and flying officers were still being paid at less than the 1920s rate in 1954.

While these raw figures provide a crude indication of how pay had stagnated, they tell only half the story, because a deadly combination of taxation and inflation had more than halved the purchasing power of the pound. At six shillings in the pound, the basic rate of income tax in 1922 had been 30%; by 1947 it was nine shillings, a swingeing 45%, and this had fallen only marginally (by sixpence) by 1954. Inflation had been relatively insignificant until the late 1940s but from then on its influence had become increasingly corrosive.[52] The cumulative effect of all this was that the pound in the wallet of a flight lieutenant in 1947 was worth only 61% of what it would have been worth in the 1920s, and by 1954 this had dwindled to just 47%. None of this is intended to suggest that servicemen were being particularly poorly treated. Similar declines in relative income were experienced by most sectors of British society during the early years of a slow post-war economic recovery. The final column has been provided to show that, reflecting the general increase in national prosperity, the position did improve considerably over the next fifty years or so. The startling increase in rates of pay are a little misleading, however, as much of this was absorbed by inflation, which reached an annual rate of 20% at one stage. Nevertheless, allowing for the fact that the basic rate of income tax has fallen to 23%, in real terms a wing commander at the turn of the century is at least twice as well off as his predecessor of 1922.

Rank	1922	1947	1954	2000
Pilot Officer	18/0d	16/0d	17/6d	£39.20
Flying Officer	£1/3/0d	18/0d	19/6d	£59.70
Flight Lieutenant	£1/9/0d	£1/3/0d	£1/9/0d	£76.12
Squadron Leader	£1/14/0d	£1/15/0d	£2/7/0d	£95.89
Wing Commander	£2/0/0d	£2/7/6d	£3/1/6d	£135.26

Fig. 26. *Comparative daily rates of pay (on promotion) for General Duties officers in 1922, 1947, 1954 and 2000.*

[48]The terminology used here is not precise. Commissioning arrangements are subject to continual change in an attempt to devise regulations which are mutually beneficial to the Service and to the individual. It is not considered necessary to explore this complication here, beyond noting that in 1955 a GD officer could be serving on: a Permanent Commission, a National Service Commission, a Direct Commission Scheme A, a Direct Commission Scheme B, a Short Service Commission, an Extended Service Commission or a Branch Commission.

[49]AMO A.111/55 of 31 March.

[50]In fact, once the demands of the Korean War expansion had been satisfied, the main reason for continuing to train any National Service pilots had been to provide the 100 needed annually to sustain the twenty fighter squadrons of the RAuxAF. Although there were few openings for aircrew after 1957, the call-up continued on a selective basis until January 1961, the last conscripted airman not being discharged until January 1963.

[51]Rates of pay for 1922 are taken from AMWO 137 of 21 February, for 1947 from AMO A.758/47 of 31 October and for 1954 from AMO A.70/54 of 1 April. Those for 2000 were current at the time of writing.

[52]See Chapter 7, Note 1. While the value of the pound had dropped somewhat in the mid-1930s, this decline had been reversed by the outbreak of war and its value in 1945 was virtually the same as it had been in 1921. So far as the years reflected in Fig. 26 are concerned, using the long term RPI, and assuming the purchasing power of the pound to have had a notional value of 1 in 1999, its value in 1922 had been £31.98, compared to £21.04 in 1947 and £15.42 in 1954.

Chapter 25

Navigator training during the first post-war decade

Following the run down of the BCATP in 1945, the RAF needed to re-establish a UK-based training system. This resulted in a spate of unit redesignations and renumberings during the early post-war period but the situation had stabilised by mid-1948 with most navigators being trained to 'wings' standard at Nos 1 and 2 Air Navigation Schools (ANS). In that year, however, to take advantage of better weather factors, they were joined by No 3 ANS at Thornhill in Southern Rhodesia, graduates of this school subsequently passing through No 201 Advanced Flying School (AFS) at Swinderby for a period of acclimatisation training.

These arrangements sufficed until 1951 when the expansion of the RAF, due to the Korean War, created an urgent need for additional training capacity. This obliged the Service to turn to civilian contractors, much as it had had to do in 1938. Air Service Training and Airwork Ltd were contracted to run Nos 1 and 2 Basic Air Navigation Schools (BANS), at Hamble and Usworth respectively. These, Anson-equipped, units offered a twenty-eight-week course for National Servicemen, the syllabus being completed by a stint at one of the Service-run schools, three more of these having been opened to provide additional capacity.[1]

Meanwhile, with NATO having been formed in 1949 and the Cold War intensifying, Canada had agreed to reassume its wartime role of acting as 'the aerodrome of democracy'.[2] In a scheme very reminiscent of the wartime BCATP, the RCAF undertook to train pilots and navigators for the air forces of the western alliance. The British were quick to take advantage of this scheme, the first batch of RAF navigators beginning their courses in February 1951. Over the next two years, the focus of RAF navigator training shifted increasingly towards Canada, permitting No 3 ANS to be closed down in September 1951, only to reform at Bishops Court a few months later.

No 3 ANS's second lease of life was relatively brief, as it disbanded again in 1954, by which time all but one of the other ANSs, and both BANS, had already closed down. By the end of that year, therefore, the only UK-based unit still involved in navigator training was No 2 ANS at Thorney Island. Since the bulk of the syllabus was now being covered in Canada, No 2 ANS's primary function in the mid-1950s was similar to that of a wartime (O)AFU in that it provided UK/European acclimatisation flying and practical experience of using aids which were not available on the other side of the Atlantic.

Along with the Anson, the Wellington T.10 was the standard early post-war navigation trainer. This one, NC793/FFOG, was with No 2 Air Navigation School at Middleton St George in 1950. (B.A. Forward)

[1]All three of these units, Nos 4, 5 and 6 ANSs, proved to be relatively short-lived. This was particularly true of the Langford Lodge-based No 4 ANS which, having been established on 22 September 1952, assumed the identity of No 5 ANS on 15 November when that unit disbanded at Lindholme. Never having received any aeroplanes as No 4 ANS, the unit had no better luck as No 5 and it closed down on 31 January 1953, having contributed nothing of any consequence to the navigator training programme.

[2]This stirring phrase was first used to describe Canada's hosting of the BCATP by Robert Lovett, US delegate to the Ottawa Training Conference of 1942.

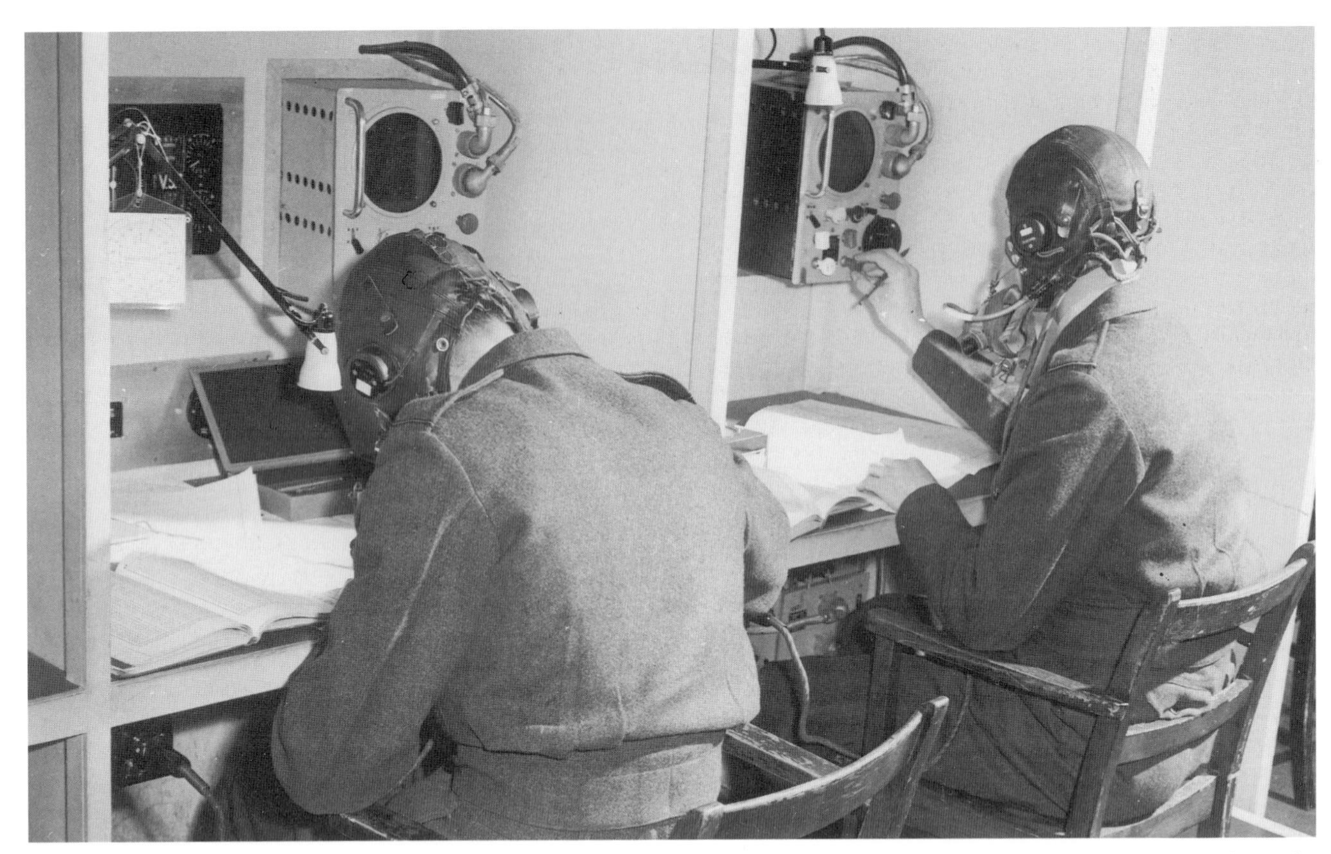

A synthetic training which had first been introduced during WW II, Thorney Island's Dead Reckoning Trainer (DRT) in 1954. The 'radar set' is a Universal Indicator which was used, in this instance, to produce simulated GEE signals; the other black box visible in the left hand cubicle is an API Mk 1. There was another student on the other side of the back wall of each cubicle, following his leader's plot but applying the 'actual' winds, rather than those being found by the trainee. Since this second player knew where the 'aeroplane' really was, he was able to manipulate the readings on some of the instruments to reflect this and to work out the appropriate sextant 'readings' when his 'navigator' used astro. While this system was primitive by modern standards, it was very effective and provided valuable real time plotting practice for both members of the team. (CRO, RAF Finningley)

The Valetta T.3 was a not entirely successful concept. Inside there were ten student navigator stations, each fitted with an API, a radio compass, GEE and REBECCA and there were five astrodomes, permitting 'all those on the left' to use a sextant, followed by 'all those on the right'. Responsibility for the actual navigation of the aircraft was vested in a member of the staff who was on the flight deck and this represented the major weakness in the flying classroom system. Only one navigator can be in charge and it was the adrenaline factor associated with this function that students needed most. Apart from the fact that one was up in an aeroplane, albeit as a 'passenger', most of what went on inside could actually be simulated quite effectively on the ground. (CRO RAF Finningley)

As regards aeroplanes, all post-war RAF navigators had learned their trade on Ansons and Wellingtons until 1951 when a 'flying classroom' adaptation of the Valetta transport began to enter service. In 1952 the earlier types began to be supplanted by the Varsity, which was to become the Service's all-purpose, multi-engined crew trainer for the next quarter of a century. By this time, however, most RAF navigators were gaining their initial flying experience at Summerside and/or Winnipeg on RCAF Expediters and Dakotas. On returning to the UK navigators trained in Canada flew their acclimatisation courses on Varsities and/or Marathons until 1955 when it also became possible to provide an introduction to jet flying following No 2 ANS's acquisition of some obsolete Vampire night fighters.

The implications of the V-bombers

Beginning with the receipt of the first Valiants in 1955, squadrons of V-bombers, known collectively as the Medium Bomber Force (and colloquially as the V-Force), were to form the backbone of the RAF for the next twenty years. The introduction of bomber aircraft which differed so radically from those which had gone before was bound to affect the policy governing the composition of their crews; a policy which had last been formally reviewed in 1942. The problems that this threw up received increasingly active consideration from 1951 onwards.

It had long been agreed that all three V-bombers would be operated by five-man crews but it remained to be determined precisely what sort of men they should be. A bombing team, comprising a pilot and two navigators, was a given, but there was some uncertainty over the other two crew members. In January 1952, harking back to the tradition established by the wartime 'heavies' (and sustained in some Washingtons[3]), HQ Bomber Command recommended that the right-hand seat should be occupied by an air engineer.[4] The Air Ministry had some reservations about this, but, since the imminent withdrawal of Lincolns and Washingtons would create a surplus of air engineers, who would also be cheaper to replace than pilots, the suggestion was accepted. A year later, however, Bomber Command had changed its mind and the AOCinC, Air Mshl Sir Hugh Lloyd, proposed that the captain be assisted by a second pilot.[5]

Although detailed discussions were to continue for some time, the essentials of the composition of a V-bomber crew were settled during the summer of 1953. The two-pilot option was readily adopted, partly because it was desirable to be able to provide on-the-job training for prospective captains, and partly because it was considered preferable to employ exclusively commissioned personnel wherever the custody and/or delivery of nuclear weapons might be involved.[6]

There was no dispute over the need for two navigators and it was foreseen that this would continue to be the case, even if the long-term prospect of air-launched guided weapons were to materialise. After some debate, it was decided to refer to them as the navigator (plotter) and navigator (radar).[7] The function of the third back-seater was initially envisaged as being largely confined to the handling of communications, although it was anticipated that he might eventually have to look after Radio Counter Measures (RCM) equipment as well. At the time, and later, serious consideration was given to introducing the term radio officer to distinguish these men from traditional air signallers. Whatever they were to be called, however, it was considered highly desirable that, like the other members of a V-bomber crew, they should be officers. Some reservations were expressed over simply extending the current practice of commissioning NCOs, however, as it was felt that this did not always produce officers of the required calibre.

In the autumn of 1954 some thought was given to dispensing with the third back-seater altogether and distributing responsibility for communications among the other crew members. This option had to be rejected, however, because the design of all three V-bombers had already reached a stage at which any major modification to the layout of the crew compartment would have been inordinately expensive. There was, in any case, a far more persuasive argument for retaining a five-man crew. As the V-bomber projects had approached the hardware stage, the air staff's direct association with them had grown much closer and it had become apparent that all three types were going to be 'electric' aeroplanes. Monitoring and control of the complex, and critically important, electrical system would be the responsibility of the third back-seater and this secured his position within the crew.

The introduction of the air electronics officer and the air electronics operator

Following the RAF's post-war contraction, its residual air signals training capacity was concentrated in Madley's No 4 Radio School. In December 1946 this unit moved to its peacetime location at Swanton Morley where it continued to train signallers, its original fleet of Proctors and Dominies soon being supplanted by Prentices and Anson T.22s. On 1 April 1951 the unit was restyled No 1 Air Signallers School and, a year later, a second was opened at Halfpenny Green. Having operated for less than eighteen months, No 2 Air Signallers School closed down in September 1953, its function presumably having been to permit the Service to handle the initial Korean War bulge. By this time the RAF's attention was beginning to focus increasingly on the problems associated with the provision of aircrew for the projected V-Force, a development that was to have major implications for air signals personnel.

While the possibility of deleting the fifth member of a V-bomber crew was finally ruled out during 1954, a degree of uncertainty remained as to what he would actually do. It was assumed, however, that, whatever it turned out to be, it would be too demanding for the traditional air signaller and that it was likely to require levels of education and intelligence similar to those associated with pilots and navigators. Once

[3]The American-supplied Washington was designed for two-pilot operation but the RAF elected to make limited use of surplus air engineers to fly as co-pilots, these men being in addition to the dedicated air engineer within a crew. This practice did not read across to the contemporary Lincoln which operated on similar lines to the wartime Lancaster with a single pilot assisted, as necessary, by his air engineer.

[4]AIR20/7385. HQ Bomber Command letter BC/S.85213 dated 16 January 1952.

[5]*Ibid.* HQ Bomber Command letter BC/S.83718 dated 20 January 1953.

[6]*Ibid.* Minutes of an Air Ministry meeting held on 30 July 1953 on file CMS.2060/DDOps(B). Note that, despite the decision not to use air engineers, there were isolated cases of them flying in the right hand seats of Valiants in the early days, but this is believed to have occurred only at the OCU, not on squadrons.

[7]Note that these terms were applied merely for administrative convenience to indicate which navigators had attended which specialist post-graduate courses. They were not formal sub-categories in the sense that had been used to distinguish between the various types of wartime navigator whose specialisation had been determined by the courses they had attended during basic training.

The Anson soldiered on as a trainer for non-pilot aircrew until as late as 1958. This one, VS595, is a T.22 which belonged to No 1 Air Electronics School. (E. Taylor)

this had been agreed, it automatically followed that, since he would have to be recruited from the same pool as pilots and navigators, the third back-seater would, like them, also have to be commissioned. By 1955 it was being argued that Coastal Command might also have a requirement for the new type of 'radio officer' and the whole question was referred to the Air Council.

The main reservations that emerged during the subsequent discussions centred on the difficulties that were likely to be encountered in recruiting these men. In view of the RAF's perennial problems with providing enough pilots and navigators, it was feared that it might well be impossible to find yet more men of a similar calibre. This prompted further examination of the possibility of extending the terms of reference of navigators to embrace the responsibilities of the new trade, an interesting proposal in the light of developments anticipated in 2003 (see pages 232–233). While this approach presented a management solution to some aspects of the problem, because all three rear crew seats still needed to be filled, it would not have reduced the overall numbers required.[8] Since the recruiting challenge appeared to be unavoidable, it was decided to face it head on and in early 1956 the entirely new aircrew category of the air electronics officer (AEO) was created.[9]

It is perhaps worth recording that by 1957 the future of the new category looked particularly bright. That year's White Paper on Defence had been drafted on the assumption that the RAF's future lay in missiles, rather than aeroplanes. It followed that pilots would soon become largely redundant, the need for their manual dexterity being replaced by a demand for the more intellectual and technical capabilities of navigators and, to an even greater extent, AEOs. In the dawn of the era of Bloodhound and Thor, and with the prospect of BLUE STREAK to follow, it looked to some as if the new AEOs might eventually inherit the air force. In retrospect, this may appear to have been an exercise in wishful thinking but, at the time, the idea really did not seem to be that far-fetched, not at least to those who believed in the new gospel.

Many AEO's were directly recruited but others were found from within the Service by cross-training commissioned air signallers, by cross-training and commissioning selected NCO air signallers and by drawing on suitable ground tradesmen. Once qualified, AEOs were to wear a new 1939-pattern flying badge with an 'AE' within the laurel wreath, although this was not formally introduced until 1957.[10] The Prentice having been withdrawn by this time, the first AEOs were trained alongside air signallers on Swanton Morley's Ansons. To reflect the change of emphasis in the unit's task it was restyled No 1 Air Electronics School on 1 April 1957 before moving at the end of that year to Hullavington where it was re-equipped with Varsities during 1958.

For the first decade after their introduction the majority of AEOs were to be found within Bomber Command,[11] while air signallers still abounded in Coastal Command, although the odd stray could be found in the wrong camp and a few of each occasionally escaped to Transport Command. Nevertheless, by the time that the venerable Shackleton finally began to give way to the Nimrod in 1970, most of Coastal Command's commissioned air signals personnel were AEOs and, of equal significance, there had been a major change in the NCO complement of a maritime crew.

At much the same time as the AEO had been introduced, the increasing complexity of the detection equipment installed in Shackletons had made it desirable to raise the overall standard of technical competence of air signallers. The first step

[8]AIR6/118. Conclusions of Air Council Standing Committee Meeting SC 14(55) held on 6 June 1955.
[9]AMO A.54/56 of 8 March.

[10]AMO A.18/57 of 9 January.
[11]Although it was the RAF's intention that its V-bombers should have all-officer crews, pending the availability of adequate numbers of AEOs, it was impossible to achieve this aim. As a result, some NCO air signallers had to be substituted in the early days, particularly on Valiant squadrons.

The rearward-facing AEO's station in a Vulcan B.2. Most of the controls and displays on the bulkhead were associated with the STR 18 HF radio and a variety of electronic countermeasures, e.g. RED SHRIMP, BLUE DIVER, BLUE SAGA and chaff; the circular screen is the display for the RED STEER Mk I tail warning radar. The large panel below the porthole is a schematic representation of the aircraft's all important electrical system, the control of which was the AEO's most critical responsibility. (British Aerospace via Roger Chesneau)

in this direction was taken in 1956 when the twenty-week Air Signallers Advanced Course was set up at Swanton Morley.[12] Students who were not already graded as air signallers (A) graduated as such and this upgrade soon became one of the primary aims of the course.

Shortly after the unit moved to Hullavington, *ab initio* air signaller training was suspended because the 1957 White Paper had substantially reduced the RAF's front-line, creating a surplus of manpower. Most of the air signallers involved were disposed of during 1958 under a voluntary redundancy scheme. Not for the last time, the RAF had implemented a short-term solution to a long-term problem and within two years it was already short of airmen aircrew and Hullavington had to reinstate basic training courses in 1960.

Having previously dropped its numerical designation, to become simply the Air Electronics School, the unit moved to Topcliffe on 14 January 1962. At the end of that year, it was announced that the Air Signallers Advanced Course, which had been unaffected by the moratorium on *ab initio* training, was to be redesignated as the Air Electronics Conversion Course. Thenceforth, all graduates [and all current air signallers (A)] were to be categorised as air electronics operators (AEOp), exchanging their 'S' badges for the 'AE' which had previously been worn only by AEOs, i.e. by officers.[13] Following the creation of this new category, the training of all air signals personnel underwent a major overhaul between 1965 and 1967.

This process began when AEOps started to be trained from the outset, that is to say, without having to pass through an initial air signaller stage. Of the ten students who graduated with No 42 Air Signallers Course in July 1965, for instance, six [probably ex-tradesmen, who would have equated to the old air signallers (A)] wore an 'AE' badge and four [presumably *ab initio* students] wore an 'S'. The last four air signallers to graduate as such completed their course (No 55) in December 1966. A few weeks later the last all-officer AEO course (No 45) ended. Thereafter, AEOs and AEOps were to be trained alongside each other against a new thirteen-month syllabus. No 1 Air Electronics Course graduated in August 1967 but changing requirements dictated that the joint AEO/AEOp course would turn out to be merely a transitional arrangement.

By this time ten years' worth of officers had been trained, primarily to satisfy the needs of the expanding Medium Bomber Force. As soon as the V-Force had reached its full potential, however, it began to contract, taking with it the demand for AEOs, especially as the missile era predicted by Duncan

[12]AMO A.280/56 of 14 November.

[13]AMO N.894/62 of 5 December as amplified by AMO A.6/63 of 2 January.

Sandys had failed to materialise. In fact, the V-Force's decline had got off to a flying start as a result of the abrupt withdrawal of the Valiant in 1965. This had created an unforeseen surplus of trained AEOs sufficient to permit direct recruiting to be terminated, the last *ab initio* student officers graduating in 1967. Thereafter, as with air signallers in the past, the RAF trained all of its air electronics personnel as airmen aircrew. The much reduced requirement for officers was met by selection from the pool of NCOs, some of them being commissioned on graduation.

While these changes to basic training were being made, the school continued to run its Air Electronics Conversion Course to permit the dwindling rump of air signallers to be recategorised as AEOps, this process continuing until 1972. In October of the following year, the school (which was now also responsible for training air engineers[14]) moved to Finningley. Shortly afterwards the Varsity was retired, obliging student AEOps to gain their airborne experience on the Dominie, often during sorties primarily designed for the benefit of trainee navigators. This was hardly an ideal arrangement but its drawbacks were largely offset by the progressive introduction of increasingly sophisticated synthetic training aids. Practical experience continued to be provided in much the same manner following the transfer of all non-pilot aircrew training to Cranwell in 1997, since when the instruction of AEOps has been one of the responsibilities of the multi-faceted Navigator and Airmen Aircrew School (NAAS).

There is one other aspect of the air signals specialisation which is worthy of note. AEOps are categorised as 'wet' or 'dry' men, which is to say that they deal primarily either with sonobuoys and acoustic processing or with radar and/or electronic support measures. At one time all AEOs/AEOps were trained in both fields, the way in which they would subsequently be employed being decided at the OCU stage, but streaming is now carried out before the end of basic training. It is not encouraged, but it is possible for an AEOp to change his specialisation and some 'wet' men have converted to 'dry', although relatively few have moved in the other direction. These labels are not applied to AEOs, incidentally, although most of those who had been 'wet' specialists as AEOps tend to remain in the maritime world after they have been commissioned. By contrast, AEOs having a 'dry' background have rather broader employment opportunities, with No 51 Sqn, for instance, or as Wing Electronic Warfare Officers on strike/attack stations.

While the AEO and AEOp had virtually displaced the air signaller by the end of the 1960s, this still left a gap in the range of aircrew categories. Although the Douglas Committee had rejected the idea of special duties operators being recognised as a discrete aircrew category in 1945 (see page 191) the problem had not gone away. The post-war RAF had continued to maintain an airborne intelligence gathering capability and this had been significantly enhanced during the late 1950s by the acquisition of Canberras and Comets. The crews of these aeroplanes, particularly the latter, included a number of special operators who did not fit comfortably within any of the currently recognised aircrew categories, obliging the unit concerned, No 51 Sqn, to make its own arrangements. Most of its recruits were drawn from experienced ground radio operators who, after in-house training, flew as acting sergeants, but they wore no flying badge and drew only crew pay.

In the early 1970s the Comets were replaced by Nimrods and, since the 'S' badge was no longer being awarded, at much the same time No 51 Sqn appears to have begun to authorise its signals personnel to wear them. While this practice was presumably condoned by the squadron's operating authority, it was almost certainly improper.

In any event, the end result was a formal bid for the peculiar circumstances of this handful of men to be treated as a special case. It was argued that, because they carried out their duties in an airborne environment, they deserved to be recognised as aircrew, which would automatically entitle them to draw flying pay. After the obligatory ritual arguments with the Treasury, it was agreed to reinstate the redundant category of the air signaller. This required an increased degree of formality, however, as the change from ground to air duties now involved a remustering process.

Beginning in 1978 prospective air signallers were required to attend a short squadron-run survival course. In 1979 a formal selection board procedure was introduced and the survival course was extended to a week. While this sufficed for the next ten years, there was a widespread perception that, despite their flying badges, No 51 Sqn's, now unique, breed of air signallers were not 'real' aircrew. This inevitably caused some friction within the squadron itself, where 'instant' air signallers flew alongside formally trained AEOps. For the signallers to be recognised by their peers it would be necessary for them to attend the demanding initial training course that had to be passed by all other airmen aircrew (see pages 215–216). Negotiations began in 1989 and No 51 Sqn's *protégés*, were soon being required to clear this hurdle before embarking on the specialist phase of training, leading to the award of an 'S' badge, responsibility for all of this remaining with the squadron.

Since No 51 Sqn has been the sole sponsor of air signallers for many years, the numbers involved have been small. Nevertheless, there was still one barrier which needed to be overcome and this fell in June 1991 when Sgt Sue Rosie became the first woman ever to be awarded an 'S' badge.

The fluctuating fortunes of the air engineer

Air engineer training had continued at St Athan throughout the late 1940s but it was clear that the anticipated withdrawal of piston-engined bombers would provide a substantial surplus in this category. As a result, *ab initio* training courses ceased in August 1951. Thereafter the Service lived off the fat represented by serving direct entrants who elected to re-engage to complete twenty-two years, topped up by a few volunteers who were prepared to fly under the old five-year arrangements. These additional men were drawn from experienced ground tradesmen and trained relatively informally on Operational Conversion Units (OCU).

As with air signallers, many air engineers took advantage of the 1958 redundancy scheme to leave the Service. By 1960 they were in increasingly short supply and training had to be restarted. This had not been too difficult in the case of air signallers, as their school had remained in commission to train AEOs. The situation was very different in the case of air engineers. Because the RAF routinely moves all of its people around on a two to three-year cycle, three or four 'generations' had passed since St Athan had stopped training aircrew in 1951. As a result: the pool of resident expertise had long since dried up; all of the old training rigs had been

[14]An extension of its task had led to the unit's title being expanded to the Air Electronics and Air Engineers School (AE&AES) with effect from 30 January 1967.

disposed of; and there was very little in the way of a 'corporate memory'.

The initial attempt at, wholly internal, recruiting was confined to airframe and engine tradesmen of senior technician rank. They were offered a year's training and five years' productive flying before resuming ground duties. The prospect of flying pay provided some incentive, but this had to be set against the problems of eventual reintegration into their original trades. On balance the offer proved to be so unattractive that only six applications were received to fill the thirty vacancies on the first course which was duly postponed. The gaps that had to be filled urgently were plugged by hastily assimilating a number of crew chiefs as aircrew.[15]

To alleviate the difficulties with recruiting, the trawl was widened to include instrument and electrical fitters and the entry rank was lowered to corporal in the hope that early promotion to sergeant, as aircrew, would provide the necessary carrot. In the meantime, work had been progressing to devise a suitable training system. The easy option was to exploit an existing course, one actually intended to produce crew chiefs, since this already provided adequate technical instruction in all four of the required disciplines. Regardless of their previous qualifications (all candidates would already be skilled in at least one trade), it was decided that all prospective air engineers would have to pass through the full sequence of instruction. This involved sixteen weeks of airframes and engines with No 8 SofTT at Weeton, followed by another sixteen weeks of electrics and instruments at No 12 SofTT at Melksham. Flying badges were presented on completion of an appropriate course at an OCU, such courses generally being of five to six months duration.

It soon became apparent that lowering the entry hurdle to permit corporals to apply had failed to produce the numbers required and more courses proved to be so undersubscribed that they had to be cancelled. Meanwhile, the manning situation was growing worse, not least because Transport Command was taking delivery of a substantial fleet of Argosies.

The roots of the recruiting problem stretched all the way back to WW II when, it will be recalled, the Service had taken a long time to learn that flight engineers needed to be treated as aircrew, and not as flying tradesmen. This lesson had never been properly digested, however, as the 1946 Aircrew Scheme had shown only too clearly, the RAF spending the next five years doggedly trying to persuade groundcrew to fly on short-term contracts. The fact that it had had to resort to recruiting direct entrant professionals in 1943, and again between 1948 and 1951 seems not have made any lasting impression either. With monotonous predictability, when more air engineers were required in 1959, the Service had once again attempted to find them by misemploying technicians.

There are, and probably always will be, some tradesmen who would like to fly for a time but, despite all attempts to provide appropriate safeguards, this almost inevitably results in some career disadvantage compared to those who keep their feet firmly on the ground. As a result, there will rarely be enough of these men to satisfy the overall requirement. Just as in 1942 and in 1948, what had been needed in 1959 was a scheme offering air engineers full-time service on aircrew terms. Such an arrangement was finally introduced (again) in 1963.[16] The necessary manpower was still to be found by drawing on ground tradesmen but they were now able to remuster as full-time aircrew, as were air engineers currently serving under the old short-term arrangements and those who were back on the ground having previously done a stint of flying.

While a permanent solution to the recruiting problem was being sought, the arrangements that had been made for training had begun to unravel. Among the changes in defence policy announced in 1957 had been the ending of National Service, no further conscripts being called up after 31 December 1960. With its intake rapidly shrinking, the training machine contracted over the next few years, both of the units attended by air engineers being closed. The airframe and engines commitment was transferred from Weeton to No 4 SofTT at St Athan during 1964, responsibility for Melksham's electrical and instrument element of the syllabus being transferred to No 9 SofTT at Newton. It should be stressed that all four of the schools which were, or had been, training air engineers were essentially ground oriented and even St Athan, once the spiritual home of the air engineer, had long since lost its touch. As a result, the two-phase system had never been entirely suitable, as was demonstrated by an unsatisfactory failure rate at the OCU stage. Most of this, not least air sickness, could be directly attributed to the total lack of practical, and precious little theoretical, flying content within the technical courses.

Settling for air engineers riding piggy-back on the crew chiefs course may have been expedient, but it had never been the right answer. What was really needed was a dedicated course designed for, and preferably taught by, aircrew at a flying station. Pressure for such a course to be provided began to build up and in January 1967 responsibility for air engineer training was vested in Topcliffe where it could be conducted alongside that of AEOps in what was restyled the Air Electronics and Air Engineers School (AE&AES). The first of the new series of Air Engineers Courses began on 13 May 1967. Curiously enough, however, it was identified as No 5 Course, in order to conform to the numbering pattern already established by the resident AEOp brigade.

The new syllabus included practical airborne experience on the Varsity which permitted flying badges to be awarded, as was far more appropriate, on completion of the course, rather than after the OCU stage. To begin with, the majority of trainees continued to be ground tradesmen but direct entrants were soon reintroduced, these representing about half of the intake by the mid-1970s. The AE&AES moved to Finningley in 1973 where, in anticipation of the withdrawal of the Varsity, preparations began for its replacement by suitably adapted Argosies.

The four-engined Argosy was an improbably large airframe for the training role but, having recently been withdrawn from transport duties, it was readily available at the relatively small cost of a partial internal refit. The idea was to use these aeroplanes to train navigators and, despite their often conflicting individual requirements, AEOps, air engineers *and* air loadmasters, sometimes simultaneously. There were many in the non-pilot training community at the time who considered this a trifle overambitious. Perhaps fortunately, the reservations of the sceptics were never tested because the Argosy trainer project was cancelled in 1975.

Thereafter, and ever since, air engineers have gained their airborne experience on the Dominie. There has never been a great deal of this, but then engineers never have been over-

[15]Sponsored mainly by Bomber Command, to fill the gap left by the deletion of the air engineer from the crews of large bombers, a crew chief was a highly-trained, multi-skilled ground tradesmen capable of dealing with practically all aircraft systems. Although he had no direct responsibilities in flight, a crew chief always accompanied, what became for the duration of the exercise, 'his' V-bomber when it operated away from base.

[16]AMO A.147/63 of 24 April.

Originally procured to train navigators, the Dominie was eventually obliged to do triple duty, providing airborne experience for air engineers and air electronics operators as well. This one, XS731, belonged to No 6 FTS at Finningley when this picture was taken in the 1970s. (CRO RAF Finningley)

provided with flying time while under training – none at all during WW II. On the other hand, so long as the simulation is comprehensive and realistic, much of an air engineer's practical work can be carried out satisfactorily on synthetic training aids.

The first such device, a training rig based on the Argosy, was built at Topcliffe. The second, utilising the actual cockpit section of a redundant Argosy, was built at Finningley, as was a Dominie trainer created inside a fibreglass moulding of an actual aircraft. Apart from the provision of the Dominie 'shape', these devices were all designed and built on-site, at minimum cost by the instructional staff. It stands as mute testimony to the 'poor relation' status that the RAF has persistently conferred upon its air engineers that they were still having to provide themselves with such essential training aids on a do-it-yourself basis into the 1980s. No substantial investment of public money was made until as late as 1983 when a contract was finally let for the purchase of a Nimrod-based procedures trainer.

Along with all other non-pilot aircrew training, the air engineers moved to Cranwell in 1997 to form an element of the NAAS. The numbers required have declined steadily over the years, partly through the contraction of the Service and partly through the introduction of two-man (a euphemism for two-pilot) flight decks. Thus, for instance, while the original fleet of Hercules C.1s and C.3s had employed substantial numbers of air engineers, they will not be included in the crews of the C.4s and C.5s which have replaced them. Similarly, the air engineers who flew in the Nimrod MR 2 will not be required in the 'glass cockpit' of the refitted Nimrod MRA 4. So long as the RAF continues to operate its VC10s, Sentries and a few other types, it will continue to need air engineers but their days are numbered. At the time of writing it was expected that the annual training requirement for new air engineers would reduce to zero in 2005.

The reinstatement of the radio observer

At much the same time as the Service had been deciding to introduce the AEO to fly in V-bombers, the anticipated arrival of Javelins in 1956 had prompted a reappraisal of the qualifications that were necessary to occupy the back seat of a night/all-weather fighter. Since it was now established policy that all pilots and navigators (and AEOs) were to be commissioned, it is a little surprising to find that the RAF decided to reverse this trend by introducing a new category of NCO back-seater.

While other options were available, most of these men, whether direct entrants or serving airmen, were expected to fly on, initially, five-year engagements. They were to be taught how to carry out interceptions using airborne radar and given a course of basic navigation training which omitted astro and sundry other advanced techniques. This syllabus required some six months to complete, compared to a year for the full navigators course. Having been only partially trained, however, these men clearly could not be regarded as 'proper' navigators so the long defunct trade of the radio observer was reinstated, granting the 'RO' badge of 1941 a second lease of life.[17]

This scheme was superficially attractive, since it represented an economic use of resources, but it also represented an attempt to substitute a half-trained sergeant for a fully-trained officer. It was not quite a throwback to the days of the part-time gunner of the 1920s, but the same underlying principle was clearly at work. The new breed of back-seater served in Meteor and Javelin night-fighter squadrons where they flew alongside commissioned navigators.

It soon became apparent that, given an equal degree of experience, there was little to chose between the professional competence of an NCO and that of an officer. Nevertheless, this situation had revitalised, potentially at least, the Bristol Fighter syndrome of 1917. That is to say that the effectiveness of a crew could, because of the difference in their status, sometimes be less than the sum of the capabilities of its individual members.

In the event, the output of radio observers was to amount to a little over one hundred personnel trained on ten courses which passed through the system in 1956–57.[18] By the mid-1960s they had practically all disappeared. Some had returned to civilian life; some had reverted to their ground trades while others, having been given the additional training which had originally been withheld, had been commissioned as navigators. The latter development served to invoke further echoes of the past; it will be recalled that as long ago as 1943 the Service had concluded that, to be fully effective, all AI operators needed to be properly qualified navigators (see page 186).

A final flirtation with NCO pilots and navigators

In 1961, with the short-lived radio observers already fading from the scene, the RAF continued its reversionary trend and reintroduced, albeit 'on a limited scale', recruitment of NCO pilots and navigators.[19] The intake was expected to include both civilian entrants and internal recruits who had the necessary flying aptitude but who were considered to be unsuitable for commissioned service, plus officer trainees who had failed to make the grade. After graduating from initial training with the rank of acting sergeant, they were to undergo flying training alongside their acting pilot officer colleagues.

The first NCOs began their professional training with No 2 ANS's No 34 Course in November 1961. Peak loading occurred in July 1962 when the student body at Hullavington comprised 138 officers and thirty-nine sergeants. Intakes continued for eighteen months, the last NCOs graduating with No 51 Course in April 1964. Since the beginning of

[17]AMO A.192/56 of 8 August.

[18]Nos 1–5 RO Courses, the first of them commencing on 26 September 1956, were trained by No 2 ANS at Thorney Island. No 6 Course began there but was transferred to No 1 ANS at Topcliffe six weeks after it had started. The remaining RO training commitment was handled by Topcliffe, No 10 Course having been cancelled, the last to graduate was No 11 which ended on 26 November 1957.

[19]AMO A.193/61 of 21 June.

the scheme a total of fifty-eight navigators had passed out as airmen aircrew, compared to 198 as officers. To reward their performance during training some sergeants were commissioned on gaining their 'wings' and within five years practically all of the others who were still in uniform had become officers, demonstrating once again the very close correlation that exists between officer and pilot/navigator qualities. As a result of this experience, the RAF reverted to the 1950 policy of 100% officer intakes which still governs the recruiting of pilots and navigators today.

The introduction of the air loadmaster, *née* air quartermaster

In 1945 Transport Command had failed to persuade the Douglas Committee that the RAF should recognise air quartermasters as aircrew (see page 190). Although the proposal had been turned down, there had always been much to do 'down the back' of a transport aircraft. These duties included, for instance: overseeing the loading, lashing down and unloading of cargo; ensuring that the weight and balance of the aircraft remained within limits; supervising passengers in flight; and assisting in the delivery of air drops.[20] This sort of work, much of which tended to be delegated to the, often seriously overworked, air engineer, really was sufficiently complex, even critical, to have warranted the provision of a specialist crewman. The Service did employ airmen from the equipment trade as air quartermasters to help out, but it still declined to acknowledge them as aircrew. The perceived injustice of this situation was periodically aggravated by the fact that surplus signallers and gunners were also sometimes misemployed as quartermasters and air despatchers but, in their case, retaining their aircrew status and (after it had been introduced in 1950) full flying pay.

When it had been essential to carry a crewman in the RAF's early small and underpowered helicopters it used volunteer ground tradesmen but, following the introduction of the Belvedere, pressure for them to be replaced by rated aircrew came to a head in 1961. The idea of a dedicated category was rejected in favour of air engineers who were soon supplanted by air signallers but by 1967 it had been agreed that the task should be given to air quartermasters (later loadmasters) and this remains the most common practice today. This is No 26 Sqn's XG467, delivering a 105mm field gun to a site north of Aden circa 1963. (Gp Capt J. Price)

[20]Primary responsibility for the conduct of air drops continued to be vested in soldiers of the Air Despatch Regt, as it still is today.
[21]AMO A.117/62 of 16 May.

Transport Command tried again in 1952 but, once again, its submission was turned down. Even a request for air quartermasters to be allowed to wear the aircrew eagle was denied. Despite this rejection, one significant innovation was approved in 1952, the introduction of female cabin crew to replace the redundant air gunners who were then serving in this capacity on trooping flights to and from the Middle East. In view of the number of families involved, it was considered that it might be more appropriate to employ women and a trial period proved that this was indeed the case. Once this arrangement had become permanent, women gradually took on other aspects of the air quartermaster's duties.

Another campaign for aircrew status was mounted in 1960, this time invoking the precedent represented by BOAC whose stewards wore flying badges and drew flying pay. It was argued that RAF personnel involved in route-flying carried out much the same duties as their civilian counterparts, including in-flight catering, the safe custody of sensitive material, liasing with movements staff on the ground, and so on. Predictably, the 1960 submission was rejected, but the opposition was beginning to crumble.

Two years later, with Comets and Britannias being joined by Argosies, and the Belfast, Hercules and VC10 in prospect, the Air Ministry finally conceded that 'the qualities required of air quartermasters and the responsibilities attaching to their duties are such as to merit aircrew status.'[21] The new aircrew category was to be distinguished by its own badge, a single wing with a 'QM' motif. It was the first RAF flying badge which women were entitled to wear, there being ten female air quartermasters on active service when it was introduced. Eight years later the air quartermaster was restyled the air loadmaster; the monogram on the badge being changed to an 'LM'.[22]

When air quartermasters had first been recognised their training was carried out by Transport Command, mostly at Abingdon. Apart from the introduction of a mandatory initial training phase (see below) similar arrangements applied to air loadmasters, although this task was later transferred to Brize Norton. In 1983 responsibility for basic training was assumed by No 6 FTS at Finningley, permitting all airmen aircrew to be trained within the same unit, now restyled the Air Electronics, Engineer and Loadmaster School (AEELS). Because of the very different operating environments in which loadmasters could be required to work (ranging from the comfortable cabin of a VC10, through the noisy, and sometimes draughty, hold of a Hercules, to the wet end of a helicopter's winch cable), it was necessary for them to go elsewhere for a final special-to-type course before they gained their flying badges. In 1997 the AEELS was transferred to Cranwell where it was reconstituted as the NAAS, the new unit continuing to train loadmasters much as it had done previously.

The Airmen Aircrew Initial Training School

At the same time as a dedicated air engineer training course was being set up to run alongside that of AEOps at Topcliffe in the mid-1960s, another major innovation had been introduced. To ensure that all prospective airmen aircrew (ultimately including air loadmasters and air signallers) were made of the 'right stuff', it was decided to run them all through a common initial training course before they embarked on their professional studies. The nature of this course was very similar to the one attended by officers and it is arguable that this similarity provides yet

[22]DCI(RAF) S.159 of 30 September 1970.

more evidence to show that, regardless of their professional specialisation, officers and aircrew have to possess many of the same fundamental characteristics.

The first of these physically demanding, three-month courses began in July 1966 under the auspices of what was to become the Airmen Aircrew Initial Training School (AAITS). Those who passed embarked on their professional training already wearing the gilt aircrew eagle in the vee of their chevrons, indicating that, although they had yet to earn their flying badges, they were already considered to have aircrew status. Along with the AE&AES, the AAITS moved to Finningley to become part of No 6 FTS in 1973. It moved again in 1997, to Cranwell, where it now operates as an element of the NAAS.

The introduction of fighter controllers and airborne technicians as 'aircrew'

Following some exploratory work with Neptunes in the 1950s, the RAF eventually acquired an airborne early warning capability in 1972 when the Shackleton AEW 2 entered service. For the next ten years the business of watching radar screens and directing fighters was carried out by navigators, AEOs and AEOps. There was clearly a case for professional fighter controllers to be involved in such activities but, while they had been members of the General Duties (Ground) Branch since 1954 (see below), these men were not aircrew. Nevertheless, the prospect of the far more advanced Nimrod AEW 3 argued strongly for the employment of airborne fighter controllers and the first two, Flt Lt H. Montgomerie and FS R. Steggall, qualified to fly with No 8 Sqn in August 1983. This innovation was accompanied by a new flying badge, a single-winged 'FC', although, through some bureaucratic oversight (or administrative sleight of hand?) it appears to have been introduced without formal sanction.[23] It was at this stage that the authorities charged with regulating flying badges should have stepped in, either to prevent the issue of the 'FC' or to devise appropriate legislation to cover its use.

The RAF's acquisition of Shackleton AEW 2s (this is No 8 Sqn's WL741) created a demand for airborne fighter controllers. This began to be satisfied in 1983, although the way in which the 'FC' badge was introduced appears to have represented a major departure from a procedure for which there was ample precedent.

Although there were a number of factors which argued against recognising fighter controllers as aircrew *per se*, this did not necessarily mean that these men should have been denied the right to wear a badge. A similar situation had cropped up in the past with parachute training instructors. Since they undoubtedly flew in (at least took off in, although they often declined to land in) aeroplanes in order to do their jobs, it was decided that they should be permitted to wear an appropriate emblem. It was to be a 1939-pattern single-wing with a parachute symbol within the laurel wreath. The regulations authorising the introduction of this badge in 1945 included the statement that 'parachute training instructors are to be granted honorary aircrew status' and went on to define the training necessary to qualify.[24] The authority for the issue of this badge, which still confers honorary aircrew status on its wearer, continues to be reflected in Queen's Regulations today.[25]

Another possibility would have been to follow the precedent established by the Catering Branch in 1967.[26] Selected personnel, trained as cabin staff for VIP flights, were mustered as air stewards and identified by a dedicated badge. Since they were not rated as aircrew in the conventional sense, however, this emblem was not based on the classic 1939-pattern and it was not awarded permanently in that it had to be relinquished if the wearer remustered out of Trade Group 19 to pursue some other specialisation. Furthermore, it was worn on the upper sleeve, rather than on the chest, although, for a non-pilot flying badge, it did have the unique distinction of having its 'AS' motif flanked by two wings!

Because fighter controllers were not aircrew, it would have been appropriate to pursue one of these options or to devise some other distinctive method of distinguishing these people. In the event, however, nothing was done to regularise the situation and aircrew-style 'FC' badges proliferated in a legislative vacuum.

The Nimrod Mk 3 was to be equipped with far more sophisticated systems than the wartime AN/APS-20 radar carried by the Shackleton and this brought with it a demand for greater technical support. From 1985, therefore, technicians, mostly of Trade Group 2, began to participate in the Nimrod trials programme. While these men flew regularly, however, they were not formally recognised as aircrew in that they wore no badge and drew crew pay rather than flying pay.

With the demise of the Nimrod AEW project in 1986, the RAF ordered the Boeing E-3 Sentry for delivery in 1990. A jointly-owned, internationally-manned NATO force of E-3s already existed at Geilenkirchen and the first complete RAF crew joined this unit in 1987. This team included a number of technicians, all of whom still lacked any form of flying badge. The badge problem was subsequently aggravated by the arrival of additional fighter controllers who had not qualified for their 'FC' badges because they had not attended the course run by No 8 Sqn.

Those who were embarrassed by their lack of a flying badge soon found a way to overcome this deficiency. Strictly speaking, although the presentation of foreign flying badges may be accepted by RAF personnel, they may not be worn on RAF uniform.[27] This prohibition could be neatly outflanked, however, because day-to-day dress on the NATO

[23]Most unusually, the introduction of the 'FC' badge was not endorsed by a DCI. This alone must raise serious doubts as to its official status prior to 1998 when it was, a trifle belatedly, at least included among the recognised flying badges listed under QR 206.

[24]AMO A.1079/45 of 8 November.
[25]QR 434(2).
[26]DCI(RAF) S119 of 14 June 1967.
[27]QR 206(5).

unit tended to be flying overalls, which were, arguably, not strictly 'uniform'. As a result, it became a common practice for unbadged RAF personnel to sport an equivalent USAF emblem. This problem was finally solved in 1990 when a standard pattern, single-winged 'AT' badge began to be worn by what had become known as airborne technicians.[28] Like the earlier 'FC' badge, there seems to have been no formal authority underpinning the introduction of this new emblem.[29] By this time, however, the 'FC' badge was becoming increasingly familiar, because the fraternity of fighter controllers was now content to endorse the wearing of this (apparently) RAF-sponsored badge by men who had gained their flying experience on NATO-operated Sentries.

In the meantime, while NCOs of Trade Group 12 had been flying as controllers for several years (on the strength of a suitable specialist annotation), to meet the anticipated demands of the RAF's own Sentry force, a dedicated category of NCO fighter controller had been introduced in 1989.[30] The regulations specifically stated that these men could expect to be employed on flying duties but, curiously enough (or, on reflection, perhaps not), reference to the 'FC' badge was conspicuous by its absence, although it is known that such emblems were being worn.

As latecomers to the flying game, the status of fighter controllers and airborne technicians has sometimes been a contentious issue and there is a body of opinion which maintains that neither are 'real' aircrew. For instance, having been transferred to the recently formed Operations Support Branch, fighter control officers, are no longer even members of the GD Branch so, it is argued, they can hardly be regarded as professional aircrew.[31] Similarly, NCO controllers and airborne technicians do not have to undergo the rigours of the course run by the AAITS, a hurdle which all other non-commissioned flyers do have to clear. Furthermore, both of the new categories draw flying pay only while they are filling a flying appointment, rather than on a permanent basis which has long been the case for 'proper' aircrew.

Because the status and conditions of service of the traditional aircrew categories have been relatively stable ever since the 1950s, it is, perhaps, understandable if the new arrivals have raised some eyebrows. For instance, it has become an article of faith that aircrew earn their flying badges by successfully completing 'a prescribed course of flying training.'[32] Everyone thought that they knew what that meant, until the advent of the 'FC' and 'AT' badges for which the definition of flying training had to be stretched to embrace in-house training at squadron (even a NATO squadron) level, invoking shades of 1916. Furthermore, it was difficult (this writer has actually found it impossible) to find any written authority for the introduction of either of these new badges.[33]

All of that having been said, however, there are no absolutes where flying badges are concerned. If one looks back a little further than the 1950s one can find all kinds of practices which had official sanction at the time but which would seem very non-standard today. Without going right back to the *ad hoc* means of obtaining a flying 'O' in 1915–16, once could cite examples such as: the award of 'RO' and 'M' badges after very brief periods of instruction; the officially approved wearing of the (never formally endorsed) 'FE' badge; the award of 'E' badges to people who had yet to fly in an aeroplane; and (under AMO A.89/42) the award of appropriate badges to *de facto* aircrew who had never been formally trained at all. Then again, there have been many instances of permanent flying badges being associated with temporary crew pay. One could also add to this list the case of the parachute training instructors badge and its associated honorary aircrew status.

Furthermore, while the advent of the 'FC' and 'AT' badges may have caused a minor stir, it hardly compares to the culture shock which resulted from the introduction of non-pilot aircrew as 'instant' sergeants at the beginning of 1939, a practice that is now so commonplace as to attract little comment. The fact is that the new badges and categories are neither better nor worse than the more familiar ones, only different. In time, they will merge into the background and come to be taken for granted.

Nevertheless, it is interesting to reflect that, in days of yore, the staffs charged with protecting the sanctity of the RAF uniform and its associated badges, took their responsibilities so seriously that they spent the whole of WW II interpreting (or, arguably, misinterpreting) the regulations so as to prevent the erstwhile observers of WW I from wearing flying 'O's on their army tunics (see pages 193–94). Faced with a far more flagrant transgression of the rules in the 1980s, these ministerial guardians should surely have either outlawed the wearing of the unauthorised 'FC' badge or taken action to have it legitimised.[34] They appear to have done neither for fifteen years, by which time the 'FC' badge was a *fait accompli* and, presumably based on that precedent, the 'AT' badge had followed on.[35] Who, one wonders, will be next to award themselves a flying badge? In the late 1990s there was talk of an airborne role for imagery analysts or, as they used to be called, photographic interpreters. Should this happen, and should they too decide that they ought to have a distinctive badge, one hopes that their 'PI' in the sky will be formally authorised by a DCI.

[28]It is alleged, by some, that it had originally been intended to identify these personnel as Flying Airborne Radar Technicians.
[29]Although 'AT' badges have been in circulation since 1990, the authority under which they were being worn remains obscure as, like the 'FC' badge, they do not appear to have been sanctioned by a DCI. Indeed it was not until as late as 2000 that the 'AT' badge even figured among the officially recognised emblems listed under QR 206 when a revised (fifth) edition of Queens Regulations, dated December 1999, was distributed. In accordance with long-established practice, incidentally, QR206 notes all flying badges that have been awarded in the past, as well as those which are current; sadly, the compiler of the fifth edition appears to have overlooked the 'AQ'.
[30]DCI(RAF) S31 of 10 March 1989.
[31]Reversing the decision of 1954, the GD (Ground) Branch was abolished with effect from 1 April 1997, its place being taken by the newly established Operations Support Branch to which Fighter and Air Traffic Controllers were transferred along with RAF Regiment, Flight Operations and Intelligence Officers.
[32]QR J727(1).
[33]Since the absence of proof is not proof of absence, the possibility must remain that the 'FC' and 'AT' badges were properly sanctioned. Nevertheless, it is worth recording that, when the author wrote to the MOD in 1999 requesting that the specific authority for the introduction of these badges be identified, the specialist officers concerned were unable to do so.
[34]Since the 'FC' and 'AT' badges both appeared without the authority of a DCI, one suspects that other important formalities may also have been glossed over. It is, for instance, necessary to seek the sovereign's approval of the design of any new badge before it is introduced. As examples, AIR2/8369 preserves the correspondence covering the submission to the palace of specimens of the'N', 'B' and 'E' badges on 27 July 1942, of the 'S' on 5 October 1943 and the 'M' in March 1945, while AIR2/18211 contains a letter dated 10 January 1956 seeking royal approval of the 'AE' badge. Was this, one wonders, ever done for the 'FC' and 'AT'?
[35]This inactivity cannot be explained by ignorance of the situation, as the uncertain status of the 'FC' badge was brought to the notice of the MOD, formally and in writing, by this (at the time still uniformed) author in 1988.

Chapter 26

1950–70. The background to aircrew commissioning policy

Before summarising the later changes in post-war aircrew commissioning policy, it is worth examining two aspects of the background against which they were made.

The first point concerns the changing perception of the function of an aircrew officer. While the introduction of the RAF's all-officer approach in 1950 had gone some way towards solving the problems associated with the provision of pilots and navigators, it had created another. The RAF was now faced with a situation which it had been specifically trying to avoid ever since 1945. It was having to sponsor relatively large numbers of officers, most of whom would never actually command anything. This was inevitable, however, as the experience of WW II had shown quite clearly. Wartime aircrew had generally been too preoccupied with their primary duties to exercise any realistic measure of direct control over bodies of airmen and, as a result, ground branch officers, particularly engineers, had become the RAF's real man managers.

Furthermore, it had become increasingly common for aircraft, along with all administrative and technical personnel, to be pooled. Squadrons were no longer the self-sufficient, semi-autonomous organisations of yesteryear. In many cases, the significance of a squadron number plate had been reduced to little more than a convenient label by which to identify a particular group of aircrew. These aircrew were supported by a variety of anonymous common-user organisations with which they frequently had little direct contact. The cost of this development in terms of morale and fighting spirit was considerable, but it was also unquantifiable and therefore weighed little in the balance compared to the measurable advantages to be gained in efficiency, flexibility and economy (but mostly economy).

This trend continued after the war, and even where it did not, aircrew, serving on squadrons and working irregular hours, found it difficult to establish any kind of worthwhile relationship with airmen who often tended to work shifts.[1] Nevertheless, the RAF took many years to reconcile itself to the realities of this situation and it constantly strove to devise ways of involving junior aircrew officers in the administration and welfare of airmen. While well-intentioned, these patently artificial constructs generally served only to confuse the issue by diluting the authority of the ground officers who were really in charge. As outlined below, it was 1970 before the air force finally came to terms with the fact that it was simply impractical to keep on pretending that the function of a contemporary aircrew officer was the same as that of his predecessor of forty years earlier.

[1]This was far from being a new problem. During WW II the Service had openly acknowledged that too many of its wartime (mostly aircrew) officers holding junior executive appointments knew too little about the men under their command. See, for instance, *Tee Emm* for April 1943.

The second point concerns the way in which aircrew officers were employed. In 1954 the GD Branch had undergone a major constitutional change when it had absorbed the Aircraft Control and Fighter Control Branches.[2] Although these branches included many specialists who had no experience of flying, they had also provided employment for large numbers of aircrew officers who were 'resting' between operational tours or who had been withdrawn from flying duties. Furthermore, many purely administrative appointments, having no direct connection with flying whatsoever, continued to be filled by aircrew, particularly career officers who were 'broadening their horizons'.

During the 1960s, serious questions began to be raised over the viability of this traditional approach to running the air force, one major concern being the recruiting situation, which meant that there simply were not enough aircrew to permit them to be 'misemployed' to the extent that they had been in the past. While this alone provided a convincing argument for changing employment patterns, it was made even more persuasive by the rapidly escalating cost of training which made it increasingly undesirable to have expensive aircrew working on the ground. To put it another way, it was preferable to use specialists recruited for the purpose, because they were cheaper to train – and they did not draw flying pay. Aircrew continued to serve on ground duties from time to time but less frequently and the practice was virtually discontinued after 1970. That is not to say that aircrew were subsequently employed exclusively on flying duties but that, wherever possible, their ground tours would be in appointments closely related to flying, for instance training, planning or the direction and monitoring of operations.

1950–70. Changes in commissioning policy

Two major reviews of the terms and conditions under which officers served were undertaken during 1956–57 but these resulted in only one significant development. The GD Branch was divided into two lists, the General List, which included all officers serving on engagements offering full careers, and the Supplementary (Flying) List for the rest.[3] The first group comprised officers serving on what used to be called 'permanent commissions', the second embraced officers serving on shorter engagements, long engagements with limited promotion prospects or under branch terms.[4]

[2]AMO A.219/54 of 9 September. Other officers absorbed into the new organisation included those concerned with radar supervision, photography, photographic interpretation and balloons.

[3]AMO A.362/57 of 27 November. There was actually a third section, the Supplementary (Ground) List, but that need not concern us here.

[4]Originally introduced exclusively for ground branches in 1951 (by AMO A.627/51 of 1 November), the Branch List was a variation on the theme of permanent commissions. A year later, the scheme was extended to embrace both aircrew officers already serving on extended or short service commissions and airmen (aircrew) wishing to become officers by, respectively, AMOs A.499/52 and A.500/52 of 25 September. The main purpose of the Branch

Within certain constraints, provision was made for officers to migrate from one list to the other. For instance, a Supplementary List officer, who would not normally expect to progress beyond flight lieutenant rank, selected for further promotion would usually be transferred to the General List. These arrangements were implemented in January 1958 and two years later the lengths of the most common forms of engagement were standardised at service to age 55 for General List officers and age 38 (or sixteen years of service – the so-called '38/16 point') for the rest, an appropriate pension (strictly speaking 'retired pay') being payable in either case.[5]

Despite these improvements, manning continued to cause concern, as did the ever rising costs of training. In an effort to solve these problems, in 1965 AMP, Air Chf Mshl Sir David Lee, turned once again to the concept of longevity. He argued that the shortfall could be made up, with the added bonus of a corresponding reduction in *ab initio* training costs, if a substantial proportion (the target was 40%) of aircrew could be persuaded to continue flying beyond their 38/16 points. To provide a suitable carrot, it was accepted that the chances of promotion to squadron leader would have to be substantially improved, the annual quota of Supplementary List squadron leaders subsequently being raised from four to sixty, up to a total of 750.[6] Unfortunately, even this failed to produce the required response, partly because there were insufficient squadron leader appointments in which these officers could be employed.

Still faced with persistent undermanning, AMP took the problem back to the Board at the end of 1967. In order to expedite the programme, he sought agreement to his doubling the annual squadron leader promotion quota, thus halving the time required to reach the ceiling of 750. He also proposed to identify specific additional posts which could reasonably be filled by squadron leaders. As a first step, it was suggested that all Comet and VC10 captains should be squadron leaders. All of this was agreed.[7]

Predictably, and as the Board had feared, the decision to promote automatically pilots who just happened to have been posted to fly jet transports was widely perceived to have been divisive by all other pilots (and navigators), but especially those who flew heavy aircraft in other roles. As a result, on being introduced to a squadron leader for the first time, those who considered that they had been discriminated against were tempted to open the conversation with a question along the lines of, 'Are you a real squadron leader, or do you just fly Comets?' Beyond this, to absorb the flood of newly promoted senior officers the status of many of the lesser executive posts at squadron level was progressively raised so that a typical squadron operating multi-seat aeroplanes eventually had an establishment of four or five squadron leaders in place of the previous one.

List was to cater for personnel of flight sergeant or warrant officer/master aircrew rank whose age precluded their being commissioned under other arrangements. A branch commission offered a pensionable engagement but carried little realistic prospect of promotion beyond the rank of flight lieutenant, although this was partially compensated for by a preferential pay scale.

It is perhaps a fine point, but it should be appreciated that, while its absorption into the Supplementary List in 1957 meant that the Branch *List* ceased to exist as such, its conditions of service remained so it was still possible for an individual to be a Branch *Officer*.

[5]AMO A.45/60 of 24 February.

[6]AIR6/145. The argument for increasing the number of Supplementary List squadron leaders to 750 (there were only seventeen at the time) was articulated to the Air Force Board Standing Committee in AMP's memorandum SC (65)22 of 5 July 1965. The idea was subsequently endorsed by the full Air Force Board on 29 July at its meeting 13(65) (AIR6/143).

[7]AIR6/160. Air Force Board Conclusions 1(68) of 22 January 1968.

Even so, retention rates continued to fall below the desired level and it became necessary to introduce 'Specialist Aircrew'. Resembling, in some respects, the terms available to Branch Officers, selected experienced aircrew, who were considered to be excellent professionally but who were not regarded as good promotion prospects, were offered further service at enhanced rates of pay. These terms were introduced on 1st April 1970.[7A] Thereafter, all other things being equal, it was possible for a flight lieutenant to remain in the cockpit as specialist aircrew until the age of 55, his emoluments being roughly the same as those of a squadron leader. There was some prospect of promotion to squadron leader as specialist aircrew which provided an increase in status without, in most cases, obliging the individual to take on the kind of executive responsibilities traditionally associated with that rank. Most of the squadron leaders who had recently been promoted on the Supplementary List were transferred to specialist aircrew terms in that rank, retaining some prospects of promotion to wing commander.

In the meantime, the significant changes which had been occurring within the structure of British society, and which became increasingly apparent during the 1960s, had been forcing the RAF (and the other Services) to reappraise its approach towards the recruiting and training of officers. Traditionally, the Service academies and colleges, Dartmouth, Sandhurst, Cranwell, Henlow[8] and the others, had drawn their intakes from that slice of the population immediately below the rather less than 5% who, according to the Robbins Report,[9] went to university and who, ideally, would have attended a Public School. The proliferation of universities meant that in the 1960s places were becoming increasingly available to people who would previously have been expected to take up cadetships. As a result, the RAF had begun to offer increasing numbers of university graduates permanent commissions on terms similar to those which had previously been reserved, almost exclusively, for Cranwellians. It took time for the rash of new universities to influence recruiting but some idea of their impact can be judged from the fact that the proportion of cadets entering Cranwell from Headmasters Conference schools plummeted from 63.8% in 1958 (much the same as it had been before the war) to a mere 21% in 1962.[10]

The ideal solution, from the point of view of the Services, might have been to have their colleges recognised as degree-awarding institutions, which would probably have permitted them to continue to attract their traditional intakes. In all probability, after a little fine-tuning, the intellectual demands of the curricula on offer in 1960 would have been more than enough to satisfy the Council for Academic Awards of 1990. This Council's standards used to be far more rigorous in the 1960s, however, and, at the crucial time, military training was considered to contain too little of academic substance to impress.

Nevertheless, while the young men of the 1960s were understandably disinclined to forego the option of obtaining a university education, many of them were still keen on

[7A]DCI(RAF) S60 of 8 April 1970.

[8]The RAF Technical College had been established at Henlow on 15 August 1947. It provided cadets recruited into the Technical Branch with similar service training (and subsequent career advantages) to those offered to pilots (and a few others) at its sister organisation at Cranwell. The institution at Henlow eventually moved to Cranwell where it became an integral part of the Royal Air Force College with effect from 1 January 1966.

[9]Report of the Committee on Higher Education, 1961–63.

[10]E.B. Haslam, *The History of Royal Air Force Cranwell* (1982) and Tony Mansell, '*Flying start: educational and social factors in the recruitment of pilots of the Royal Air Force in the inter-war years*' published in *History of Education*, Vol 26, No 1 (1997).

pursuing a career in one of the Services. The difference was that they would now be joining as relatively mature 22 year-old graduates, with ideas of their own, rather than as malleable 18-year-olds, amenable to being pressed into a mould. Furthermore, in view of their age on entry, it would be impractical to expect them to spend two or three further years as cadets before entering productive service.

The upshot of all this was that, with some regret, the cadetship schemes had to be abandoned and, in order to ensure that it recruited its fair share of university-educated men, many of whom were sponsored by the Service, the RAF was obliged to offer them the prospect of a full career on the General List and a rate of pay which went some way towards recognising the three years that they had already spent studying. Once again, the indissoluble link between pay and rank, to which reference has already been made, dictated that these men would have to be given substantial antedates of seniority. In fact, these antedates were such that most graduates were flight lieutenants long before they had finished their training.

University graduates had been receiving preferential treatment of this kind for some time, but the scale of the programme had not been large enough to cause significant comment.[11] From the mid-1960s, however, the numbers involved increased markedly and 'instant' flight lieutenants proliferated. The granting of these (so-called) 'Green Shield Stamp' commissions created some resentment among non-university entrants who could expect to serve for almost six years (which would have included a full operational tour of duty) before attaining the rank of flight lieutenant. While hardly ideal, this development was virtually unavoidable and the initial discontent slowly faded as the practice became increasingly widespread.

The evolving pattern of officer recruiting had another knock-on effect which is worthy of mention. It had long been the case that, in addition to serving his time, before he could become a flight lieutenant, an officer had first to pass the associated Promotion Examination 'B'.[12] The practice of commissioning officers as flight lieutenants meant that they avoided that hurdle. Consequently, in addition to lacking practical experience, this new generation of officers had little awareness of the air force lore which their predecessors had acquired through pre-examination study. Since increasing numbers were by-passing the examination, however, it was eventually abandoned so that no officers were required to do much studying until they reached their late 20s when they began to qualify themselves for promotion to squadron leader, which required them to pass the 'C' Exam. The inevitable result was to devalue the rank of flight lieutenant so that, among aircrew at least, it became little more than a pay grade.

This downward trend was to continue. The substantial increase in the number of squadron leaders agreed in 1965, the appointment of specialist aircrew as such from 1970 and the eventual abolition of the related Promotion Examination 'C' meant that that rank was also in danger of becoming a mere pay grade by the 1980s. All of this would, no doubt, have been a considerable disappointment to Sir John Slessor who had been at pains to counter this specific tendency when he had been attempting to define the shape of the post-war air force in 1945 (see page 197).

The RAF College's last cadet entry (the 101st) began its 2½-year course in September 1970; the next intake would comprise university graduates who were required to stay at Cranwell for only eleven weeks. In the meantime, all officers joining on less favoured terms continued to gain their commissions via a four-month stint at the Officer Cadet Training Unit at Henlow.[13]

This fundamental change in the way in which the RAF recruited and trained its career officers was accompanied by a major restructuring of the entire officer corps. This was brought about as a consequence of yet another review, commissioned by AMP, Air Mshl Sir Andrew Humphrey, in July 1968. It was conducted by AVM W.D. Hodgkinson, who submitted his report almost a year later. He drew a number of conclusions, the most important of which may be summarised as follows.[14]

a. The RAF was considered to lack professionalism in many of its operational and administrative functions. This deficiency was a direct result of its having adhered to the Trenchardian principle of GD officers, i.e. pilots (and now navigators), being capable of undertaking a variety of (to them) secondary tasks long after WW II had clearly demonstrated that this concept was outmoded.

b. It followed from the above: that aircrew should concentrate on the increasingly demanding job of flying; that the RAF should employ specialists in all fields of activity; and that the career prospects of ground branch officers should be improved in order to attract high-quality recruits.

c. Another unfortunate consequence of Trenchard's legacy was that GD officers (in effect pilots) had exclusive control over the higher direction of the Service. This was not a satisfactory situation because, as pilots, they simply lacked expertise in fields which were critical to the efficient conduct of air operations.

d. Like the old Cranwell cadetships, the graduate entry scheme was considered to be fundamentally flawed. Both systems conferred special privileges on people who were as yet unknown quantities, rather than on those who had demonstrated their abilities in service.

[11]The RAF had offered permanent commissions to graduates throughout the inter-war period and had reinstated this practice when permanent commissions had been reintroduced in 1945.

[12]Promotion within the lower commissioned ranks of the RAF was initially based on time, tempered by a degree of selection. AMWO 181 of 19 March 1925 announced that an additional hurdle, a series of promotion examinations, would be introduced in the following year. In future, to be eligible for promotion to flying officer a candidate would have to pass the Promotion Examination 'A', to flight lieutenant the 'B', and to squadron leader the 'C'. At the time, these provisions were confined to the GD Branch but similar arrangements were later introduced for stores/equipment officers, the 'E' to flight lieutenant and the 'F' to squadron leader.

The insatiable demands of the much larger air force of the late 1930s meant that concessions had to be granted, e.g. AMO A.441/38 of 1 December permitted flight lieutenants who had not passed the 'C' to be made up to squadron leader. With the outbreak of war, however, promotion examinations were promptly suspended for the duration (AMO A.353/39 of 6 September). AMO A.822/48 of 14 October announced the progressive reintroduction of the 'B' and 'C', which would now be applicable to all branches, not just GD. It had also been intended to reinstate the 'A' but this was initially held in abeyance and eventually abandoned without ever being reintroduced. The 'B' followed it into oblivion in the 1970s and the 'C' in the 1980s.

[13]Post-war initial officer training for direct entrants and for airmen being commissioned from the ranks had been provided at a variety of locations but by the late 1950s the position had stabilised with No 1 Initial Training School (ITS) at South Cerney handling prospective pilots and navigators and the Officer Cadet Training Unit (OCTU) at Jurby dealing with ground branches and NCO aircrew being commissioned in their current trades. Having spent a period at Feltwell, in October 1965 the OCTU moved to Henlow which was about to be vacated by the RAF Technical College (see Note 8). In the meantime No 1 ITS had been renamed the Aircrew Officers Training School and had moved to Church Fenton in 1968. In May 1969 it too moved to Henlow where it was absorbed into the OCTU.

[14]AIR20/12267. The points listed have been extracted from AF/HC/BS/12, dated 1 May 1969, the 'Hodgkinson Report'.

In December 1969 the Air Force Board decided to implement most of Hodgkinson's recommendations.[15] This had far-reaching consequences but, in the specific context of this narrative, it led to two major changes in policy. First, with a few specific exceptions, the practice of misemploying aircrew in administrative appointments was progressively phased out. Secondly, the existing two-list system (i.e. General and Supplementary), which had effectively divided officers into 'haves' and 'have nots', virtually from the day they joined up, was superseded by a single list which offered all officers an equal chance of consideration for promotion.[16] To reflect this, it was no longer appropriate to segregate the graduate entry from the rest and eventually, in December 1978, the RAF introduced a 'single gate' officer training scheme under which (almost[17]) all prospective officers, regardless of age, sex, qualifications and ultimate branch, attended a common initial training course at Cranwell.

In short, with only minor alterations, e.g. the Cranwell course has been as short as three months and as long as six, the Hodgkinson Report of 1969 provided the mould which shaped the RAF's officer corps for the rest of the century.

The myth of equal career prospects for navigators, as compared to pilots

As early as 1941 some senior officers had begun to appreciate that the crucial importance of navigation made it necessary to afford a greater level of recognition to navigators or, as they still were at the time, to observers. This had eventually provoked a crusade in support of captaincies for non-pilots (see pages 187–189) and a similar campaign to extend their opportunities for attaining higher ranks. While the then AOCinC Bomber Command, Air Mshl Sir Richard Peirse, had felt unable to lend his support to the specific case for observer captains, he was, in all other respects, in favour of enhancing their career prospects.

At the time, the handful of Station Navigation Officers were only flight lieutenants (and in 1941 many would still have been pilots), as were Squadron Bombing Leaders. There was no establishment at all for Squadron Navigation Officers. Sir Richard considered that, apart from imposing an unreasonably low rank ceiling, the overall effect of these arrangements, at squadron level, actually emphasised the less demanding aspect of the observer's job. He also pointed out that, while current planning envisaged that observers might eventually fill 50% of navigational staff appointments in the future, this would still involve only relatively small numbers. As a result, the observer was 'up against a brick wall; he sees contemporary pilots getting promotion while he himself can hope for little more than to become a Squadron Bombing Leader.'[18]

To maintain the pressure, Bomber Command fired off another letter two months later, specifically urging the early establishment of flight lieutenant Squadron Navigation Officers and raising the rank of Station Navigation Officers to squadron leader.[19] This persistence was finally rewarded in June 1942 when appropriate establishments were amended to satisfy Bomber Command's demands, although it was 1944 before a similar upgrade was authorised for Coastal Command.

While these changes had provided a handful of observers with something which might, at a pinch, be passed off as a career structure, the Service was soon obliged to consider the future of its entire officer corps. The award of permanent commissions to RAF officers (in practice, only to pilots) had been suspended on the outbreak of war on the grounds that the future was so uncertain as to make it impossible to determine the number of regular officers that would be required. By 1943 it had come to the attention of the Air Ministry that the Admiralty and the War Office were both still offering permanent commissions. After some reflection, despite the improving war situation, the Air Ministry concluded that its original rationale had been valid and that it was still too early for the RAF to be entering into long-term commitments with individual officers. Nevertheless, there was no doubt that this would eventually become appropriate and, in anticipation of this, it was decided to invite applications.[20]

Very large numbers of officers expressed an interest and by early 1945 it was apparent that it would take some considerable time to review all the applications that had been received. Nevertheless, some of the conditions of service which were expected to apply had been more clearly defined by this time and details were circulated in March.[21] Quite astonishingly, the RAF revealed that it had decided to insist that officers selected for permanent commissions in the GD Branch 'who are not already pilots will normally be required to qualify as such.' Disinterring this hoary old Trenchardian chestnut of 1919 vintage, demonstrated once again that old air force habits die hard.

At the time it was not known whether a discrete Technical Branch was going to be maintained after the war. If it was not, however, engineering officers would have to be transferred to the GD Branch and those likely to be offered permanent commissions were put on notice that they too might have to learn to fly.[22] In the event it was eventually decided to retain a separate Technical Branch in which it was anticipated that 'a proportion' of officers would be trained as pilots, although this was no longer to be a precondition for the granting of a permanent commission.[23]

To some of the senior officers who could remember 1917, and there were still a lot of them about, all of this must have seemed perfectly reasonable. After all, in the 'good old days' an observer could not even attain the rank of captain without first becoming a pilot. Why change now? Because, by 1945,

[15]AIR6/173. Conclusions of Air Force Board Meeting 15(69) held on 15 December 1969.
[16]DCI(RAF) S60 of 8 April 1970.
[17]Prospective officers of the 'professional' branches, i.e. doctors, dentists, lawyers and chaplains, and ex-officers of the RN, Army or RAF, joining/rejoining the Service also pass through Cranwell, but via a relatively short induction course.
[18]AIR2/8270. Bomber Command letter BC/S.22453/Air dated 17 December 1941 from AOCinC to USof S at the Air Ministry, Capt H.H. Balfour.
[19]*Ibid.* Bomber Command letter BC/S.22453/Air dated 15 February 1942 to Capt Balfour from AOCinC (but actually signed on his behalf by AVM Saundby).
[20]AMO A.188/44 of 2 March.
[21]AMO A.297/45 of 26 March. This order explained, *inter alia*, that the Air Ministry recognised the need to notify successful applicants as quickly as possible. Rather than waiting until the entire assessment process had been completed, therefore, the granting of permanent commissions was done piecemeal, the first batch being announced immediately in AMO N.332/45 of 26 March.
[22]*Ibid.*
[23]AIR20/4324. The Report of a Committee on the Future of the Technical Branch, chaired by Air Mshl Sir Roderic Hill and published in September 1945, presented a very convincing case for the retention of a discrete specialist branch to handle engineering matters. The Committee's recommendations were accepted, a summary of the report, including details of the anticipated arrangements, being published as AMO A.1026/46 of 12 December.

while none of them had been permitted to attain very high ranks, a handful of non-pilots had demonstrated that they were quite capable of functioning as captains of crews and of commanding flights and squadrons.[24] *That* is why.

It would seem, however, that, rather than being a considered response, the requirement for all holders of permanent commissions within the GD Branch to be pilots, as initially stated, may have been more of a knee-jerk reaction on the part of staff officers who had simply assumed that the system would wish to re-establish the pre-war situation. Fortunately, when the question was examined by a committee studying the Selection and Training of Officers of the GD Branch under the chairmanship of the Director General of Personal Services, AVM D. Harries, it concluded that, while all Cranwell cadets and university entrants would have to be trained as pilots, this need not otherwise be an essential precondition to the granting of a permanent commission.[25]

Despite this conclusion, there was no immediate public retraction of the previously published 'everyone will have to be a pilot' policy, suggesting that some of the more influential officers lurking within the bureaucracy may have been reluctant to see this concession actually implemented. One also suspects that the air establishment's apparent willingness to embrace a more liberal philosophy may have been more in the nature of a pragmatic acceptance of the inevitable than a considered choice. The fact was that, in the immediate post-war years, the training system simply lacked the capacity to indulge in such pointless exercises as training one sort of competent aviator to become another.

By the summer of 1946 the Air Ministry was having to come to terms with this situation and a statement was released to the effect that the question of flying training being a precondition of a permanent commission was under review and that no further applications for such courses were to be submitted until further notice.[26] It was clear that the establishment was now having serious second thoughts about the viability of sustaining this time-honoured, if totally unnecessary, tradition. The following year it was announced that there was no prospect of the air force being able to offer the necessary flying training courses before 1949 at the earliest.[27] The 'must-be-a-pilot' requirement was finally withdrawn in May 1948.[28]

At the same time, it was announced that 'all navigators entering the Royal Air Force should have career prospects comparable to those open to pilots.'[29] In fact this announcement was actually represented as being a clarification of the equal careers policy which, it was claimed, had been enshrined within the 1946 Aircrew Scheme. In real terms, this had meant very little, beyond the fact that it took an N3 as long to make N2 as it took for a pilot to progress from P3 to P2. While the RAF evidently viewed this sort of meteoric rise as a 'career prospect', it would seem that most navigators had failed to recognise it as such, hence the need to point it out.

All of this had been the outcome of a lengthy examination of the place of the navigator conducted by the Post-War Manning Committee in 1947–48 and sparked largely by the considerable difficulties that were being encountered in recruiting enough of them. The committee had concluded that the ideal solution would be to do away with navigators altogether and to provide all pilots with comprehensive training in navigation (shades of 1937 – see pages 121 *et seq*). Accepting that this was impractical, largely because of the costs involved, rather than because such an approach was inappropriate, the committee's second-best solution was to retrain navigators as pilots after one tour. This approach was no cheaper, of course, and it is worth noting that the air staff members of the committee specifically distanced themselves from both of its preferred approaches. DCAS, Air Mshl Sir Hugh Walmsley, went on record as saying that 'navigators should be kept as a specialist category. To be both a first-class pilot and a first-class navigator (*is*) beyond the capacity of any but the most exceptional officers.'[30]

In the end, it was accepted that there was no real alternative to the permanent retention of navigators. When presenting the committee's conclusions to the Air Council Standing Committee in March 1948, AMP, Sir Hugh Saunders, stated that 'there can be no doubt that the mental capacity and professional skill required of a navigator is as high, if not higher, than that required for a pilot. It is obvious therefore that the career open to navigators as a class must be not less attractive than that open to pilots.'[31] The committee's recommendations were accepted and the Air Council subsequently stated, quite unequivocally, that pilot and navigator aircrew were to have an equal chance of being selected for officer training and that 'navigators shall be selected for permanent commissions in the GD Branch in the same proportion as pilots.' Furthermore, it was noted that appropriate unit establishments would be changed to permit navigators to fill appointments as Flight and Squadron Commanders.[32]

Few of the navigators of 1948 are likely have been aware of the very similar announcement that had been made with respect to observers as long ago as June 1918 (see pages 89–90). In view of the way that that undertaking had been honoured, however, even if they had known about it, it would have been unlikely to have had a very positive effect on their morale. Nevertheless, the fact remained that the air force had publicly committed itself to providing navigators with similar opportunities to those which were available to pilots. Perhaps to underline this change in policy, from 1948 onwards the Air Force List recorded pilots and navigators on a common gradation list, rather than separately as had been the case since the reintroduction of commissioned observers in 1940.

For any of this to have much real meaning, of course, it would be necessary for navigators to attend the RAF College, since

[24]Some examples of wartime non-pilot executives are at Notes 37, 38, 39 and 43 to Chapter 23. So far as ranks were concerned, the Air Force List for July 1945 records the names of twenty-five squadron leader navigators while the combined list for air gunners and WOps included twenty-one plus a single wing commander. By comparison, there were 2721 wing commander and squadron leader pilots. In practice, some of these officers (of all categories) would have been holding acting ranks one, or even two, notches higher than those listed so there will have been a few wing commander navigators about, and possibly even the odd group captain. Two years later, with the initial post-war run-down approaching completion, the List named just seven senior officer navigators, five wing commanders and two squadron leaders; there were two wing commanders and two squadron leaders on the gunner/signaller list; there were now 1343 wing commander and squadron leader pilots. Neither list, incidentally, had featured any flight engineers above the rank of flight lieutenant.

[25]AIR2/6830. AMP (Sir John Slessor) submitted to the Air Council a summary of the Harries Committee's proposals in his note AC 24(45) of 19 June 1945. With one or two minor reservations, the Air Council endorsed the content of AMP's paper at its meeting 7(45) held on 17 July.

[26]AMO A.766/46 of 5 September.

[27]AMO A.431/47 of 29 May.

[28]AMO A.410/48 of 20 May.

[29]*Ibid.*

[30]AIR6/101. This statement is quoted in paper AC (54)35 of 9 June 1954 submitted to the Air Council by AMP, Air Chf Mshl Sir Francis Fogarty.

[31]AIR6/95. The conclusions of the Post-War Manning Committee were presented to the Air Council Standing Committee in AMP's memorandum SC (48)19 of 25 March 1948; its recommendations were accepted at its April meeting.

[32]AMO A.410/48 of 20 May.

that was the only realistic means of gaining a secure footing on the RAF's fast-track career ladder. It was all very well granting a few navigators 'PCs' at a later stage, but it was difficult to make up the lost time and these Johnnies-come-lately never really enjoyed all of the privileged treatment which the Service reserved for its Old Cranwellians.

The establishment had no illusions about this situation incidentally, as AMP had made quite clear in 1949 when he stated that 'it is generally accepted that the Cranwell or University entrant has advantages over the SSC (*Short Service Commission*) officer appointed to a permanent commission and has in addition better prospects of advancement to higher rank.'[33] This observation had been made in a paper raised to establish the case for navigators to be admitted to Cranwell; a proposal that was subsequently accepted by the Air Council.[34] Unfortunately, however, this acceptance had been only 'in principle' and at the time it was deemed to be too difficult to put the idea into practice, although sufficient room was found to permit equipment and secretarial officers to be admitted in 1953.

If a full career, offering all of the opportunities available to pilots, remained a rather vague prospect for navigators, it was even further out of reach for the SEG categories. Technically, they had been entitled to be considered for permanent commissions ever since these had been reintroduced in 1945 but this had initially presupposed that they were prepared to transfer to a ground branch, their options being extended in 1949 to include retraining as pilots or navigators.[35] The bulk of the relatively small requirement for officers to serve as gunners, signallers and engineers had, therefore, continued to be met by employing wartime veterans or by commissioning selected airmen aircrew on a succession of extended, short service or branch terms.

By 1954 an overt degree of dissatisfaction with their promotion prospects was becoming apparent among navigators. This led AMP, Air Chf Mshl Sir Francis Fogarty, to re-examine, in the light of the '100% officers' decision of 1950 (see page 203), the equal careers policy which had been introduced in 1948. On investigation, he was able to demonstrate that the number of junior officer navigators being promoted did represent a reasonable reflection of their proportional representation within the GD Branch. Nevertheless, there were some discrepancies in this and in other respects, the numbers being selected for Staff College for example, and where these occurred the balance was invariably in favour of pilots.[36]

The most serious shortfall had been in the career management of young navigators caused by a seemingly permanent manning deficit. This had begun as early as 1947–48 when, in order to compensate for a shortage of pilots, many navigators had taken up offers to retrain. Unfortunately, it had subsequently proved to be impossible to balance this outflow with a corresponding increase in recruiting. In 1949 AMP, Sir Hugh Saunders, had written that 'we have barely sufficient Navigators for the squadrons'.[37] Under those circumstances it had proved very difficult to provide commissioned navigators with the non-flying appointments in which, as budding career officers, they could gain the experience of administration which was essential if they were to move on to positions of greater responsibility in higher ranks.

Although the Air Council had long been aware of the adverse implications of this situation, because most navigators were still relatively junior in rank it took time for sufficient evidence to accumulate to enable them to see that, as a group, they were failing to make much progress. Nevertheless, by 1954 the problem was becoming increasingly apparent at Flight Commander level where a mere 4% of the 210 posts available at that time were being filled by navigators, rather than the 26% which might have been expected.[38] Hence the growing crew room perception that the equal careers policy of 1948 had been a sham.

In presenting this problem to the Air Council, AMP stated that 'there was a widespread impression among navigators that this policy was not being implemented and a belief in some quarters that the policy was unworkable and should be abandoned.'[39] The question, therefore, was whether the Council should renege on its promise to navigators or stand by its earlier decision and restate the policy, bearing in mind what that implied in the context of captaincy and command. Six months of debate ensued, during which VCAS, Air Chf Mshl Sir Ronald Ivelaw-Chapman, among others, pointed out that if navigators were going to be seen to have the same status as pilots, some of them really would have to admitted to Cranwell.[40]

The operational CinCs were eventually invited to contribute their views. Bomber and Coastal Commands both came out in favour of continuing the equal careers 'experiment'. On the other hand, Fighter Command and 2nd TAF were opposed to any form of executive authority being vested in navigators.[41] These reactions were entirely predictable, of course, and served only to demonstrate that people who tend to fly alone and in small aeroplanes are likely to have limited horizons.

The eventual outcome of these deliberations was a formal public restatement of the RAF's commitment to equal careers.[42] Furthermore, it had been agreed actually to make provision for navigators at Cranwell. A mere seven years after it had been decided to admit them (longer than it had taken to fight WW II), the RAF College's 74th Entry, of January 1956 was the first to include any navigators.

Their presence at Cranwell having finally been secured, it is of some interest to consider how the scheme was being implemented two years later. In the course of routine forward planning, a study of pilot and navigator intakes was carried out in 1958. At that time the projected front line strength of the RAF of 1970 was expected to amount to some 520

[33]AIR6/92. Air Mshl Sir Hugh Saunders' paper SC (49)14, of 27 May 1949, the conclusions of which were accepted in principle by the Air Council Standing Committee at a meeting held four days later.
[34]AIR6/78. Conclusions of Air Council Meeting 11(49) held on 16 June 1949.
[35]AMO A.900/49 of 22 December.
[36]AIR6/101. Paper AC (54)35 of 9 June 1954 submitted to the Air Council by AMP, Air Chf Mshl Sir Francis Fogarty.
[37]AIR6/92. See Note 33.

[38]AIR6/101. Paper AC (54)35 included some contradictory and potentially misleading figures. It stated, for instance, that 'the proportion of navigators to pilots (all categories and ranks of officers) is approximately 1 : 4'. A few paragraphs on, however, it also stated that the 'figure would be 26% if equal proportions of navigators and pilots were appointed'; this would indicate that the ratio of navigators to pilots was actually 1 : 3. Furthermore, by confining the figures to officers the global representation of navigators was minimised as was shown only four months later when another paper, (AC (54)56, which dealt with training navigators at Cranwell and was jointly sponsored by AMP and AMSO) stated that 'the overall ratio of pilots to navigators in the Service is 2.4 : 1'. In 1949, incidentally, paper SC (49)14 (see Note 33) had contained three statements to the effect that the pilot : nav ratio was 2 : 1 and it was 2 : 1 again in 1958 (see Note 43). Beware statistics compiled by anyone other than oneself.
[39]AIR6/98. Conclusions of Air Council Meeting 14(54) held on 5 July 1954.
[40]AIR6/98. Conclusions of Air Council Meeting 15(54) held on 15 July 1954.
[41]AIR6/98. Conclusions of Air Council Meeting 22(54) held on 2 December 1954.
[42]AMO A.44/55 of 10 February.

The Varsity was one of the mainstays of the RAF's training system from 1951 until 1976. This photograph dates from 1959 and shows TG622 wearing the blue fuselage band of the RAF College, making the point that Cranwell had finally started to train navigators. (MAP)

aeroplanes. It was calculated that to man these aircraft, to fill the associated staff and non-operational flying appointments and to sustain the associated training system would require between 2500 and 2800 pilots and 1300–1350 navigators. Allowing for wastage over the intervening years, it was calculated that to provide these the Service would need to recruit annual intakes of 456 pilots and 224 navigators, a ratio of almost exactly 2 : 1. The figures showed that ninety-six of each year's pilot intake would enter through Cranwell. In view of the RAF's professed commitment to equal careers, it followed that these pilots should be accompanied by forty-eight navigators. Surprisingly (or perhaps not), the calculations made provision for only fourteen.[43]

These figures may not have been quite as outrageous as they might at first appear, because of the 'allowance for wastage' factor. Although the paper did not include specific details, it is reasonable to assume that contemporary performance in flying training will have been taken into account. This would have suggested that some 25% of both pilots and navigators could be expected to fail and that about half of the unsuccessful pilots might be 'salvaged' as navigators. From the intake of ninety-six plus fourteen, therefore, it would be reasonable to anticipate an output of seventy-two plus twenty-three. Even so, this still represented a pilot:navigator ratio of 3.1:1, compared to the air force wide 2 : 1, leaving navigators still under-represented among the select group of officers whose personal files carried the prestigious 'made in Cranwell' stamp.

Although these calculations might be regarded as betraying a certain lack of enthusiasm for the RAF's proclaimed equal careers policy, we should bear in mind that they were merely the paper projections of a planner. In reality, the situation was far worse. Between December 1958 and March 1973 (the output dates of the 74th and 101st Entries, the first and last to include navigators) 931 pilots graduated from Cranwell so there ought to have been about 465 navigators. In fact, there were only 149, a ratio of only 6.5:1, less than a third of what 'equality' would have led one to expect.[43A]

Meanwhile, in 1960, the Air Council had been moved to announce, once again, that 'all navigators have career prospects comparable with those of pilots holding the same type of commission.'[44] Why did the RAF find it necessary to keep on repeating this mantra? Perhaps it was to encourage navigators to have faith in a truth which some were still finding it difficult to accept. After all, the average navigator, surveying the air force of 1960, would still have been hard-pressed to see much concrete evidence of all the equality that was supposed to have been about since 1948 (or, arguably, since 1946).

While obvious signs were still scarce, however, the equality really was there, even if it did seem to be taking a long time to show itself. This was practically unavoidable, because it was bound to take something like twenty years for a twenty-year old recruit, even a 'fast runner', to achieve the rank of group captain and thus begin to get his head far enough above the parapet for his contemporaries to be able to see him. It must be remembered, of course, that there were no commissioned navigators (observers) until 1940, so one could not realistically expect to see many of them begin to attain high ranks until 1960 at the earliest. This is not to say that no navigators had been promoted or been appointed to command squadrons, but those who had had been men of a distinctly earlier, and therefore, 'different' generation, wartime veterans with rows of campaign medals.[45]

Nevertheless, post-war navigators did start to make the grade during the 1960s and by the mid-1970s they were filling increasingly influential staff appointments and beginning to command squadrons, and even stations, in significant numbers. In terms of rank, for instance, the spring 1976 edition of the Air Force List shows that of 643 GD wing commanders, 167 (26%) were navigators; there was also a single AEO and a solitary air signaller who had yet to convert to the new electronic faith. While this clearly represented reasonable progress, navigators had yet to make their mark at the next level up, pilots still constituting 83% of the 250 listed group captains.

By the 1980s individual navigators were occasionally managing to penetrate the innermost circles of the air establishment but there was, and still is, a significant imbalance in favour of pilots at the highest levels of the Service.[46] This was almost inevitable, because the RAF employs more pilots than all other aircrew categories put together. Notwithstanding this fact, however, compared to navigators, pilots were (and they still are) over-represented in the upper reaches of the hierarchy.

In this context it is interesting to consider one of the observations raised by the Hodgkinson Report of 1969 (see page 220), that it was inappropriate that so many of the RAF's most senior officers should be pilots. This implied that more of them should be drawn from branches other than GD which, in turn, pointed towards some sort of common gradation list for air officers. This was not a new idea; indeed it had not even been new in 1956 when it had first been given serious consideration. At that time, a committee, which had been investigating such matters under the chairmanship of Air Mshl Sir Charles Guest, had decided not to recommend its adoption, stating that:[47]

> 'What seems to us important is not that the names of Air Officers should be in a common list, but that the senior appointments of the Service should be allocated to the best man for

[43]AIR6/116. Memorandum AC (58)80 of 2 December 1958 submitted to the Air Council by VCAS, Air Mshl Sir Edmund Hudleston.

[43A]Statistics on the output from Cranwell were provided by Jean Buckberry, the College Librarian and Archivist, by permission of the AOC and Commandant.

[44]AMO A.29/60 dated 10 February.

[45]An example is provided by No 101 Sqn which had a navigator CO in 1956. He was Sqn Ldr B. Moorcroft DSO DFC, a wartime Pathfinder who, incidentally, and quite improperly, still sported a flying 'O'.

[46]The first (and to date, the only) navigator to gain a seat on the Air Force Board was Air Mshl Sir Charles Ness who was Air Member for Personnel in 1980–83.

[47]AIR8/2123. Report of a Committee to Review the Entry and Subsequent Training of Future Permanent Officers in the Royal Air Force, PEC(56)R.1 dated 10 February 1956.

the job, taking into account ability and experience, but ignoring the Branch to which an officer happens to belong.'

Needless to say, the Air Council was content to accept this relatively low key approach. A cynic might consider that this was because it would, in effect, permit a generation of senior pilots, who had been brought up to believe that, with very few exceptions, pilots were the best men for the job (whatever it was) to continue to rule the roost. This would probably be unkind, however, as the Council subsequently asked the Inspector General to review (all) the Guest Committee's recommendations. Finding grass roots support divided between the introduction of a common list and the implementation of Guest's solution, Air Chf Mshl Sir Walter Dawson chose to endorse the less formal, 'best man for the job', approach.[48] This was duly implemented, although the Air Council forbore to make any public announcement to the effect that a new policy had been adopted.

The idea resurfaced in 1961 in the course of yet another review of the officer structure, this time conducted by Air Chf Mshl The Earl of Bandon who, *inter alia*, recommended the introduction of a common list for officers of air rank.[49] While this was still a highly controversial proposal, it is evident that, with the passage of time, it was becoming possible to promote the idea more positively. The Air Council was still very nervous about its implications, however, and AMP, Air Mshl Sir Arthur McDonald, was invited to review the Bandon Report and suggest alternative means of implementing its findings. It fell to his successor, Air Mshl Sir Walter Cheshire, to present McDonald's proposals which modified some of Lord Bandon's recommendations but continued to advocate a common list.

In subsequent discussion, the uniformed members of the Council were practically unanimous in rejecting this idea, CAS, Air Chf Mshl Sir Thomas Pike, stating that 'it would have little practical meaning and would be bad for morale as it would make it more obvious than ever that the General Duties officer had better promotion prospects.' On the other hand, Mr W.J. Taylor MP, the Parliamentary Under-Secretary, considered that the Service was failing to face up to the fundamental issue raised by the Bandon Report, that is, 'whether the RAF should continue to consist of a flying élite with technical advisers or alter its organisation radically so as to make full use in higher management of all the skills available.' He went on to argue that, while leadership was the essential quality, as in commerce and industry, this could be found among the practitioners of many different professions.[50] Despite this spirited opposition, however, the Council elected not to introduce a common list, although it did agree to 'multiple annotation' where appropriate, i.e. the identification of selected senior appointments which could be filled by officers from branches other than GD, although, once again, it elected not to make a public announcement to this effect.

From this brief review, it is clear that AVM Hodgkinson had not been breaking new ground when he brought up the idea again eight years later. Nevertheless, despite its being repeatedly advised that it should introduce a common list for air officers, the Air Force Board could not bring itself to do so until the 1980s. The Air Force List for 1986 was the first to feature all air officers on a single gradation list which appeared under the new heading of the 'Policy Branches', finally reflecting an egalitarian philosophy which had first been tentatively mooted thirty years earlier. Thereafter, while certain senior posts would, for obvious reasons, always have to be filled by officers of particular 'trades', in general there was to be no quota system based on branch and selection for promotion to higher ranks was to be based on merit alone. Theoretically, therefore, it was perfectly possible that most air vice-marshals and above might eventually turn out to be navigators – but there was no technical reason why a substantial proportion of them should not be engineers, suppliers or, for that matter, physical training officers.

What has happened in practice? At the time of writing, the latest (2000) List includes 108 active air officers.[51] Of these, sixty-seven have been drawn from the GD Branch, a number which, when compared to the overall composition of the officer corps, is considerably in excess of a statistically predictable result (for a comparison of the relative sizes of the GD and non-GD Branches, see Note 18 to the Epilogue). Moreover, if we look a little closer, we find that fifty-seven of these GD officers are pilots. Only ten are navigators, substantially fewer than one might expect in view of their representation within the branch. Furthermore, all ten navigators are 'mere' air commodores.

Looking a little closer still, we find that, of the total of 108 air officers, all four air chief marshals, six of the seven air marshals and seventeen of the twenty-five air vice-marshals are pilots. Yet forty-two of the seventy-two air commodores are *not* pilots (thirty-two drawn from branches other than GD plus the ten navigators). In other words, as one climbs the four highest rungs of the RAF's career ladder, the proportion of non-pilots one is likely to encounter falls progressively from 58% to 32% to 14% to zero. It is quite clear, therefore, that for all practical purposes equality actually begins and ends with air commodores – strictly speaking, it does not even begin with air commodores because pilots are substantially over-represented even at this level.

There could be many explanations for this curious situation but it is difficult to dismiss the parallel with 1918 (see pages 89–90). It would seem that pilots still have a natural tendency to favour other pilots and that the pilots who still fill all of the most influential positions in the air force, automatically select others of their kind to succeed them. Intentional or not, because of the self-perpetuating nature of such a nepotistic culture, change is unlikely to become apparent for at least fifteen years. This is because it will take that long for the current generation of pilot air marshals and their heirs apparent, the several generations-worth of senior pilots who are already being groomed to take their places, to have their turn before much space will become available in the upper echelons of the hierarchy for officers schooled in other disciplines.

Despite this writer's evident scepticsm, however, it would seem that the Service may actually be about to embrace the 'best man for the job' philosophy with some degree of commitment. While this concept was already supposed to have been applied to air commodores and above for several years, it was announced in 1999 that the entry level to 'the executive' is to be lowered to wing commander. For obvious practical reasons, many posts will have to continue to be 'trade annotated' but where specialisation is not a significant consideration, employment opportunities at middle and senior management levels are to be considerably broadened. As the Minister cautioned at the time, however (presumably, because of the 'generation factor') it is likely to be several years before the impact of this policy has much tangible effect.

[48] *Ibid*. Inspector General's Report No 542, IG306 dated 1 October 1956.
[49] AIR8/2337. Report on the Officer Structure of the Royal Air Force, dated 1 May 1961.
[50] AIR6/131. Conclusions of Air Council Meeting 24(61) held on 21 December 1961.
[51] The 2000 List actually reflects the position as at 6 July 1999.

The politics of 'twin-wings for navs' in the post-war era

Although it had been raised and dismissed in 1942 (see page 164) and again in 1944–45 (see pages 191–193), it was almost inevitable that the question of twin-wings for navigators would come up again after the war. The catalyst turned out to be the RCAF which introduced a new style of navigators badge in August 1948. Very similar to the pilots badge in overall design, the central 'RCAF' monogram was supplanted by a globe bisected by a lightning flash. The appearance of this rather stylish fashion accessory was bound to provoke popular demand for something similar in the RAF, especially as American navigators had always worn a double-winged badge. Furthermore, in the opinion of some navigators, the Air Council's declaration of the previous May, that they were to have the same career prospects as pilots, provided ample grounds for claiming equality in badges.

In 1949, in order to assess the extent of the perceived demand for change, AMP, Air Mshl Sir Leslie Hollinghurst, found himself committed to another survey. This one was to be far more comprehensive than either of the two previous exercises. A letter was duly despatched to all home and overseas commands in September, which, allowing for the inclusion of No 90 Gp and the Rhodesian Air Training Group, provided thirteen returns. Replies were required by the end of November and a wide cross-section of opinion was to be canvassed, taking in the entire rank structure (which, so far as navigators were concerned, did not extend much beyond flight lieutenant at the time). The specific aim of the exercise was to 'obtain the general consensus of opinion amongst navigators' (NB *not* pilots) regarding the introduction of a double-wing.[52]

With the exceptions of Maintenance and Bomber Commands, especially the latter, which were opposed to change, the rank and file supported the case for a double-wing. In one or two instances the majority in favour was fairly narrow but in some it was as high as four to one. It is interesting to note, however, that only two AOCinCs/AOCs endorsed the opinions of their subordinates. Eight, all of them pilots of course, unashamedly took issue with the views expressed by the men they were supposed to be representing by specifically opposing the introduction of a twin-winged badge; the remaining three declined to offer any comment.

The responses reflected a number of recurrent themes, some of which are noted below.

a. Many reports noted that support for change was very strong among younger navigators but that it waned with age and seniority.
b. There were several observations to the effect that twin-wings were perceived to be associated with captaincy and it was considered that their significance would be degraded if they were to be worn by non-pilots. (This observation patently failed to take account of the fact that non-pilots had been eligible for captaincy since 1942, which is some indication of how rare it still was for any of them actually to be appointed as such.)
c. It was evident that twin-wings were widely associated with status and awarding them to navigators was seen to be a way of demonstrating their alleged equality with pilots. This would also serve to elevate them above 'lesser mortals', i.e. the SEG categories.
d. Many of those who opposed change did so on the grounds of tradition and pride in their 'N' badges.
e. Some who responded simply disputed the assumption that navigators were in any way 'second class'. Since they contended that they were not, they considered that there was nothing to be gained by changing their badge.
f. Many of the respondents who opposed the twin-wing advocated the reintroduction of the flying 'O' (probably betraying their age in the process).

The replies had all been received and collated by the end of 1949 and they were then passed to the Air Council for consideration. Opinion was divided. Some members suggested that the introduction of a double-wing might serve to improve navigator recruiting, which was causing concern at the time. Others thought that such an esoteric consideration would be of little significance to the civilians, as yet unfamiliar with air force ways, that the Service needed to attract. There was concern over the possibility of an adverse reaction by pilots and a suspicion that introducing twin-wings for navigators would eventually be bound to provoke similar demands from the lineal descendants of the wartime 'non-PNB' aircrew categories.

Nothing was decided and on 1 March 1950, AMP minuted the file to the effect that he had better things to do and that it had been a mistake ever to have embarked on this exercise. He directed that, unless someone else raised the matter, no further action was to be taken for twelve months. A year later, the file was brought forward and, since no further correspondence had occurred, it was promptly put away again.

In July 1954 this sleeping dog was reawakened during the Air Council's debate over the policy of equal careers (see page 223), and kept awake by continuing concerns over navigator recruiting. Sir Ronald Ivelaw-Chapman, VCAS, suggested that the gesture of twin-wings might exert a positive influence in both cases and AMP was asked to investigate further. Although this exercise led him to draw the personal conclusion that it would not be appropriate to change the 'N' badge, Air Chf Mshl Fogarty laid a variety of options before the Air Council for its consideration.[53] At a meeting held in December AMP even displayed specimens of a number of possible twin-winged designs but members were still unable to reach a consensus over the desirability of introducing a new style of badge and AMP was asked to take air force wide soundings.[54] On 22 December he wrote to much the same thirteen headquarters as had been approached in 1949 (the only difference being the substitution of AHQ Malta for Rhodesia). They were all asked to test the water once again.

The responses had all been received by the end of January 1955 and they revealed that a significant shift in opinion had taken place.[55] This time only one return was actively in favour of introducing a double-winged badge; eight were against. Four were evenly divided and in three of those cases, predictably as ever, the (pilot) CinCs threw their weight behind retention of the single wing. Much the same detailed comments were elicited as before and, once again, it was clear that attachment to the 'N' badge increased markedly with age and experience. It was concluded that the design of flying badges had little bearing on recruiting and the matter was dropped.

[52]AIR2/10835. The correspondence relating to this survey is on Air Ministry file A.25201/49/P1.

[53]AIR6/101. Paper AC (54)67 of 13 November 1954.

[54]AIR6/98. Conclusions of Air Council Meeting 22(54) held on 2 December 1954.

[55]AIR2/10835. The correspondence relating to this survey is on Air Ministry file A.25201/49/P1.

On looking back at the history of this question, a cynic might conclude that the Air Council had simply persisted in asking it until it finally got the answer that it had always wanted to hear. Be that as it may, the subject lay dormant until the autumn of 1962 when the question of twin-wings for navigators was raised once again, this time by CAS, MRAF Sir Thomas Pike. Not wishing to stir up the AOCinCs, the task of sounding out opinion was delegated to the Director-General of Personal Services, AVM J.R. Gordon-Finlayson, who dealt with commands at an equivalent rank level, i.e. via the Air Officers Administration.[56] Once again, the feedback was represented as being strongly in favour of retaining the single wing, the only apparent dissent being expressed by NEAF. 'Apparent' because the responses will all have been submitted by pilots and, in view of their track record in such matters, one has reservations as to the extent to which navigators were actively consulted. There are also some grounds for suspecting that navigators may have been their own worst enemies in this matter and that the results of such polls as were taken may have been 'fixed'.[57]

Whatever the truth, the result of the survey appeared to be another resounding rejection of twin-wings and CAS was advised to drop the matter.[58] He did, and although the idea continued to surface from time to time, it was always on a relatively informal basis thereafter. The review of 1962, therefore, appears to have been the last time that officialdom gave the idea any serious consideration until the very end of the century.

Navigator training since 1957

Although some nations continued to have their aircrew trained in Canada under bilateral arrangements, the NATO scheme, which had been in operation since 1951, closed down in 1957. In that year, therefore, the RAF reinstated all-through navigator training at No 2 ANS, its output later being supplemented, albeit at a much lower rate, by that of No 1 ANS which reopened at Topcliffe.[59] Apart from some early use of the Marathon, which soon faded from the scene, the flying content of the course was conducted on Valettas, Varsities and Vampires. In 1959 the Vampires were replaced by Meteors, but only at No 2 ANS, students from Topcliffe and Cranwell being obliged to spend a few weeks at Thorney Island to complete the jet phase of their courses.

The navigator training system was completely reorganised in January 1962 when No 2 ANS moved to Hullavington where, flying only Valettas and Varsities, it became the basic air navigation school. At the same time, No 1 ANS moved to Stradishall where it assumed responsibility for the advanced phase of the course which was flown on Varsities and the Meteors it had taken over from No 2 ANS. Three years later No 2 ANS moved to Gaydon while No 1 ANS began to receive Dominies.

The Dominie represented such an advance in training capability, compared to the old Meteors, that a streaming policy was introduced. For a time, students earmarked for 'high and fast' types flew their advanced phase solely on the Dominie while those destined for 'low and slow' operations stayed on the Varsity. This approach did not last for long, however, perhaps because it had omitted the crucial combination of 'low and fast' which had become the cornerstone of RAF tactical doctrine by the mid-1960s. In any event, the system was changed so that all students flew both the Varsity and the Dominie during their time at Stradishall, No 1 ANS continuing to provide appropriate facilities for Cranwell cadets, since the RAF College's resident fleet of navigation trainers did not cater for jet flying.

Eight years after the two-stage system had been introduced, a reduction in throughput permitted the schools to be amalgamated, both ANSs moving to Finningley during 1970. In the long term it was envisaged that all non-pilot training facilities would be concentrated there, which meant that it would be inappropriate for the unit to be designated as an ANS. The identities of the old navigation schools were, therefore, suppressed in favour of that of a defunct pilot training school, No 6 FTS.

At the beginning of 1971, in an effort to keep up with the times, a 'low and fast' phase was introduced using Jet Provosts. Another major advance occurred in that same year when the Dead Reckoning Trainers of the 1940s, 50s and 60s were succeeded by a computer-based synthetic training system. It was hardly a flight simulator, as a pilot might understand the term, but it did permit sorties to be 'flown' on the ground in real time under relatively realistic conditions. Since the machine was required to function as both a Varsity and a Dominie, however, the generic instrument panel represented neither aeroplane. Nevertheless, the simulator did reproduce the very different performance characteristics of both types

Navigators first began to be exposed to the high-speed, low level tactical environment at the ab initio *stage in 1971 when a squadron of Jet Provosts was established at Finningley. The badge on the dorsal fin of this Jet Provost T.4, XP560, shows that it belonged to No 6 FTS.* (CRO RAF Finningley)

[56]AIR2/18211. Letter A.355766/61/DGPS dated 16 October 1962, from AVM Gordon-Finlayson to all command HQs.

[57]The author, who was serving on a squadron in Singapore in late 1962, recalls a notice being pinned up inviting navigators to append their names if they favoured the introduction of a twin-winged badge. The proposal attracted the support of most of the fairly numerous junior officers, including this writer. One of the squadron's handful of grizzled old master navs took us all to one side and forcefully 'explained' the error of our ways, leaving us in no doubt as to where our loyalties ought to lie. Suitably shamed, most of us sheepishly crossed off our names. It is suspected that similar scenes, in which the age and sentiment of the few overcame the youth and enthusiasm of the many, may have been played out in crew rooms right across the air force. Being predominantly of the aged and sentimental variety, most of the relatively few senior navigators at group and command HQs would have had strong emotional ties to their traditional badges and, because of their elevated positions within the chain of command, their voices would have been far more easily heard than the stifled murmuring filtering up from the coal face. Thus, through its liberal interpretation of the democratic process, did the 'executive of the navigators union' continue to delude itself into believing that its semi-badges really did have as much significance as those worn by pilots and unwittingly connive at sustaining the second-rank status of their own trade, notwithstanding repeated assurances over equal careers.

[58]AIR2/18211. Unreferenced memo, dated 10 January 1963, from AMP, Sir Walter Cheshire, to CAS.

[59]No 1 All Through Course began at No 2 ANS on 3 April 1957. Only Nos 1 and 2 Courses graduated using this terminology, however, as the title was changed to Navigation Course in April 1958, No 9 being the first to start as such. This series of numbers remains in use today. No 1 ANS' first intake, also No 1 Course, began on 11 December 1957 but the main preoccupation at Topcliffe was refresher training, *ab initio* courses having reached only No 4 by the end of 1959 by which time Thorney Island was dealing with its No 19.

In 1971 the relatively primitive, if effective, DRTs were superseded by this computer based system. The tracks being followed by each of the 'aeroplanes' were displayed on the large electronic maps in front of the controllers, permitting them to detect major problems as they developed and to intercede as required. If necessary, it was possible to freeze time within an individual cubicle, effectively stopping that 'aeroplane' in mid-air while a problem was sorted out. (CRO RAF Finningley)

quite convincingly; it could even provide something like the appropriate background noise in the cubicle.

As intended, the trainee navigators were joined at Finningley by the remaining categories of non-pilot aircrew students during 1973 and three years later the venerable Varsity was withdrawn from service. Since the planned replacement for this workhorse, the Argosy, failed to materialise (see page 213), No 6 FTS was left to do the best it could with its remaining Jet Provosts and Dominies.

By the mid-1980s the navigation school had finally moved out of its 'temporary' wartime accommodation into a purpose-built, permanent building but this was already too big, as the numbers passing through the system had declined significantly in the intervening years since the new facilities had first been requested. For instance: the two-nav Vulcans had been replaced by single-nav Tornados; the remaining Victor tankers were being adapted for single-nav operation and the recently acquired TriStars had dispensed with navigators altogether. The breaching of the Berlin Wall in 1989 and the subsequent collapse of the USSR was inevitably followed by a reduction in the overall size of the RAF, the disbandment of several squadrons during the 1990s further reducing the numerical requirement for navigators.

While the numbers of navigators needed by the RAF had declined steadily, those that were required had still to be trained and the course has been progressively adapted in an effort to reflect the changing demands of the front-line. The first major innovation had been introduced as early as 1976 when the Dominie had begun to operate at low-level in order to provide students with practical experience of radar navigation in that very demanding environment.

While the use of the Dominie at low-level did represent some progress, it has to be said that its EKCO 190 weather radar and its V-bomber style, backwards-facing seating arrangements fell a long way short of simulating the conditions in a Buccaneer. The limitations of the Dominie, operating in a role for which it had never been intended, were well understood from the outset. Some early improvement was made by the introduction of a navigational computer (Decca TANS) but it was many years before it became possible to provide the major upgrade which was really required. In the mid-1990s the eleven remaining aircraft of the Dominie fleet were finally fitted with entirely new avionics, including a proper ground-mapping radar (Thorn EMI's Super Searcher). The seating arrangements for the crew were also revised, the student navigator now facing forwards, like his pilot (thus removing any potential confusion as to who meant what when somebody said, 'Look to your left').

The Dominie refit was only one element of a completely new approach to the training of navigators which had been implemented in 1992. The most obvious external signs of this new philosophy were the introduction of an initial flying phase on the Bulldog, the progressive replacement of the Jet Provost by the Tucano and the adoption of the Hawk for advanced tactical flying. Not long afterwards, however, further contraction of the RAF meant that No 6 FTS had to be disbanded in 1996. The residual non-pilot training commitment was transferred to Cranwell where it is currently carried out under the aegis of the NAAS, operating as an element of No 3 FTS. For the previous quarter of a century it had been possible to carry out all aspects of navigator training at one base but pressure on space at Cranwell, and the logistic complications arising from operating four different aircraft types, meant that this was no longer practical and the fleet had to be dispersed.

At the time of writing, all *ab initio* RAF navigators begin their training at Cranwell where they fly in the Tutor (originally the Bulldog) before being detached to Topcliffe to gain further flying experience on the Tucano. On returning to Cranwell all students undergo a period of synthetic training after which they are earmarked for one of three styles of operation, their subsequent courses being outlined below.

a. Those who are expected to fly high performance combat aircraft spend a little more time at Cranwell, flying in the Dominie, before moving on to Leeming (originally Valley). There, they eventually gain their flying badges after successfully completing their training on the Hawk, the later stages of this phase differing in content depending upon whether they have been streamed to fly in the attack or air defence roles.
b. Students selected to fly heavy, multi-engined types remain at Cranwell for the remainder of their course, all of their subsequent flying being conducted on the Dominie, this experience being reinforced by extensive use of synthetic training facilities.
c. Trainee navigators destined for helicopters spend a little more time at Cranwell, flying in Tutors, before transferring to Shawbury where they qualify for their flying badges after gaining experience of rotary-wing operations on the Squirrel and Griffin.

The art of air navigation becomes a science

This writer was trained as a navigator in 1960, but the equipment he used and the techniques he was taught would have been very familiar to his predecessor of 1943. He flew in a Varsity, which could fairly be described as a 'tin Wellington'. The basic method of navigation in vogue was still the mechanical air plot, using an API Mk 1, with reversion to manual procedures as and when required. The primary fixing aid was still GEE. The aircraft was equipped with a drift sight and position lines could be obtained via an astro-compass or a Mk 9 Bubble Sextant. Radio bearings could be coaxed from a GEC radio compass, as could CONSOL counts, but in the latter case better results could be obtained by using the Marconi R1155 radio receiver at the signaller's station. Ranges from EUREKA beacons could be read off the REBECCA oscilloscope, the same display being used in its BABS mode to practise airfield approaches. All of this equipment was of wartime vintage, the radio dating from as early as 1940.

The 1960s was a decade of change, however, and when the newly qualified navigator was assigned to an operational role, he would more than likely find that his aeroplane was equipped with a Doppler radar which measured drift and groundspeed. Since heading and airspeed were already known, the availability of Doppler meant that the navigator could always calculate the direction and speed of the local wind. In other words, from the 1960s onwards, since the navigator (nearly) always knew the dimensions of all three sides of the triangle of velocities, he had a permanent solution to the problem which his predecessors had spent much of their time trying to solve.

In much the same way as the API had been used to resolve airspeed around the aircraft's heading to provide an indication of the aeroplane's notional position in still air, it was now possible to resolve the output of the Doppler radar around heading in a Ground Position Indicator (GPI) which provided a read out of the actual position of the aircraft. As a result, the air plot technique, which had provided the basis of air navigation since before WW II, was replaced by the track plot.

Although they suffered from certain limitations, the first-generation of Doppler radars (GREEN SATIN and BLUE SILK) were remarkably accurate, the biggest errors within the overall system arising from the heading which was still being taken from a magnetic compass, albeit a distant reading model. So, while an automatic track plot was much more convenient and easier to interpret, like the air plot, its overall accuracy decayed with time and it was still necessary to obtain fixes against which to reset the GPI. Thus, while the overall accuracy of navigation had been substantially improved, the navigator's workload had been only marginally reduced.

In much the same timeframe, GEE was being superseded by TACAN, a system which provided range and bearing from any one of a large number of ground beacons which were being deployed worldwide. Although GEE was being withdrawn, other wartime systems (like LORAN) which operated on very similar, i.e. hyperbolic, principles, were still available while others were being introduced. Some of these (like DECCA) were far more accurate while others (like OMEGA) provided far greater coverage. Furthermore, intensive development of the H_2S radar of WW II had eventually created a system which was able to provide the V-bombers with fixes to a notional accuracy of about 400 yards.

The RAF also gained its first operating experience with inertial navigation during the 1960s. Developed as the primary guidance system for the BLUE STEEL stand-off bomb, it was required to be accurate only for the relatively brief duration of its free flight, which presupposed that it would be working from a precise datum when the missile was released. This was achieved by combining the short-term accuracy of the missile's inertial navigation system (INS) with the long-term accuracy of the Doppler radar in the mother aircraft and

The RAF gained its first experience of inertial navigation in the 1960s via the BLUE STEEL missile. This one is being carried by a Vulcan B.2, XM572 of the Scampton Wing. (CPRO, HQ Bomber Command)

resolving the resultant velocities around the very accurate heading output of the inertial platform, positional information being periodically updated by H_2S radar fixes. For its time, this was an extremely accurate system and it was totally self-contained, requiring no inputs from any external sources.

By the 1970s student navigators were being taught to handle Doppler radar and analogue computers, like the GPI Mk 4, from the outset. Needless to say, by that time the 'sharp end' of the Service had moved on, leaving the training system still a generation in arrears. Any self-respecting combat aeroplane, from the Phantom to the Nimrod, was now equipped with a digital computer fed with very accurate velocities, usually derived from a hybrid system incorporating both inertial and Doppler inputs. Updated by radar fixes and fully integrated with the autopilot and attack systems, such a computer was capable of guiding an aeroplane around a route and providing its crew with accurate weapon-aiming data. At the same time, it could be expected to have sufficient spare capacity to calculate instant answers to practically any navigational problem that the crew chose to set, e.g. heading, distance, elapsed time and fuel required to reach a diversion.

While traditionalists could still find a use for their old Dalton computers for a while, they were finally rendered obsolete by the advent of the Tornado for which even flight planning facilities were computerised. Since a late-model Doppler/inertial system provided both a precise heading reference and very accurate velocities, the only remaining scope for improvement lay in fixing. This loophole was finally closed by the introduction of the satellite-based Global Positioning System (GPS) which is capable of locating a receiver within a matter of yards. In fact, it is no longer simply a question of locating the aeroplane so much as that part of the aeroplane in which the GPS receiver happens to have been installed.

It could be argued that it might be unwise to rely too heavily on the use of satellites because such systems are vulnerable to enemy action, and to such random influences as Sun spot activity. On the other hand, GPS provides only the ultimate refinement in positional accuracy, the icing on the cake. So long as it knows its position at the start of a mission, i.e. the precise geographic co-ordinates and the alignment of its dispersal or hardened aircraft shelter, the error accumulated during a sortie by a state of the art INS, which requires no external reference whatsoever, is measured in yards, not miles. Furthermore, the three-dimensional mapping databases which can be loaded into a modern navigational computer are now so accurate that they can be used both to navigate and to fly at low level on autopilot in the dark and/or in cloud by comparing radar altimeter returns with the stored information on the terrain profile.[60] Such systems are also self-contained and more or less unjammable, short of using nuclear weapons to rearrange the landscape and/or to release a pulse of energy intense enough to disrupt the computer's circuitry.

Under the circumstances, by the late 1980s it was becoming difficult to foresee a situation in which a navigator might have to revert to the relatively primitive manual techniques of yesteryear. In other words, the traditional 'navigator' was rapidly becoming redundant. The extent to which this was true varied, but the RAF was already operating aeroplanes (like the TriStar) entirely without navigators in roles in which they would have been considered essential only a few years earlier. Furthermore, because navigation was now hyper-accurate and largely computer-based, even where they were being retained, few navigators needed to devote much time to establishing their aeroplane's position. During an operational sortie, a *fin de siècle* back-seater in an attack aircraft will concentrate relatively briefly on the aiming and delivery of whatever weapons his aeroplane is carrying, spending most of his time monitoring and operating the array of warning and defensive systems carried by his aircraft.

It could be argued that this represents a full turn of the wheel, as this was pretty much what the observer of 1918 used to do.

A rose by any other name?

A backward glance to WW II reveals the emergence of a curious discontinuity in the employment patterns of back-seaters which continued to be reflected in their functions more or less permanently. Bomber and Coastal Commands had always operated large aeroplanes equipped with increasingly sophisticated devices, but, despite being in the same air force, they tended to employ some of their non-pilot aircrew in very different ways.

Within the wartime Bomber Command H_2S radar had been installed at the navigator's station, although when it had first been introduced, exclusively within the Pathfinder Force, it had been regarded as a bombing, as much as a navigational, aid. As a result, it became common practice for a target marking crew to include a second air bomber to act as 'set operator'. This was not the case in Main Force squadrons when they too eventually received H_2S, although, even here it would often be operated by the air bomber. In a much developed form, the same equipment served as both navigation aid and 'bomb sight' in the V-bombers where it was operated by the lineal descendant of the air bomber, the navigator (radar).

Evolution had followed a very different path in the maritime world where radar had been introduced to supplement the 'Mk 1 eyeball' in the detection of submarines and surface vessels. Since it was a piece of electronic equipment, responsibility for it had been given to the WOp/AG who had passed it on, via the WOM/AG, the WOM(air) and the air signaller, to the AEO/AEOp.

By the early 1970s Bomber and Coastal Commands had become mere groups within Strike Command. Despite this nominal unification, however, they had adhered to their traditional operating procedures which resulted in some curious contradictions. For instance, while a sergeant AEOp could operate the ASV Mk 21 radar in a Shackleton, the H_2S Mk 9A in a Victor was the exclusive preserve of a commissioned navigator. Conversely, the AEO in a Nimrod was a screen-watcher, whereas his counterpart in a Vulcan was not.

In this respect, at least, the division between the functions associated with different aircrew categories had become a trifle blurred. At the same time, the divergence between individuals within the same nominal trade had become increasingly marked so that the navigator of, say, a VC10, had very little in common with his namesake in a Buccaneer. This is of no great significance, however; after all, a pilot is a pilot, whether he flies a helicopter, a heavy transport aircraft or a V/STOL strike-fighter. It followed that there was little

[60]As originally planned, the upgraded equipment fit for the Tornado GR 4 would have included a Terrain Referenced Navigation System (TRNS) of this type, GEC's Spartan, but this was subsequently deleted from the programme. Nevertheless, the technology exists and, while the hardware may not be available literally 'off the shelf', it could probably be purchased and installed at relatively short notice.

Above: *The rearward-facing navigation suite in a Vulcan B.2* circa *1965, nav (radar) on the left, nav (plotter) on the right; the back end of a Victor looked much the same. This picture shows only two-thirds of the instrument panel, the section belonging to the AEO being illustrated on page 211. Since this particular aeroplane was equipped to carry BLUE STEEL there were further displays to do with the missile underneath the hinged lid of the plotter's desk. Displays such as these probably represented the ultimate in analogue computing but the system was prone to partial failures. The navigators could intercede to compensate for these but, with so many dials to be monitored and so many manual controls to be manipulated, one can perhaps see why it took two men to handle the system effectively. Once the requirement for bombing had been deleted, however, it became feasible to dispense with one of the navigators in Victors employed solely as air-to-air refuellers.* (British Aerospace via Roger Chesneau)

Left: *The availability of the microchip has permitted cumbersome analogue navigation and bombing computers to be replaced by lightweight, digitally processed, solid state devices which have introduced entirely new standards of accuracy, reliability and flexibility. This picture shows the navigators station in a Tornado GR 4 of the 1990s. It is clearly still a very busy place but comparison with photographs of the rear crew compartment of a V-bomber make it equally clear that it is now possible for one man to do what it had taken three men to do in the 1950s. Whether it is really practical to dispense with the back-seater altogether, while still retaining a true all-weather day/night offensive capability, as some pundits would have us believe, remains to be seen.* (BAE Systems, Warton) justification for differentiating between different types of navigator or AEO.

This point could be stretched to the extent that it could even be argued that there was actually no need even to differentiate between navigators and AEOs. Indeed, in 1955, in the context of the forthcoming V-bombers, some consideration had been given to the idea of broadening the terms of reference of navigators to produce an all-purpose back-seater (see page 210). Had this proposal been adopted at the time the AEO would have been stillborn. Thereafter, the idea of the multi-disciplined crewman resurfaced from time to time, notably in 1978, and again in 1983, when it was informally suggested that pilot-practice might usefully be imposed upon most of the remaining non-pilot trades.[61] It was proposed that navigators, AEOs and AEOps should be merged into a single category to be known as, perhaps, Tactical Co-ordinators or Systems Operators – or even Observers! These proposals served to fuel some lively discussions but 'the establishment' declined to be drawn and there was no official public response. It was inevitable that, in the course of these debates, the idea of a twin-winged badge would be dusted off yet again, only to provoke an equally predictable defensive reaction from the traditionalists.

Like the idea of a single executive gradation list, which had been around for at least thirty years before it was actually introduced (see pages 224–225), the idea of merging non-pilot categories was not new, having first been suggested at least as early as 1943.[62] Nevertheless, while the great and good of the air force community appeared to have shown little interest in merging categories in 1980, it seems that a seed may have been sown. Twenty years later it was to germinate and in August 2000 the Air Force Board Standing Committee announced that the navigator, AEO, AEOp and air signaller specialisations were to be combined.[63] In future, they are to be known as Weapons Systems Officers or Operators (WSO/WSOp), depending upon whether or not they are commissioned. When this announcement was made it was being forecast that the new trade structure would be introduced in the autumn of 2001. It is difficult to see, incidentally, how these people can avoid being referred to as 'Wizzos', as tends to be the case with many American back-seaters.

As this book has shown only too clearly, history has taught us two lessons in the context of non-pilot aircrew. First, while superficially attractive, previous attempts to economise on them have generally proved to be deeply flawed. The most notable example was the ill-conceived policy of making do with part-time airmen between the wars, but there have been more recent failures; in the 1960s, for instance, there was the attempt to train engineer aircrew by making do with a course specifically designed for ground crew and, at much the same time, the short-lived reintroduction of NCO radio observers and navigators.

The second lesson is that experience has shown that, while multi-skilled personnel may suffice in peacetime, under the stress of sustained wartime operations, it has twice been necessary to introduce progressively increased degrees of specialisation. Thus, from the RFC's standing start in 1914, the RAF of 1918 was on the point of rationalising its existing collection of rather ill-defined non-pilot trades into Brancker's seven discrete categories (see Fig. 15). Similarly, having gone to war with just three varieties of non-pilot aircrew in 1939, the RAF had fourteen categories and sub-categories by the spring of 1945. In both instances, this crystallising process had been evolutionary, rather than planned, but the fact that evolution has twice followed the same path must surely tell us something.

[61]*Air Clues*, correspondence columns, various issues in 1978 and 1983.
[62]See Chapter 23, Note 51.
[63]*RAF News*, 18 August 2000.

It is possible that modern technology really will permit the Service to dispense with the wheel this time; we can only hope that it will not have to go to the trouble and expense of having to invent it all over again (again).

The last new aircrew badge?

It was inevitable that the planned merging of trades would raise questions over the retention of the old 'N', 'AE' and 'S' badges, all of which would clearly be too specific for the new, 21st Century, jack-of-all-trades back-seaters. It was decided, therefore, to introduce a completely new badge but, perhaps wisely, in view of the refusal of old hands to give up their 'O' and 'FE' badges in the past, it was agreed that anyone who was already entitled to wear one of the current emblems would have the option of continuing to do so.

The new badge is to take the form of a single-winged 'RAF' monogram within a laurel wreath, surmounted by a crown. While this addresses concerns first raised by the rank and file as long ago as 1942, in that it confers a token of royal approval and actually identifies the wearer as being a member of the RAF (see page 192), it seems that the Service still cannot countenance anyone but a pilot wearing two wings.

In recent years, successive administrations have spoken enthusiastically of 'transparency' and 'open government' and even of 'freedom of information' legislation, but little of this ethos seems to have percolated down to the Ministry of Defence. As a result, presumably, of a perceived risk to national security, we may well have to wait thirty years before being permitted some insight into the real depth of the deliberations which led to the introduction of the new flying badge.

In the meantime we may have to be content with the simple statement that the two-wing option had been considered, but that it had been dismissed on the grounds that its introduction might have been controversial and that it would have run counter to RAF and RFC traditions.[64] Neither of these arguments is particularly persuasive. In the first instance because, whatever solution was imposed, if it involved change, as it was almost bound to, it was equally certain that it would provoke controversy for that reason alone.

So far as traditions are concerned, it would seem that, in the eyes of the pilots who still manage practically all air force affairs, these are associated only with the badges which *they* wear. It is plain that, since pilots evidently fail to appreciate the historical significance of the badges worn by navigators and others, these emblems are regarded as being readily disposable. Furthermore, is it not a trifle selective to invoke only RFC-derived RAF traditions? What of the RNAS and its contribution to the RAF's heritage? In stark contrast to RFC practice, the first generation of naval back-seaters wore a twin-winged badge, as do their successors in today's FAA. Is it not time to honour the naval element of the RAF's parentage?

The fact is that while there may be some merit in honouring RAF traditions, this particular one leaves the Service in

[64]This rationale was offered in an unreferenced, unclassified briefing paper produced by the MOD when the aircrew categories of the WSO/WSOp and the associated badge were announced. It was anticipated that this announcement might well provoke a number of questions and the document provided appropriate official responses.

The WSO badge was originally to have been introduced in the autumn of 2001 but the date has since been put back to April 2003. It is suggested that, if the Air Force Board really believes in equal careers for navigators, this delay provides it with an ideal opportunity to demonstrate its commitment to this half-century-old policy by authorising a pilot-style, twin-winged badge for their successors. After all, if the 'traditional' 'N' can be dispensed with there is no reason to regard its single-winged design as being sacrosanct either. While the RFC's generals (may have) had some grounds for regarding the observers of 1915 as being less important than pilots, the Bailhache Committee soon showed that this had been a misconception. Since it had clearly gone in the wrong direction, relatively few air forces (including the RNAS) opted to follow the RFC's lead and practically all of those which did have subsequently abandoned the blatantly discriminatory half-badge. It is very late in the day, but it is not too late for the RAF to acknowledge that its retention of the single-wing has always been more to do with bias than with tradition. It is, of course, entirely appropriate that anyone who was originally presented with a single-winged badge and who wishes to continue to wear one, for reasons of pride or sentiment, should be permitted to do so, but the RAF of the 21st Century really ought to stop trying to imply that its professional non-pilot aircrew are anything less than fully fledged.

an increasingly isolated position, as most other major air forces have long since abandoned single wings – if they ever adopted them.[65] Thus, while pilots may choose to present the defence of their exclusive right to wear a twin-winged badge as the preservation of a tradition, others may see this as merely clinging to an outdated privilege.

Interestingly, an air force study, conducted shortly before it was decided to merge most rear crew categories, had concluded: that fast-jet navigators shared a common level of responsibility with their pilots; that pilots and navigators required comparable skills, training and leadership qualities; and that the demands placed on the tactical co-ordinator in a maritime crew equated to those of the fast-jet navigator.[66] In other words, that pilots and navigators are far more alike than they are different.

This conclusion should hardly have come as a surprise, however. After all, Bailhache had said as much as long ago as 1916 (see page 30), as had AMP in 1938 when he had directly challenged the validity of the prevailing assumption that 'the observer need not be of the same high standard as the pilot' (see page 132). Indeed, it was because the RAF had finally recognised the essential similarity between pilots and navigators that it has been fishing in the same pond for them ever since the introduction of the PNB scheme of 1942. Furthermore, in 1948 AMP had acknowledged that navigators needed to possess degrees of intellectual ability and levels of professional skill *at least* as great as those demanded of pilots (see page 222). It was for precisely that reason that the Air Council had begun to offer navigators the same career prospects as pilots, as it has done ever since, although, as we have seen, this equality has always tended to be of a somewhat Orwellian kind.

Under the circumstances, it is arguable that the RAF missed an ideal opportunity to demonstrate its professed commitment to equality in 2000. Since all of the very different kinds of pilot have always worn a common badge and all of the very different rear crew categories are soon going to do so, and, since all aircrew are so alike, it would have been but a short step to accepting that they might as well all wear the same emblem. It is most unlikely that such a radically heretical idea will have even been considered but, if anyone did have the temerity to advance it, it would undoubtedly have been given short-shrift.

Instead it was decided to offer non-pilots a new badge which would be 'a respected and attractive symbol that formally acknowledged completion of a syllabus of flying training.'[67] The last clause is interesting in the light of the rogue 'FC' and 'AT' badges which are not associated with a flying training course but which will continue to be tolerated. The upshot is that, despite the Air Force Board's paying lip service to tradition, these latter day quasi-aircrew will continue to wear traditional style badges whereas the last of the real back-seaters will have to put up with a design resembling an airman's cap badge to which a wing has been stapled.

Reverting (for the last time) to the possibility of a twin-winged badge, there was a significant contemporary development that makes it particularly surprising that this option was so easily dismissed in 2000. One of the last remaining bastions of the single-winged badge had fallen as recently as 1999. In that year the Australians had finally broken ranks by introducing twin-winged badges for navigators, thus following the example set by their Canadian cousins half-a-century earlier. The new Australian badge features a representation of the Southern Cross in place of the 'RAAF' monogram sported by pilots. One hesitates to predict what the eventual impact of this might be, but it seems most unlikely that this antipodean initiative will be allowed to pass without provoking some sort of comment from the non-pilot community in (what used to be known as) the mother country.

The distaff side

Leaving aside the imminent introduction of the WSO, the position with regard to non-pilot aircrew at the end of the

[65]Practically all of the air forces which were established by, or in association with, the RAF, notably those of Commonwealth countries, all of which more or less had the single-wing foisted upon them, have since abandoned it. The only other substantial air force to adopt a simple flying 'O' was the USAS of WW I but they had replaced it with a twin-wing by 1920. The French Air Force also used a single-wing but this was set within a wreath, the whole being presented as a metal brooch. Pilots wore a very similar device, their wreath enclosing a double winged emblem, but the brooch was the same size as that worn by observers. Today, all qualified French aviators wear twin-winged flying badges. Other major air forces, eg those of imperial Russia and the USSR, Poland, imperial and Nazi Germany, Italy, Holland, etc. all used variations on the twin-winged theme or a variety of brooches but in all cases, while most of these emblems differentiated between pilots and observers they were of similar sizes and patterns, thus avoiding the 'half-an-aviator' stigma implicit in assigning the latter smaller badges and/or designs featuring only one wing.

[66]See Note 64.

[67]*Ibid.*

1990s remained much the same as it had been for the previous thirty years except for the introduction of female aircrew officers. The first one, an air loadmaster, had been commissioned as early as 1973 but the real breakthrough in this context came in July 1989 when it was announced that the RAF would accept women for training as pilots, navigators, AEOps and air engineers. The first three navigators, all of whom had been internally recruited, began their professional training in September; the first to qualify, Fg Off Anne-Marie Dawe, graduated in March 1991.

To begin with the employment of female pilots and navigators was confined to helicopters and transport aircraft operating in support roles. This constraint was to be short-lived, however, and on 16 December 1991 the Ministry of Defence announced that women would be permitted to fly combat types as well. By the end of 1994 the RAF had sixty-nine female navigators and pilots. A dozen of the navigators and eight pilots had gained their 'wings'; the remainder were still undergoing training. Most of the operational navigators had been posted onto heavy aircraft but one was flying Tornado F.3s. Women still represented only a tiny proportion of the 900 pilots and 300 navigators who had passed through the training system between 1989 and 1994, but they were sufficient to make their presence felt and their numbers were growing. By mid-1999 there were fifty-two women qualified as pilots or navigators flying operationally and there were forty-two more in the pipeline.

Having broken through one layer of the glass ceiling to gain access to the previously male preserve of the Crew Room, it remains to be seen whether women navigators (or WSOs) will be any more successful than their male counterparts in securing executive appointments and, the ultimate test, in gaining access to the (almost) exclusively pilot inhabited domain of the Air Force Board Room. Only time will tell, but in 1992 an air loadmaster, Sqn Ldr Sue Bancroft-Pitman, became the first woman to attain senior officer rank as aircrew and in 1996 Flt Lt Sarah Heycock, a navigator with No 206 Sqn, became the first woman to captain a (Nimrod) crew. Furthermore, Gp Capt Joan Hopkins, a fighter controller, had been appointed to command an operational station (RAF Neatishead) as early as 1982, so the portents are good.

Postscript

When the RAF came into existence in 1918 it inherited large numbers of back-seaters. Nevertheless, it chose to ignore the obvious implications of this and made a determined effort to do without them in the 1920s. Somewhat reluctantly, the Service was eventually obliged to accept that this policy had been ill-conceived and that, to enable it to manage its affairs efficiently and operate effectively, it needed the expertise of professionals other than pilots – on the ground, as well as in the air. So far as non-pilot aircrew were concerned, their place in the scheme of things was secured during WW II and it remained so until the turn of the century.

By that time, however, although the RAF was still employing navigators, air electronics officers and operators, air engineers, air loadmasters and a few air signallers, it was plain that this would not continue to be the case indefinitely. User-friendly computers of ever-increasing capacity and flexibility have already displaced both the navigator and the air engineer from the flight decks of many of the RAF's larger aircraft. In the specific case of navigators, for instance, according to officially released figures, the annual into training target for 2000 had fallen to forty-three, compared to 100 in 1988; it was forecast to be a mere fifteen in 2010.[68]

How accurate this forecast will turn out to be remains to be seen, but it is interesting to observe that, coincidentally, the most recent batch of officers to graduate from Cranwell at the time of writing, No 186 Course, just happened to include twenty-two prospective pilots and eleven student navigators[69] – much the same 2 : 1 ratio as had been required in the 1950s (see page 224). Nevertheless, with numbers declining inexorably, the Air Force Department contended that it was becoming increasingly difficult to sustain a viable career pattern for individual non-pilot aircrew. Since officers of the GD Branch are supposed to have had equal career prospects, irrespective of their flying badges, for the previous half-century, it is not entirely clear why the numbers wearing any particular badge should have affected the issue. Nevertheless, the decline in numbers was cited as one of the main reasons for deciding to restructure the non-pilot element of the GD Branch by combining most of the remaining categories in 2001.

Pilots are not immune to this evolutionary process, of course, and even those who fly high-performance combat aircraft may eventually become superfluous. Unmanned Air Vehicles (UAV) are becoming increasingly commonplace for reconnaissance and surveillance duties and, although there will (almost) certainly be at least one more generation of piloted fighters and bombers (or dual-capable 'strike fighters'), it is quite possible that the next one will be 'flown' under remote control from the safety of an underground bunker.

It seems less likely that pilots will ever be completely replaced in large, long-range/endurance aeroplanes, although their function may increasingly become one of monitoring, rather than operating, the controls and systems. Almost no one, it would seem, will be indispensable. With pilots having expended so much energy for so long on preserving their position at the top of the aircrew heap, it would be ironic in the extreme if the dominant member of the crews of the last generation of manned RAF aeroplanes turned out to be the air loadmaster. Nevertheless, until someone invents a machine that knows which knots are required, where and when, and is actually able to tie them, the 'loadie' could well prove to be the most difficult man to replace.

[68]*Ibid.*
[69]*RAF News*, 8 December 2000.

Epilogue

While observers have long since faded from the RAF scene, because their successors still serve, it is worth looking back to WW I in an attempt to find some rational explanation for the RFC's determination to exclude observers from even the lowest levels of the chain of command. Since a lack of regard for aircrew other than pilots was to prevail for so many years within the RAF, we should also consider some of the long-term implications of the RFC's unfortunate attitude.

Had there really been an anti-observer bias within the RFC and, if so, why?

There had been a gradual, if marginal, improvement in the conditions of service of observers between 1914 and 1918, and there were signs that the situation might have improved significantly had the war been prolonged. It is quite clear, however, that they had never commanded the same respect as contemporary pilots – at least, not in the eyes of the senior officers who wrote the rules.

The nature of the problem appears to have been that the RFC had permitted a natural inclination (for pilots to favour other pilots) to become a *de facto* policy. Since this policy was bound to influence practice, it inevitably led to the interests of pilots being promoted at the expense of those of all other trades. Because of the way in which its generals had stacked the cards, therefore, only pilots were able to win at the RFC's flying game. This may be an oversimplification but, in essence, it is what happened.

Whether this unfortunate situation had arisen by accident or by design may be debatable, but what is certain is that Sir Clement Bailhache's investigations had clearly identified the problem as early as 1916. The RFC's subsequent failure to implement his Committee's only specific recommendation relating to observers permitted its discriminatory attitude to become even more deeply entrenched. Once this opportunity had been ignored there was little chance of the system's ever being put to rights, as the plainly prejudicial practice of restricting the rank of observers to lieutenant ensured that very few spokesmen emerged with the authority to question the *status quo* or to press the back-seaters' case.

As suggested above, it is possible that the RFC's apparent bias against observers was actually a bias in favour of pilots – which is not quite the same thing. Wherever the emphasis lay, however, the outcome would have been the same. Reduced to their essentials, there would appear to be three possible explanations for the RFC's attitude.

a. All observers really were inherently inadequate.
b. All pilots were arrogant and ambitious and therefore connived to protect their privileged status.
c. Discriminatory tendencies towards minorities are endemic within any social group and within the RFC this was bound to manifest itself at the expense of the less numerous observers.

The major, and very obvious, flaw in the first of these possibilities is that a substantial proportion of observers subsequently became pilots. They can hardly, therefore, have been incompetent as individuals.

The second proposition has a number of weaknesses. First, since most pilots were very junior officers they wielded insufficient influence to affect matters as remote to them as personnel policy. Secondly, even if they had been able to, since many of them had been observers themselves, they might well have been inclined to be sympathetic, rather than vindictive, towards them. Finally, if pilot-preference really was the dynamic, why was there no significant bias against observers in the RNAS?

The fact that there was no significant anti-observer bias within the RNAS seriously undermines the third argument, that discrimination is inevitable. It is true that the Admiralty had been comparatively slow to realise that it needed professional observers, but once it had, it treated them no differently from its pilots. Since none of the more obvious propositions provides a convincing justification for the RFC's attitude towards its observers, it is necessary to look for a more subtle explanation.

It is interesting to note that, as is clearly shown by the succession of regulations which they devised, the dismissive attitude towards observers displayed by the upper echelons of the RFC never diminished. This contrasted sharply with what had been happening at the working level. A certain lack of respect for observers may have been apparent in the early days but with the passage of time this had largely faded away. Hubert Griffiths, for instance, writing of his time with No 15 Sqn in 1918, went so far as to describe the pairing of a pilot and observer as being '... more binding than that of a marriage. (It) was, I suppose, the most personal relationship that ever existed.'[1] This recollection of a deep mutual respect was a far cry from the lack of regard for the observer of 1915 recalled by Robert Money (see page 17). Perhaps this remarkable change in attitude in such a short time provides a clue which might help to explain the whole phenomenon.

Twentieth century warfare on an industrial scale effectively compressed time in that social and technological changes which might normally have occurred over a lifetime or more took place in just a few years. Among the more obvious examples of this process during the Great War are the meteoric careers of certain soldiers who were fortunate enough to have been in the right place at the right time. Their experience and seniority were such that they were suitable for rapid promotion within the hugely expanded wartime army, many of these men attaining ranks which they could hardly have even dreamt of reaching in peacetime.[2] What implications might this have had within the microcosm of the RFC?

[1]Hubert Griffiths, *RAF Occasions* (1941).
[2]Examples of accelerated promotion within the RFC are legion. For instance Majs J.F. A. Higgins, C.A.H. Longcroft, W.S. Brancker and J.M. Salmond had all become major-generals within four years, some of them in three. Similarly, captains in 1914, T.I. Webb-Bowen, L.E.O. Charlton, G.S. Shephard, H.C.T. Dowding and C.L.N. Newall were all brigadiers in 1918. Even more

Although they were already wearing their flying badges when they arrived in France, most newly qualified pilots still had much to learn, certainly until late 1917. This was one of several 1½ Strutters bent by 2/Lt Norman Macmillan when he first joined No 45 Sqn; indeed he narrowly avoided being sent home for further training. Nine months later he was Capt Macmillan MC, a Flight Commander with ten victories to his credit. This sort of progress towards maturity was less apparent among early observers because they tended to leave to become pilots themselves once they had become proficient, their places being taken by another generation of tyros. (J.A. Brown)

A volunteer observer, arriving on his first squadron directly from the trenches in 1915, was of very little immediate use. He had never been up in an aeroplane and, since he had no training whatsoever, he had only the vaguest idea of what was expected of him. A newly certified contemporary pilot was only a marginally better prospect, of course, since he too needed to be 'shown the ropes' and he may well have tended to break aeroplanes at a rather distressing rate to begin with.

Once a new pilot had found his bearings and gained a little confidence, however, he became an increasingly capable and valued member of his squadron. New observers matured at a similar rate, of course, but as soon as they had acquired some 'air sense' and begun to make a positive contribution most of them disappeared to become pilots themselves. Their places were promptly taken by more bewildered tyros and the whole process had to be repeated. From the perspective of a hard-pressed CO, the early observers passing through his hands in an endless procession may often have appeared to have been rather more trouble than they were worth. Similarly, once the newly-trained pilot had found his feet, he began to accumulate wisdom and, eventually perhaps, sufficient *gravitas* to become a Flight Commander. In the meantime, he was obliged to fly with a series of green observers, the contrast between his own expanding capabilities and those of his 'passengers' becoming more and more apparent as time went by.

It is easy to see that constant repetition of this cycle meant that within each squadron there would have been the permanent presence of a floating population of what amounted to dangerously inexperienced, semi- or unskilled comparative incompetents – the observers. Under the circumstances, while there would doubtless have been many exceptions to the rule, it would be quite understandable if the bulk of early observers had failed to inspire much confidence in some of the pilots who had to fly with them. In fact they evidently failed to inspire much confidence among the more experienced observers either. For instance, when Lt A.J. Insall was considering applying to have (another) try at pilot training in May 1916, after ten months of active service as an observer with No 11 Sqn, his perception of his colleagues was a significant factor in his calculations. Insall was strongly inclined to go for single-seaters because 'the idea of entrusting my skin to some of the observers I knew did not seem to appeal to me overmuch.'[3]

The Wing and Brigade Commanders of 1917–18 had been the Flight and Squadron Commanders of 1914–15. Could it be that their personal experience of observers during their active periods of relatively early combat flying had created an impression of inadequacy so marked that it stayed with them long after their rapid ascent through the ranks had taken them out of the cockpit? They must all have been aware of the progressive improvements that had been made to training and there were even isolated instances of senior officers, like Geoffrey Salmond, actually taking the observer's part. It seems, however, that most of them may have developed, perhaps unconsciously, a permanently jaundiced view of observers.

While it is impossible to prove that this syndrome actually existed, it is not too difficult to identify individuals who fitted the pattern, perhaps the most prominent example being John Salmond. As a major, Salmond had commanded No 3 Sqn for the first eight months of the war, a period during which he would have been exposed to the apparent inadequacies of the first cohorts of untrained observers. Later, in 1917, as the brigadier responsible for RFC training, he had such confidence in the *professional* capabilities of the observers being produced by his organisation that he actively (if unsuccessfully) supported the case for the award of their badges on completion of their courses and the abolition of the mandatory period of probationary active service. A year later, however, by then a major-general, back in France and commanding the RAF in the Field, he strongly opposed the suggestion that observers should be given the opportunity to exercise *executive* authority

It would seem, therefore, that by 1918 many of the pilots at the bottom of the RFC's hierarchy, that is those who were flying with them on operations, had come to accept observers as being more or less their equals. It is also clear, however, that those at the top were still quite unable (or unwilling) to acknowledge their potential. In fact, since they were drawn from substantially the same pool of manpower, observers and pilots would obviously have had much the same ability as individuals. It is easy to see, however, that the long-term and widespread practice of converting observers into pilots meant that few observers plied their trade for long enough to become truly expert in their field. This was bound to create a poor impression of the overall capabilities of observers and the system simply protected itself from them, the aim perhaps being not so much to preserve the paramountcy of pilots, as to prevent perceived incompetents from filling positions of authority.

The resultant regulations did serve to institutionalise an anti-observer bias within the RFC but they were not simply a manifestation of an illogical prejudice. The RFC's discriminatory attitude towards its observers was based on a false impression which was actually created and sustained by the corps' own practices and procedures.

Why did the peacetime RAF dispense with observers in 1919?

There seems to be no specific record of the thinking behind the RAF's decision to abandon observers, so one can only

remarkable were the cases of Maj-Gens E.L. Ellington and W.G. H. Salmond, both of whom had begun the war as captains, and Brig-Gen P.H.L. Playfair who had gone to France in August 1914 as a mere lieutenant. Most of these officers (and the list is far from being exhaustive) were holding their senior ranks on a temporary basis, of course, but this did nothing to diminish either their authority or their influence.

[3]A.J. Insall, *Observer* (1970).

speculate on what it might have been.[4] It is possible that the RAF was forced to dispense with non-pilot aircrew (along with most of its commissioned specialists) by financial stringency. It could have been that, with only minimal funding available, the Service felt that the only way to make ends meet would be to employ, as officers, only people who were capable of flying an aeroplane and then making them double-up to act in other capacities. In army terms this would equate to recruiting only artillery officers and then expecting them to spend some of their time building bridges, mending tanks or galloping about on horses. Needless to say, the Army, which was subject to much the same budgetary constraints as the RAF, did not elect to pursue such an unrealistic option. It would hardly have been a sensible response to a shortage of funds in any case, because it is very expensive to train people in two disciplines, especially when they can function effectively in only one speciality at a time.

Since the financial argument is unconvincing, there must have been some other reason for the RAF's electing to do what it did. It is suggested that the most likely explanation for this decision lay in the previous experience of the man who made it. Hugh Trenchard, in common with practically all of the RAF's first generation of generals, was a pre-war pilot who had turned to flying relatively late in life. While all of these men had been impressed by the military potential of the aeroplane and did their best to exploit it, they had actually been trained as soldiers (or sailors). Only later had they become airmen.[5]

Nevertheless, despite their evident enthusiasm, they can only really have been airmen by conviction. Circumstances had denied them the opportunity of spending the crucial formative years of their careers as aviators. Their personal experiences had conditioned them to have an instinctive 'feel' for what it was to be a soldier but most of their awareness of what was involved in being a flyer had to have been relatively superficial. This observation does nothing to belittle their subsequent achievements, quite the contrary, but it is difficult to see how a group of men who had spent their youth pig-sticking Pathans, bombarding the Boer or coaling-ship on the China Station could really have had an intimate appreciation of the day-to-day life, attitudes, outlook or opinions of an experienced professional flyer.

Trenchard's postwar concept of an air force in which every officer would be able to fly an aeroplane plainly failed to take account of the fact that most pilots enjoy doing what they do so much that many of them tend not to want to do anything else. More often than not this 'anything else' includes flying in any capacity other than as a pilot. As a result, the Air Ministry's declaration of January 1920, that 'as no provision has been made for observers in the permanent Air Force, all officers (*i.e. pilots*) are to be considered available for the duties of observers' (see page 106) proved to be little more than an exercise in wishful thinking. Despite the stated policy, the majority of pilots simply declined to occupy the back seat, the responsibilities of the non-existent observers soon being delegated almost universally to non-commissioned ground tradesmen who flew on a part-time basis.

Such a fundamental misjudgement can surely have been attributable only to an inability to understand what it really meant to be a committed practical aviator? Furthermore, Trenchard, in common with all of the RAF's early air marshals, had been a pilot from the outset. None of these men had come up the 'hard way' via an apprenticeship as an observer. Since they had little, if any, first-hand experience of flying as a back-seater on operations, they simply could not have had a very firm grasp of their work or of the problems that it involved.

Indeed, many of the more senior and influential personalities in the RFC and the early RAF, Henderson, Trenchard, Sykes, Brancker, Game and Ellington for instance, had rarely (if ever) even flown in combat. Yet these men were the legislators and makers of policy. When arriving at their decisions they would have relied heavily upon the advice offered by the brigadier-generals commanding in the field; men with whom they were well acquainted from their time at the CFS, where most of them had attended pre-war courses, men like Pitcher, Longcroft, Ashmore, Webb-Bowen and Newall. As suggested above, however, it would seem that this group of officers may well have had little regard for observers as a result of their having been exposed to their inadequacies in 1914–16, when these men had been flying operationally.

With only seven years' experience of military aviation on which to draw, Trenchard could perhaps be forgiven for attempting to devise an ideal on which to base his peacetime air force. Perhaps it is only with hindsight that we are able to appreciate how unrealistic the concept of a pilots-only organisation would prove to be. On the other hand, as discussed below, it does seem to have been almost perverse to have virtually discounted so much of what had been learned between 1914 and 1918.

Was the RAF justified in dispensing with its observers and with officers of other key trades?

Did it really matter that the postwar RAF elected to do without commissioned back-seat aircrew, along with officers of most other specialisations? In the light of later developments, the answer to this question can only be – yes, it mattered. While this may be obvious today, however, it clearly cannot have been the case in 1919.

Trenchard freely acknowledged that 'technical experts' would be required for development work in the fields of 'navigation, meteorology, photography and wireless', all of which he recognised as being 'primary necessities.'[6] He envisaged, however, that all of these experts would be pilots holding permanent commissions, all of whom would be required to specialise in a technical discipline after five years of service. Unfortunately, this approach was bound to breed officers who would be pilots first and foremost. Since Trenchard evidently failed to understand this, he could not be expected to foresee that many of these men would find that their subsequent technical responsibilities were more irksome than stimulating.

There must surely also have been a considerable element of self-deception at work to have enabled Trenchard to persuade himself that his future pilots would not need professional

[4]AIR8/19 might appear to be the most promising source of clues, as it contains a substantial quantity of papers and correspondence raised between 1919 and 1923 dealing with the provision of personnel for the *post bellum* air force. Unfortunately, it sheds no light on the reasons behind the decision to dispense with observers.

[5]The most extreme example of a late conversion to the faith is probably represented by Trenchard's first DCAS, RAdm Mark Kerr, who had acquired his RNAS seaplane pilot's 'ticket' in Greece during the war at the age of fifty.

[6]AIR1/17/15/1/84. These quotations are taken from the famous 'Trenchard Memorandum' of 25 November 1919 which was subsequently endorsed by Parliament to become the blueprint for the peacetime RAF.

assistance. How else could he have explained away the fact that during the recent war it had been found necessary to employ thousands of technical and administrative officers – not to mention non-pilot aircrew? Taking the December 1918 Air Force List as a reasonable reflection of the manning situation at the end of WW I, and leaving aside doctors, dentists and chaplains, we find that the officer corps numbered 21 018 graded personnel (of all kinds) who flew (or who were immediately involved in the direction and control of air operations), plus 9198 who did not.[7] In other words, for every 2.3 officers notionally available as aircrew, the wartime RAF had needed one on the ground. This groundcrew:aircrew relationship was no late-wartime, new-fangled, 'air force' phenomenon incidentally, as the Air Force List for April 1918 reveals that the new Service had inherited a ratio of 2.4 : 1 from its forebears.

In the specific case of observers, there can be no doubt that by late 1918 the RAF had been fully aware of their value as navigators, especially within Trenchard's own Independent Force. In September, for instance, his OC 83rd Wg, Lt-Col J.H.A. Landon, had expressed the opinion that 'the success of every raid probably depends upon the Observer as much as on the Pilot, and that the success of long raids depends rather more on the training of the Observer than on the training of the Pilot.'[8] Even so, within a matter of months the air force had decided to do away with observers.

The same fate was to befall most of the officers who had been engaged on ground duties. By 1917 a squadron never had fewer than three officers established in support roles, a Recording Officer, a Stores Officer and an Armament Officer. As operations became more complex these numbers could be increased, depending on a squadron's role. Thus, for instance, by the summer of 1918 a Handley Page squadron had four Technical Officers, rather than the usual two, while a corps reconnaissance squadron had two additional officers specialising in wireless equipment. If a wartime squadron had so recently required three, four, five and sometimes as many as six, ground-based officers dedicated to sustaining its operations it seems remarkably short-sighted to have assumed that this would not be the case in the future.

Operational efficiency was a very secondary consideration in the early postwar years, however. The problems which were far more likely to focus the Air Council's attention were financial and political. In its efforts to stimulate economic recovery the Government sought to restore Sterling to the Gold Standard which meant maintaining a balanced budget which, in turn, meant that the Treasury was obliged to impose extremely tight constraints on public expenditure. Paradoxically, this turned out to be a mixed blessing so far as the RAF was concerned. Tiny annual allocations of funds meant that research and development were under-resourced, which meant that there were few significant technical advances. Those developments that were introduced into service were hardly revolutionary and thus they did little to expose the myth of the pilot's ability to cope unaided. On the other hand, it was only this same financial stringency that enabled the RAF to survive as an independent Service at all, air power proving to be a highly cost-effective means of maintaining imperial control, particularly over the vast tract of the Middle East which had become a British responsibility following the collapse of the Ottoman empire.

Lack of funds also served to inhibit the RAF's expansion plans. Thus, despite parliamentary approval having been granted for a metropolitan air force of fifty-two squadrons as early as 1923, this aim had still not been achieved ten years later. Since the RAF was unable to buy all the additional aeroplanes to which it was entitled, it followed that it would have been equally incapable of paying all of the men who would have been needed to fly and maintain them. It was obliged, therefore, to minimise its manpower requirements. This financial imperative provided further justification for a manning policy under which all officers would be pilots, some of whom would be required to do double duty in other fields. Furthermore, keeping the RAF small and lean, made it deceptively easy (for pilots) to organise and administer.

If economic conditions had served to promote reliance on pilots, what of political considerations? Was the international situation really so benign as to justify the RAF's adopting such an unrealistic manning policy? In short – yes. On 15 August 1919 the government declared that its defence planning would be based on the assumption that there would be no major war for at least ten years. In 1928 this policy was made annually renewable and it was so renewed every year until 1933, hence the lack of urgency attached to the RAF's authorised expansion during the 1920s.

This consideration aside, there was a considerable degree of popular support for international disarmament in the years following the Great War. Many governments, including those of the UK, subscribed to this ideal. While none was prepared to go so far as to disarm unilaterally, so long as there was some prospect, however faint, of an effective disarmament conference being held it would have been counterproductive to adopt anything resembling a warlike posture. So far as British politicians were concerned, therefore, there were no votes in rearmament until Hitler came to power, and not very many even then.

On balance, therefore, it could reasonably be argued that, in the prevailing economic and political climate, the RAF's decision to concentrate its limited funds on pilots had made the best use of the available resources. Nevertheless, as discussed below, this policy would inflict damage which took many years to repair.

Did the lack of observers have any effect on the development of air navigation?

Would it really have made any difference to the development of navigational techniques if the RAF had retained observers in peacetime? Almost certainly – yes. It will be recalled that the Bailhache Committee had made only one recommendation with respect to observers – in effect, that they should be recognised as a separate trade, equal in status to that of pilots, and that there should be no bar to their promotion. Had this far-sighted measure been implemented promptly it would have provided both an effective counter to the prejudice that was becoming increasingly deep-rooted within the existing system and the catalyst that was needed to foster the creation of a professional class of specialist back-seaters.

Although Bailhache did not actually say so, it followed that his recommendation would, by permitting observers to attain ranks at which their voices could be heard, probably have

[7]The 21 018 'aircrew', which did not include any officers above the rank of lieutenant-colonel, broke down as: 14 111 Aeroplane Officers; 689 Seaplane Officers; 412 dual-rated Aeroplane and Seaplane Officers; 339 Airship Officers; 1033 Kite Balloon Officers; and 4434 Observer Officers. The corresponding division of the 9198 officers of ground branches (three of whom were full colonels) was: 783 Staff Officers; 5276 Technical Officers; 3109 Administrative Officers; 25 Motor Boat Officers and 5 Gymnastic Officers.
[8]AIR1/1982/204/273/88. Letter 83W/A12/6 dated 5 September 1918 from Lt-Col Landon to HQ VIII Bde.

ensured that some of them would have risen to become members of the 'air establishment' and this might well have had a significant influence on inter-war developments. In view of the financial constraints which prevailed during the 1920s, it may be stretching a point to suggest that the retention of observers would have prevented air navigation from stagnating to the extent that it did. On the other hand, it might have done – and the example set by the Fleet Air Arm certainly tends to support this contention.

Maintaining an awareness of air navigation within the RAF was clearly the responsibility of the graduates of Calshot's Long Navigation Courses. In practice, however, throughout the 1920s, the majority of these officers tended to be employed merely as instructors, either at the Navigation School itself, where they kept the faith alive by preaching the gospel to the next course, or at an FTS, where they taught *ab initio* pilots a ten-hour syllabus of elementary air pilotage, involving nothing that they had learned at Calshot.[9] Furthermore, it should not be assumed that all of these men were necessarily enthusiasts for their subject, simply because they had passed through Calshot. Some will have chosen to specialise in navigation only because they perceived it to be the least distasteful option when the time had eventually come for them to give up being full-time pilots and broaden their horizons by becoming an expert in some other field.

Nevertheless, while it was not possible to make a silk purse of a navigator (engineer, armament officer, etc) out of every sow's ear of a pilot, there were some who did become deeply committed to their chosen specialisation. So far as air navigation was concerned, the RAF's handful of experts would surely have known enough to have been able to specify some of the devices which were needed, and probably enough to have assisted in their practical development as well. Whether they really were capable of solving the problems of air navigation must remain a moot point, however, because, until the mid-1930s, no one ever asked them to – and that was the real problem.

It could be argued that contemporary technology would not have permitted much progress to have been made before this in any case. This is true of some of the more sophisticated navigational aids introduced during WW II, which had to await the development of radar. On the other hand, astro could certainly have been introduced as a standard technique in the 1920s. Similarly, there is no reason why airborne radio direction finding should not have been in general use by the early 1930s. Furthermore, German exploitation of the directional properties of radio transmissions permitted the *Luftwaffe* to employ practical blind-bombing techniques long before the RAF did. Then again, an Air Position Indicator could probably have been in use ten years before such devices actually entered service. None of these examples required a technical breakthrough; all were based solely on the application of well-understood physics. The missing ingredient was a demand for such devices, because without it there could be no investment in their development.

The root of the problem lay in market forces and, within the RAF, there simply was no market. The experts could almost certainly see the problems that needed to be solved,

[9]Between 1924 and 1933 twenty-one officers graduated from Nos 4–13 Long/Specialist Navigation Courses. Fourteen of them were subsequently employed on routine instructional duties; four were posted to squadrons or stations. Only three were assigned to posts having anything to do with policy or development work (one went to the Air Ministry, one to the Admiralty Compass Observatory and one was assigned to work with the British Arctic Air Route Expedition of 1930).

The nearest thing to navigators in the inter-war RAF were the Calshot-trained pilots of flying boats, but even these majestic machines rarely ventured out of sight of land. This is S1263, an Iris V of No 209 Sqn; she was lost in January 1933 when she sank in Plymouth Sound following a collision with a naval pinnace. (MOD H1792)

but no one else was interested. Had there been a substantial number of observers in the air force, however, they would surely have been clamouring for more efficient navigational and bombing aids. But there were none, and the average pilot, having little interest in the more esoteric aspects of navigation, was quite content to find his way by following a railway line. Since most of the tiny handful of enthusiasts were mere flight lieutenants, they had virtually no influence in matters of policy and navigation marked time.

The consequences of the RAF's policies were summed up in late 1936 by Gp Capt Arthur Harris when he wrote, in characteristically forthright style, that 'the trouble with Service navigation in the past has been the lack of knowledge and of interest in the subject evinced by senior officers, down to and including the majority of Squadron Leaders' and lamenting that 'the junior officers that have been responsible ... for navigational equipment and methods ... have not carried sufficient guns to get these vital requirements properly co-ordinated and put across.'[10]

It is suggested that, if the RAF had, for the previous fifteen years, been employing observers having a status equal to that of pilots, Harris would not have had to write what he did. Even if he did have to write it, however, he would at least have had the satisfaction of having someone else to blame. As it was, *any* inadequacy revealed within the RAF of the 1930s could be attributable only to pilots.

Did the RAF's 'pilots only' policy of the inter-war era distort its perceptions and limit its effectiveness?

Having no pretensions to being a sociologist or a psychologist, one hesitates to dabble in either of these black arts. Nevertheless, one does not need to be an expert to be able to appreciate that common personality traits and shared beliefs will tend to influence group behaviour while inducing a conformity of individual opinion. One would expect such trends to be particularly marked within a relatively closed society, especially one which selected its members very carefully and then spent two years conditioning them. The Cranwell-experience clearly tended to create a common mindset among the junior career officers of the 1920s – that was, after all, one of the objects of the exercise. Since this will have influ-

[10]AIR2/2860. Memorandum, concerning the state of navigation within the RAF, dated 3 November 1936 on Air Ministry file S.47629, from Harris, as Deputy Director of Plans, to the Director of Staff Duties (Air Cdre W.S. Douglas) and the Director of Training (Gp Capt R. Leckie).

enced the attitudes of these officers in the 1930s, this mindset is worth examining in a little more detail.

There can be little doubt that, quite understandably, many pilots (and, in the 1920s, all Cranwell graduates were pilots) feel a certain innate sense of superiority. After all, they, and they alone, control fast, powerful machines which can manoeuvre in three dimensions. The attractions of flying an aeroplane are obvious and those who are able to do so have always been much admired. This is still the case today, but it was even more so when pilots were as rare as they were in the 1920s. The RFC having done much to establish the image of the omnipotent pilot, the RAF subsequently did absolutely nothing to curb the growth of this myth. In fact, by dispensing with all other aircrew (and practically all other officers), it actively fostered the impression that pilots were able to do almost anything.

Since they routinely indulged in an extremely glamorous and exciting activity, not to mention one which had the undeniable *frisson* of a significant risk of injury or even death, it is hardly surprising that many of these young men came to believe in their own myth. If the nature of his occupation tended to encourage a military pilot to believe that he was a cut above the average, this tendency was reinforced by the status he was afforded within the Service. Apart from a handful of sergeants, all pilots were automatically commissioned. Oddly enough, however, only a few of them were subsequently called upon to exercise any powers of command. In the 1920s more than half of the RAF's officer pilots were serving on five-year engagements during which they were required to do little more than fly their aeroplanes.

Beyond an obligation to try not to break their aeroplanes, even Cranwell-trained career officers did not begin to acquire any significant responsibilities for the first four or five years or so of their productive service.[10A] Yet practically all pilots were officers. Why? Because flying demanded the standards of education, intelligence, discipline and initiative traditionally associated with commissions in the other Services. If the RAF was to be successful in recruiting such men it would have to offer them similar terms to those which they could obtain from the RN or the Army. Furthermore, it would be necessary for a pilot to be an officer in order to be able to pay him a reasonable salary. It was never a lot, but a 25 year old flying officer still earned more than twice as much as a 35 year old sergeant in a skilled trade and, combined with the irresistible attractions of being able to fly, it was enough.

While the relationship between recruiting and pay clearly contributed to the close association between pilots and commissions, social class was another important factor. In 1920 a typical Cranwell cadet was required to contribute about £125 per annum towards the cost of his two-year course.[11] At 1999 prices this would equate to a total of something in excess of £6000.[12] To be able to afford this sort of investment, a cadet's parents would clearly have had to be reasonably well off. British society was still rigidly based on class during the inter-war years and, for the sort of outlay that they were being required to make, the heads of the comfortable middle-class households, from which the RAF drew the majority of its career officers, would have expected nothing less than a commission; after all, in effect, they were buying it.

During the 1920s, therefore, the RAF established that, regardless of whether they actually commanded anything, most of its pilots would be officers. By obliging its career officers to specialise in some other trade after a few years of service, it helped to foster the image of the pilot, as 'General Duties' officer, being able to turn his hand to anything and to excel at it. So far as pure flying was concerned, whether they actually spent their time droning across the deserts of Iraq in Vickers Vernons or trying to coax their war surplus DH 9As through the mountain passes of India's North West Frontier Province, most young pilots considered themselves to be, indeed they were, of the same breed of men as those who thrilled the crowds at Hendon. To be an RAF officer in the 1920s, therefore, was to be a member of a very glamorous and exclusive club. Exclusive, that is, of anyone other than pilots.

By the mid-1930s some of these men had matured, been promoted to middle management and were occupying some of the offices which opened onto the 'corridors of power'. What was their outlook? Devoted to the Service which had nurtured them, their instinctive conservatism would have made them resistant to any suggestion that there might be something amiss with the officer corps. After all, their personal experience indicated that pilots were quite capable of dealing with practically anything.

What their experience did not reveal, however, was how well they had coped. Since all of the RAF's officers were pilots, whenever a problem cropped up the only solutions offered were those that occurred to pilots. Perhaps there had been other ways to do things, perhaps even better ways. But even to admit to such a possibility would have represented a form of self-criticism – and an ego-involved opinion change is not one that is easy to embrace. If the state of air navigation in the early 1930s is anything to go by, however, it would appear that the all-knowing pilots were not even aware of some of the air force's problems, or if they were, that they had chosen to ignore them.

Even worse, by having no professional aircrew other than pilots, the RAF had deluded itself into thinking that being able to fly an aeroplane was all that really mattered. In fact, being able to fly an aeroplane is merely a means to an end. As was to be repeatedly demonstrated during WW II, assisted only by a flight engineer, a Lancaster could be successfully flown by a single pilot – some of them ladies even! In later years, even a V-bomber could be safely flown by a pilot and an AEO. In neither case, however, could anything worthwhile be achieved, beyond moving the machine from A to B. The point of flying a Vulcan, a Lancaster – or a Virginia – was to be able to do something destructive with it and that required a competent crew of professional aviators, all of whom were just as important to the success of the enterprise as the pilot.

By late 1918 the RAF was, somewhat reluctantly, just beginning to come to terms with the implications of this. Unfortunately, however, the RFC had spent the previous four years belittling its back-seaters and it would probably have taken at least another four for the RAF to have fully accepted them as being of comparable status to pilots. The influence of the more enlightened RNAS had obliged the RAF to adopt

[10A]The Trenchard Memorandum of 1919 had anticipated that career officers would fly for five years before having to select a technical specialisation; AMWO 426/28 of 21 June reduced this honeymoon to four years.

[11]AIR10/160. AP 121, published in September 1920, contained the provisional regulations governing the RAF (Cadet) College at Cranwell. A gentleman cadet was expected to contribute £100 towards the cost of uniform and books plus, for each year of his two-year course, £75 to cover tuition fees. While the majority of cadets were obliged to pay their way, provided certain conditions could be met, some relief could be obtained, particularly for the sons of Service families, through a variety of concessionary schemes and bursaries. In addition, cadetships were awarded to a handful of the most deserving airmen graduating from each apprentice entry.

[12]See Chapter 7, Note 1. A brief period of early postwar inflation meant that by 1925 the same £250 would have been worth more than £8000 of 1999 money.

a more even-handed approach, but the new Service had not really experienced a change of heart; there had been no 'Road to Damascus' transformation. Within a matter of months it had become quite clear that the RAF's new attitude had been no more than a pose and that it was still firmly wedded to the idea of the inherent superiority of the pilot.

Nevertheless, when the peacetime RAF finally began to recognise that it was still faced with much the same problems that had to be solved in 1914–18, it came up with much the same answers. From 1934 onwards specialist non-pilot aircrew began to be reintroduced, but with a significant difference. The RFC had understood instinctively that the majority of aircrew, including back-seaters, would need to be officers. Its pilots having (apparently) successfully managed, more or less, on their own for the previous fifteen years, the RAF thought that it could get by with corporals – and part-timers at that.

One imagines that one or two of the more thoughtful Squadron Commanders of this period might have had some niggling doubts about this approach. How, for instance, was his unit supposed to cope with maintenance in wartime if a substantial proportion of its tradesmen were flying on operations? What if some of them failed to return? If their replacements were qualified as aircrew (which was unlikely, as much of their training was to be carried out in-house), this would do nothing to solve his servicing problem. On the other hand, if they were unqualified, he would have no one to fly with his replacement pilots. But there is little evidence to show that such considerations caused much concern.

The *Zeitgeist* of the 1920s had provided little incentive for officers to dwell on operational matters such as these. For example, one might have expected the majority of papers published in the *RAF Quarterly* to have explored alternative methods of persuading a bomb to hit a target or to have considered the best means of determining the number of bombs required to destroy it or to pondering the problem of how to find the objective in the dark. Articles dealing with such topics did appear, of course, but (as has been pointed out elsewhere[13]) a disproportionate amount of space was devoted to describing the delights of riding to hounds or the experience of travelling by camel train in some remote outpost of the empire.

While its junior- and middle-ranked officers may not have been devoting too much thought to solving intractable operational problems, what they did do well was to keep the RAF in the public eye through the medium of its annual Air Pageants at Hendon. These permitted its pilots to demonstrate what they were really good at – precision flying. A pilot's ability to execute a spectacular display of aerobatics was impressive, of course, but it was not enough. Since career officer pilots were responsible for practically all air force activities, they needed to be equally as proficient in many other fields.

Unfortunately, some of these officers will inevitably have had limited aptitude for their 'secondary' specialisation and many more lacked much enthusiasm for it. On reflection, this was hardly surprising for young men who had, for the previous four or five years 'slipped the surly bonds of earth/And danced the skies on laughter-silvered wings' on a more or less daily basis.[14] This experience had turned many of them into committed professional flyers and, for them, the prospect of spending many months in the classroom, grappling with abstruse formulae, unscrambling wiring diagrams and poring over endless Air Publications – while simultaneously having to become an expert on King's Regulations and Air Council Instructions – will have held few attractions.

This was especially true when the prize to be won was likely to be *another* three years during which the earthbound aviator would have to occupy himself with servicing schedules, exposure times and focal lengths, the storage of explosives or establishing the wavelength to use to maintain W/T contact with a remote detachment. All of these tasks were undeniably important, even vital, but they can have had little appeal to a substantial proportion of pilots.[15] Such matters would have been of absorbing interest to specialist officers, of course, but the RAF had elected to dispense with them.

Once the Service had elected to implement its pilots-only policy, it was committed to making it work. Since it did (or appeared to) work for some time, the officers involved came to have faith in the system and the all-embracing capabilities of the General Duties officer on which it was based. Unfortunately, it was all an illusion. The system had only coped because it had not been subjected to stress. Once the RAF began to expand, it became increasingly apparent that it had actually been operating on what had amounted to an amateur basis for fifteen years.

For the Service to function efficiently it needed the same level of professional support that it had had in 1918 but for the career officers of 1935 to acknowledge this and introduce such a system would be to acknowledge that they had failed. As a result, only limited progress was made and it took several more years for the second generation of upstart, 'second class', non-pilot corporal aircrew to penetrate the pilots-only bastion of the air force's commissioned establishment.[16] Nevertheless, the reality of war would eventually force the hand of the conservatives and in 1940 the RAF finally reintroduced dedicated commissioned engineers, administrators – and non-pilot aircrew.

What were the long term effects of the RAF's 'pilots only' philosophy on officers of other trades, and navigators in particular?

Until the mid-1930s (apart from a handful of doctors, dentists, lawyers and chaplains) the only officers employed by the RAF as professional specialists were those of the Stores and Accounts Branches. All else was the business of the pilots of the so-called General Duties Branch. While this approach sufficed to sustain colonial police actions, conducted in daylight and in fair weather against technically unsophisticated and ill-equipped opponents, it was unable to cope with real warfare and in 1940 the RAF had been obliged to reinvent the wheel by reinstating the arrangements which had prevailed in 1918.

[13]By, for instance, Dr Robin Higham on page 46 of the 19th *Journal* of the *RAF Historical Society*.

[14]From the opening lines of the poem *High Flight* written by Plt Off James Gillespie Magee of No 412 Sqn in 1941.

[15]Needless to say, there were some notable exceptions to this general rule, the most prominent example probably being Sir Frank Whittle, whose work on gas turbines was to be of such fundamental importance. As an ex-apprentice, however, it could be argued that Sir Frank was such an exception because he was essentially an engineer and only incidentally a pilot, albeit a very competent one.

[16]There are striking similarities between the situation of the underprivileged observer/navigator of the 1930s and 1940s and his need to overcome the prejudice of pilots, and the struggle of women to break down similar barriers throughout the present century and, during the last twenty years, within the RAF itself.

Apart from the time that it had wasted in having to rediscover how to keep itself operational, by adopting a pilots-only policy the RAF had also denied itself access to a great deal of human potential. Trenchard's premise, that it was necessary for practically every RAF officer to be able to fly an aeroplane, had proved to be false. Not least because, as Geoffrey Salmond had tried to point out as early as 1917, it failed to take account of those individuals who, while they may have lacked a certain degree of hand and eye co-ordination, were in all other respects well motivated and highly competent.

During the 1930s, the Trenchardian doctrine, that *all* officers must be able to fly, gradually began to give way to a more realistic concept, that all officers must be professional specialists, only *some* of whom needed to be pilots. This approach was initially introduced on a somewhat *ad hoc* basis but pragmatism had been largely transmuted into policy by mid-1940. From 1948 onwards the regulations were progressively refined until it would eventually become possible, at least in theory, for an officer of more or less any branch to achieve high rank.

That it took such a long time for this aim to be realised, was because history had first to be allowed to repeat itself. Despite the RNAS' legacy of regulations which should have enabled back-seaters to rise within the newly formed RAF, no ex-RFC officer ever became a major whilst still graded as an observer. It is simply inconceivable that of some 4400 commissioned observers listed at the end of 1918 not one had shown the potential for promotion, especially as several of them did achieve relatively high ranks after they had become pilots. All that the observers of 1918 had needed was a little patronage, but this had been universally withheld by the pilots who were then exclusively responsible for recommending candidates for promotion.

The circumstances of 1918 were to be very closely mirrored by those of 1945 when, with a very few exceptions, practically every officer holding the rank of squadron leader or above was a pilot.[17] Belonging, as they did, to the 'old school', many of these officers passed on their outdated attitudes regarding the assumed supremacy of the pilot to their successors. As a result, although it did slowly fade away, there continued to be a degree of prejudice ingrained within the system.

Prejudice aside, when navigators were finally granted access to the career ladder in 1948 they found that all thirty years' worth of the rungs above them were already occupied by pilots. As a result, navigators could not be expected to get anywhere near the top until the 1970s. Furthermore, the term 'career equality' had a real meaning only for those officers fortunate enough to have been offered permanent commissions, like Cranwell cadets. So far as navigators were concerned, it would be 1959 before any of them were able to take advantage of the preferential treatment reserved for graduates of the RAF College and even then only in disproportionately small numbers.

Despite this slow start, it had been accepted, at least in principle, as early as 1943 that non-pilots were capable of discharging executive functions, and before the war ended a few of them had been appointed as Flight and Squadron Commanders. This was never a common practice, however, and non-pilot executives continued to be a rarity during the early postwar years. They eventually came into their own during the 1960s when relatively large numbers of navigators began to fill Flight, Squadron and even Station Commander appointments.

[17]See Chapter 26, Note 24.

In 1980 the General Precisions Trophy was presented to the best individual crew in navigation in that year's Strike Command Bombing and Navigation Competition, Exercise DOUBLE TOP. Under the circumstances, for the purposes of this commemorative photograph, it might have been more appropriate for the trophy to be held by the nav (plotter) but it is interesting to see that it is actually in the hands of the captain. It would, of course, have been quite possible for the plotter to have claimed this privilege on the basis of his trade, or even, in this instance, by pulling rank, but this would simply have been alien to the prevailing culture within the V-Force.

Curiously enough, although it had become perfectly feasible for a navigator to command a squadron of V-bombers, even an entire station, as a number of them did, there was no question of his being able to captain a single crew. While pilots had, in the name of equal opportunities, been obliged to relinquish their exclusive grip on executive appointments, they had covered their embarrassment at this loss of prestige by clinging steadfastly to the fig leaf of captaincy. The sole exception to this pattern occurred in the world of maritime operations where the appointment of a navigator or an AEO to command the crew of a Shackleton or Nimrod was to become a relatively unremarkable event.

Within the V-Force, the combination of constituted crews and captaincy being the prerogative of the first pilot meant that an entire crew could be identified solely by reference to him. This commonplace custom inspired riddles along the lines of, 'What has five heads, ten legs but only one name?', the answer, of course, being a V-bomber crew. One consequence of this unfortunate practice was that, regardless of where the real strength lay within a crew, its achievements tended to be associated with its captain, invoking echoes of 1917 when pilots were credited with all victories over enemy aircraft, including those shot down by their observers. While, in the interests of brevity, it obviously made sense to use the captain's name as a convenient label, it also represented a very subtle form of discrimination. This may well have been unintentional but the fact remains that, simply because their names appeared on tote boards, flying programmes, statistical returns, etc., pilots were more easily identified as individual personalities than the relatively anonymous back-seaters. In an ideal world, this should have made no difference, but, in reality, because pilots' names made a far greater impression on the corporate consciousness, their careers were far more likely to flourish than those of the men who flew with them.

While the RAF has always been reluctant to permit navigators to be nominated as captains of fast-jets, a ranking back-seater may well feel the heat if his pilot gets his fingers burned through ill-disciplined flying. This Tornado GR 1 of No 27 Sqn is approaching the dramatic shape of the Devil's Tower in Wyoming in 1986 – on a properly authorised sortie. (British Aerospace, Warton/Sqn Ldr Terry Cook)

From the 1970s onwards the 'sharp end' of the RAF began to replace its three-man Canberras and five-man V-bombers with two-seat Phantoms, Buccaneers and Tornados. Here too, the pilot has retained the exclusive right to captaincy. Even so, a wing commander navigator, sitting behind a flight lieutenant pilot, might be unwise to assume that he would emerge unscathed from a Board of Inquiry convened to investigate his captain's indulgence in a little unauthorised low-flying – a classic case of inferred responsibility without conferred authority.

By the 1980s a few navigators (and officers from non-aircrew disciplines) were beginning to attain relatively high ranks but pilots continued to fill the majority of senior appointments – as they still do. In 2000 no fewer than twenty-seven of the RAF's most senior thirty-six officers (75%) were pilots. This suggests that something like three out of every four officers must have been pilots. This was far from being the case; the actual proportion was only *one* in four.[18]

That the RAF's instinctive preference for pilots had meant that it had taken navigators (and others) a long time to achieve high rank may have been a disappointment to the individuals concerned, but it could be said that was of secondary importance. What really mattered was that, for (at least) the first half-century of its existence, the RAF had failed to exploit the potential of many very capable people, simply because they were not pilots. Only now (since 1999) is the Service allegedly adopting a policy of appointing 'the best man for the job' and it is bound to take several years for the effects of this to become apparent.

It is sobering to reflect that if Charles Portal had not elected to trade in his flying 'O' for a pilots badge during WW I the RAF would soon have dispensed with his services. Had he remained an observer, he would have been demobilised, still a mere lieutenant, in 1919 and the RAF would have had to look elsewhere for its CAS in WW II. One wonders how many potentially great men the RAF has overlooked because they were wearing the wrong flying badge – or no badge at all?

Conclusion

Historians are often accused of judging past events in the light of later knowledge, rather than by that which was known at the time. While this writer cheerfully admits to having a somewhat partisan point of view where non-pilot aircrew are concerned, it is contended that his opinions were not formed by taking undue advantage of hindsight. The basic facts are these. The RFC of 1913 had suspected that it might well need aircrew other than pilots. The RAF of 1919 *knew* that it did – and it knew a good deal about them. It then either misunderstood, chose deliberately to misinterpret or simply ignored these facts. The facts were still there, however, and the RAF of the inter-war years had ample opportunity to study the Great War and to learn the lessons that it had taught.

Among the more obvious of these lessons were: that professional non-pilot aircrew were essential; that, in order to recruit observers of a suitable calibre, they would need to be paid the rate for the job, which meant that they would probably have to be commissioned; and that they should have career prospects similar to those offered to pilots. If the gift of hindsight was required to be able to perceive what was necessary then the admirals of the inter-war years were plainly blessed with it, whereas contemporary air marshals were not. But it is suggested that the RAF's persevering with its unfortunate, pilots-only approach had less to do with a lack of hindsight than it had with a fundamentally flawed policy which led to an increasingly blinkered attitude.

The philosopher Georg Wilhelm Hegel (1770–1831) once wrote, 'What experience and history teach is this – that people and governments never have learned anything from history, or acted on principles deduced from it.' He was not alone in reaching this conclusion, the Spanish writer George Santayana (1863–1952) observing that, 'Those who cannot remember the past are condemned to repeat it.' While the RAF may not have conformed to these patterns entirely, it has certainly tended to do so where its non-pilot aircrew have been concerned. Exactly as Hegel would have predicted, it is quite astonishing to observe that the RAF largely ignored the lessons of 1939–45, which, so far as non-pilots were concerned, had been *exactly* the same as those taught by 1914–18. While the RAF of 1946 did not go quite so far as to dispense with all non-pilot aviators, as it had done in 1919, the ill-conceived 'aircrew' scheme of 1946 was clearly an attempt to downgrade the status of those who remained and to foreclose on their having any realistic prospect of a worthwhile career.

Whether the arguments presented here have been accepted or not, there can be little dispute that the following statement is true. Having, in 1919, rapidly reinstated the practices of 1913, the RAF had permitted its pilots to re-establish their original and undisputed hegemony. This fostered the fiction that pilots could do almost everything associated with the operation of aeroplanes and that what they could not do themselves in the air could be safely delegated to a misemployed volunteer ground tradesman. Unfortunately, this philosophy was based on a false premise. As a result, the lessons of 1915 had to be learned all over again in the 1930s and *again* in the late 1940s.

The sad part is that all of this wasted time could probably have been saved if the War Office had only heeded the advice of Sir Clement Bailhache's Committee in 1916.

[18]Leaving aside doctors, dentists, lawyers and the like, the 2000 Air Force List contains the names of 10 056 officers ranked as group captains or below – I know because I counted them! Of these, 4289 (42·6%) are members of the GD Branch. For the record, the Ops Support Branch numbers 1636 (16·3%) and there are 1880 (18·7%) engineers, 710 (7·1%) suppliers and 1541 (15·3%) administrators. Of the aircrew, however, only 2618 are pilots; that is just 26% of the overall officer corps, or one in four.

Another interesting statistic revealed by this exercise is that, despite the advertised impending extinction of back-seaters, the fact is that in 2000 they actually represented a higher proportion of the total than ever, the long term pilot:nav ratio of 2:1 having fallen as low as 1·8:1.

The underpowered and inadequate Marathon T.11 which flew with Nos 1 and 2 ANSs between 1954 and 1958. (MoD)

A contrast in crew accommodation. Student navigators at work in a Wellington T.10 in the late 1940s (left) and in a Dominie T.1 in the 1970s. (MoD)

The admirable Varsity T.1 on which all navigators, and practically all other non-pilot aircrew (and many pilots who were destined to fly heavy aircraft), were trained between the mid-1950s and the type's withdrawal in 1976. This one, WF331, is seen here with No 6 FTS in 1972. After basic training many navigators encountered the Varsity again on post-graduate courses at the Bomber Command Bombing School and/or the College of Air Warfare or as instructors. (MoD)

Annexes

Annex A. Photography, 1914–18

The RFC went to war primarily to gather intelligence. It followed that, since a photograph provided an accurate and permanent record of what had been seen during a sortie, cameras should have been the most useful items of role equipment in the inventory. This appears not to have been quite as blindingly obvious at the time as it is today, however, and in August 1914 the RFC had just five Pan Ross cameras available. By early 1915 three of these had been lost or damaged but the pictures that they had taken had been valuable enough to persuade the most sceptical of generals that aerial photography was essential. In January Lt J.T.C. Moore-Brabazon was put in charge of a small experimental photographic section which had been set up within 1st Wg to review the situation and determine the way ahead. Within a few weeks, with the co-operation of the Thornton-Pickard Manufacturing Company, a new camera, the Type A, had been designed, built, tested and put into production.

The Type A was first used operationally in March 1915 and the lessons learned from this experience led to a series of progressively improved designs. The salient characteristics of the most common types of wartime camera are listed at Fig. A1. It will be seen that each model generally tended to be heavier and more complex than its predecessor but, at the same time, it also became simpler to operate. Reliability was improved by the introduction of metal construction. Utility was enhanced by the provision of a range of lenses, so that by 1918

Model	Service Date	Type & Construction	Operation & Installation	Focal Length	Weight or Size
Type A	1915	Single shot camera of wooden construction with manual changing of 5″× 4″ plates and manual adjustment of controls.	Multiple manual adjustments. Usually operated in hand-held mode by the observer, but some eventually carried on fixed external mountings.	8″ lens.	10 lb
Type C	1915	Manually operated camera of wooden construction with (usually two) eighteen-plate (5″× 4″) magazines.	Much simplified operation. Fixed, external mounting. Controlled by the pilot on, e.g. BE2s, or by the observer on, e.g. FE2s and Vickers.	10″ lens.	26 lb
Type E	1916	Manually operated camera with eighteen-plate (5″× 4″) magazine. Some metal components to overcome distortion of focus experienced with wood shrinkage on earlier models.	Variable focal length. Fixed, external mounting, as above. Could be remotely installed and operated by either crew member via a Bowden cable.	Adjustable 8″–10½″ lens.	31 lb
Type L	1917	Semi-automatic, eighteen-plate (5″× 4″) magazine-loaded camera of metal construction (but with wooden magazines). Prismatic adapters were available for oblique work.	Some early external mounting but usually internal and remotely operated via a Bowden cable controlling a flexible rotating shaft powered by a small wind-driven propeller. Able to take a series of sequential pictures automatically (10 secs interval at 50 mph).	Adjustable 8″–10½″ lens.	37 lb
Type LB	1918	Similar to Type L in overall design but of metal modular construction (but magazines still made of wood). Operation further simplified and improved with 'jam-free' mechanisms.	As above.	Alternative 4″, 6″, 8″, 10″ or 20″ lenses.	52 lb
Type BM	1918	Semi-automatic camera, entirely of metal construction, including (usually three) twelve-plate (9½″× 7″) magazines.	As above.	Alternative 7″, 10″, 14″ or 20″ lenses.	82 lb
Type F	1916	Only British film camera used in WW I; employed operationally only in the Middle East. Automatic operation, using 5″ film on 25 or 50 feet spools (50 feet gave 120 exposures).	Carried externally, usually on a bomb rack. Integral, wind-driven propeller to provide power – approx 300 revolutions giving one exposure. Automatic recording of height and heading on each frame.	8″ lens.	Size: 14½″× 7½″× 7½″

Fig. A1. Salient characteristics of the most common types of camera used by the RFC/RAF.

Left: *Too cumbersome to be used sensibly as a hand-held camera, the Type C was usually mounted alongside the pilot's cockpit, as on this BE2c.* (T. Treadwell) Right: *The pilot of an Armstrong Whitworth FK3 adjusting a Type L camera mounted on the wing root while the corporal in the rear cockpit wields one of the handy P-series.* (M. Goodall)

it was possible to take photographs from 20 000 feet with sufficient discrimination to be able to distinguish barbed wire entanglements. While the major customers, the planning and intelligence staffs, the map-makers, the artillerymen and, to an extent, balloon observers, all required vertical photographs, there was still a frequent need for oblique pictures to amplify specific details or to record fleeting events. These were usually taken by the observer, using a hand-held camera.

So far as organisation was concerned, on Moore-Brabazon's recommendation, each wing was established to have its own photographic section in the spring of 1915.[1] This arrangement sufficed for a while but within a year it was unable to cope with the volume of work. The problem was not so much the processing of plates, which were being exposed in steadily increasing numbers, but in supplying prints for which the demand was insatiable and which were always required urgently. To speed up the service it was decided both to expand and to decentralise the system. From April 1916, therefore, every corps reconnaissance squadron was established to have its own photographic section staffed by an NCO and three men.

By the summer of 1918 the establishment of photographic personnel on a corps reconnaissance squadron equipped with twenty-four RE8s or FK8s had grown to sixteen: a sergeant; a corporal and fourteen air mechanics. There was no corresponding provision on bomber or fighter reconnaissance units, which suggests that, although DH 9s, Bristol Fighters and other types could certainly be fitted with cameras, relatively little use was being made of them in other roles.

A Bristol Fighter with its fabric stripped to reveal the observer groping towards a floor-mounted Type L to fit a magazine. (J.M. Bruce/G.S. Leslie collection)

[1]The other members of Moore-Brabazon's original pioneering team had been Lt C.D.M. Campbell, F/Sgt F.C.V. Laws and 2/AM Gorse.

Some idea of the scale of the work carried out is conveyed by some statistics compiled shortly after the war which indicated that the numbers of prints produced annually in France were:[2]

Year	**No of Prints**
1915	(Est) 80 000
1916	552 453
1917	3 925 169
1918	5 946 096
Total	**10 503 718**

Compared to the work done by the army, the navy devoted relatively little effort to the development of cameras. This was because vertical photography had little practical application in the maritime field and for overland work the RNAS would have had access to the excellent range of cameras which was being developed by the RFC. Mounting cameras externally on seaplanes had proved to be problematical in any case due to salt deposits from sea spray. The navy did have a need for hand-held cameras for very long range oblique work and suitable devices were developed to meet this requirement, but they were produced only in very small batches. As a result there was little standardisation but most naval cameras were of simple box design with a double dark slide for manual plate changing. A variety of lenses gradually became available, these giving focal lengths of between 4″ and 15″. The proliferation of shore-based coastal reconnaissance and anti-submarine flights in 1918 created a demand for more cameras of this general type. The RAF eventually introduced standard models for this purpose, notably the P14 and P18.[3] These were produced in substantial quantities, seeing extensive service with land-based squadrons in France and elsewhere as well as at sea.

[2]AIR1/724/91/6/1.

[3]Late in 1918 a new system of nomenclature was introduced whereby plate cameras were classified as P types, the Type LB, for instance, becoming the P7. Cameras using film became F types and gun cameras G types. Designations derived from this system, e.g. the G45 and the ubiquitous F24 and F.95, remained in use to the end of the century.

Annex B. Communications, 1914–18

While crews had been using W/T to transmit to the batteries whose fire they were directing ever since 1914, this one-way system did not cater for long-range work, i.e. when the target was too far away for the ground signals of the 'Gunners' to be read from the air. To solve this problem it was necessary to provide two-way radio communications. Associated trials with airborne W/T receivers were well under way by 1916 and in the spring of 1918 a start was made on deploying an operational system. To begin with small numbers of suitably equipped Bristol Fighters were distributed among the existing corps reconnaissance squadrons.

This piecemeal approach proved to be difficult to manage, a problem that was overcome by an organisational change. In July the modified aeroplanes available to I Bde were pooled to form an autonomous unit manned by crews who were to be dedicated to long-range artillery work. Once this unit, L Flight, had worked out the most appropriate operating procedures, it became clear that this was a much more efficient solution and it was decided that each RAF brigade should have its own Bristol Fighter-equipped long-range artillery flight. The next one, III Bde's N Flight, was formed in September and three more had come into being before the Armistice. The equipment used comprised a Type 52A transmitter, powered by a wind-driven alternator, and a Mk III receiver. Although the long-range system had clearly served to demonstrate the advantages of two-way radio communications, it had been introduced too late to have a major impact on operations.

While the provision of airborne Morse receivers had provided the RFC with a worthwhile increase in operational flexibility, it did not represent much of a technical advance, since the use of two-way W/T was already well-established elsewhere, notably within the RNAS. A far more significant innovation was the introduction of wireless telephony, i.e. voice communication, later to become better known as radio telephony or R/T. Experimental work on speech transmission was under way in the UK by May 1915 (possibly earlier) and the RFC first employed R/T in France during July 1917 when Nos 11 and 18 Sqns carried out a series of field trials. This activity was carried out behind the lines, using apparatus made up in the workshops of the Signals Experimental Establishment at Woolwich. The success of this programme led to large-scale orders being placed, the aim being to have all two-seater squadrons fully equipped by 1919.

Training of Bristol Fighter and DH 4/9 crews began at Biggin Hill in January 1918, the Wireless Experimental Establishment accepting intakes of up to thirty students per week, drawn both from squadrons working up in the UK and from those already in France. On 2 April, by which time sufficient aircrew had been trained to man ten squadrons, the task was taken over by the newly established Wireless Telephony School which moved to Chattis Hill a fortnight later. At much the same time No 1(T) Wireless School began turning out large numbers of appropriately trained technicians from Farnborough. The deployment of hardware started in March when the Bristol Fighters of Nos 11 and 22 Sqns began to be fitted with R/T equipment but the entire programme was thrown into disarray by Ludendorff's spring offensive. Once stability had been restored the process was resumed with No 22 Sqn being fully equipped by the end of April, Nos 11 and 88 Sqns during May and No 18 Sqn, along with some of the corps squadrons working with Second Army, in August.

Steady progress was maintained thereafter but the programme still had a long way to go when the war ended, although all nine fighter squadrons based in the London Air Defence Area had been equipped before the end of the summer. Nevertheless, it is indicative of the RAF's intention to provide telephony universally that the establishments of all squadrons were amended in July 1918 to reflect the provision of the necessary additional tradesmen, including a Technical Officer (Wireless), or two in the case of a corps reconnaissance squadron.[4]

Many applications for R/T were found and tried with varying results and in many cases it was the observer who handled the radio. The practical experience gained included the transmission of reconnaissance reports direct to Army Headquarters (by No 18 Sqn), the direction of tanks by aircraft (by No 8 Sqn) and two-way communication between forward troops and aircraft during contact patrols. R/T had also been used to pass landing information and/or diversion instructions from operating bases to returning night bombers of the Independent Force, and fighter reconnaissance squadrons were beginning to use air-to-air communications to control formations. The latter was found to be highly effective in training new crews behind the lines and before the war ended the use of R/T was being actively investigated for the tactical control of combat formations (by No 22 Sqn) and for the co-ordination of bombers and escorts (by Nos 88 and 103 Sqns).

There were many teething troubles due to equipment failures and limited power output, the practical range for an airborne transmitter being not much more than 10 miles. Problems were also experienced with discomfort from ill-fitting headphones and the concentration necessary to operate the equipment tended to detract from other vital tasks, not least the need to maintain a sharp look out for enemy aircraft. The greatest practical limitation, however, was the need to use a trailing aerial up to 150 feet long. This was a potential hazard when flying in formation and an unacceptable hindrance in air combat. If a fight developed the aerial had to be reeled in or jettisoned; in either case it put an end to the use of R/T when it might have been most valuable. Work was in hand to provide fixed or 'cartridge' aerials to solve this problem when the war ended. Despite the many difficulties being experienced, solutions to all of the problems which had been encountered were being devised and R/T showed great promise. Had the war continued into 1919 there can be little doubt that it would have provided the RAF with a significant tactical advantage.

[4]AIR1/835/204/5/254. HQ RAF DRO No 732 of 24 August 1918 reproduced an Air Ministry amendment of 26 July to establishments AF/F/17, 18, 19 and 20 (among others) covering the provision of additional personnel for squadrons equipped with radio telephony.

Annex C. Gun Armament, 1914–18

Although some pre-war experimental work had been done on the carriage of guns, when the RFC flew to France in 1914 none of its aeroplanes was armed. Indeed the most appropriate weapon(s) had yet to be identified and there were no practical gun mountings. To begin with, therefore, the more aggressive crews began to arm themselves with Lee-Enfield rifles, supplemented by the occasional shotgun or even a Service revolver, none of which was very effective.

What was needed was a machine-gun, of which the British Army had two standard types. Both were of rifle (.303 inch) calibre, the recoil-operated, belt-fed, water-cooled Vickers, and the gas-operated, magazine-fed, air-cooled, Lewis. Because it was a little lighter, generally 'handier' and lacked the complication of cartridge belts, the latter was considered to be best suited for use in the air and more than 1000 had been ordered for the RFC by mid-1915. Although only a quarter of these had been delivered by that time, these guns sufficed to arm the relatively small force which was in the field.

While it was obviously important to have an effective weapon, if it was to be of any real use, it was also necessary to devise an efficient means of bringing it to bear. Many different types of mounting were designed, some of them specific to particular types of aircraft, and most of these were serviceable enough, at least in pusher aeroplanes. As discussed in the main narrative, however, none of them were of much real use to an observer occupying the front cockpit of a tractor biplane. The biggest constraint was the need to avoid damaging the aircraft's propeller, which effectively created a large cone in the forward hemisphere into which it was impossible (or extremely inadvisable) to fire a gun.

The same constraint applied to pilots, of course, although several methods of mounting a fixed forward-firing Lewis were devised. The best of these, designed by Sgt R.G. Foster in 1916, permitted the gun to be fitted, parallel to the aircraft centre-line, on top of the upper wing where it was high enough to shoot above the propeller disc. Foster-type mounts were used on single-seaters for the remainder of the war. While the Foster mount was a satisfactory means of outflanking the problem created by the propeller, what was really needed was a solution – a means of firing *through* the disc swept by the airscrew.

Methods of doing this had been available since 1914 but it was not until 1916 that the British authorities actually adopted a system. The first to find official approval was the Vickers-Challenger synchronisation gear, which was followed by Ross gears and Kauper gears. Meanwhile, the potential of the Vickers gun had been re-examined. It had been found that, if it could be carried on a fixed, rather than a flexible, mounting, the belt feed need not be an encumbrance. It had also been shown that, in an airborne environment, it was possible to dispense with the water jacket. By 1917, therefore, the Vickers gun, in combination with the definitive synchronising system, the CC (Constantinesco-Colley) gear, became the standard armament in practically all single-seat fighters. It was also adopted as the pilot's (fixed) weapon in two-seaters.[5]

Above: *An observer demonstrating the way in which the Strange mount might permit him to use his gun to provide a modicum of defensive fire to the rear, albeit at some inconvenience (not to say risk!) to his pilot.* Below: *A, probably kneeling, sergeant demonstrating the use of a gun mounted on the No 4 Mk IV swivelling pillar of an FE2b. Both guns are Lewis Mk IIs and both are fitted with bags to collect spent cases, a very necessary precaution to avoid their striking the pilot and, in the case of the FE2, the propeller.* (Sqn Ldr H. Cockerall via W. Wiggins)

In the Sopwith 1½ Strutter of 1916, and in all subsequent two-seaters, the observer occupied the rear cockpit, giving him a relatively unrestricted field of fire. Since it needed to be flexibly mounted, the weapon of choice for back-seaters remained the Lewis gun, which was progressively refined with the aim of reducing its weight while increasing both its

[5]Although the end result would be the same, it is a common error to refer to synchronising systems as 'interrupter gears'. As the name implies, the CC system synchronised the firing of the gun to permit the bullet to pass through the arc of the propeller; it did not stop the gun from firing.

Yoking two Lewis guns together, as on this RE8 of No 5 Sqn, C2731, created the so-called 'Huntley & Palmer'. Note the stencilled notice under the sill of the observer's cockpit warning that 150 lb of ballast was necessary if the aeroplane was to be flown solo. (J.M. Bruce/ G.S. Leslie collection)

ammunition capacity and its rate of fire. Fitted with a 47-round magazine, the Mk 1 Lewis of 1915 weighed a little over 25 lb and could fire 550 rounds per minute. Despite having a 97-round drum, the Mk III of 1918 weighed only 17 lb and fired 700 rounds per minute.

Early methods of mounting the observer's gun varied in detail but most designs involved the weapon's being free to move in elevation, usually with a degree of counter-balance, while it was trained in azimuth by swinging it around a 'rail' fitted to the rim of the cockpit. By the end of 1916 the 'Scarff ring' (named for its designer, WO F.W. Scarff, RNAS) had been adopted as standard, the most common pattern being officially identified as the No 3, Mk II Barbette.

By 1918 it was quite common to mount Lewis guns in pairs, this combination being known colloquially as the 'Huntley and Palmer'. While it was quite a handful to manage in the 70 mph slipstream, since they could be fired together or independently, the two-gun arrangement gave the observer the very useful options of being able to double either the firing time or the weight of fire. That having been said, however, it should perhaps be pointed out that, for two reasons, it was unwise to fire the Lewis in spectacular Hollywood-style sustained bursts. First, because the barrel was susceptible to damage ('blueing') from overheating and, secondly, because of the limited capacity of its magazine. If the gun were fired continuously, the early 47-round magazine would be emptied in five seconds and, because of the increased rate of fire of the Mk III, even the later 97-round magazine would last for only eight. The idea was to fire the gun in *well-aimed* three-to-four round bursts rather than to use it as a hose.

With only minor modifications, the fixed Vickers gun and the Lewis gun/Scarff ring combination remained the standard armament of British aircraft until the adoption of the Browning machine-gun and power-operated turrets in the late 1930s.

For more detail on the guns employed (by both sides) during WW I, the reader is referred to Harry Woodman's excellent *Early Aircraft Armament* (1989) from which much of the above has been condensed.

Effective gunnery required extensive training facilities, including target tugs, like this obsolete RE7, 2386, probably at Hythe. (Sqn Ldr H. Cockerall via W.H. Wiggins)

Annex D. Navigation, 1914–18

Although back-seaters and pilots had shared an interest in navigation from the outset, by 1918 it was becoming increasingly common for observers to assume responsibility for this task. The extent to which this was occurring varied from role to role but it was most marked where navigation was most demanding, in the squadrons of the long-range heavy night bomber force. Solutions to the problems of air navigation had been incremental, improvements in tools and techniques being introduced piecemeal from 1915 onwards, so that by 1918 substantial progress had been made. Despite these advances, practically all of which had been made by RNAS personnel, for most practical purposes air pilotage, i.e. navigation primarily by reference to a map, remained the basic means of navigation over land.

It was one thing to keep track of one's position while flying in daylight over a relatively confined area of what soon became very familiar terrain, which is how the RFC's tactical aeroplanes operated, but it was quite another to fly deep penetration raids into enemy airspace at night. Recognising the need to raise navigational standards, Lt Cdr Lord Tiverton,[6] arguably the RN's leading theoretician in the field of applied air power, nevertheless recommended that map-reading should remain the cornerstone of bomber navigation, rejecting other methods as being insufficiently precise to justify their increased complexity. This did not mean that crews were restricted to flying from one readily identifiable feature to another. To assist them with route navigation they were encouraged to apply simple air pilotage techniques. Drift, for instance, could be assessed by eye by reference to lines drawn on the map in advance and displaced at (say) 10° intervals from the desired track. Similarly, groundspeed could be measured by using a stopwatch to record the time taken to fly between two identifiable points, ideally cross-track line features. In fact, to assist the Anglo-French night bomber force based near Nancy, the French positioned lights at predetermined intervals so that an outbound crew could obtain an accurate groundspeed check by overflying them before crossing the lines.

Tiverton also advised that bomber crews should be required to spend many hours poring over appropriate maps so that they would become thoroughly familiar with the entire region over which they might be required to operate. They would also need to have a particularly detailed knowledge of their specific objectives and, to provide the material to meet this requirement, he recommended the use of dedicated photographic reconnaissance units. Many years later Tiverton's ideas would be put into practice and 'Target Study' was to become a regular feature of the training routine for bomber crews of the Cold War era, but it never became a well established procedure in 1917–18.

While map-reading also sufficed for inshore coastal operations, it provided no solution to the navigational problems of crews operating well out to sea on anti-submarine patrols. This presented particular difficulties for the crews of the naval airships which often flew over the North Sea or the Western Approaches for many hours, even days, out of sight of land and in winds of unknown velocity. The speed of these winds could easily exceed the speed capability of the 'ship and under these circumstances it was impossible to stay on station and extremely difficult to maintain a sensible plot of the craft's position. Thus, while an airship might sight something of interest, this information was of limited value if the crew could not establish their own position with reasonable accuracy.

Navigating by reference to the Sun, Moon and stars was a familiar procedure to sailors and (when cloud cover permitted) the crews of RNAS airships and flying boats made some attempt to employ these techniques.[7] The use of astronomical sightings was only moderately successful, however, as established nautical practice did not transfer easily to the airborne environment.[8] The problems that were encountered

[6]Viscount Tiverton was very influential in developing the *practical* aspects of the doctrine of strategic bombing. Adopting a rigorously scientific approach, he applied mathematical analysis and statistical method to many problems. By such means he was able, for instance, to identify the most critical sectors of the enemy's war industries, e.g. the production of chemicals for use in the manufacture of explosives. By establishing both the ballistic characteristics of bombs and the actual, rather than the theoretical, accuracy of bombing by experiment, he was then able to determine the number of sorties which would be required to disable a particular target complex. If a serious attempt had ever been made to apply Tiverton's calculated force levels to his target list it is arguable that the Independent Force, small as it was, just *might* have been able to damage vulnerable choke points within Germany's war economy to an extent sufficient to have had a real impact on her capacity to continue fighting. In the event, much of the effort of Trenchard's bomber force was dissipated in attacks against tactical targets (mostly aerodromes and railways) and the concept of strategic air warfare remained an untested theory. Like so many of the innovations which were essential to the *application* of air power that were developed during WW I, Tiverton's pioneering work in the field of what would later come to be known as 'Operational Research', was largely forgotten and had to be reinvented a quarter of a century later.

[7]An early, perhaps the first, serious attempt to use astro in the air had been made as early as 1913 when, flying from Eastbourne, F.B. Fowler had taken an experienced maritime navigator, Mr Rainey of the Royal Mail Steam Packet Company, on a flight sufficiently far out to sea to be out of sight of land. Using a chronometer and a nautical sextant, Rainey claimed to have established his position within a (quite remarkable) quarter of a mile; see R. Dallas Brett, *History of British Aviation*, 1908–1914 (republished by Air Research 1988).

[8]Celestial, or 'astro', navigation depends fundamentally upon the *precise* measurement of the angle between the horizontal (i.e. the horizon at sea level), the observer and the heavenly body – this angle being known as the body's 'altitude'. As a rule of thumb, an error of one minute of arc in measured altitude will result in an error of one nautical mile in the calculated position. As soon as the observer is raised above the surface of the Earth, however, problems begin to multiply. Because of his elevated position, the observer's 'horizon' is effectively depressed, since he can see further round the curvature of the Earth. The higher he is, the further away is the horizon and the more likely it is to become indistinct in haze and/or to be obscured by cloud. Assuming that the horizon can be seen clearly, however, the error caused by measuring altitude from this depressed 'false' datum can be calculated precisely, so long as the observer's height above sea level is known accurately. Unfortunately, contemporary barometric instruments did not permit height above the surface to be measured with much precision. An alternative approach to measuring the body's altitude 'upwards' from the horizon

were compounded in the case of airships by the vast bulk of the vessels themselves which obscured the upward view from the underslung crew car like a permanent overcast. A real enthusiast for celestial navigation, lucky enough to be assigned to airships of the North Sea or Coastal classes, could overcome this limitation, however, so long as he was prepared to abandon the relative security of the crew car and clamber up a tube *through* the ship to a gun position perched precariously on top of the envelope.

While operating within sight of the coast it was, of course, far more practical to take compass bearings of coastal features to establish an aircraft's position. Furthermore, when escorting a convoy, such missions representing a substantial proportion of airship activity: navigation could generally be left to the ships which were being accompanied.

Calculators and tools

During 1917, a gradual increase in the intensity of relatively long-range overland operations, particularly bombing sorties, began to focus attention on the potential of dead reckoning.[9] Here the RFC/RAF was able to take advantage of the fact that RNAS activities over the sea had already inspired the development of a range of useful tools. Most of these had been devised by naval officers, extrapolating their experience of nautical practice, who gave their names to these devices. Thus in the summer of 1916, for instance, Lt Cdr G.R.C. Campbell and Lt Cdr G.B. Harrison were able to adapt the principle of the naval 'Battenberg' to produce the Campbell-Harrison Course and Distance Calculator. From July 1917 this instrument was embellished by Cdr Rollo Appleyard RNVR who added his eponymous Time and Distance dials. A combination of the two produced a handy calculator which could solve all the common problems involved in aerial navigation and by September 1918 more than 16 000 examples were on order. Other aids to navigation included Flt Cdr A.W. Bigsworth's plotting board, Cdr H.P. Douglas' protractor (still standard issue to all RAF navigators in the 1990s) and the Aero Bearing Plate, the latter being additionally available in a luminous model for night use.

The bearing plate was an adaptation of another long-established nautical device, the *Pelorus*. The version developed for use in the air had a fixed, depressed sighting angle which made it particularly useful. Having first aligned the plate with the passage of objects on the ground, thus establishing drift, one could time the interval from an object's entering the field of view until it was directly beneath the aircraft. This, combined with a knowledge of the aircraft's height, the depression angle of the sight and some elementary trigonometry, provided groundspeed, which, since heading, airspeed and drift were already known, permitted the wind velocity to be determined. Once a means had been found to assess the local wind in flight it became theoretically possible to deal with the triangle of velocities, the key to aerial navigation.

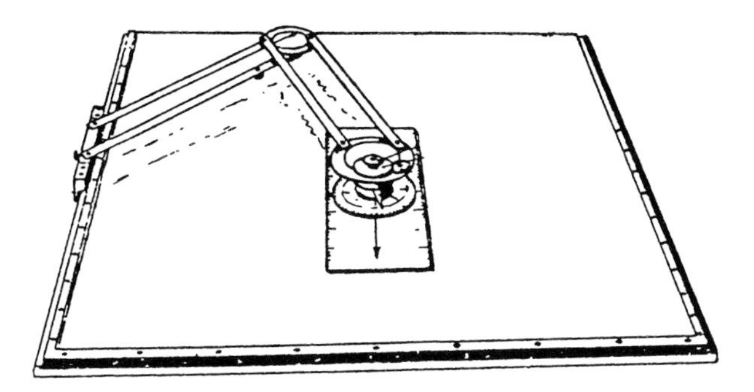

Perhaps better known for his work as an RNAS pilot, Flt Cdr A.W. Bigsworth also gave his name to this combined chartboard, straightedge and protractor. The 'Bigsworth Board' was produced in substantial numbers and remained in service until the early years of WW II when it was still providing a conveniently portable and self-contained navigation station in aeroplanes (like Blenheim Mk Is) in which adequate facilities for the observer were still lacking.

The availability of these tools and the increasing awareness of the need for *all* aircrew to be able to handle them constructively led to navigation displacing artillery co-operation within the curriculum of the SoMAs in January 1918. It also began to feature increasingly in the syllabuses of a number of role-related courses, particularly those concerned with day and night bombing.

Compasses

The RFC was not alone in increasing the amount of attention being paid to air navigation during training and as late as March 1918 the RNAS was considering setting up a course to train specialist instructors in map-reading, compasses and aerial navigation. Once qualified they were to preach the gospel at naval flying training units where classroom exercises were to include the application of the wind velocity to calculate the headings and times to fly to negotiate a triangular course. Since the RAF assumed responsibility for all aircrew training only a few weeks later, it is doubtful whether this RNAS-sponsored scheme was ever implemented. Nevertheless, it is informative to consider the content of one of its proposed practical exercises. In the air, from a known start point, a pilot would have had to fly a pre-calculated heading for ten minutes 'under the hood' after which he would have had five minutes to locate himself by reference to his map. The interesting thing is that the average permitted error in the heading steered was to have been as much as 20°, it being envisaged that the instructor would monitor this by logging the compass reading every fifteen seconds.

This level of tolerance may seem remarkable today, but, as had been demonstrated by a recent series of trials, it was a reasonable reflection of the performance to be expected using a contemporary air compass. In November 1917 the RFC Experimental Station at Orfordness had been engaged in an investigation of the feasibility of instrument flying.

would be to measure its co-altitude 'downwards' from the vertical but a practical means of defining the local vertical would not emerge until the 1920s.

Some idea of what all this meant in practice can be gained from the experience of Maj G.H. Cooke, navigator of the R.34 on its Transatlantic crossings in 1919. Only three of seventeen astronomical observations taken during the westbound flight could be made with reference to a clearly defined sea horizon; the remainder had to be estimated against a cloud horizon and were thus inherently inaccurate. Furthermore, with no information available on the surface pressure, the ship's altimeters became highly unreliable, so it was not possible to apply a height correction with any confidence. At one stage, by innovative use of his sextant to measure actual height above sea level, Cooke calculated that the ship's altimeters were nearly 1000 feet in error, this assessment being validated shortly afterwards when a sea level pressure reading was obtained by W/T from a nearby surface vessel. Cooke later estimated that in mid-Atlantic he had probably known the whereabouts of his craft to within about 50 miles. This information has been extracted from *R.34* by E.M. Maitland (1921).

[9]Dead (a corruption of the original 'Deduced') Reckoning is the method of determining position by keeping an account (or 'reckoning') of the distances covered on each of the courses steered since leaving a known position, the 'Point of Departure'.

As part of this work, a number of pilots had each been required to demonstrate their ability to fly due north, south, east and west. During each exercise the heading was to be maintained for five minutes without using any external reference. A test observer recorded the compass reading at fifteen second intervals. The trial results were eventually presented as graphs indicating error to the left or right of the required heading. At Fig. D1 the outcome of one of these test flights has been replotted to show the headings actually steered by the aeroplane on each of its four runs.

It is significant that the logged readings were to an accuracy of only 5°. This will have been partly because it was difficult to read the instrument with any greater precision, but this problem would have been considerably aggravated by the instability caused by the meandering course being steered as the pilot 'chased the needle'. Of the eighty readings which are reflected in Fig. D1 there were only eight instances of this particular pilot holding the same heading for 30 seconds. Six (unidentified) pilots took part in the trial. The example illustrated here was the worst case but none of the others was particularly impressive. The best that anyone achieved was to wander 10° either side of a mean course, this mean course often being displaced by as much as 30° from that which was intended. The results of this trial were not so much a reflection on the flying skills of the pilots involved, however, so much as an indication of the limitations imposed by the state of the art of instrumentation.

The aircraft used (a BE2e) would have covered about five miles in five minutes, yet it is plain from the diagram that in three of the four cases shown the (presumably relatively experienced) trials pilot was already at least a mile away from where he would have expected to have been. The student pilots on the projected RNAS course would have been even less capable of steering a heading accurately. Since they would have been required to remain 'heads down' for twice as long, it was only to be expected that they would be displaced by several miles by the time that they were permitted to look out. As they were also quite likely to have been further disorientated by finishing up pointing in the 'wrong' direction, it is perhaps understandable why the navy had thought it necessary to allow them as long as five minutes to sort themselves out.

If nothing else, the Orfordness experiment had served to highlight the inadequacy of the most common compass then in use (the RAF Mk II).[10] This will hardly have been a surprise, as all early aircraft compasses were acknowledged to be notoriously inaccurate. They were all far too easily disturbed by a variety of factors, including the magnetic field created by the whirling metallic mass of a rotary engine, the electromagnetic effects generated by magnetos, mechanical vibration, the accelerations caused by aircraft manoeuvres and

A Bristol Fighter, F4405, having its compass swung. (J.M. Bruce/ G.S. Leslie collection)

[10]The initials RAF stood for Royal Aircraft Factory in this instance.

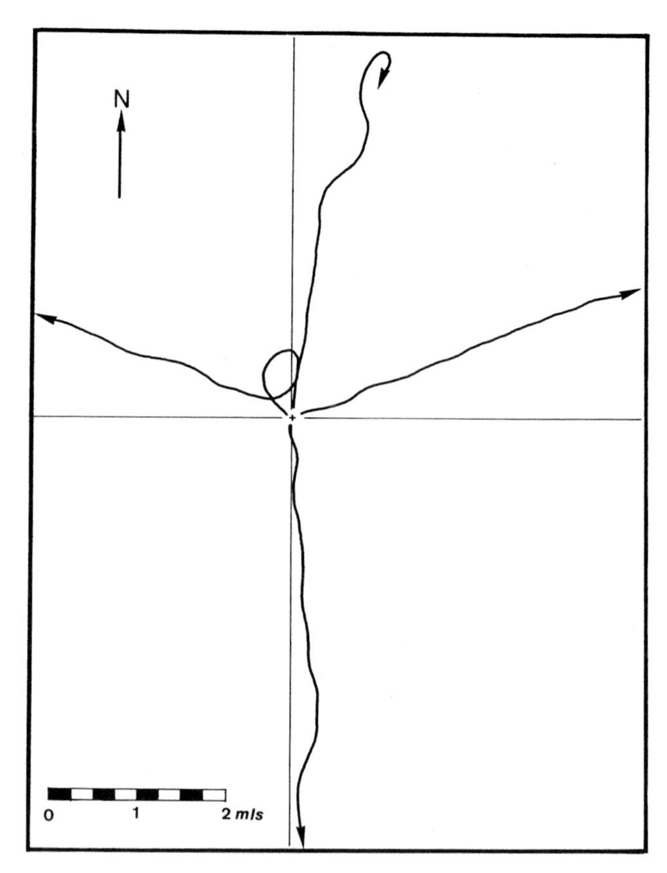

Fig. D1. The headings actually flown by an unidentified pilot on 4 and 5 November 1917. He was attempting to maintain courses of due north, east, south and west using an RAF Mk II Air Compass but with no external reference. Weather conditions were noted as being good with smooth air. The aircraft was a BE2e, 4560.

the magnetic implications of the carriage and release of bombs. Vibration alone, for example, was known to be capable of inducing a permanent deflection in excess of 40° in the Type 259 Compass.

Apart from these problems, early aircraft compasses were deeply mistrusted, indeed often ignored, as they were all prone to the mysterious, so-called, 'northerly turning error'. For no apparent reason, beyond the fact that his aeroplane just happened to be pointing north(ish) at the time, if the pilot applied bank (and nothing else) he would find that the compass immediately indicated that his aircraft was actually turning. This was the most straightforward example of a false reading but, when manoeuvring, as the aircraft's orientation and attitude changed, the compass could be induced to present a variety of contradictory indications. Confusing at the best of times, northerly turning error could sometimes be quite alarming, especially in conditions of poor visibility.

This problem was investigated by Capt K. Lucas at Farnborough and his explanation of the phenomenon resulted in the RAF Mk II Compass.[11] This minimised the problem, but at the expense of the instrument's being somewhat

[11]Like the nautical compasses from which they had been derived, early aircraft compasses were designed to detect and respond to the Earth's magnetic field, but only in the horizontal plane. When in banked flight, however, the compass was also affected by the vertical component of the Earth's field and, depending upon its orientation, it could behave in a disturbingly erratic fashion as it attempted to indicate the resultant of the two forces, i.e. to align itself with the Earth's actual magnetic field and thus to reflect the angle of dip as well as the direction of the pole. The phenomenon was known as 'northerly turning error' because the symptoms were at their worst on northerly headings.

insensitive and sluggish. Once the Mk II had been deflected it would tend to swing lazily back and forth before settling back on north. If the pilot attempted to follow its indications too closely, while it was still swinging, this could set up a cycle in which he 'chased' the instrument. The error could sometimes build up to the extent that he could be seduced into flying in a circle, following the compass as it eventually took the 'short way' back to north (Fig. D1 almost certainly shows instances of this having occurred).

Thus, while Lucas' rationale had served to dispel the mystery surrounding the previously unpredictable behaviour of air compasses, the RAF Mk II was insufficiently responsive to cope with violent or prolonged manoeuvres and thus it too tended to inspire little confidence among many of the crews using it. On the other hand, those obliged to fly in the 'bumpy' conditions which were frequently encountered in the Middle East often came to appreciate the Mk II's relative lack of sensitivity.[12]

Although Farnborough continued to make its contribution, the acknowledged repository of compass lore lay within the Admiralty Compass Branch and in February 1917 it was given responsibility for all aircraft compasses by the Cowdray Air Board. This led to the Branch being elevated to Department status, still under the overall control of its original Director, Capt Frank Creagh-Osborne (RN Retd). The Department was subdivided into a Magnetic Compass Branch under Lt Cdr Colin Campbell, a Gyro Compass Branch under Lt Cdr Geoffrey Harrison and an Air Compass Branch. Since the need for an efficient airborne compass was common to both the RNAS and the RFC, the latter Branch was to be jointly staffed. With remarkable magnanimity the navy installed a soldier as Superintendent, Capt M.K. Cooper-King RFC. Shortly afterwards the whole empire moved from its London address at 47 Victoria Street to the Admiralty Compass Observatory at Slough. A period of intensive effort soon produced the Type 5/17 Air Compass, the designation indicating the month in which it became available for general Service use, i.e. May 1917. While still subject to, the now understood and therefore no longer alarming, northerly turning error, the Type 5/17 was more sensitive, yet more stable, than the RAF Mk II and thus had a significantly improved performance.

Not satisfied with this, however, the team at Slough went on to develop the ultimate wartime compass, the Type 6/18, Lt Cdr Campbell and Dr G.T. Bennett generally being given the credit for having led this project. The Type 6/18 was the first practical aperiodic compass, which is to say that, while being very responsive, it was also 'deadbeat', i.e. if the needle was deflected it would return rapidly to north but without any significant overswing. Its relatively late introduction meant that insufficient Type 6/18s could be produced in time to equip more than a tiny fraction of the 3300 aeroplanes that were on charge to operational squadrons when the war ended, let alone the other 19000 which were flying with training units and/or being held in reserve. Nevertheless, where it was available it had the potential to enhance the precision of dead reckoning and, perhaps more importantly, its reliability, its accuracy and its predictable behaviour encouraged pilots to place more faith in all of their instruments.

Along with progressively upgraded versions of both the RAF Mk II and the Type 5/17, the Type 6/18 remained in use as a standard air compass well into the post-war era. In fact, so successful was the basic design of the latter that the post-war P and O Series compasses which began to appear in the 1920s (and which could still be found in the cockpits of many RAF aeroplanes forty years later) were really progressive refinements of the Type 6/18 rather than new concepts.

As a footnote to the above, it is interesting to note that in 1919, when the post-war RAF required all of its officers to become pilots, one of the tests that they were required to undertake involved an exercise not unlike that which had been proposed by the RNAS in March 1918.[13] The subject was required to fly on a nominated compass heading, his instructor checking the reading every 30 seconds. The average error was not to exceed 15°, the maximum permitted deviation being 30°. After fifteen minutes the student was handed a map on which he was expected to mark the position of the aircraft.

Dead reckoning

Since it was often necessary to maintain some kind of plot in the context of maritime operations, the RNAS had been well ahead of the RFC in the application of dead reckoning (DR), having adapted long-established nautical practices for airborne use. Regardless of how accurately it was maintained, however, a DR plot provided only an indication of where an aeroplane would be in still air. For this to be of any practical value in establishing where the aeroplane actually was, it was also necessary to know the speed and direction of the wind. Over the sea it was possible for an experienced observer to assess the local surface wind by inspection (by 'drift and wind-lane') and then, using a rule of thumb, to adjust this to provide a likely approximation of the wind at his operating height. Alternatively, he could measure the actual wind velocity aloft by, for instance, tracking back and forth over a nominally static object, like a smoke float, and using a suitable device, e.g. a bearing plate or a bomb sight, to measure the drift on a variety of headings.

Wind finding was a time-consuming procedure, however, and in practice aeroplane crews would usually have accepted and applied the wind values provided at briefing. Since most sorties would have been of relatively short range, if not duration, this would normally have sufficed, although one imagines that crews would have been able to request an update from their parent ship or shore station by W/T, should they ever have considered it necessary.

Airships carrying out extended patrols over the North Sea or the Western Approaches could also attempt to assess the wind themselves. One way of doing this would have been to head the 'ship into wind until its drift had been neutralised and then to have reduced power until it ceased to make any headway. Once this 'hovering' condition had been achieved, the reciprocal of the craft's heading and its true airspeed would have matched the direction and speed of the local wind. If this method was ever used, however, it would still have been a fairly laborious process and it seems far more likely that crews would have been notified by a broadcast from a shore station if a significant change in the wind had occurred or have requested one if they thought this to be the case. Alternatively, they could have obtained the current surface wind value from a friendly naval vessel in the area.

Despite the increased attention being paid to the problems inherent in air navigation, it is questionable to what extent

[12]Not long after completing his work, Capt Keith Lucas was killed while flying a BE2c which collided with another being flown by 2/Lt G.P.L. Jacques near Farnborough on 5 October 1916.

[13]AMWO 1051 of 18 September 1919 laid down the flying standards to be achieved by an officer, required to qualify as a pilot, in order to accept the grant of a permanent commission in the post-war air force.

DR techniques were actually used in the air. Although improvements in instrumentation were being made, it was still not possible to measure airspeed, altitude or temperature to any great degree of accuracy and, as Fig. D1 clearly shows, the performance of most compasses left much to be desired. Even the relatively advanced Type 6/18, would show an apparent change of heading whenever an adjacent Lewis gun was swung on its Scarff ring. All of this would, of course, have tended to confound any attempt at maintaining a precise plot. Furthermore, simply handling a chart, let alone plotting on it, at sub-zero temperatures with a gale of sleet howling through an open cockpit, presented considerable practical difficulties. The Bigsworth Plotting Board, with its chart clamps and integral compass rose, parallel rule and measuring scale, all mounted on an articulated arm, was an attempt to minimise this problem but it was hardly a complete solution.

Within the RFC/RAF the most useful practical application of DR techniques was at the planning stage of a long-range sortie. Although the science of meteorology was still relatively primitive, forecasts were regularly produced (see Annex H) and the observer could use these to lay his course using the best available wind information. Having made allowance for the anticipated wind effect, crews were then able to fly pre-calculated headings, refining these as necessary *en route* by observation of the actual drift being experienced and checking progress by reference to a map. Thus, despite the notional introduction of DR, it was essentially only an adjunct to map-reading and, so long as the weather did not change suddenly, such changes being very difficult to predict at the time, air pilotage provided an adequate practical solution to the problem of aerial navigation over land.

When the weather did change, however, it could cause considerable difficulty, especially at night. Contemporary instrumentation made prolonged flying in cloud an unrealistic proposition and if the ground became obscured the crew was deprived of its only fixing aid. If, as was very likely, the sudden development of clouds was associated with a marked change in the speed or direction of the wind (or both) a crew's problems were considerably exacerbated. Bombing raids, even those carried out by the big Handley Pages of the Independent Force, only occasionally ranged as far as 150 miles from base and most targets were within 100 miles, but even so the return leg could become a painfully long drawn out affair if the prevailing westerly wind changed unexpectedly. In this event the headwind component at 5000 feet could easily approach that of the aeroplane's cruising speed of about 70 mph; conversely a strong wind from the beam could result in a disorientating 45° of drift.

Lighthouses

Locally devised illuminated beacons had been in use on a makeshift basis before the end of 1914 but there was little call for night flying facilities in France prior to the advent of the Light Night Bomber Force in early 1917. The first lighthouses employed by the British were lit by acetylene but these were being progressively replaced by electric arc lights when the war ended. All the lights were mobile and they were periodically moved to reflect squadron deployment patterns (and to confuse the enemy?). To support night operations from a total of eleven designated aerodromes, thirteen navigational lighthouses had been deployed by June 1917.[14] By early November 1918 the RAF had twenty-four lighthouses available, of which seventeen were actually in use, the remainder being held in reserve.[15] There was a further concentration of ten British lights in the vicinity of the Independent Force's aerodromes in Lorraine.

It is worth noting that British crews were often able to exploit the enemy's night navigation facilities (this undoubtedly, if inadvertently, having been a reciprocal arrangement), although the Germans tended to use pyrotechnics, rather than lighthouses. While these were probably less reassuring than the more or less permanent British beacons, they did have the significant advantage of being visible above low cloud and fog banks. Despite their apparent preference for fireworks, the Germans did deploy some lighthouses, a very powerful one near Lille being of particular value to British bomber crews, since it could be seen on a clear night virtually from take off.

The original lighthouses used in France were lit by acetylene. Later models, like this one, used electricity.

[14]The eleven landing grounds nominated as being available for night operations as at 20 June 1917 were:

Formation	Primary	Emergency
I Bde	Treizennes	Auchel
II Bde	Bailleul	Abeele
III Bde	La Bellevue	Izel-le-Hameau
IV Bde	Estrées-en-Chausée	Longavesnes
V Bde	Abeele	Droglandt
9th Wg	Boisdinghem	Liettres

[15]While they had not been positioned on designated aerodromes, twelve of the active lighthouses were annotated as being located at sites suitable for use as emergency landing grounds by night-flying Handley Pages, FEs and (apart from two cases) Camels.

Annex E. Hydrophones, 1918

Trials with hydrophones designed to be used in aeroplanes began in 1917. While these early devices did permit the presence of a submarine to be detected, they could give no indication of its location which meant that they were of very limited tactical value. By early 1918 a much more useful directional system had been developed and, following successful experiments using flying boats, it entered service.

While the trials work had demonstrated that a suitably equipped seaplane could alight to listen for a contact and, if it found one, take off again to engage it, it had also shown that it was quite likely to lose track of its prey in the process. To solve this problem a second aeroplane needed to be on hand, airborne and ready to strike. Large twin-engined, manpower-intensive flying boats were not an economic proposition, however, so the preferred operational tactic was to employ pairs of floatplanes. Nevertheless, some big boats were also equipped with hydrophones and by the end of the war a further variant of the system optimised for use by airships had been developed, although this never became operational.

The interpretation of hydrophone signals was made the business of the observer and to teach the necessary techniques, rather than continuing to use an RN training facility at Portland, the RAF established its own school at Aldeburgh. The system did become operational late in the war but the onset of autumnal weather, and seas too choppy to permit the frail floatplanes of the day to alight, prevented its achieving any success against U-boats.

'You dunk it; I'll listen.' A hydrophone being deployed from a Felixstowe F.3 (N4230) during trials conducted off Shoeburyness in May 1918. (J.M. Bruce/G.S. Leslie collection)

Annex F. Wireless Direction Finding, 1914–18

Ground-based wireless direction finding

The problem of fixing an aircraft's position when operating out of sight of land had been very apparent from the outset and steps were taken to solve it in August 1915 when the Admiralty authorised the Marconi Company to build direction-finding (D/F) stations at a number of coastal sites. In effect these were an extension of an existing system set up to intercept radio transmissions in order to detect and track enemy submarines – and the much feared Zeppelins. By December the Admiralty was able to issue standing instructions to aircrews operating over the North Sea. Thereafter it became routine for patrolling aircraft to make an hourly Morse transmission consisting of its callsign repeated ten times. This was sufficient to permit a receiving station to establish the bearing of the incoming signal and, by comparing this with bearings taken at the same time by other stations, it was possible to fix the source of the transmission by triangulation and relay this information to the crew.

The system was far from perfect, however, and in July 1917 there was an exchange of concerned correspondence in naval circles to establish why the system was not being exploited to the full. An investigation, based on the use of the D/F stations at Lowestoft and Flamborough Head by Howden-based airships, revealed that the best accuracy that could be expected would provide a fix within a 5 mile square but that 10–15 miles was more usual and greater than 20 miles far from unknown.

Naval aircrews were already well aware of this, of course, and tended not to trust radio fixes, putting their faith in them only when no better information was available. Since RNAS airships and seaplanes routinely carried wireless sets, it was probably easier for their crews to keep track of their whereabouts by simply asking one of the friendly ships in the relatively crowded North Sea. By September, with attention being focused on the D/F system, the incidence of gross errors had been significantly reduced, with the notable, and critical, exception of fixes provided for airships operating close inshore. Unfortunately, without the provision of many more D/F sites, the geometry of bearings taken by coastal stations on an airship which was also close to the coast was bound to result in a poor 'cut' and a fix of doubtful accuracy. Under foggy conditions, therefore, a crew carrying out an inshore patrol or one attempting to return to base had little alternative but to hold off a safe distance out to sea and wait for the visibility to improve.

While W/T was used extensively for air-to-ground communications over the Western Front, the RFC made only limited use of direction-finding. This was largely because the majority of air operations were conducted within a relatively confined area which meant that navigation presented few problems. A D/F service might have been of some value to crews operating at longer ranges but, since few of the RFC's aeroplanes carried receivers, it would not have been possible to inform their crews of their position. Nevertheless, one practical application was developed, following the establishment of a network of D/F sites in France during 1917. These were able to pinpoint the location of German aeroplanes by triangulating their radio transmissions, this information then being relayed to patrolling fighters by visual signals. This primitive form of 'GCI' (Ground Controlled Interception) did achieve some success in frustrating enemy air activity.

In contrast to RFC practice, most of the RNAS patrol aircraft based on the coast were equipped with two-way radios. Early in 1917 three naval D/F stations were deployed to France with the primary aim of detecting and plotting the movements of Zeppelins and of enemy submarines operating from Belgian ports. After some initial instability these facilities were more or less permanently located at Coxyde (La Panne), Lampernisse and St Pol and they soon began to provide a similar oversea fixing service to that offered by the D/F stations in the UK.

Airborne wireless direction finding

While ground D/F stations had considerable potential, the success attending experiments with airborne direction finding probably had even greater significance for the long-term future of air navigation. This work was begun by the RNAS and continued under the auspices of the RAF. Initial trials were conducted at Cranwell in 1917 under the direction of Lt S. Smith RNVR, using an RE7 with a single fixed coil installed athwartships to see whether it was possible to home on a transmission. While not entirely successful, this experiment had shown some promise. Once the problem of magneto interference had been overcome (by Capt J. Robinson RFC) and a second, fore-and-aft, coil had been included, the system was demonstrated to work. By turning the aeroplane until the strength of the received signal indicated that it was pointing directly at the transmitter, bearings were successfully obtained from stations as close as Cleethorpes and as distant as Paris.[16]

The next improvement was to devise a set of moveable coils so that bearings could be measured without the aeroplane having to deviate from its course and by October 1917 a system suitable for use in Handley Pages had been developed. An early example was sent to Dunkirk for trials but concern over the possibility that the technology would be compromised if it fell into enemy hands caused these to be cancelled before the equipment had even been installed.[17] It was decided not to introduce airborne D/F until the associated machinery could

[16]In fact exactly the same indication would be obtained if the aeroplane were pointing directly *away* from the transmitter, the appropriate direction having to be established by common sense.

[17]This decision highlights a problem associated with all 'secret weapons'. Unless they can be employed to overwhelming effect, commanders are often reluctant to use them for fear of their being duplicated and used against their own forces. Similar prudent hesitation delayed the operational deployment of 'Window', the magnetron and a number of other devices and techniques during WW II.

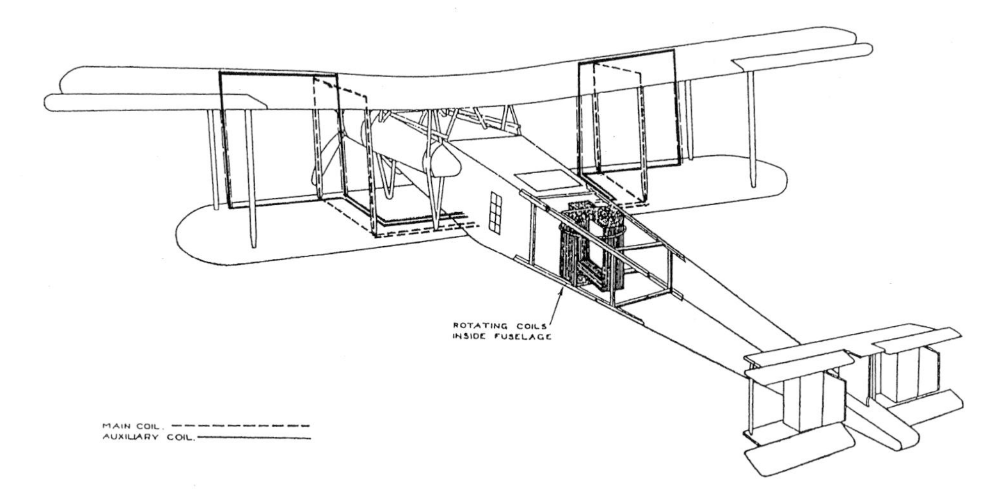

This sketch shows the alternative wiring arrangements for the airborne D/F facility in an O/400. Fixed coils, aligned with the lateral and longitudinal axes, could be wound within the wing structure and/or a rotating coil could be mounted in the rear fuselage. Since there was ample space, it was recommended that both systems should be installed in HPs, but in early post-war continuation experiments conducted with Bristol Fighters from Biggin Hill only the fixed arrays were used.

be manufactured in quantity and to concentrate in the meantime on training.

To support the airborne D/F system a series of radio beacons would be required and the identification and/or construction of a suitable selection of transmitters began in February 1918, the chosen sites eventually including Poldhu (Helston), Stonehaven, Ipswich, Chelmsford and Horsea Island (Portsmouth). With each of these transmitting for three (different) minutes in every hour, it was theoretically possible to take a bearing from several stations in turn, permitting the position of an aircraft to be established with reasonable accuracy. Development work continued at Cranwell with Capt J.D. Greenwood RFC supervising the installation of a set of rotating coils in an O/400. After some local trials, the first true radio navigation exercise, a flight from Cranwell to Stonehenge, was undertaken on 23 March 1918. The navigator was Sqn Cdr H.F. Towler, a pilot who, following a lengthy stint as CO of the RNAS Observers School at Eastchurch, had become a prominent member of the development team.

As a result of the success of this flight, preparations were put in hand to introduce airborne D/F training at No 1 School of Navigation and Bomb Dropping. In April 1918 No 97 Sqn moved to Stonehenge where its crews were to be taught how to use the system. In the event, the Sunbeam engines of the squadron's Handley Pages proved to be troublesome and little progress was made until they were replaced by Rolls-Royce powered aeroplanes. In the meantime, confidence was gained by driving the trainee observers and wireless operators around Salisbury Plain in a Crossley tender fitted with the coils so that they could take bearings at ground level.

Although trials had shown that the equipment worked well enough when it was maintained and operated by skilled personnel, there was some doubt as to whether this would be the case if it were in the hands of an ordinary squadron. Furthermore, large scale deployment would demand the provision of many more highly trained technicians, as the equipment required a certain degree of skilled adjustment and fine tuning. There were also reservations over the acceptability of the disruption in aircraft production which might occur if the equipment were to be installed. To cap all of this, doubts were being expressed as to the real extent of the tactical advantage that deployment would provide.

With enthusiasm for the new-fangled technology rapidly waning, it was decided to postpone deployment, pending the availability of the very long-range Handley Page V/1500. Early in July, therefore, No 97 Sqn's trained personnel were transferred to the recently formed No 2 School of Navigation and Bomb Dropping at Andover where they were to continue directional wireless training. The squadron's five O/400s (B9446, C9636, C9641, D4571 and D5417 plus a couple of FE2bs and a Curtiss JN4) were bequeathed to No 115 Sqn at Netheravon. No 97 Sqn was issued with unmodified aeroplanes and the following month it joined the Independent Force as a standard heavy bomber squadron.

In a memorandum dated 1 October 1918, Lt-Col G.P. Grenfell (O.4 at the Air Ministry), summarised the overall position regarding directional wireless.[18] All associated aircrew training had been suspended, since the technology had 'not yet proved its value as a means of navigation'. Qualified personnel had been earmarked for recall in the event of a resumption of the programme but were otherwise available to the Director of Training for other instructional duties. So far as specialist technicians were concerned, training, which had been under way at No 1(T) Wireless School at Farnborough since January under the direction of Capt C.K. Chandler, had been severely cut back, although it had not been stopped altogether.

In the meantime tests were to continue with an O/400 at Bircham Newton, where Lt-Col R. H. Mulock was then forming the 27th Group to control the operations of the projected four-aircraft squadrons of V/1500s. Further trials would also continue to be conducted by the Wireless Experimental Establishment at Biggin Hill. In addition, two fully-equipped O/400s had been sent to eastern France for field trials and familiarisation with the Independent Force, at least one of these evidently still being in commission at the Armistice (see below).

To support this residual experimental work the high-power transmitters at Chelmsford and Poldhu would be available, as were low-power stations at Andover, Borden and Milton. It

[18]AIR2/97/B.847. Lt-Col Grenfell's memorandum was prompted by a conference held on 30 September 1918, to discuss matters relating to the Independent Force. The Chairman, Maj-Gen Trenchard, had observed that, since progress with the D/F equipment was slow, the system was unlikely to become operational before the following spring and he had recommended that training be cut back.

Too many struts! This O/400, D9712, has been fitted with the additional struts necessary to carry the fixed D/F loops – see previous diagram. (J.M. Bruce/G.S. Leslie collection)

was also hoped to persuade the French to co-operate, permitting use of their very powerful transmitters at Paris and Lyons. All three organisations still working on the system were to exchange reports and keep the Air Ministry informed of progress. At much the same time American requests to be given access to British D/F technology were rebuffed. It was argued that the system was not yet sufficiently developed for it to be deployed and that widening the circle of those 'in the know' might compromise the techniques involved. Furthermore, it was considered that, working in isolation, the Americans might well make some unforeseen breakthrough.[19]

So far as feedback from France was concerned, Sir Hugh Trenchard showed no great enthusiasm for the system. His overriding priority was to sustain the strength of his existing squadrons and, if possible, to obtain more of them. The GOC was certainly not prepared to accept an interruption in the supply of replacement aeroplanes in return for the uncertain advantages which, its advocates claimed, might accrue from the deployment of an airborne D/F capability. He even declined the offer of a local low-powered beacon to support development work in France, since he was content that the existing lighthouse network provided adequate navigational facilities, particularly in assisting in recoveries to base.

Only a few weeks after Lt-Col Grenfell had circulated his memorandum, the situation was transformed by the flight, made in conditions of marginal visibility, of a wireless equipped O/400 (C9694) from Biggin Hill to Paris on 19 October; a return flight being completed three days later. In addition to a qualified W/T Operator, AM Joyce, the crew included a *very* senior W/T Officer, Col L.F. Blandy, to supervise the handling of the D/F equipment. The designated navigator was Maj Towler who flew buried in the centre fuselage from where he had no sight of the ground throughout either flight.[20] His only instruments were a compass and altimeter, no airspeed indicator having been provided. Using only the meagre information available to him plus radio bearings taken from Paris, Horsea Island, Chelmsford, Poldhu and, ironically, on the return journey, two from Nauen (near Berlin), Towler maintained a plot of the aircraft's position, calculated the wind and passed headings for the pilot, Lt A. Woodward, to steer. As verified by an independent observer, Maj W.H.D. Acland, who was able to monitor progress by map-reading, the aircraft stayed close to its planned track on both occasions and arrived within two miles of its destinations.[21] Another

[19]This would appear to have reflected a significant change in policy as it is known that officers of both the US Army and Navy had spent some two months at Cranwell in early 1918 observing British D/F trials work.

[20]Some O/400s were being fitted with a telephonic intercommunication system before the war ended to permit crew members in the rear cabin to speak to the pilot. Whether C9694 was one of these aeroplanes is uncertain but it would seem quite likely.

Another form of intercommunication between crew stations was a 'Steering Indicator' which was to be an integral element of the fully developed airborne D/F installation. It presented the pilot with a permanent indication of the heading (course) that he was required to maintain through a light display on his instrument panel which was remotely controlled from the navigator's station. Since this device is known to have been in use as early as March 1918 it would seem more than likely that it would have been available to Towler in the following October. It was, incidentally, also intended to use the same light display to pass steering demands to the pilot when using the Gray gyro-stabilised bomb sight which, had it ever entered service, was to have been installed in the rear cabin.

[21]AIR2/97/B.847. The report on this flight includes a typewritten copy of the navigator's logs and a pair of charts showing the activity undertaken during each flight (the charts are most unlikely to be those which were actually used in the air, however, as they do not appear to have had any coffee spilled on them . . .). It is interesting to note that the bearings logged are to the astonishing accuracy of a quarter of a degree. The preserved charts are Mercators projections on which a straight line represents a rhumb line and, since a radio bearing follows a great circle, it would have been necessary to have applied conversion angle to some of the bearings taken in order to plot these accurately. There is no indication that this was actually done, but the trials team were certainly well aware of the need for this refinement. It is suspected that the necessary calculation will have been made 'in the margin', the bearing actually logged being the observed reading +/− conversion angle, the magnitude of which could well have been assessed to within a fraction of a degree, hence the *apparent* accuracy of the result.

officer who had come along to see fair play was Maj-Gen Brancker.

The flight to Paris was deemed to be the convincing demonstration that had been required and on 21 October, before the aircraft had even made its return journey, an amendment to the establishment of O/400 squadrons was issued to support the introduction of directional wireless. The cost, in both equipment and manpower, turned out to be quite substantial, so one can perhaps understand some of the earlier misgivings over the implications of this technique. Over and above its normal entitlement, a squadron operating D/F equipment was to be provided with a repair lorry and three tenders, two light and one heavy. Its establishment of personnel was amended to reflect no fewer than twenty-five additional men: a Technical Officer (Wireless), seven wireless mechanics (one of them a sergeant), fourteen wireless operators (one of them a corporal) and a driver for each of the three tenders.

At the same time arrangements were put in hand to restart training at Andover and negotiations were hastily started with the French, who had also been working on directional wireless, with a view to co-ordinating the use of the high power beacons available to the Allies. At a conference held in Paris on 24 October it was agreed that, when required, the designated stations would transmit for two three-minute periods in each hour.[22] The minutes of the conference recorded that the French claimed to have been achieving an overall accuracy of $+/-3°$, which was comparable to British experience (but see Note 21). The minutes also noted that it was not foreseen that there would be any call to activate the system to support operations before 1919.

In the event, the Armistice intervened long before preparations to use the system could be completed. Three days later, in preparation for its disbandment, orders were issued directing the entire Independent Force to withdraw to western France.[23] Among the units to be redeployed was No 97 Sqn which was to move from Xaffévillers to St Inglevert, where it would be subordinated to HQ RAF. HQ Independent Force wrote to the squadron's prospective new 'owners' to let them

One of two types of moveable coil developed for Handley Pages. Both stood about five feet tall and occupied virtually the entire depth of the centre fuselage immediately aft of the rear cabin. The upper ring was graduated in degrees. The whole device was rotated to find the position of maximum received signal strength (this procedure was not quite as straightforward as it sounds) and the bearing, relative to the aeroplane's heading, read off a datum fixed to the aircraft's centre line

know that one of its O/400s (presumably one of the two trials aircraft noted above) was 'fitted with directional wireless apparatus' and that 'directional wireless observers and operators' were attached to this unit. Technically, despite the Armistice, a state of war still existed with Germany and this was underlined by the fact that the letter also advised that the Air Ministry had ruled that 'until further instructions, directional wireless is not to be employed on the enemy's side of the lines.'[24]

Thus, while the practicality of airborne D/F had been convincingly demonstrated during the last few weeks of the war, and a cadre of observers and technicians had been trained to handle the system, it is clear that the considerable potential of this technology had never been exploited operationally. Development work continued for a while and by December 1918 a set of moveable coils had been installed in a Felixstowe F.3 at the Isle of Grain. Andover was subsequently directed to build three more sets for the F.5s which were to be used by the Long Navigation Course when this was set up at Calshot in 1920. It has not been established whether these coils were ever installed but, whether they were or not, airborne D/F activity soon faded away.

In reality, while the D/F system itself may have worked to the claimed tolerance of $+/-3°$, the overall accuracy of the system would have been considerably degraded by the errors arising from the aircraft's compass, the accuracy of which would rarely have been better than $+/-5°$. Another form of error to which radio D/F systems are inherently vulnerable is 'night effect'. The ability to transmit over extended ranges at night by 'bouncing' signals off the ionosphere was being exploited long before the war but, prior to the 1920s, it is doubtful whether it was appreciated that the simultaneous reception of the, out-of-phase, direct and reflected signals gave rise to anomalies in the apparent bearing of the transmission. But, whether it had been appreciated or not, unlike the complications arising from plotting on a Mercators chart, there was no easy answer to the problem of night effect, not least because it is variable in its sense, its magnitude and its duration. While they cannot be entirely eliminated, means were later devised to minimise the inaccuracies caused by night effect but these were certainly not available during WW I.

While it would have served well enough as a homing device, since airborne D/F was subject to so many errors, it is questionable whether the system really would have been as valuable to night bomber crews in 1918/19 as its advocates claimed.

[22]The agreed transmission sequence was as tabulated below:

Station	Transmission 1	Transmission 2	Wavelength
Chelmsford	H + 21 to H + 24	H + 51 to H + 54	3200 mtrs
Lyons	H + 24 to H + 27	H + 54 to H + 57	4500 mtrs
Paris	H + 27 to H + 30	H + 57 to H + 60	4500 mtrs

[23]AIR1/1988/204/273/128. HQ Independent Force Order No 44 of 14 November 1918. The run-down was remarkably rapid. Maj-Gen Trenchard relinquished command on 20 November, leaving Brig-Gen C.L. Courtney to finish tidying up. HQ Independent Force ceased to function at 2359 hrs on the 25th.

[24]AIR1/1996/204/273/234. Brig-Gen E.B. Gordon's letter IFG 92/1/20 dated 13 November 1918.

Annex G. Bomb Sights, 1914–18

The policy decision which transferred responsibility for bomb-aiming from pilots to observers in the summer of 1918 was, in part, a reflection of the success which had finally attended a prolonged, if uncoordinated, effort to develop an efficient bomb sight. Fertile minds within both the RNAS and the RFC had been at work since before the war, creating a variety of increasingly complex devices all of which were intended to introduce a degree of science into the art of bomb-aiming.

Personalities who made notable pre-war contributions to this process included Maj H. Musgrave and Lt C.G.S. Gould within the RFC's Military Wing and Lt R. H. Clark-Hall and Sub-Lt J.L. Travers of the Naval Wing. Despite their efforts, when the war began the RFC had no effective means of aiming bombs while the RNAS had only a primitive 'lever sight'. Before the end of 1914, however, 2/Lt R.B. Bourdillon had produced a promising design. After further development at Upavon, in collaboration with Henry Tizard and Lt G.M. Dobson, this emerged as the CFS Bomb Sight. Bourdillon's basic concept was produced in a number of variants, the most numerous, the Mk IVb, being used by both the RFC and the RNAS until well into 1917.[25]

Seen here after it had been forced to land in Holland on 16 August 1918 (and very unusually), this DH 9 of No 211 Sqn (B7623) had a drift bomb sight mounted alongside the observers cockpit. (J.M. Bruce/ G.S. Leslie collection)

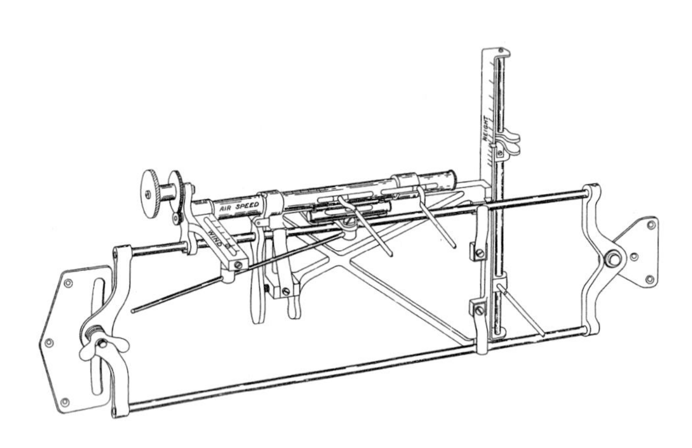

Lt Cdr H.E. Wimperis' Drift Sights were the most common bomb-aiming devices in operational use during 1918. Top: *The Low Height Mk II on which, uniquely, the height adjustment was made by pinching the clamps and sliding a datum up and down a calibrated vertical scale.* Bottom: *A Low Height Mk IIa fitted to a Wight seaplane; on this, and all of Wimperis' other Drift Sights, the adjustment for height was made by moving a lever against a curved scale.* (J.M. Bruce/ G.S. Leslie collection)

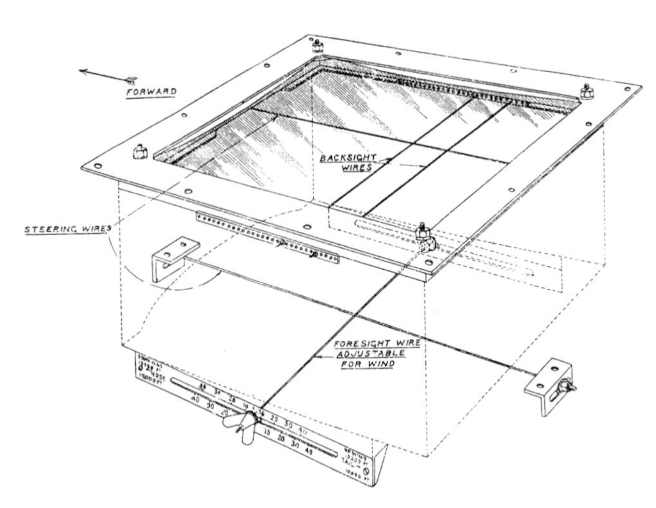

The Negative Lens Sight. There were often three lateral backsight wires, rather than two as in this diagram.

[25]Robert Benedict Bourdillon was to spend two years working on bomb sights as an EO, mostly at the RFC Experimental Station (originally No 37 Sqn) at Orfordness. He would later be decorated with the MC while flying with No 27 Sqn, which just might explain the effort devoted to developing a periscopic sight for the Martinsyde G.100.

In the meantime development continued with the RNAS introducing the Equal Distance Sight (which was used in conjunction with a special reversing stop-watch) in 1916, and the RFC devising a means of using the CFS principle in conjunction with a periscope on the RE7 and the Martinsyde G.100/102 in an attempt to overcome the problems involved in direct sighting. While these devices did permit a notional degree of accuracy to be achieved they were all quite difficult to use effectively and they all required a timed run to establish groundspeed – which, under combat conditions, was often extremely inconvenient, to say the least.

To overcome this limitation Lt Cdr H.E. Wimperis developed his Drift Sight which began to enter service in substantial numbers during 1917. By adjusting three scales to reflect the aircraft's height, its airspeed and (the reciprocal of) the wind velocity, the sight automatically produced the correct bombing angle. If time and the enemy permitted, it was also possible to use the sight to assess the local wind velocity, but in practice it was more usual to set the forecast wind which was available at briefing. Wimperis' basic design was eventually produced in five sub-variants: the High Altitude Drift Sight (HAD) Mks I and Ia, and the Low Height Drift Sight (LH) Mks II, IIa and III. The Mks I, II and III were all calibrated in knots for use at sea (the Mk III being specifically calibrated for airships), and the Mks Ia and IIa in mph for use over land. Like all of the preceding designs, the family of Drift Sights was intended to be used while flying directly up- or downwind, which imposed a significant tactical limitation, although Wimperis' sights could be used for cross-wind attacks at the expense of some theoretical accuracy.

With the exception of the periscopic variety (which never became widely available, apparently being abandoned after field trials), all of the sights described thus far were normally fitted on the outside of the fuselage, requiring the user, usually the pilot, to grope about in the slipstream while making the necessary adjustments. Ultimately he had to sight the target by leaning out of the cockpit to position his eye directly above the sight, to ensure that the target tracked along the drift wires, while simultaneously doing his best to keep the aeroplane on an even keel by reference to spirit levels. To do this properly required a long and articulated neck and rather more arms than the average pilot possessed, these inadequacies having to be compensated for by a great deal of contortion.

With the aim of producing a more 'user friendly' system the RFC introduced the Negative Lens Sight in 1917. In essence this amounted to a rectangular box set in a hole cut in the floor of the pilots cockpit. The upper face of the box was a lens, suitably shaped (plano-concave) to provide an extended view of the ground beneath and ahead of the aircraft. Longitudinal sighting wires were stretched centrally across the upper and lower faces of the box to establish an approximation of the vertical (so long as the wings were kept level) and to facilitate lining-up on the target. Three fixed wires were arranged laterally across the top of the box, serving as backsights – one for each of three predetermined bombing heights, 6000, 10 000 and 15 000 feet, each of which was associated with a specific airspeed. The foresight was another lateral wire stretched across the bottom of the box, its fore-and-aft position being adjusted by setting the forecast windspeed for the upwind or downwind case.

This sight was much easier and more comfortable to use, although it still required attacks to be made directly up- or downwind. It was not very accurate, however, as it had to be pre-set before take off, any subsequent adjustment of the wind speed or deviation from the three bombing altitudes/airspeeds for which the sight was calibrated having to made by eye. It also had a tendency to become obscured by oil leaking from the engine. The extent of this problem varied, depending upon the aircraft in which the sight was installed, but it virtually ruled out its use on rotary-powered types in which oil spillage was actually a design feature.

Because of its limitations the Negative Lens Sight was soon relegated to being a back-up system, only to be used for bomb-aiming *in extremis*. On the other hand, the fact that it enabled the pilot to see directly beneath and, to some degree, ahead of the aircraft actually made it of more practical use for reconnaissance work than it was for bombing. While the sight was too crude to permit accurate assessment of the forward throw for bombing, it was perfectly adequate for ensuring that the aeroplane actually overflew the target and this made it very handy for photographic work. At one stage it had been intended to fit Negative Lens Sights in all corps types but it proved to be very difficult to install in the RE8. A remote installation was eventually devised, with the 'view' being presented to the pilot via a series of lenses, but this system was deemed to be overcomplicated and it was finally decided not to persevere with the RE8 programme.[26] Although it had a number of drawbacks the Negative Lens Sight was a very useful adjunct to the range of tools available to a crew and they were produced in far greater numbers than any other type of sight.

The most efficient wartime aiming device, the Course Setting Bomb Sight, was also designed by Wimperis. Development work was initiated by the RNAS in 1917, the project being taken over by the RAF in the following year. In the ultimate Mk IIb version the integral compass was an aperiodic type and the sight was calibrated for bombing, on any heading, at heights up to 14 000 feet with allowance being made for such refinements as the trail angle associated with the ballistic characteristics of each type of bomb. While it was relatively complicated, this complexity conferred a useful degree of flexibility and it could also be used for wind-finding using the principle of multiple drifts - the so-called 'wind star'

This upended Bristol Fighter reveals two holes cut in its undersides. The rectangular one in the centre section of the lower wing permitted the pilot to see the ground via his Negative Lens Sight; the circular cut out was for a camera. (J.M. Bruce/G.S. Leslie collection)

[26]AIR1/946/204/5/1000. In view of the technical problems which were being encountered, HQ RFC letter CRFC 1638/53 OB1 of 7 March 1918 withdrew the requirement for the installation of the Negative Lens Sight in the RE8.

Type	1915	1916	1917	1918	Total
CFS	50				50
CFS 'Trombone'	275	295			570
CFS Mk IV		850			850
CFS Mk VI		450	150		600
Equal Distance		400	200		600
Low Height Drift Mk II		200	1 050	2 850	4 100
CFS Mk VII			500	1 150	1 650
High Altitude Drift Mk I			400	8 700	9 100
Low Height Drift Mk III (Airship)			150	200	350
Negative Lens			1 050	18 700	19 750
Electric gyro stabilised (Gray)				20	20
Wind-spun gyro stabilised (Horsley				200	200
Course Setting				720	720

Fig. G1. *Production figures for WW I bomb sights.*

method. Very few Course Setting Sights saw service before the Armistice but they became standard post-war RAF equipment, as did Wimperis' earlier Drift Sights which also remained in use for many years.

Another avenue that was being explored was the exploitation of the principle of the pendulum in order to provide a level datum for sighting. The possibility of using electrically driven and/or wind spun gyroscopes to achieve the same aim was also being investigated by 1916 and by mid-1918 two practical applications had emerged, the Horsley and the Gray Sights. The Gray Sight appears to have shown the greater promise and it was being actively developed for Handley Pages as the war ended.[27]

In the event no stabilised sights ever reached the squadrons, but it is interesting to note that the Gray Sight was to have been installed in the rear cabin of the O/400, necessitating the provision of a remote steering indicator to enable the bomb-aimer to direct the pilot towards the target. This may have been the relatively simple device introduced by the RNAS in 1917 which permitted the observer to instruct the pilot to turn left or right or to fly straight ahead by illuminating one of three lamps on the instrument panel. This system had proved to be rather crude and insensitive, however, and it is more likely that the Gray Sight was intended to be used in conjunction with a steering indicator which enabled the observer to give the pilot a precise heading to maintain (see Note 20).

The table at Figure G1 provides some indication of the production figures for wartime bomb sights of various models.[28]

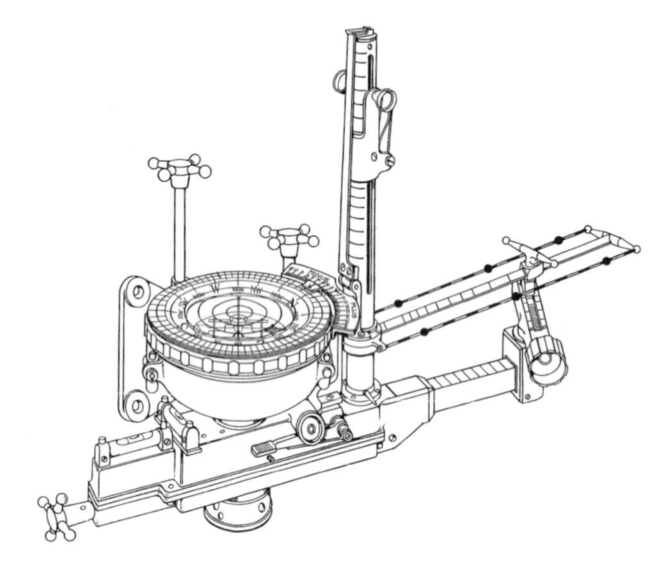

Although it was probably never used on operations, the best wartime bomb sights were later versions of the Course Setting Bomb Sight (CSBS) originally developed by H.E. Wimperis for the RNAS and which he subsequently perfected under the auspices of the RAF. This particular version is the Mk Ia which was intended to be used at altitudes of between 300 and 2500 feet, the Mk II variants being calibrated for high level work up to 14000 feet. By taking drifts on different headings, the CSBS could also be used to measure the local wind velocity at height. Theoretically this wind could have been measured very precisely but in practice the results would have been degraded by the relative inaccuracy of the means available to measure other essential parameters, including the aircraft's course (heading), its indicated airspeed, the air temperature and the atmospheric pressure (altitude).

An observer (wearing the short-lived pale blue RAF uniform, as revealed by his gold captain's rings) wielding a hydrophone probe (see Annex F). In front of his left arm can be seen a CSBS. (J.M. Bruce/G.S. Leslie collection)

[27]In *The Cross & Cockade Journal*, Vol 24, No 2 Harry Clarke contributed a very interesting and lengthy article on the wartime career of Capt G. McKerrow, an Experimental Officer at Orfordness. McKerrow spent much of his time on bomb sight development work, including operational trials in the field, and Clarke's account is strongly recommended as further reading.

[28]AIR1/724/91/6/1. A survey of bomb sight development, compiled by Capt H. Batsford shortly after the war, had appended to it a table (reproduced at Figure G1), which purported to show the annual production figures for various types of sight. The figures are far too neat to be totally convincing but they presumably provide a fair indication of the pattern of production, although the total for Negative Lens Sights is astonishingly high. If production really did run to 19 750 units someone must have *seriously* miscalculated when placing the order. It is generally accepted that the RAF had about 22 000 aeroplanes on charge when the war ended but the majority of these were single-seat fighters, trainers, flying boats, airships and sundry obsolete types, none of which would have been fitted with a lens sight – 10 000 would have been more than sufficient to equip every aeroplane that needed one and to provide a substantial reserve stock.

Unless it proves possible to verify Batsford's statistics, however (which now seems unlikely), they would appear to remain the best available indication of wartime bomb sight production.

Annex H. Meteorology, 1914–18

Apart from needing to know the direction and strength of the wind in order to navigate with any accuracy, other aspects of the weather were crucial to the planning and conduct of air operations. Although there was a sound understanding of the concept of air masses long before 1914, detailed knowledge of the upper air was still scanty and the concept of frontal systems, essential to successful forecasting, did not materialise until the early 1920s.[29] Nevertheless, from the summer of 1915 periodic observations of actual conditions were reported to 'Meteor' (the Meteorological Service, RE) at GHQ in France and regular releases of balloons from half-a-dozen or more sites, permitted the winds aloft to be assessed by theodolite tracking. While it was sometimes possible to follow these balloons to 15 000 feet or even higher, the cloud base often intervened and they would be lost to view at much lower altitudes. Early in 1918 a Meteor Flight was set up to carry out upper air observations of temperature and humidity using aeroplanes, a most valuable incidental contribution being a series of air-to-air cloud photographs taken by Capt C.K.M. Douglas and Lt E.H. Sessions.

All of this current information, combined with a knowledge of what had happened in the recent past 'upstream' in the British Isles and/or in southern France, permitted Capt (later Lt-Col) E. Gold to maintain a reasonable plot of the developing weather pattern. From this he was able to forecast ahead for several hours with reasonable confidence. He could not, however, guarantee to get it right every time.[30]

It should be appreciated, incidentally, that aviators were not the only people who required meteorological information. The artillery needed to allow for the wind aloft in calculating ballistic trajectories, for instance, and the forecast surface wind was of absolutely critical importance to those concerned with gas warfare.

A Meteorological Officer about to release a clutch of balloons to permit the upper winds to be assessed by theodolite tracking. This picture is associated with No 143 Sqn, which suggests that it will have been taken at Detling, but the same procedure would have applied in France. (J.M. Bruce/G.S. Leslie collection)

[29]The first frontal analysis of a weather system over the UK was not carried out until 1925.
[30]After the war Ernie Gold DSO, FRS was to become a prominent figure in the Meteorological Office and an internationally acknowledged authority in his field.

Bibliography

Primary sources

Extracts from Crown copyright material in the custody of the Public Record Office have been reproduced courtesy of that institution. The documents listed below include the more important Piece Numbers which have been consulted at the PRO. Many of these Pieces contain a number of separate files which have not been individually identified here, although in most cases the appropriate one(s) will be evident from their titles. On the other hand, where a particular file has been used to support the main narrative, it has been specifically identified in a related footnote.

AIR1/16 AIR1/27 AIR1/30
AIR1/59 AIR1/71 AIR1/109
AIR1/113 AIR1/115 AIR1/120
AIR1/122-123 AIR1/127-131 AIR1/133
AIR1/134 AIR1/137-138 AIR1/143
AIR1/160 AIR1/161 AIR1/168
AIR1/274 AIR1/279 AIR1/365-366
AIR1/373 AIR1/377 AIR1/393-408
AIR1/457 AIR1/459 AIR1/461-463
AIR1/502 AIR1/522 AIR1/533
AIR1/616 AIR1/625 AIR1/643
AIR1/654 AIR1/662-664 AIR1/667-668
AIR1/674 AIR1/676 AIR1/678
AIR1/683 AIR1/687 AIR1/699-701
AIR1/724-725 AIR1/756-757 AIR1/771
AIR1/785 AIR1/799 AIR1/803
AIR1/806 AIR1/814 AIR1/818-819
AIR1/821 AIR1/823 AIR1/827-830
AIR1/832 AIR1/834 AIR1/861
AIR1/864 AIR1/867 AIR1/872
AIR1/899 AIR1/913 AIR1/920
AIR1/937 AIR1/946 AIR1/994
AIR1/997 AIR1/1001-1002 AIR1/1025-28
AIR1/1036 AIR1/1057 AIR1/1075
AIR1/1078 AIR1/1084 AIR1/1135
AIR1/1141 AIR1/1143 AIR1/1169
AIR/1214 AIR1/1266 AIR1/1273
AIR1/1283 AIR1/1288 AIR1/1290
AIR1/1305 AIR1/1326 AIR1/1830-1831
AIR1/1839 AIR/1951 AIR1/1988
AIR1/1990 AIR1/1996 AIR1/2011
AIR1/2086 AIR1/2103 AIR1/2108-2112
AIR1/2148-9 AIR1/2162 AIR1/2217
AIR1/2283 AIR1/2362 AIR1/236
AIR1/2386-2390 AIR1/2400 AIR1/2405
AIR1/2424 AIR1/2433-2434 AIR1/2521
AIR2/8 AIR2/9 AIR2/15
AIR2/36 AIR2/38 AIR2/60
AIR2/78 AIR2/84 AIR2/91
AIR2/97 AIR2/118 AIR2/121
AIR2/125 AIR2/163 AIR2/291
AIR2/2005 AIR2/2075 AIR2/2421
AIR2/2660-2662 AIR2/2860 AIR2/2968
AIR2/3077 AIR2/3160 AIR2/4021
AIR2/4062 AIR2/4456 AIR2/4459
AIR2/4467 AIR2/4692 AIR2/5837
AIR2/6146 AIR2/6336 AIR2/6830
AIR2/8065 AIR2/8137 AIR2/8179
AIR2/8181 AIR2/8270 AIR2/8349
AIR2/8350 AIR2/8352 AIR2/8369
AIR2/8482 AIR2/8494 AIR2/8636
AIR2/8638 AIR2/8714 AIR2/10835
AIR2/11646 AIR2/11672 AIR2/18211
AIR5/351 AIR5/498 AIR8/3
AIR8/5 AIR8/6 AIR8/19
AIR8/204-205 AIR8/1541 AIR8/1545
AIR8/1882 AIR8/2123 AIR8/2300
AIR8/2337 AIR9/36 AIR10/64
AIR10/7 AIR10/150 AIR10/160-162
AIR10/190 AIR10/192-193 AIR10/223
AIR10/258 AIR10/276 AIR10/290
AIR10/315-316 AIR10/336-337 AIR10/358
AIR10/820-821 AIR10/922 AIR10/947
AIR10/991 AIR10/1082 AIR10/2012
AIR10/5551 AIR14/8 AIR14/16
AIR14/43 AIR14/67 AIR14/1012
AIR14/1941 AIR14/3906 AIR14/4129
AIR16/20 AIR20/492 AIR20/496
AIR20/498 AIR20/1334 AIR20/4101
AIR20/4324 AIR20/7385 AIR20/9060
AIR20/9072 AIR20/12267 AIR28/598
AIR30/191 AIR32/15 AIR41/4
AIR41/65 AIR41/69-71 AIR41/81
AIR46/7

Various Orders drawn from the AIR/72, ADM/182 and WO/123 series.
Sundry pieces from the AIR/6 series, i.e. memoranda submitted to, and the conclusions of meeting held by: the Air Council; the Air Council Standing Committee; the Secretary of State's Progress Meetings on RAF Expansion Measures; the Air Force Board and the Air Force Board Standing Committee.
Various maps from the WO/153 and WO/293 series.
Various unit and station records, mostly drawn from the AIR/27, AIR/28 and AIR/29 series.

Published works

Ashton, J. Norman (2000) *Only Birds and Fools*. Airlife.
Baring, Maurice (1920) *Flying Corps Headquarters 1914–1918*. Bell & Sons.
Bartlett, C.P.O. (1974) *Bomber Pilot*. Ian Allen.
Bewsher, P. (1919) *Green Balls*. Blackwood.
Bickers, Richard Townshend (1988) *The First Great Air War*. Hodder & Stoughton.
Bott, A. aka 'Contact' (1917) *An Airman's Outings with the RFC*. Kimber.

Bourgain, Louis (1991) *Nuits de Feu sur l'Allemagne*. Private publication.

Bowyer, Chaz (1978) *For Valour, The Air VCs*. William Kimber.

Bowyer, Chaz (1979) *Guns in the Sky*. Dent.

Boyle, Andrew (1962) *Trenchard, Man of Vision*. Collins.

Brandon, Lewis (1961) *Night Flyer*. Kimber.

Brett, R. Dallas (1988) *History of British Aviation, 1908–1914*. Air Research (reprint of the original two-vol. 1933 edn.).

Brookes, Andrew (1982) *V-Force, The History of Britain's Airborne Deterrent*. Book Club Associates.

Brown, Alan (2000) *Airmen in Exile*. Sutton.

Carroll, Warren (1997) *Eagles Recalled*. Schiffer.

Chandler, Chan (1999) *Tail Gunner*. Airlife.

Charlton, Lionel (1931) *Charlton, an autobiography*. Faber.

Chorley, W.R. (1992–98) *Bomber Command Losses of The Second World War, I–VI*. Midland Counties.

Collier, B. (1959) *Heavenly Adventurer*. Secker & Warburg.

Coombs, L.F.E (1997) *The Lion Has Wings*. Airlife.

Connon, Peter (1984) *An Aeronautical History of the Cumbria, Dumfries and Galloway Region, Part 2: 1915–1930*. St Patrick's Press.

Conyers Nesbit, Roy (1996) *Eyes of the RAF*. Sutton.

Cormack, Andrew (1990) *Men At Arms 225; The Royal Air Force 1939–45*. Osprey.

Cormack, Andrew & Cormack, Peter (2000) *Men At Arms 341; British Air Forces 1914–18, Vol I*. Osprey.

Critchley, Brig-Gen A.C. (1961) *'Critch'*. Hutchinson.

Cronin, Dick (1990) *Royal Navy Shipboard Aircraft Developments, 1912–31*. Air Britain.

Davis, Brian L. (1983) *British Army Uniforms and Insignia of World War Two*. Arms and Armour.

Donnelly, G.L. (2000) *A Quest for Wings*. Tempus.

Dunmore, Spencer (1994) *Wings for Victory*. McClelland & Stewart.

Ellis, Geoffrey (1983) *Tool Box on the Wing*. Airlife.

Eyton-Jones, Arthur (1998) *Day Bomber*. Sutton.

Falconer, Jonathan (1997) *Stirling Wings*. Sutton.

Franks, N., Guest, R. & Alegi, G. (1997) *Above the War Fronts*. Grub Street.

Gold, E. (1955) 'The Meteorological office and the First World War', *Meteorology Magazine* Vol 84, pp173–178.

Golley, John (1993) *Aircrew Unlimited*. Patrick Stephens.

Gould-Lee, Arthur (1968) *No Parachute*. Kimber.

Grey, C.G. (1940) *History of the Air Ministry*. Allen & Unwin.

Griffiths, Hubert (1941) *RAF Occasions*. Cresset Press.

Hamlin, John F. (1995) *Stand by Yer Beds*. GMS Enterprises.

Harbord, Frank (1998) *Familiar Voices*. Able Publishing.

Haslam, E.B. (1982) *The History of Royal Air Force Cranwell*. HMSO.

Hatch, F.J. (1983) *Aerodrome of Democracy*. Directorate of History, Department of National Defence, Ottawa.

Henry, Mike (1964) *Air Gunner*. Foulis.

Henshaw, Colin (1995) *The Sky Their Battlefield*. Grub Street.

Hering, P.G. (1961) *Customs and Traditions of the Royal Air Force*. Gale & Polden.

Hobson, C. (1995) *Airmen Died in the Great War, 1914–1918*. Hayward.

Hurren, B.J. (1951) *Fellowship of the Air*. Flight.

Insall, A.J. (1970) *Observer*. Kimber.

Irving, David (1973) *The Rise and Fall of the Luftwaffe – the Life of Erhard Milch*. Weidenfeld and Nicholson.

James, John (1990) *The Paladins*. Macdonald.

Jefford, C.G. (1989) *RAF Squadrons*. Airlife.

Jefford, C.G. (1995) *The Flying Camels*. Self-published.

Jones, H.A. and Raleigh, Sir Walter (1922–37) *War in the Air, Vols I–VI*. (Clarendon Press).

Jones, Neville (1973) *The Origins of Strategic Bombing*. Kimber.

Keith, C.H. (1946) *I Hold My Aim*. Allen & Unwin.

Kilduff, Peter (1991) *Germany's First Air Force, 1914–1918*. Arms and Armour.

Kimber, Charles T. (1977) *Son of Halton*. Thorley Publications.

Kington, John A. and Rackliff, Peter G. (2000) *Even The Birds Were Walking*. Sutton.

Kirk, T.H. (1950) 'Meteorology in the First World War.' *Weather Magazine* Vol 5, pp301–304.

Laffin, John (1964) *Swifter than Eagles*. Blackwood.

Layman, R.D. (1996) *Naval Aviation in the First World War*. Chatham.

Leaf, Edward (1997) *Above All Unseen*. Patrick Stephens.

Lewis, Bruce (1991) *Air Crew, the story of the men who flew the bombers*. Leo Cooper.

Lewis, Bruce (1997) *A Few of the First*. Pen & Sword.

Liddle, Peter H. (1987) *The Airman's War*. Blandford.

Lomas, Harry (1995) *One Wing High*. Airlife.

Mason, Francis K. (1969) *Battle Over Britain*. McWhirter Twins.

Macmillan, N. (1935) *Sefton Brancker*. Heinemann.

Mansell, Dr Tony (1997) 'Flying Start: educational and social factors in the recruitment of pilots of the Royal Air Force in the interwar years'. *History of Education* Vol 26, pp71–90.

McCudden VC, James (1930) *Flying Fury*. John Hamilton.

Originally published in 1918 as *Five Years in the Royal Flying Corps*.

McInness, I. & Webb, J.V. (1991) *A Contemptible Little Flying Corps*. London Stamp Exchange.

Mead, Peter (1983) *The Eye in the Air*. HMSO.

Middlebrook, Martin (1985) *The Bomber Command War Diaries*. Viking.

Money, R.R. (1936) *Flying and Solidiering*. Nicholson and Watson.

Morgan, Hugh (1990) *By the Seat of Your Pants*. Newton.

Morris, Alan (1968) *First of the Many*. Jarrolds.

Morris, Alan (1970) *The Balloonatics*. Jarrolds.

Nesbit, Roy Conyers (1996) *Eyes of the RAF*. Sutton.

Neumann, Georg Paul, ed., trans. by Gordon, J.E. (1920) *The German Air Force in the Great War*. Hodder & Stoughton.

Nichols, Edward (1996) *We Held the Key*. Newton.

Noble, W. (1920) *With a Bristol Fighter Squadron*. Andrew Melrose. (Reprinted 1977 by Cedric Chivers.)

Paine, J.R. (1990) *Getting Some In*. Square One.

Parsons, Leslie (2001) *Over Hell and High Water*. Woodfield.

Passmore, Richard (1981) *Blenheim Boy*. Thomas Harmsworth.

Radford, R.V. (1980) *Watch Opened*. RAF Finningley.

Richards, D. (1977) *Portal of Hungerford*. Heinemann.

Richardson, Gp Capt F.C. 'Dickie' (1997) *Man Is Not Lost*. Airlife.

Roberts, E.M. (1988) *A Flying Fighter*. Greenhill Books (1988). Originally published in 1918 by Harper & Bros.

Roskill, S.W. (1969) *Documents Relating to the Naval Air Service, Vol I, 1908–18*. Naval Records Society.

Rotherham, G.A. (1986) *"It's Really Quite Safe!"*. Hangar Books.

Royle, Trevor (1986) *The Best Years of Their Lives*. Michael Joseph.
Shire, F.J. (1981) *The Diary of a PBO*. Boston Mills.
Sholto Douglas (1963) *Years of Combat*. Collins.
Shores, C.F. (1991) *Fledgling Eagles*. Grub Street.
Shores, C., Franks, N. & Guest, R. (1990) *Above the Trenches*. Grub Street.
Silver, L. Ray (1995) *Last of the Gladiators*. Airlife.
Slessor, Sir John (1956) *The Central Blue*. Cassell.
Smith, Malcolm (1984) *British Air Strategy Between the Wars*. Clarendon Press.
Steel, Nigel and Hart, Peter (1997) *Tumult in the Clouds*. Hodder and Stoughton.
Strange, L.A. (1933) *Recollections of an Airman*. John Hamilton.
Stringman, Flt Lt D.C. (1984) *The History of the Air Engineer*. RAF Finningley.
Sturtivant, R., Hamlin, J. and Halley, J. (1997) *Royal Air Force Flying Training and Support Units*. Air Britain.
Sykes, Frederick (1942) *From Many Angles*. Harrap.
Taylor, John W.R. (1958) *CFS, Birthplace of Air Power*. Putnam.
Terraine, John (1985) *The Right of the Line*. Hodder & Stoughton.
Treadwell, Terry C. & Wood, Alan C. (1997) *German Knights of the Air*. Brasseys.
Tredrey, Frank D. (1939) *Pilot's Summer*. Duckworth.
Tredrey, F.D. (1976) *Pioneer Pilot – The Great Smith-Barry*. Peter Davies.
Trevenen James, A.G. (1976) *The Royal Air Force; The Past 30 Years*. Macdonald and Janes.
Voss, Vivian (1977) *Flying Minnows*. Arms and Armour. Originally published in 1935 under author's pseudonym "Roger Vee"
Wallace, Gordon (1993) *Carrier Observer*. Airlife.
Webster, C. and Frankland, N. (1961) *The Strategic Air Offensive Against Germany*. HMSO.
Wheeler, Edwin (1990) *Just To Get A Bed*. Square One.
Whitehouse, Arch (1965) *The Fledgling*. Vane.
Williams, James N. (1984) *The Plan: memories of the BCATP.* Canada's Wings.
Woodman, Harry (1989) *Early Aircraft Armament*. Arms and Armour.
Operational Research in the RAF. Air Ministry (1963). HMSO.
'Flying Training in Peace and War', various contributors, *Proceedings of a seminar conducted and published by the RAF Historical Society*, 1993.
'A History of Air Navigaton in the Royal Air Force', various contributors. *Proceedings of a seminar conducted and published by the RAF Historical Society*, 1997.
RAF Flying Training – Policy and Planning. AP3233, Vol 1 (1952). HMSO.
Air Navigation. AP1234 (1944). HMSO.
Army, Navy and Air Force Lists.
Report on the Committee on Higher Education, 1961–63; Cmd 2154 'The Robbins Report' (1963). HMSO.

Periodicals and journals

Various issues and editions of the following: *The Aeroplane*, *Air Clues*, *Flight*, *The Hawk*, *Intercom*, *RAF News*, *Roosters and Fledglings*, *The Royal Air Force Quarterly*, *Tee Emm* and the Journals of *The Royal United Services Institute*, *The Royal Aeronautical Society*, *The Royal Air Force Historical Society* and *Cross & Cockade International*. The last of these provides a rich source of information on all aspects of the first war in the air. Examples of particularly relevant articles, many of them biographical notes on individual observers, appeared in the following Volumes: *2/1*, *3/1*, *4/4*, *5/2*, *6/2*, *7/4*, *8/1*, *9/3*, *9/4*, *10/1*, *13/4*, *14/4*, *17/3*, *19/2*, *20/2*, *20/4*, *23/3*, *23/4*, *26/4*, *26/4*, *27/1*, *27/3*, *27/4*, *28/1*, *28/4* and *29/4*.

Abbreviations

A&SD	Administrative and Special Duties
AA	Anti-Aircraft
AA&QMG	Assistant Adjutant and Quartermaster General
AAF	Auxiliary Air Force
AAG	Assistant Adjutant General
AAS	Air Armament Station
AAITS	Airmen Aircrew Initial Training School
AC1 (or 2)	Aircraftman 1st (or 2nd) Class
ACAS	Assistant Chief of the Air Staff
ACDC	Air Crew Despatch Centre
ACI	Army Council Instruction
ACRC	Air Crew Reception Centre
ACSB	Aviation Candidates Selection Board
ACTW	Air Crew Training Wing
ADGB	Air Defence of Great Britain
AE&AES	Air Electronics and Air Engineers School
AEELS	Air Electronics, Engineers and Loadmasters School
AEO	Assistant Equipment Officer (1915–18) *and* Air Electronics Officer (post-1956)
AEOp	Air Electronics Operator
AFC	Australian Flying Corps
AFO	Admiralty Fleet Order
AFS	Advanced Flying School
AG	Air Gunner
AGS	Air Gunners School
AG/FM(A)	Air Gunner/Flight Mechanic (Airframes)
AG/FM(E)	Air Gunner/Flight Mechanic (Engines)
AHB	Air Historical Branch (of the Air Ministry, later Ministry of Defence (Air))
AI	Airborne Interception (radar)
ALO	Army Liaison Officer
AMO	Air Ministry Order
AMP	Air Member for Personnel
AMSO	Air Member for Supply and Organisation
AMT	Air Member for Training
AMU	Air Mileage Unit
AMWO	Air Ministry Weekly Order
ANBS	Air Navigation and Bombing School
ANS	Air Navigation School
AO	Air Organisation (Memorandum)
AOC	Air Officer Commanding
AOCinC	Air Officer Commanding-in-Chief
AONS	Air Observers Navigation School
AOP	Air Observation Post
AOS	Air Observers School
AP	Air Publication
API	Air Position Indicator
ASV	Air-to-Surface Vessel (search radar)
(Aux)SAG	(Auxiliary) School of Aerial Gunnery
BANS	Basic Air Navigation School
B&GS	Bombing and Gunnery School
BCATP	British Commonwealth Air Training Plan
BFTS	British Flying Training School
CANS	Civil Air Navigation School
CAS	Chief of the Air Staff
CFS	Central Flying School
CGS	Central Gunnery School
CNS	Central Navigation School
CO	Commanding Officer
CSBS	Course Setting Bomb Sight
DAO	Director/Directorate of Air Organisation
DAPS	Director of Air Personal Services
DCAS	Deputy Chief of the Air Staff
DCI	Defence Council Instruction
DofT	Director of Training
DDTArm	Deputy Director of Training (Armament)
DDOps	Deputy Director of Operations
D/F	Direction Finding
DGM	Director General of Manning
DGMA	Director General of Military Aeronautics
DMA	Department of Military Aeronautics
DNav	Director of Navigation
DR	Dead Reckoning
DRO	Daily Routine Orders
DRT	Dead Reckoning Trainer
DTF	Director of Training (Flying)
DTT	Director of Training (Technical)
EANS	Empire Air Navigation School
EATS	Empire Air Training Scheme
EFTS	Elementary Flying School
EO	Equipment Officer
EPM	Secretary of State's Progress Meetings on RAF Expansion Measures, i.e. Expansion Progress Meetings
ERFTS	Elementary and Reserve Flying Training School
FAA	Fleet Air Arm
FM(A)	Flight Mechanic (Airframes)
FM(E)	Flight Mechanic (Engines)
FS	Field Service (Publication)
FTS	Flying Training School
GD	General Duties (Branch or officer)
GHQ	General Headquarters
GOC	General Officer Commanding
GPI	Ground Position Indicator
GPS	Global Positioning System
GSO	General Staff Officer (graded 1, 2 or 3)
HAD	High Altitude Drift (bomb sight)
HCU	Heavy Conversion Unit
IAF	Indian Air Force
INS	Inertial Navigation System
ITS	Initial Training School
ITW	Initial Training Wing
JATP	Joint Air Training Plan
KBS	Kite Balloon Section
KR	Kings Regulation
LAC	Leading Aircraftman
LFS	Lancaster Finishing School
LH	Low Height (drift bomb sight)

MOD Ministry of Defence
NAAS Navigator and Airmen Aircrew School
NCO Non-Commissioned Officer
NEAF Near East Air Force
non-PNB all aircrew categories other than pilot, navigator and air bomber (1942–45)
(O)AFU (Observers) Advanced Flying Unit
OC Officer Commanding
OCTU Officer Cadet Training Unit
OCU Operational Conversion Unit
OR Operational Requirements (Branch of the Air Ministry)
ORB Operations Record Book (the RAF Form 540)
(O)SoA (Observers) School of Aeronautics
(O)SoMA (Observers) School of Military Aeronautics
(O)SAG (Observers) School of Aerial Gunnery
OTC Officers Training Corps
OTTW Officers Technical Training Wing
OTU Operational Training Unit
PAA Pan American Airways
PACT Preliminary Air Crew Training
'PBO' Poor Bloody Observer
PDC Personnel Distribution Centre
PDRC Personnel Disposal and Reception Centre
PFF Pathfinder Force
PNB **P**ilot/**N**avigator/Air **B**omber categories (1942–45)
PRC Personnel Reception Centre
PRO Public Record Office
PTI Physical Training Instructor
QR Queens Regulation
RAeC Royal Aero Club
RAF Royal Air Force
RAAF Royal Australian Air Force
RAFME Royal Air Force Middle East
RAFO Reserve of Air Force Officers
RAFVR Royal Air Force Volunteer Reserve
RAS Reserve Aeroplane Squadron
RASC Royal Army Service Corps
RATG Rhodesian Air Training Group
RAuxAF Royal Auxiliary Air Force
RCM Radio Counter Measures
RCAF Royal Canadian Air Force
RDF Radio Direction Finding, i.e. radar
RE Royal Engineers
RFC Royal Flying Corps
RFS Reserve Flying School
RM Royal Marines
RN Royal Navy
RNAS Royal Naval Air Service
RNR Royal Navy Reserve
RNVR Royal Navy Volunteer Reserve
RNZAF Royal New Zealand Air Force
RPI Retail Price Index
RS Radio School
SAAF South African Air Force
SAG School of Aerial Gunnery
SAN School of Air Navigation
SASO Senior Air Staff Officer
SEG Generic acronym used in the late 1940s to cover Signallers, Engineers and Gunners
SFTS Service Flying Training School
SNBD School of Navigation and Bomb Dropping
SNCO Senior Non-Commissioned Officer, i.e. sergeant or above
SoA School of Aeronautics
SofAF&G School of Aerial Fighting and Gunnery
SofI School of Instruction
SoMA School of Military Aeronautics
SofTT School of Technical Training
TAG Telegraphist Air Gunner
TDS Training Depot Station
UAS University Air Squadron
UAV Unmanned Air Vehicle
USAF United States Air Force
USAAC United States Army Air Corps
USAAF United States Army Air Force
USAS United States Air Service
VCAS Vice-Chief of the Air Staff
VR Volunteer Reserve
WOp Wireless Operator
WOp/AG Wireless Operator/Air Gunner
WOM Wireless Operator Mechanic
WOM/AG Wireless Operator Mechanic/Air Gunner
WSO Weapons Systems Officer
WSOp Weapons Systems Operator

Index